KU-216-304

THE
Which? Wine Guide

Edited by ROSEMARY GEORGE MW
& CHRISTINE AUSTIN

Published by Consumers' Association
and Hodder & Stoughton

Which? Books are commissioned and researched by
The Association for Consumer Research and published by
Consumers' Association, 2 Marylebone Road, London NW1 4DF and
Hodder & Stoughton, 47 Bedford Square, London WC1B 3DP

First published October 1992
First edition of *The Which? Wine Guide* published in 1981

Editorial consultant: Aileen Hall
Acknowledgements to: Maureen Ashley MW, Francessa Beckett, Liz Berry MW, Jim Budd, Margaret Harvey MW, Helena Harwood, Maggie McNie MW, Richard Mayson, Hazel Murphy, Gabrielle Shaw

Design of cover and taste wheels: Paul Saunders
Cover photograph: The Anthony Blake Photo Library/Gerrit Buntrock
Illustrations: Bina Haria-Shah

British Library Cataloguing-in-Publication Data
A catalogue record for this book is available from the British Library

ISBN 0 340 57682 0

Thanks for choosing this book...

If you find it useful, we'd like to hear from you. Even if it doesn't do the job you were expecting, we'd still like to know. Then we can take your comments into account when preparing similar titles or, indeed, the next edition of the book. Address your letter to the Publishing Manager at Consumers' Association, FREEPOST, 2 Marylebone Road, London NW1 4DF. We look forward to hearing from you.

Typesetting by Page Bros (Norwich) Ltd
Printed and bound in Great Britain by Richard Clay Limited, Bungay, Suffolk

Contents

Part III Where to buy wine

Part IV Find out more about wine

Introduction

Welcome to the new edition of *The Which? Wine Guide*!

One of the main reasons for the *Guide*'s existence has always been to direct readers to the very best of British wine merchants, supermarkets, high-street off-licences and so on. A constant editorial preoccupation over the years has been the calibre of service offered by these suppliers to the customer, a concern held no less strongly by the current editors.

This time we have looked particularly carefully at the effort given to training the staff who come into contact with the customer. It is no good for the buyers at Head Office to be highly qualified if the person actually selling the wine doesn't know the difference between Muscadet and Moscatel, say. Supermarkets often fall down in this area and it is sad, considering the huge amounts of money flowing into their tills, that so little provision is made to give staff some wine training. Even a small amount of guidance on pronunciation and an occasional tasting would work wonders.

What has been worrying, indeed, as we have compiled this edition, is the number of businesses where staff are apparently encouraged to dish out advice on wine to customers but who are not exposed to any training beyond being told to read the labels. It is this need for good wine knowledge behind the sales counter that prompted us to give our 'scroll' award to those merchants who provide quality training and, hence, good advice. Some merchants have gone one step further and taken to educating their customers as well, with wine courses, tutored tastings and accompanied trips to the vineyards. This not only brings the whole world of wine to life but it generates a band of loyal, knowledgeable customers who will never forget the taste of wine straight from the cask.

Wine clubs and societies can also be of great value in this gentle process of education, since they offer the chance to taste a wide variety of wines at a fraction of the cost. See page 474 for more information on such enterprises.

To arrive at the eventual list of just under 250 merchants we have reviewed nearly 700 and picked out those which we feel offer the best deal to the customer in terms of range and value as well as service. For those businesses without a retail licence, willingness to sell mixed cases was an important criterion in our choice since it indicates a basic level of service that should be available from all merchants selling to the public.

There is no doubt that the recession has hit the wine trade. Some merchants have reported that customers are buying fewer bottles and looking for better quality from less well-known areas. General lack of disposable income has made the quality of the wine in the bottle more important than its perceived reputation from the label. Regions such as the new, improved south of France and Australia are capturing more sales than ever before.

One casualty of the recession seems to be organic wine, the success of which in previous years has been part of a general 'trading up' in price. This year, a great many merchants have been abandoning those organic wines which do not meet their standards of quality for money.

WINES BY TASTE

As well as finding out where to buy, readers over the years have been no less interested in finding out more about the wines they buy and enjoy. For this edition we have broken away from the traditional country-by-country survey of the world's wines. Broadly speaking, most of us choose our wines by flavour and price rather than by country, so our new approach is to compare wines by their taste, even if they come from regions that are thousands of miles apart.

To this end we have compiled *The Which? Wine Guide* Taste Wheel, or rather Wheels – one large wheel for table wines and two smaller ones for fortified and sparkling wine. Quite simply, we have divided up the world's wines according to their different taste components, taking into account acidity, body, sweetness, tannin and so on, in order to demonstrate how seemingly disparate wines do in fact stand side by side when it comes to how they taste. Conversely, not all wines from the same grape variety fall within the same section of the wheels as provenance and method of vinification have a considerable effect on flavour.

However, the prime objective of our Taste Wheels is to encourage experimentation and to expand our readers' wine-drinking horizons. It is easy to remain faithful to the wine you know you like, but to try something new is much more exciting and palate-broadening. With our Taste Wheels for guidance, we hope to make your wine-buying decisions easier and more adventurous at the same time.

Of course, taste is firmly subjective. Everyone's tastebuds are individual so you may find that you disagree with some of our suggestions. On the other hand, you will probably be surprised by similarities that would never otherwise have occurred to you.

FEATURES

Enormous changes in wine-making techniques worldwide over the past twenty years or so have wrought great improvements in the bottle, and brought wholesome, well-made wine within reach of most budgets. The technical side behind the end result – the wine in the glass – is explored in our feature on page 34.

For some years Consumers' Association has not been assessing South African products in any of its publications. Now that the structures of apartheid are being dismantled, the Association's Council has decided to amend this policy, which will be kept under review in the light of political developments. Accordingly, we have included a feature on South African wines on page 27, and have also covered those wines in the Where to Buy Wines section.

Finally, this year, we have particularly enjoyed the opportunity to ship certain bottles destined for the shores of the islands where our celebrity castaways are languishing (see Desert Island Wines on page 17). The wines they have chosen range from the nearly impossible-to-find Château Latour 1970 to uncomplicated wines that will simply evoke happy holiday memories. Just like music, wines weave their way into our lives and become markers for certain times, places and people. It is perhaps surprising that so little champagne was included in the selections, although David Gower recalls fondly a bottle of Bollinger and an axe . . .

As in previous years, do please continue to let us have your views on the *Guide* and alert us to wine merchants – both those we know about and those new ones we may not. And enjoy your drinking.

CHRISTINE AUSTIN
ROSEMARY GEORGE

ABOUT THE EDITORS

Rosemary George became one of the first women Masters of Wine in 1979. Her numerous books include *The Wines of Chablis and the Yonne* (Sotheby's), which won both the André Simon award and the Glenfiddich Prize, *French Country Wines* (Faber & Faber), *Chianti and the Wines of Tuscany* (Sotheby's) and *Lateral Wine-Tasting Guide* (Bloomsbury). She also contributes regularly to wine and consumer magazines in Britain and North America.

Christine Austin is an established wine writer, broadcaster and lecturer, who began her career as a wine technologist. She has travelled extensively, especially in Europe and most recently in Australia,and, like Rosemary George, is a member of the Jurade de Saint-Emilion.

The Which? Wine Guide Awards

As in previous editions of the *Guide*, we have given awards based on specialities in order to help readers to pursue particular enthusiasms. Remember that one speciality does not exclude another, and that any merchant of award-winning merit will have an enormous amount to offer even the uncommitted wine enthusiast.

Bordeaux Specialist Award
Thos Peatling
For sheer variety at all quality levels

Burgundy Specialist Award
Howard Ripley
For his singleminded dedication to the cause of good burgundy. Strongly challenged by *Haynes Hanson & Clark* and by *Morris & Verdin*

Rhône Specialist Award
Yapp Brothers
For beating a path to the glorious wines of this region long before anyone else, and for continuing to do so

Italian Specialist Award
Winecellars
For making sense of this complicated country and its wines, and going for quality every time

German Specialist Award
Summerlee Wines
For concentrating solely on top-quality estates, and waiting patiently for the upturn in interest in these wines

Spanish Specialist Award
Laymont & Shaw
For a well-presented, quality range and good communication skills

Australian Specialist Award
The Australian Wine Centre
For the most comprehensive selection of well-made Aussie wines

Fine Wine Specialist Award
T & W Wines
For a glorious collection of all that is great and good

Best Supermarket Award
Safeway
For a massive leap forward in the quality and variety of its range at all price levels

Best High Street Chain Award
Oddbins
Innovative, comprehensive, competitive and fun. What more could any customer want?

Best Mail-Order Merchant Award
The Wine Society
For a quality range, reliable service and well-written, digestible information

Best Independent Merchant Award
The Wine House
If every wine shop were as good as this one, the world would be a happier place

Best Out-of-Town Merchant Award
The Nobody Inn
For daring to go for quality wines in wonderful variety without the reassurance of a huge population on the doorstep

Best New Shop Award
Robersons
For an excellent range, an exciting shop, knowledgeable staff and a regular programme of tastings

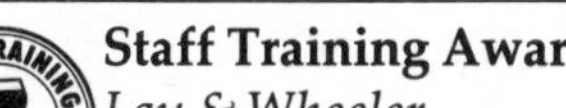

Staff Training Award

Lay & Wheeler

For enthusiastic, knowledgeable and loyal staff – all employees, no matter what their job, are given every opportunity to learn about wine from courses and tastings. This must be good news for customers

Best Wine List Award

Adnams

For clear information, interesting reading, stylish presentation and quality wines

Part I

Features

DESERT ISLAND WINES

Christine Austin

Have you ever wished you could get away from it all? Away from the telephone, fax machines and bleepers... no supermarkets, car parks, motorways or city centres... just peace and quiet, perhaps on a desert island, where the sun is warm, a sandy beach is gently washed by waves and life takes on a distinctly relaxed style?

Here at The Which? Wine Guide *(with a reverent bow in the direction of Roy Plomley) we dreamt up such a fantasy island – somewhere in the middle of an ocean, with a pleasant climate, freshwater streams and plenty of fruit and vegetables growing around the place. We then invited a series of well-known personalities to be cast away on our island, first asking them which wines they would choose to be washed up alongside them on the beach and why. Just so that life was bearable we made sure that the stream was the right temperature to chill white wines, and that there was a deep cool cave to store bottles in perfect condition. Stocks would be inexhaustible and successive vintages would float conveniently to shore to replace those consumed. Bearing in mind the mountain of bottles which may end up littering the beach, we thought they could be used to send messages to would-be rescuers or (not strictly allowed) made into a stylish beach hut.*

Naturally, a good set of glasses would also float to the beach and that all-important implement, a good corkscrew. Now all we need is a few castaways. Our first volunteer is actor **Terence Alexander**, *well known for his TV role in* Bergerac, *as Charlie Hungerford, a character who enjoys good living.*

In 1941, when I was 18, I was the leading juvenile in the twice-nightly rep at the Lyceum in Sheffield. There was a pub we used to go to with a wine bar attached called Hays Wine Bar. It had an enormous cellar stretching under the road which was absolutely full of pre-war wines. I got to know the barman very well because I used to buy a lot of wine, though I didn't know a lot about it then. One day he said to me: 'You should try this wine. It's a bit expensive but I think you'll like it.' It turned out to be Château Mouton-Rothschild 1924 and it cost me 7/6d. I took the bottle home to my digs and drank it over the weekend with whatever my landlady had prepared for dinner and thought it was *very* nice. I haven't drunk a lot of it since.

My second wine is very different and would be the wine for everyday quaffing that one would need. I was filming in Rome and one night we were having dinner sitting outside a café in the Piazza del Popolo. We ordered a carafe of wine to start with – the local Frascati made up in the hills. Frascati hasn't got a good reputation but this one was crisp, the most delicious thing. When you drink wine on the spot it makes all the difference.

In fact, I was in Italy for two and a half years while I was in the army. I got wounded just before the war finished and spent the whole of the summer of 1945 in a convalescent home in Sorrento, where we mostly drank Lacryma Christi. I love Italy and don't really dare go back in case it has been spoilt. Anyway, I developed a great love for Italian wines, and my third choice would be a Brunello di Montalcino, which I also had once or twice while convalescing – not too heavy but full of fruit, and better than a heavier Rhône for drinking on a desert island.

Memories also played a big part in helping the **Bishop of Peterborough, the Rt Rev William Westwood**, *make his selection.*

I have drunk wine since my teens but always in those early years with a certain innocence as to the quality of one wine against another. However, in my thirties I began to teach once a week in a prep school and the headmaster said that to pay me would cause confusion to tax arrangements on both sides and he would rather give me a crate of wine from time to time. He had a passion for German and Alsace wines and began to let me have cases of Hugel's Sylvaner, Riesling and Gewürztraminer. Most German wine is really just that bit too sweet for my taste, but tasting the consistency of a wine from a good shipper marked a total change in my wine-drinking habits.

When I became a bishop, we moved to London and one of my clergy introduced me in 1975 to that palace of wine bars, Don Hewitson's Cork & Bottle. My wife had just begun her long training as a counsellor and I was a very new bishop, and we hardly ever saw each other in the week. So at Saturday lunchtimes we would arrive in the 'Cork' just after noon and stay there till 3 p.m., sitting in a corner, discussing the week. Such discussions could become somewhat tense and our rows are still remembered by some of the staff of those days. It always ended cheerfully, possibly because of the good food and wine and it was there, as French wine got more and more expensive, that I was introduced to Australian wine, to which I am now devoted. I suppose it was the Chateau Tahbilk Shiraz vintage shipped by Don himself which did the trick for me and gave an absolutely fresh dimension to wine-drinking.

In 1991, my diocese celebrated its 450th anniversary. We went on seven pilgrimages, planted 450 trees, commissioned music and rang bells, but the only thing noted by the newspapers was that I took my clergy to the races at Towcester. We also selected some diocesan wine through a local wine merchant (the family of one of my curates). We shipped Côtes de Bergerac vin rouge and Bergerac Sec from the vineyards of the Guibert family in the Dordogne. After many tastings we chose well, for the red won a silver medal and for a time replaced the Bulgarian Cabernet, that great standby at parish parties!

None of these is marred by the curse of 'sacred drinking', but on my desert island they would have just the right combination of bouquet, taste, colour, fragrance and memories which would fit those long evenings when, resigned, I would feel I was to be there forever, and those happy days when hopes of rescue would spring within me. What more can you ask of a wine?

Julia Neuberger, *rabbi, writer and broadcaster, generously included some champagne to share with her hoped-for rescuers.*

There is no question that it would be a great comfort to have with me on my desert island a limitless supply of my favourite wines for quaffing – almost any good-quality Pinot Noir, and in recent months a wonderful Pinot Blanc from Rolly-Gassmann in the Alsace, shipped by Bibendum. The depression which would inevitably be caused by my acute myopia, being unable to see any ship out there even if there were one, would be much helped by the ability to drink as much as I wanted, enjoying the lightness and delicacy of the wine and not worrying about the quality of the next day's work as a result.

But it would make a change to have an occasional glass of my favourite dessert wine, Muscat de Beaumes-de-Venise. I can't remember exactly when I first had it – it was by no means the first dessert wine I tasted as a child. But by the time I had it to drink regularly, it had become synonymous, largely via Posy Simmonds and her 'Mrs Weber's Diary', with the wine of seduction for the residents of NW1 and NW5. At that time we were living in NW5, though I was never actually seduced with it. However, I have memories of carefully packed picnics on weekend outings, before we had children, with proper food rather than sandwiches, with wines chosen to accompany the food and, best of all, a half-bottle of Beaumes-de-Venise to finish off the meal with its rich sweetness and its delightfully somnolent effect. One could chat in a half-doze or sleep away the rest of the afternoon in the secure knowledge that it never left a bad taste, that one would want another glass as soon as one woke up, and that it would cause a smile or two on the faces of those at home who saw the empty bottles.

Other than those two, all I would want is a small supply of some very good champagne for when the ship did come in to rescue me – for the crew and for me – to celebrate the end of a stay on a desert island much improved by the fine wines available on tap.

Politicians are perhaps not the ideal candidates for desert islands as they really need a more responsive audience than a flock of seagulls, but our political castaways entered enthusiastically into the spirit of the game. **Bryan Gould**, *a New Zealander by birth who came to Britain as a student and now Shadow Minister for the National Heritage, returned to his roots for two of his wines.*

The first wine is the Kumeu River 1989 Chardonnay. My friend Michael Brajkovich, who is New Zealand's first Master of Wine, is now in charge of this long-established New Zealand family winery, which we visit whenever we go to New Zealand. The Kumeu River is a brilliant Chardonnay which strikes an intriguing balance between French subtlety and New World opulence.

Secondly, a top vintage red burgundy, preferably a Chambertin. I agree with Hilaire Belloc. This is the wine I would really like to be able to afford to buy and drink. There is no substitute for that combination of fruit and rotting vegetation!

Thirdly, another wine from my native New Zealand – one of the brilliant Sauvignon Blancs for which New Zealand is famous – possibly Hunters, Stoneleigh or Delegats. This is the ideal drinking for the desert island, provided the weather is sunny and the wine is cold.

(For those who are still wondering, Hilaire Belloc said: 'I forget the name of the place; I forget the name of the girl; but the wine... was Chambertin.')

Lord Archer of Grantchester *was less specific about his wines but just for once he agreed with Bryan Gould in choosing a New Zealand Chardonnay, as well as a Californian Cabernet. His third choice would be an Italian Barolo 'because I always enjoy it at my favourite restaurant in Milan'.*

Paddy Ashdown, *leader of the Liberal Democrats, recalls holidays in France in his selection.*

I particularly love the wines of northern Burgundy (around the Chablis area). Furthermore, we go there frequently for holidays and know the people in this area well, and so all our wines would be chosen from people who are both friends and excellent wine-makers.

I will choose the wines of Irancy and St-Bris-le-Vineux – in particular the Bourgogne Irancy of Daniel Quintard (a red wine), the Bourgogne Aligoté of Yvon Daudier of St-Bris, and a Chardonnay of Roget Delaloge of Irancy.

Enoch Powell *also stays firmly in France for his selection, taking just one wine and some cassis to make into Kir.*

I have become even more addicted to Sancerre blanc since spending a delightful summer holiday in 1991 on that striking vineyard-clad hill in the still inadequately known Upper Loire region.

Summer in our home commences and ends respectively when Kir starts and stops being drunk. I remember, on a visit to Alésie (which was once the parish of the reverend canon who invented and provided the name for Kir), that I burst out in affectionate laughter on finding his memorial bust set in the outside south wall of the church.

Peter Sissons, *BBC journalist and* Question Time *anchorman, has had his fair share of reporting disasters at sea, but so far there have been no latter-day Robinson Crusoes to tell the world about. His choice of wines provides him with companions from California, Spain and Australia.*

I am not an expert on wines, so I approach the prospect of being stranded with a few cases in a very practical way. These wines are going to have to be very versatile and very reliable. I also object to paying a lot for wine. I have tasted expensive clarets that have left me wondering what all the fuss was about. But my wife Sylvia and I have sat with friends in a French farmhouse kitchen drinking country wine that has been magnificent. And in the heat of the midday Mediterranean sun, whether in our favourite Crete or the Algarve, there is nothing to beat opening that first bottle of something crisp and dry, straight off the ice, with the beads of condensation soaking a crisp white tablecloth.

But the choice I make first is The Wine for Special Occasions. I am sure I am not alone in remarking the formidable competition champagne now faces from other sparklers, and how much more agreeable it is knowing that you can get twice as much wine for your money, while it still tastes expensive. So my first Desert Island Wine is the pink sparkling wine we served to our local friends and neighbours on Christmas Day before lunch. Indeed it was such a success that we didn't have the strength to cook the family lunch until two days later. It's Blanc de Noirs from Mumm Napa Valley.

My second Desert Island Wine is a white for everyday drinking – and it's also not quite as alcoholic as some (10.5 per cent) so I find it an ideal lighter glass of wine. There's no particular story attached to why I like it – indeed, there are a number of dry whites that could get my vote. But I have shared it with friends on hazy, lazy, impromptu occasions, so I suppose one comes back to reliability and availability, and never having had a bad experience. It's an increasingly popular Spanish white, Viña Sol, which is one of the range made by Miguel Torres.

I was tempted to keep things simple and go for just these two wines, which on my parched island would keep me very happy. But I think one does need a red in the portfolio, and on this scorching desert island a red that will not only be excellent served at beach temperature, but which is also good chilled. I find that a chilled red wine, provided it's suitable, can be uniquely refreshing. For such a red I'm going Australian. It's taken me a long time to get back to Australian wine. My first really bad experience with drink was nearly 30 years ago in a Yates Wine Lodge in Liverpool, when the Australian white made me fall over.

There, the only Australian wine served was called white, but it tasted and looked like inferior sweet sherry. Anyway, I've got over that and would take to my island a recent newcomer from Australia, Old Triangle Cabernet Sauvignon from Hill-Smith.

These three very distinct tastes of Australia, Spain and California – such uncomplicated companions – could turn being cast away into something just about bearable.

Someone who should at least be able to use more than seaweed to predict the next day's weather is BBC weatherman **Michael Fish**.

About 15 years ago I, my wife and my two children, then aged four and eight months, were travelling home through France. We were due to spend the night in Cahors, where we intended to arrive at about 6 p.m. The roads were very busy and I decided to take what looked on the map like a short cut, using quiet backroads through the countryside. As the afternoon wore on, we all grew hotter and the children became restless but Cahors seemed to be just as far away as when we started! We eventually arrived at the hotel at about 10 p.m. – the baby (who had been fed en route, unlike the rest of us) was fast asleep, and the hotel dining-room was closed and shuttered. The concierge recommended a small restaurant close by that was still open, where we were able to order a super meal, accompanied by the local wine – Cahors. The relief of finally having arrived made the wine taste like nectar. Needless to say, the family have never let me take a 'short cut' again.

The white Italian wine, Vernaccia di San Gimignano (DOC), always reminds me of a smashing holiday we had in Tuscany some years ago. The weather was perfect (of course), the cottage super, the countryside beautiful and peaceful, Siena and Florence fascinating and, of course, the food and wine superb. San Gimignano itself was very near to us and it seemed only natural to drink the local wine. A glass of well-chilled San Gimignano always reminds me of the peace and quiet of the Tuscan countryside in the early evening, after the hustle and bustle of a day spent in Florence.

Cuckmere White Wine is special for two reasons. I was born in the area and, therefore, it brings back memories of a happy childhood. (I even used to row on the Cuckmere when I was at school!) We bought this wine at the English Wine Centre in Alfriston, where I was delighted to discover several very good white wines, all of which compared favourably with other, more famous, wine-producing countries. We always try to serve English wine when entertaining guests from abroad to show them just how good it is.

John Duval *is chief winemaker at Penfolds in Australia and is responsible for the outstanding Grange as well as the rest of the huge Penfolds range. It is not surprising that he would take some of his own wines to our desert island as well as a French wine – but only the best.*

The three wines I have chosen are 1970 Lindemans Hunter River Bin 3875 (Semillon), 1971 Penfolds Grange and 1970 Château Latour.

This Lindemans Hunter River Semillon is a remarkable wine. Almost iridescent yellow in colour, it is still fresh and youthful with great depth of flavour while retaining elegance. This wine, to me, shows what a great variety Semillon is.

While claiming to have something of a cellar palate, I can't imagine myself not having access to a good bottle of Grange. It was Grange in particular which was instrumental in my decision to work for Penfolds.

I must admit to a preference for red wine and so I have chosen a second red. I have always been impressed by the quality of the wine produced by Château Latour and their ability to make good wine even in difficult years. The 1970 was the first vintage of Château Latour that I tasted and it has always been a favourite.

Novelist **Maeve Binchy** *is our only castaway to include a Sicilian wine.*

I discovered Jacobs Creek – Brokenwood, New South Wales – on my honeymoon. I loved it then and now.

Corvo de Casteldaccia, a very strong ruby red table wine from Sicily, reminds me of sun and holidays and laughter. And then I would choose Fleurie, a great warm, smooth red wine. The day I sold my first book, *Light a Penny Candle*, we drank two bottles at lunch and the taste reminds me of triumph.

Angus Deayton, *well known for his satirical wit on BBC's* Have I Got News For You, *decided to take five wines in his collection.*

My first choice is a Pauillac – Château Lynch-Bages Grand Cru Classé 1979 – because it reminds me of one of the joys of the Channel Islands, namely that they serve fine wines duty-free in the most unexpected places. I remember sitting in a fish and chip shop at 4.30 in the afternoon enjoying a plate of cod and chips washed down by a bottle of Lynch-Bages.

My second choice is Houghton's 'white burgundy' from Perth, Australia. It's a perfect example of the Aussie white but without the sickliness of some of their Chardonnays. I recall a very orderly trip up the Margaret River to their winery for a wine tasting in 1983 and an extremely disorderly one back three hours later. They laid on a band for us, on the sadly correct assumption that we might want to sing. I can never taste their 'white burgundy' today without being reminded of my rendition of 'Moon River', which was apposite if excruciating.

Then Nutbourne Manor, Bacchus 1986. English wines are very underrated in my opinion. This one is every bit as light and summery as a New World wine but with a taste that is quite distinctively British. At the moment English wines are still a bit pricey for what they are but hopefully the more we drink the more the price will come down. Well, it's a good excuse anyway.

My last choices are Sancerre Le Clos du Chêne 1985 and Châteauneuf-du-Pape Domaine de Mont-Redon. One of my favourite tricks if ordering for other people in a restaurant is to make the rather cliché'd choice of a Sancerre and a Châteauneuf-du-Pape in order to see how they react when it turns out to be a white Châteauneuf-du-Pape and a red Sancerre. It somehow appeals to my perverse nature. I'm hoping they'll invent a fish called fillet steak. Happily, they are very good wines.

Last of our valiant contributors is **David Gower**, *cricketing supremo of Hampshire and England.*

To be cast away on a desert island for more than a couple of weeks is not a pleasant notion, but at least the coincidence of being found in such a position with some of one's favourite wines might lessen the shock. I have to say, however, that without company and food of the same quality, even that consoling factor would be diminished.

So the first selection would be Bollinger. This will come as no shock to my friends. The 'Bollie' tent at Lord's has always been a haven to seek at the end of a long day in the field, but the stuff is my favourite liquid with which to celebrate, whether it be hundreds against Australia, weddings, or just a particularly pleasant Wednesday evening in the sun!

Secondly, I would go for an Australian wine, that continent being the source of many happy memories for me. There is a man out there, a legend in his own cellars, called Geoff Merrill, who makes some beautiful wines in the McLaren Vale in South Australia. His handlebar moustache is known throughout the cellars of Australia and some in England too, and his wines are delicious, especially his '86 Cabernet Sauvignon. But, as we are desert island bound, I am going to choose his Chardonnay from the same year (I think that was the good one!) to remind me of the days and the barbecues at his Mount Hurtle Winery, especially the day when Allan Lamb decapitated a bottle of errant Bollinger with an axe – it was just unfortunate that the bottle was balanced on my head at the time, but fortunate that the only casualty was the bottle!

Finally, we need some port, and to rekindle memories of the odd trip to Oporto and up the Douro to see how the stuff is produced in the first place, I shall have to ask the Symington family to see if they can find any Dow '55 left in storage somewhere. We did once play cricket at the sporting club in Oporto, and the game certainly wasn't the same after lunch – it's very much just as well that the same supplies are not furnished on the lunch tables at the first-class grounds of England, or the County Championship would degenerate in a hurry.

SOUTH AFRICA

Rosemary George

South Africa is coming in from the cold. With the lifting of trade sanctions, after an embargo of nearly 25 years, wines from the Cape are beginning to reappear on wine merchants' and supermarket shelves. What began as a tiny trickle is gathering momentum. The political isolation of South Africa has been strongly felt within its wine industry. For the past few years it has operated in a vacuum, unable to pit its wines against those of other New World countries. Import duties in South Africa itself are so high that to drink a wine from, for example, France or California would be a distinctly unattractive choice. With the exception of the odd bottle of champagne, South Africa fulfils the requirements of its own domestic market, consuming its own table wines as well as its own sparkling and fortified wines.

Perhaps this is why the technological advances of the last decade have passed it by. Here is a country that led the way in temperature-controlled cool fermentation at the end of the 1950s, and the use of cultured yeasts for fermentation, but is only now learning how to make Chardonnay in new oak barrels. However, there is a feeling of optimism in the winelands of the Cape. Things are changing. A new generation of winemakers – qualified oenologists, many of whom have travelled the world – is coming into its own, and the flavours of the Cape are becoming more refined with every vintage.

The Cape winelands are some of the most beautiful in the world. Rugged mountains form a dramatic backdrop to every vineyard; the effect is breathtaking, whether it is the Simonsberg, Drakenstein or Hildeberg mountains. The Paarl valley narrows into that of Franschhoek (meaning, literally, 'French corner') where many of the exiled Huguenots settled after the Revocation of the Edict of Nantes in 1685. The names have a French ring, in some cases distorted by Afrikaans pronunciation, such as L'Ormarins, La Bri, La Motte and Le Bonheur. Many of the estates have architectural gems in the form of Cape Dutch manor houses, distinctive with their gabled roof lines and brilliant white paint. Some, such as Boschendal and Groot Constantia, are museums, with antique Delft china and fine wooden fittings in yellowwood and stinkwood. Compared to the average vineyard holding in Europe, they are enormous, with large tracts of vineyards, as many as a hundred or two hundred acres, often growing other crops as well, and containing small villages housing the farm workers.

THE STORY SO FAR

The history of winemaking in South Africa is as old as the colony itself, dating back to the middle of the seventeenth century, long before vines reached California, let alone Australia and New Zealand. Jan van Riebeeck, the governor of the young Dutch colony, who had been responsible for bringing vines from Europe in the first place, recorded in his diary on 2 February 1659: 'Today, praise be to God, wine was pressed for the first time from Cape grapes'. There is no record of how the wine tasted but the grapes were described as French and Muscadel. The next governor of note, Simon van der Stel, who gave his name to the town of Stellenbosch and the mountain that dominates the skyline, Simonsberg, helped the nascent wine production by welcoming French Huguenots to the country. He was also the owner of the most famous estate of the Cape, Groot Constantia, which produced a dessert wine, Constantia, which gained a reputation in Europe long before the great châteaux of Bordeaux. The industry flourished; the wine regions gradually spread, fanning out over the Cape, until phylloxera struck at the end of the last century, causing, as it did elsewhere, considerable havoc.

Today the production of fine table wines is concentrated in the districts of Paarl and Stellenbosch. Over the past decade or so there has been a noticeable shift away from dessert wines, or fortified port and sherry styles and muscadels, to lighter table wines for consumption with a meal. The hotter regions, such as Olifants River and Klein Karoo, which depend upon irrigation, produce grapes not only for dessert wines but also for grape concentrate and distillation, as well as table grapes. The cooler vineyards of the Coastal Region, along with parts of Robertson and Worcester – which are further inland and separated from the Coastal Region by a mountain range – are the source of the best table wines.

CLASSIFICATION OF SOUTH AFRICAN WINES

The 1973 wine law of South Africa concentrates on the origin of a wine and does not encompass the type of restrictions imposed by, for example, Appellation Contrôlée in France, so yields, grape varieties, pruning methods and so on are all the decision of the producer. However, the vineyards of the Cape are carefully demarcated, with five principal regions: Boberg, the Breede River Valley, Klein Karoo, the Coastal Region and Olifants River. Within each region there are districts, such as Paarl and Stellenbosch (these are in the Coastal Region). Further down the line, there are smaller wards, which are part of either a region or a district, such as the Franschhoek Valley, which is in Paarl, and Constantia, which is included in the Coastal Region. Finally, the smallest demarcation is an estate (there are a total of 79 registered), which produces and sells wine only from its own grapes. Wines are classified not only according to provenance, which is confirmed by a blue band on the capsule, but also by vintage, with a red band, and grape variety, or cultivar, with a green band. Thus, origin is guaranteed, but not necessarily quality.

The wine industry of South Africa is dominated by an organisation known as the KWV (Ko-operative Wijnbouwers Vereniging van Zuid-Afrika Beperkt, to give it its full name) which is a co-operative of wine farmers, both producers of table wines and growers of grapes. It was established in 1918 with the particular objective of expanding the export market in an attempt to solve the problem of overproduction and surplus on the domestic market. Today it remains an important commercial organisation, but in the past it was frequently criticised for the implementation of a system of quotas which, until May 1992 when the system was abolished, controlled the amount of grapes and wine a farm could produce. In the successful table wine regions of the Cape, notably in the Coastal Region, the quota system had outgrown its use, as well as often having a stifling effect on the development of new areas which might be suitable for grape-growing. The demise of the quota should therefore help the development of vineyards in hitherto unexploited cooler sites.

CLIMATE

There is no doubt about the suitability of the Cape for making wine: the climate is Mediterranean, but the cold waters of the Atlantic Ocean have a cooling effect on temperatures. Paarl and Stellenbosch rarely suffer from extremes of temperature. Usually there is sufficient, but not too much, rain, with enough variation to provide vintage differences. Humidity can cause problems and spraying against rot is standard practice. Organic viticulture is virtually unheard of in the Cape, although serious producers assert that they keep treatments in the vineyard to a minimum.

GRAPE VARIETIES IN RED WINES

The grape varieties of South Africa are those of Europe, with just one exception, Pinotage, which was developed at Stellenbosch University by a Professor Perold in 1925. The problem with Pinotage – a cross between Cinsaut (also known as Hermitage in the Cape) and Pinot Noir – is that it is a very undemanding grape variety, easy to grow and generously productive. As a result, few people take it seriously, treating it very much as a poor relation of Cabernet, Shiraz and Pinot Noir. Yet it has the potential to make some of South Africa's most individual red wines. At Kanonkop, which is establishing a reputation for Pinotage, it is vinified quite differently from Cabernet Sauvignon: with Pinotage sufficient tannin and extract is obtained after only a two- or three-day period of skin contact at fermentation. Nevers rather than Allier is the better oak for it, and it benefits from ageing in large as well as small barrels. In the vineyard, bush vines work much better than the trellises used for other varieties. Good Pinotage has ripe raspberry flavours, with some body, and with age it takes on some of the vegetal characteristics of Pinot Noir.

Blending

A 25 per cent leeway on a stated grape variety allows for considerable flexibility in blending, and Cabernet Franc and Merlot are often added to Cabernet Sauvignon. However, many of the wines labelled Cabernet Sauvignon are pure varietals, whilst those which imitate a Bordeaux blend tend to have 'fantasy' names like Kanonkop's Paul Sauer, Rustenberg's Gold, or Warwick Farm's Trilogy; the latter consists of 75 per cent Cabernet Sauvignon, 20 per cent Merlot and 5 per cent Cabernet Franc. The leader in these was Rubicon (the name was inspired by Julius Caesar's historic crossing of the Rubicon) which was first made at Meerlust as recently as 1980. Often these Bordeaux blends seem more successful than pure Cabernet Sauvignon. The use of Bordeaux *barriques*, as opposed to the traditional large oak casks which are now really only used for Pinotage, is a relatively recent innovation and has become standard practice only in the past few years.

Perhaps the most exciting of the red varietals is Pinot Noir. Tim Hamilton-Russell at Hamilton-Russell vineyards really takes the credit for pioneering this grape variety in the Cape, and his estate at Hermanus consists of Africa's southernmost vineyards. The starting point in his search for a suitably cool site was Cape Agulhas, the most southern tip of the continent. He found the conditions he was looking for at Hermanus, planted his first vines in 1976, made his first wine in 1981 and is now producing Pinot Noir with some fine varietal character. His example has been followed by others – Meerlust, a beautiful estate outside Stellenbosch with an Italian winemaker, produces Pinot Noir, as does the newly created estate of Bouchard Finlayson, which combines Burgundian money and experience from Paul Bouchard with the expertise of Peter Finlayson, Hamilton-Russell's ex-winemaker. Glen Carlou, which belongs to Walter Finlayson (Peter's brother), is another estate well on the way to making fine Pinot Noir.

GRAPE VARIETIES IN WHITE WINES

As for white wines, every winemaker in South Africa is succumbing to the craze for Chardonnay. The country had something of a false start with that grape variety in the mid-eighties, when stringent quarantine regulations restricting the import of vines resulted in smuggled cuttings being incorrectly identified, and what was thought to be Chardonnay turned out to be Pinot Auxerrois. Things are easier now, but most of the plantings of Chardonnay are still very young and often the wine lacks the stature and body to take the amount of new oak that it is generally given. In many of the wines oak replaces fruit, with a buttery vanilla flavour, or a clumsy stewed taste that comes from oak not grapes. Happily, there are exceptions, such as the wines of Hamilton-Russell, Klein Constantia and Neil Ellis (a winemaker without an estate). Best of all is Meerlust, unfortunately not yet available in commercial quantities.

Sauvignon is more successful, with some fresh pungent flavours being achieved by estates such as Klein Constantia, Boschendal, L'Ormarins, La Bri and others. The term Blanc Fumé describes a Sauvignon that has been in oak, but the results are usually as unhappy as with many Chardonnays. There are some flavoursome Rhine or Weisser Rieslings, as opposed to Cape or Paarl Riesling (the rather insipid Cruchen under another name). More original is Pinot Gris, which so far is produced only by a couple of estates, notably Van Loveren in Robertson, with some wonderful spicy, mushroomy fruit.

It may be that the chief source of untapped white wine potential will come from Chenin Blanc, which is also known as Steen. Like Pinotage, this workhorse grape variety is very much taken for granted. It has been used for sherry, sparkling wine, table wine and distillation. In irrigated vineyards its yields can be enormous, making for some pretty diluted flavours; if kept to a sensible limit, it can provide wine with some concentration of taste. The other distinct advantage is that Chenin Blanc actually ripens every year in South Africa, a vain hope in the Loire Valley. Properly vinified, it could, and indeed does, make some fresh, lightly honeyed, easy-to-drink dry or slightly sweet white wine – Simonsig is one such example. Chenin Blanc is also a source of Noble Late Harvest wines, notably the famous Edelkeur that was pioneered by Günter Brözel at Nederburg. In the right conditions, Noble Late Harvest wines – the term Noble, as in 'Noble Rot', implies botrytis – can also be made from Sauvignon and Pinot Gris, with some success.

THE FUTURE

South African export figures for 1991 showed a dramatic increase of 60 per cent on the previous year and, with the continued growth in interest, a similar success is predicted in 1992. There is no doubt that evidence of the government's policy of reform being implemented will help make South African wines socially acceptable in a way that they never could have been during the years of apartheid. There are good wines available, with some representing good value for money. But others are still too expensive for what they are, a consequence of the isolation to which the Cape has been subjected. South Africans have yet to appreciate the full scope of the competition from Europe and the rest of the New World.

However, there is no doubt that the potential of the Cape is fantastic. It has the climate, the soil, the vines; producers are gradually acquiring better virus-free clones. Temperature-controlled fermentation in insulated cellars is standard practice; small oak *barriques* are coming into use. The Cape made great wine in the form of Constantia in the early nineteenth century and there is no reason why it cannot do so again. A feeling of optimism certainly prevails amongst a new young generation of winemakers who are poised to bring South Africa out of its vinous backwater into the limelight.

Names to look out for

Numerous estates are now making their mark on the export market. The author's top ten names to look out for, in alphabetical order, are as follows:

Backsberg
Neil Ellis
Hamilton-Russell
Klein Constantia
Meerlust
Owergaauw
Rustenberg
Simonsig
Vriesenhof
Warwick Farm

Stockists of South African wines include: *ASDA, Averys, Augustus Barnett, Barwell & Jones, Berry Bros, Bottoms Up, Cape Province Wines, Harrods, Lay & Wheeler, Marks & Spencer, Oddbins, Thos Peatling, Sainsbury's, Selfridges, Tesco, Thresher, Unwins, Victoria Wine, Waitrose, Wine Rack*

Artisan *versus* technologist?

Christine Austin

'Of course, wine doesn't taste the same as it used to – it's all the chemicals they add.' You would be surprised just how common that kind of statement is, as if people believe that white-coated scientists spend their days stirring chemicals into our drink like witches around a giant cauldron.

In one respect they are right that wine doesn't taste the same as it used to, particularly at the affordable end of the market. Do you remember the unspeakable quality of cheap Spanish wine twenty years ago, or the early Australian imports with high alcohol and tongue-curling flavours? Compare those with the good, clean, well-made wines, priced from as little as £2.50, that are stacked high on present-day supermarket shelves. Take one home and you will find that it doesn't smell of drains or taste like battery acid; it is probably quite good. If you pay a little more you will get slightly more flavour, more fruit and more complexity, but any wine will be palatable. Gone are the days when wine didn't travel – that was just an excuse for poor winemaking.

So what has caused these changes? In a word, technology – and that is a problem in itself. As the advertisement said, 'Get an 'ology and you're a scientist', but no one likes the idea of a scientist messing about with something we drink. Even a glimpse of the quality-control laboratory in a winery can make people suspicious, so, for a good public image, winemakers must be seen as artisans, preferably dressed in a checked shirt tasting wine from a cask, not measuring its acidity or residual sugar.

But technology is the best thing that has happened to wine in a very long time. It has brought wholesome, well-made wine into the reach of every family's budget. Technology doesn't mean chemicals, it means understanding all the processes of growing grapes and making wine and getting the best out of them.

Fermentation has been occurring naturally for thousands of years, but it was only in the 1800s that Louis Pasteur discovered that yeast was the cause. That simple discovery showed that winemaking isn't magic but that it *can* be controlled. Once you are in control, quality and consistency are not far behind.

IN THE VINEYARD

Technology begins in the vineyard even before the vines are planted. To get good grapes you have to choose your site carefully: the right drainage, altitude, soil type and sunshine are all-important. Grape type matters too: just as there are differences between cooking and eating apples, grapes used for winemaking are different from those intended for eating. Cabernet Sauvignon, Chardonnay or Pinot Noir? It all depends on what the area is suited to and the type of wine you want to make.

Clones and vine types

Whichever grape you decide to grow there is an additional choice: which clone to use? The very word 'clone' conjures up dreadful images of genetic engineering, but, in fact, many clones are naturally-occurring variations that already exist in vineyards. They are like twins in a family: they may look identical but once you get to know them you will find that each has a different character. Some have a particular nuance of flavour, some are more resistant to disease and still others suit a particular soil type. A few winemakers are happy to select the one clone that seems ideal for a particular site; others prefer to use different clones to add complexity to the wine – it all depends on the winemaker.

Not all winemakers have an unlimited choice when it comes to selecting clones or even vine varieties. Quarantine regulations in some parts of the world have restricted the types available. One vineyard in Australia decided to plant one particular clone and after a seven-year wait it was allowed just four precious vine cuttings. The technologists got to work and in one year they provided 2,500 identical, healthy, plants. Tissue and leaf culture work faster and more cheaply than the traditional ways of planting and collecting seeds, and this leads to lower prices at the checkout.

Technologists do not just select types of vine, they can create them too. The stalwart variety of middle-priced German wine, Müller-Thurgau, was developed in the 1800s by crossing Riesling and Sylvaner. Now it is widely planted and produces good wines from sites which cannot ripen the more demanding Riesling.

Rootstocks

An additional complication is choosing the right rootstock. Ever since the phylloxera plague swept around the world in the late 1800s, most vines have been grafted on to resistant roots. The exceptions are in a few areas, such as Cyprus, Chile and South Australia, which the little aphid never managed to reach. There are hundreds of different vine rootstocks, each one suited to different circumstances. Therefore, by varying the rootstock, as well as the variety and the clone, the winemaker can control yields, improve resistance to disease and keep phylloxera at bay. It sounds like unnecessary interference but the alternative is more disease, uncontrolled high yields and poor wine. Even now, California is again wrestling with the phylloxera problem, for a new super-strain, Biotype B, has appeared. Current rootstocks, mainly AxR1, are not resistant to this type and so a programme of regrafting on to more resistant rootstocks is taking place.

Irrigation

Eventually the vineyard is planted on the right roots, at the right density of plants per hectare and using the right trellising to comply with legislation (in some areas) or the winemaker's current practice. Water is the next important point. Generally, European vineyards receive enough rain to grow good grapes so irrigation is banned throughout Europe except in a few experimental areas. But outside Europe irrigation is essential.

Water is like the engine of the vine – it 'drives' transpiration and photosynthesis. Too little, and the vine becomes stressed and fruit quality suffers; too much and the grape flavours are diluted. The winemaker can decide when to water the vines by kicking the soil and seeing how much dust it creates but electronic measurement gives a more accurate result and can trigger drip irrigation systems to deliver the right amount of precious water to each vine. Once again, the winemaker is in control.

The grape-pickers are replaced

With the grapes gently ripening in the sunshine, our winemaker's thoughts turn to the vintage and how to harvest the crop. He or she might book the regular team of pickers who will toil in the sunshine for weeks, discarding poor or unripe grapes and generally picking a quality crop. However, not all parts of the world have experienced grape-pickers to call on.

Machine-picking is the order of the day in many New World areas. You will never see machines on the steep slopes of the Mosel or in certain hallowed vineyards, but in large, fairly flat vineyards in Australia, California and Chile, say, and even in parts of Bordeaux, they do an excellent job. They work quickly when the crop is ripe, they don't need feeding three times a day or fall asleep after lunch and, most importantly, they work at night. That way grapes are cool and reach the winery in a much better condition than if they had been harvested in hot sunshine.

It is typical of many Australian companies to have vineyards at different sites and truck grapes through the cool of the night over hundreds of miles to a central winery. Sometimes the grapes are crushed and the juice is transported in chilled tankers like milk. Having centralised wineries keeps costs down and concentrates the technical expertise on one site. This system also allows for blending grapes and wines from different areas.

If you pick by machine, then when winter comes you might as well prune your vines mechanically too. Widely used in the New World, the machine works rather like a hedge clipper, slicing off shoots along the top and sides of the vine. It even mulches the clippings around the base of the vines to fertilise next year's crop. Not only is this cheaper than hand pruning but it changes the way the vine produces its grapes. Instead of three or four large bunches the vine sprouts 20 or more small bunches of tiny grapes. Because small grapes have a high skin juice ratio they have greater flavour.

IN THE WINERY

Once at the winery, the winemaker is still in control. If grapes were left to their own resources they would relentlessly ferment, first into a poor-quality wine and then into vinegar. Whether our winemaker wears a checked shirt or a white coat, it is his or her job to get the best from the grapes and to make the best possible wine. Wineries have moved on from the days when everyone danced around in a sludgy mass of purple grapes. Winemaking, particularly white wines, is clean, cool and controlled.

White wines

White wines are generally made by fermenting the juice off the skins; even white grape skins contain enough tannin to make a wine taste astringent. To separate juice from skins, the grapes are gently pressed so that the juice runs out; from this point onwards the juice must be protected. Just as the surface of a cut apple goes brown if you leave it in the air, so grape juice oxidises and loses its fresh fruit flavour if it is not protected in some way. This is where sulphur dioxide (SO_2) comes in.

This chemical has long been used by winemakers all over the world, as well as by home winemakers in the form of Campden tablets. Mothers also use it to sterilise their babies' bottles. Its preservative properties were discovered centuries ago: we know, for instance, that the Romans burnt it in casks and amphorae in order to clean them. Nowadays, it is used in solution and added in tiny doses to prevent the oxidation of wine. As technology has improved, the amount of SO_2 used in winemaking has fallen and legislation has been passed to control its use. Very few winemakers can do without it: even most organic producers use small amounts of sulphur. Sulphur does not just stop the juice going brown, but it kills off some of the bacteria and wild yeasts lurking on the skins and in the juice that can give odd flavours to the wine. Once rid of them, the juice becomes stable.

The cloudy bits in grape juice settle out in about 12 hours to give a clear juice which ferments cleanly, leaving bright fruit flavours in the wine. To help this process, some winemakers may add an enzyme which, unfortunately, sounds like the chemistry set being opened again. But enzymes are naturally occurring substances which act as catalysts – they can be extracted and used. Anyone who has eaten a wafer-thin after-dinner mint is guilty of enjoying the results of enzyme technology.

AND SO TO FERMENTATION

The whites

Grapes have a natural bloom composed of yeasts. In well-established winegrowing areas these yeasts are likely to be 'good' ones which would ferment the juice into wine, but in newer areas they may be spoilage yeasts which have quite a different effect. The choice is simple. Do you risk the natural yeasts and bacteria taking hold of a large tank of wine and turning it into expensive vinegar or do you add your own yeast? Unless you are very sure of your natural yeast you will add a pure culture which works at the temperature you want. Yeast selection has become a science of its own, with special strains being developed to produce exactly the right type of fermentation at the right temperature.

Temperature control is one of the keys to modern winemaking. By controlling temperature you can control the rate of fermentation and the resulting flavours. Cool fermentation (about 20°C for whites) for 10 to 15 days retains the flavour of the fruit, but if it is allowed to proceed without control then the temperature will rise and the wine will become dull and 'cooked'.

Some of the most dramatic improvements in quality have been brought about by controlling temperature; the easiest way to do this is in a stainless steel tank. By simply running water over the outside of the tank or using cooling coils inside, the temperature of fermentation can be controlled. From the top names in Bordeaux to the giant company Gallo in California, stainless steel glints in every corner of a winery. Its other great advantage is that it is easy to clean, so 'off' flavours from bacterial contamination are avoided.

The old alternative

The down-side to the 'clean is good' approach to winemaking is that these squeaky-clean wines may lack character and depth. After all, some of the most wonderful white wines in the world are made in wooden casks in Burgundy. That is why people like Len Evans of Rothbury in Australia and Jim Clendenen of Au Bon Climat in California are going back to using cloudy juice and barrel fermentation. They get toasty flavours which just can't be matched by oak ageing. At about £300 a cask this option is open only to makers of top-quality and expensive wines, but it does demonstrate how one winemaker's new discovery may be just a refinement of another's established technique.

... and the reds

Red winemaking differs from white in that the skins are included in the fermentation process. Peel a red grape and the flesh is pale green; consequently, in order to make a red wine, the colour and flavour in the skins must be extracted. Long maceration on the skins provides a lot of the colour but the tannin comes too and this is why big Bordeaux wines need time to soften.

To make a red wine for early drinking it is important to strike a balance between extracting the colour and flavour and leaving harsh tannins behind in the skins. In a tank of fermenting red wine the skins float to the surface, forming a 'cap', so pumping the wine over that cap or submerging the layer in the tank helps to extract the colour and flavour. Some tanks slowly rotate like giant washing machines to keep the cap broken up and in the wine.

The idea behind making Beaujolais demonstrates another way of leaving the tannin behind. Carbonic maceration uses whole grapes which are fermented in an atmosphere of carbon dioxide. This allows a different type of reaction to take place; after five days or so the free-run juice is run off and fermentation continues normally. The result is a wine with low tannin and acidity and lively fruit flavours.

Temperature control is just as important for red wines as it is for whites. Higher temperatures (nearer 30°C) extract the colour quickly without all the accompanying tannin. The result is a soft, well-coloured and full-flavoured wine which does not need years to mature.

A touch of oak

Young red wines, even those for relatively early drinking, may be aged in oak casks for a short period. Oak adds another dimension to the flavour of both reds and whites. To describe a wine as oak aged is only part of the story: there are many different sources of oak and ways it can be used. European oak, for example, causes flavours and effects on the wine that are different from casks made of American oak, which gives a fuller, more sappy flavour and is used widely in Rioja. European oak, particularly from France, has a more subtle flavour but even this varies from forest to forest; Limousin, Tronçais and Nevers have different characteristics and effects on the wine. The very best winemakers not only specify what type of oak is to be used but also the caskmaker and the amount of 'toast' inside the cask. When ageing a wine in cask, the winemaker can play tunes on the flavour by ageing only a proportion for a few months and blending that oaked wine with some that is unoaked. Only the best wines can stand up to the positive flavours of new oak and many will be aged in oak that is a year old. After a few years all the flavours will have been lost from a cask and it becomes merely a storage vessel.

Malolactic fermentation and clarification

Malolactic fermentation is the process whereby natural bacteria in wine transform harsh malic acid into softer, creamier lactic acid. It used to be regarded as a bit of a mystery but now that it is understood and can be controlled many winemakers promote malolactic fermentation in just part of their wine to give it added complexity.

Both reds and whites have to be fined to get rid of cloudy particles which might spoil the appearance of the wine. Top-quality wines are fined by the addition of egg whites but most are clarified by a special earth called bentonite which falls to the bottom of the vat before being removed. Some wines, though, do 'fall bright' given low temperatures and sufficient times.

Ready for the market

Not surprisingly, when the wine is ready to bottle, technology still plays a part. A badly cleaned bottling line will negate all the good work done so far. Many white wines are chilled to get rid of excess tartrates in the wine. These don't do the wine any harm but they can form crystals in the bottle. If you have ever complained to your wine merchant about broken glass in a bottle, it is almost certain that the bits you could see were tartrates.

Protection from oxidation continues even at the bottling line. A little dissolved carbon dioxide in the wine helps keep it tasting fresh but too much gives a slight fizz on the tongue.

Pulling the cork is the consumer's first experience of a bottle of wine. It can be disappointing when the cork crumbles or fails to come out of the bottle, but occasionally the cork can fail altogether and allow in oxygen. This spoils the wine and makes it smell like stale cabbage: this is described as 'corked'. Little bits of cork floating around in the glass are not the same thing at all – that generally means the bottle has been badly opened.

As supplies of good-quality cork cannot keep up with the demand, inevitably some poor-quality cork is used, thus increasing the incidence of cork failure. Not all these wines will be strongly corked but some – a higher proportion than many would credit – can be tainted by a taste of cork, known as corkiness.

From the vineyard to the bottling line, today's winemaker has more information and more resources at his or her disposal than ever before. The result is clear to see – a wealth of good wines at very reasonable prices. New technology has transformed wine from a luxury into an everyday item, but the consumer should not confuse technology with chemistry. Winemakers are an inquisitive bunch, always striving to improve the quality of their product. They experiment with viticulture and vinification in a constant search for improvement and, as with all development, as soon as one goal is reached another comes into view. Their work hinges on getting the best out of what nature can provide and they know that the answers they seek are not to be found in a chemistry set. If you do visit a winery and see a white coat, it probably belongs to the person who makes sure that the bottling line is clean and that the wine is up to standard. The winemaker will almost certainly be wearing a checked shirt. And it is quite probable that the nearest the wine in your glass has been to chemicals is the washing-up liquid lingering around the rim.

Part II

The taste of wine

INTRODUCTION TO THE TASTE WHEELS

The country-by-country approach to wine has become too rigid and, at the same time, too confusing. Britain now imports wines from over forty different countries, from all continents, with each year bringing new wines and new flavours from hitherto undiscovered vineyards. Consequently, the consumer is presented with an ever-increasing choice. Small wonder, then, that many of us prefer to stick faithfully to the familiar old favourites and hesitate to spread our vinous wings.

Since it is the intrinsic taste that determines whether we enjoy a wine, and not the fact that it comes from such and such a grape variety or this or that vineyard, it seems more logical and useful to discuss wines by flavour rather than by country. What follows is a breakdown of the world's wines into three taste wheels – for table, fortified and sparkling wines – particularly featuring those most readily available on our wine merchants' shelves.

The taste wheels show the similarities between wines from different countries and regions and demonstrate that grape varieties, flavours and wine styles *do* cross national boundaries. They draw comparisons and contrasts between the basic taste components, acidity and body, tannin and oak. For example, if you like the firm, crisp flavour of Muscadet, you will see that you are not condemned solely to the dry whites of the Atlantic end of the Loire Valley, but can find taste parallels not only in other parts of France, but also in New Zealand, Portugal and Italy. Conversely, the identical grape variety produced in two completely different parts of the world, or indeed in two adjacent wine regions, may not taste at all the same.

Any attempt to put wine into categories of taste can only ever be purely subjective and is open to discussion. You may find that you disagree with some suggestions, but that does not matter. The aim is to provoke thought and encourage experimentation in your wine-buying. We have split the world's wine up into broad bands of flavour, determined by such fundamental factors as oak, body, acidity, sugar and tannin. There are several wines which find a place in more than one taste band. New Zealand Sauvignon Blanc is one such wine for, depending on how it is vinified, it may be crisply pungent, or ripe and full-flavoured with hints of oak. Chablis is another example which crosses the bands, depending on whether it is village Chablis or a Chablis grand cru, and whether it is fermented in stainless steel or aged in oak. The taste wheels are no more than guidelines: with something as subjective as taste in wine, nothing can be permanent, for flavours change as the wines mature and develop. Nor are our palates infallibly consistent from day to day.

THE FUNDAMENTALS

First, it is worth considering the four fundamental factors that make a wine taste the way it does. They are the grape variety or blend of grape varieties; the soil in which the vines are grown; the climate to which they are subjected; and the hand of the winemaker.

Grape varieties

An infinite number of different grape varieties can be used for making wine, although, in practice, those that make the world's finer and better-known wines are limited to perhaps a hundred. In Europe, centuries of tradition and experience have determined which are best suited to which vineyards, while parts of the New World are still experimenting with the better-known vines of France, Germany and Italy, to establish which perform best and where. Efforts are concentrated above all on Cabernet Sauvignon and Chardonnay, but Riesling, Gewürztraminer, Sauvignon, Sémillon, Chenin Blanc, Cabernet Franc, Merlot, Pinot Noir, Syrah and Sangiovese all have their counterparts in other continents. In addition, there are the occasional individual grape varieties of the New World, such as California's Zinfandel and South Africa's Pinotage.

Soil and climate

Soil and climate explain, in part, why two wines from the same grape variety, grown in different parts of the world, can taste quite diverse, without any apparent similarity of flavour. Chardonnay is an obvious example, as the world's most fashionable and popular white grape. The soil components of chalk, limestone or clay may affect the flavour. In a cool climate, where the grapes find it hard to ripen, the wine will be lean with firm acidity – compared to a wine born in a hot sunny climate, where a lack of acidity in the grapes may present a problem and the wine will taste ripe and buttery. Winemakers in the New World are more cavalier in their attitude towards what the French call *terroir* – the all-encompassing term for the combination of soil and microclimate of a vineyard, as well as other factors such as aspect and altitude – and think nothing of trucking grapes for hundreds of miles to blend with other grapes grown elsewhere.

On the northern edge (in the northern hemisphere) of the band where grape growing is feasible, the annual differences in climate account for vintage variations, with rain, frost, hail, drought, sunshine – at the right or wrong time – making a wine great or merely indifferent. The permutations in climate are much less pronounced the further south you go, until you reach southern Italy and southern Spain where unlimited sunshine and unfailingly ripe grapes are assured. However, in Europe's most northern vineyards the annual differences in weather can be quite significant, and can vary quite dramatically from one region to another within the same country. For example, a great claret year does not necessarily mean a good burgundy vintage. The climatic conditions of the two regions can be quite different, for one enjoys a continental climate and the other is determined by the maritime influence of the Atlantic Ocean. The contrast between two consecutive years can be equally marked: 1990 in Bordeaux may be one of the contenders for 'the vintage of the century', while 1991 was affected by spring frosts and then by rain at the harvest, producing merely average wines.

The winemaker

Finally, the winemakers play their part. It is their decision when to pick the grapes, how to vinify them and when to bottle the wine. Tradition and experience dictate some of the choices, but experimental curiosity also features, especially in the vineyards of the New World, or in regions that are undergoing dramatic transformation, such as Tuscany or the Midi. The use of oak, of which more later, is the most obvious way in which the winemaker can directly influence the taste of the wine, but there are numerous other possible nuances of technique, all of which contribute something to the final result – the bottle on your dining-table, and the wine in your glass.

> *A man cannot make him laugh; but that's no marvel; he drinks no wine.*
>
> Shakespeare, *Henry IV (Part II)*

THE BASIC COMPONENTS

The basic components of taste have determined the shape of the taste wheels. For white wine, the first consideration is sweetness, or otherwise, so the initial division is between dry, medium and sweet. Body, or weight, which originates not only from sugar, but also from alcohol, must then be taken into account. A dry white wine with a high alcohol content will taste full-bodied, while a crisp wine with little alcohol will seem quite light and ethereal. There is the same difference in red wines, too, with a mouth-filling Châteauneuf-du-Pape from a warm climate contrasting with a light-bodied Pinot Noir from a much cooler region. Red wines may also have more or less weight, depending on how long the juice has spent in contact with the grape skins during fermentation: a long period of skin contact will give a wine more extract and substance than one which has spent only three or four days on the skins. Most sweet wines seem positively mouth-filling because of the high sugar content.

Acidity

Acidity is an essential ingredient in all wines, although it is most apparent to the tastebuds in light, dry, crisp whites and rosés. However, even red and richly sweet wines still need a quota of acidity, or they will taste flabby and lifeless. Acidity is mainly a function of climate: the warmer the climate, the riper the grapes, the more sugar and less acidity; conversely, the cooler the climate, the harder it is for grapes to ripen, so they are picked with higher levels of acidity which transfer to the wine. With modern vinification techniques it is possible to remove acidity from a wine, or add it, but this can sometimes be detected in the mouth as an unbalanced citric taste.

Oak

Oak is another key taste in both red and white wine. Ideally, a wine should not taste obviously of oak. It should be used in the same way that garlic is used in cooking: the taste should be well-integrated and harmonious, without dominating or overwhelming the fruit. However, without it, the wine would be that much poorer and would lack complexity or dimension. Small oak barrels have been used in parts of France for winemaking for centuries; after all, they were all that was available for storing wine before the advent of concrete and, subsequently, stainless steel. Now winemakers have a choice and many are abandoning their concrete tanks and stainless steel vats and returning to the oak barrels of their grandfathers. They are mastering the techniques required of new oak barrels; a fundamental difference is that nowadays barrels tend to be renewed at least every three or four years, whereas their grandparents continued to use the same barrels for ten, or even twenty, years.

The taste of oak from a new barrel can drown, rather than enhance, the intrinsic fruit flavour of wine and can produce what some call an infusion of oak chippings. With older barrels the effect diminishes significantly. A wine, therefore, needs to have sufficient body and structure in its own right in order to absorb the effect of the oak, without detriment to the flavour. Compare a fine white burgundy vinified in oak with a Muscadet fermented in oak. With the Muscadet there is the proverbial tisane of oak chippings, for there is insufficient structure in the wine to cope with the oak, while the burgundy takes on even greater stature and finesse. Having said that, the effect of the oak on the flavour of the wine also varies in relation to the age of the wine. A young burgundy that has just been bottled, after spending a few months in new oak, will taste ripe and buttery. It will not only have some youthful fruit, but also the vanilla flavours of the new oak, although these flavours will not yet have come together. As the wine matures it loses its youthful characteristics, and enters a rather awkward phase, when the oak overwhelms the fruit. And then, when the wine is two or three years old, it begins to take on more mature flavours, with a harmonious balance between the oak and the fruit.

Winemakers in California, Australia and elsewhere in the world, who aspire to emulate the finesse of Meursault or Puligny-Montrachet, are aware of the importance of oak barrels. They appreciate the qualities and effects of different barrels, whether they are heavily charred or only lightly so, whether they come from the Allier or the Vosges or one of the other oak forests of central France and, perhaps most important of all, who the cooper is. They have also come to realise that the flavours originating from the barrel are very much better integrated into the wine if the wine is not only aged, but also fermented, in oak. It seems that a wine put into wood for a few months will result, more often than not, in two distinct layers of flavour, oak and fruit.

Similarly, with all the great red wines, oak maturation is a vital part of the production process. While white wine can sometimes be fermented in small oak barrels, red wine is only ever matured in them, although some traditional estates may still ferment their wine in large open-topped wooden vats. However, that has little bearing on the final taste in the glass. It is the maturation in oak that is important in contributing to the ultimate quality and flavour of a red wine. Maturation in oak allows the wine to absorb some extra tannin from the wood; it also allows for a period of gentle oxidation, or rather oxygenation, which may soften the youthful tannins in a new wine. Depending on the style of the wine and the producer's aims, this period of maturation may be only a few months, or a couple of years, or even longer. While small barrels are usual in the classic regions of France, such as Bordeaux, Burgundy and the Rhône Valley, Italy has traditionally favoured large barrels, or *botti*. These have little effect in adding tannin to a wine, but provide a useful vessel for a period of gentle maturation, with some subtle oxygenation. Traditionally, Italian red wines, such as Barolo or Brunello di Montalcino, have been kept in wood for longer periods than the red wines of France.

The taste of oak in red wine is most obvious in a young wine. An immature classed-growth claret, which has only been in bottle for a few months, is likely to have the spicy vanilla flavours of new oak, combined with a powerful impact of tannin. The oak will fade as the wine matures but will have added structure and tannin rather than actual flavour. The taste of oak is also very apparent in and is essential to Rioja. Its characteristic vanilla flavour originates from American oak, traditionally used in Spain.

Age

Age is another factor which, to a certain extent, is linked with the use of oak. A very high proportion of the dry white wines available on our wine merchants' shelves are destined for consumption within a year or two of the vintage. Oak has not played a part in their vinification process and there is no virtue in laying them down as they will not improve with age. However, fuller-bodied wines, which have probably spent a little time in oak, do last longer. They have more body, originating partly from the oak, and are intended to develop with age. The prime example is, of course, white burgundy, but most Chardonnays from elsewhere in the world also benefit from a little bit of bottle age. However, their ageing ability is also determined by the amount of acidity in the wine, for acidity is one of the factors that helps a wine to retain its youth.

With red wines too, it is those most suitable for ageing that are matured in oak before bottling. Young, fruity red wines, of which Beaujolais is the most typical example, are bottled a few months after the vintage for drinking in relative youth. Wines with structure and tannin are matured in oak in order to soften the harsh, aggressive flavours of the young wine. Once bottled, they may then need several years of ageing before becoming really enjoyable. The best classed-growth clarets should age for twenty years at least, as should great Rhônes, while burgundy is a little lighter in body and not blessed with quite the same longevity.

Tannin

It is tannin that features largely in red wines, but hardly at all in white wines, and is what determines, above all, their longevity. Tannin originates naturally from the grape skins, pips, and perhaps stalks, as well as from contact with new oak barrels, and is what gives a red wine its backbone and enables it to develop with age. However, tannin must always be balanced with sufficient fruit, for a wine with high tannin and no fruit will taste dry and puckering, while a wine with neither tannin nor acidity will seem dull and lifeless. Tannin fades with age, but enough fruit must always remain. Some wines with a tannic flavour are not worth ageing, as the austerity of the tannin is part of their character and nothing will be gained from further bottle age. Others, with a relatively high tannin content – in fact, virtually all fine red wines – benefit enormously from ageing, first in barrel in the winemaker's cellar and then in bottle, hopefully in the consumer's cellar.

A large amount of tannin is not always desirable in a young red wine. To avoid this, a vinification process has been developed, particularly designed for wines intended for early consumption, which aims to extract colour, fruit and flavour from the grapes, but not tannin. This is called carbonic maceration. Whole bunches of grapes, which have not been destalked or crushed, are put into a vat that is already filled with carbon dioxide. Some juice is released by the weight of the grapes, which begin fermenting, releasing more carbon dioxide and, at the same time, fermentation starts inside the grapes themselves. After a few days, the grapes are pressed and, whereas in most vinification it is the free-run juice that is best of all, with carbonic maceration the pressed juice is prized. In Beaujolais, they have adopted a variation of this technique called semi-carbonic maceration, where no additional carbon dioxide is added to the vat. Carbonic maceration is used particularly in the south of France to soften the flavours of the rugged Carignan. In the traditional regions of France, vinification methods are classic, with the colour, fruit and tannin coming from a period of contact between the juice and the grape skins, which may only be a few days or as much as three weeks.

Sweetness

Sweetness in wine comes about in various ways. The best sweet wines are the result of grapes affected by noble rot or *Botrytis cinerea*, which is a type of fungus which attacks the ripening grapes in the early autumn just before the vintage, causing them to dehydrate, shrivel up and become raisin-like, with an immense concentration of juice and flavour. The margin between noble and grey rot is very slender and it is all too easy for grey rot to develop rather than noble rot. Noble rot requires very special climatic conditions, ideally damp misty mornings, which must be followed by warm, sunny afternoons, to dry the grapes. Sauternes is the epitome of sweet wine made in this way. The great sweet wines of Germany and the Loire Valley also depend upon the presence of noble rot, while an increasing number of New World vineyards are producing botrytis-affected wines. Noble rot gives a wine an inimitable taste, a slightly roasted, distinctive burnt taste, which the French call a *goût de rôti*, and which ensures that the wine is sweet, but never cloying.

However, if you have very ripe grapes but no botrytis, it is still perfectly possible to make delicious sweet wine. Fermenting yeasts die when a certain level of alcohol is reached. In the case of very ripe grapes, this may happen naturally while some sugar remains in the wine or, with the increasing improvements in modern wine technology, it is feasible to stop the fermentation by chilling and filtering, in order to obtain a wine with the desired balance between alcohol and sweetness. This is often done in vineyards where botrytis is desired, but where the climate is less kind. Some medium-sweet wines are also made in this way, so that some grape sugar is retained in the wine. Alternatively, especially in Germany, they use what is called Süssreserve, or sweet reserve – unfermented, and therefore sweet, grape juice – which is added to the finished wine, to provide additional sweetness and richness.

The final option is to dry the grapes, either while they are still on the vines, or after they have been picked. The first procedure is favoured in Jurançon, where it is called *passerillage*. There is little or no botrytis here, for the climate of the Pyrenees is too dry. Alternatively, for vin de paille or Recioto di Soave and other traditional Italian *passiti* wines, the grapes are dried after they have been picked. Once, this was done on straw, hence the origin of the name, but it is now more usual to hang up the grapes so that they are better ventilated. The juice concentrates and the grapes become sweet and raisin-like before they are pressed, a month or two after the harvest.

THE TASTE

It must also be remembered that the taste of any wine is ultimately determined by the food with which you drink it. A simple experiment illustrates this vividly. Take a lightly tannic red wine, such as a young Bordeaux Rouge. Taste it and then take a bite of apple or carrot. Taste it again and the apple will have emphasised all the tannin and astringency in the wine. Now take a mouthful of a hard cheese, like Cheddar or Caerphilly, and taste the wine again. It will seem quite different now, for the cheese will have softened all of the rough edges in the wine and brought out all of the fruit, almost to the extent that it is hard to believe that it is one and the same wine.

This introduction has concentrated on table wines and, while some of the same factors apply to fortified and sparkling wines, the specific details are considered in the introduction to their respective wheels. With all three wheels, we hope to offer some guidance through the maze of different labels that abound on our wine merchants' shelves, thereby encouraging experimentation and enhancing your drinking enjoyment. The merchants' directory which follows will help you to decide what to buy and where.

DRY WHITE WINES

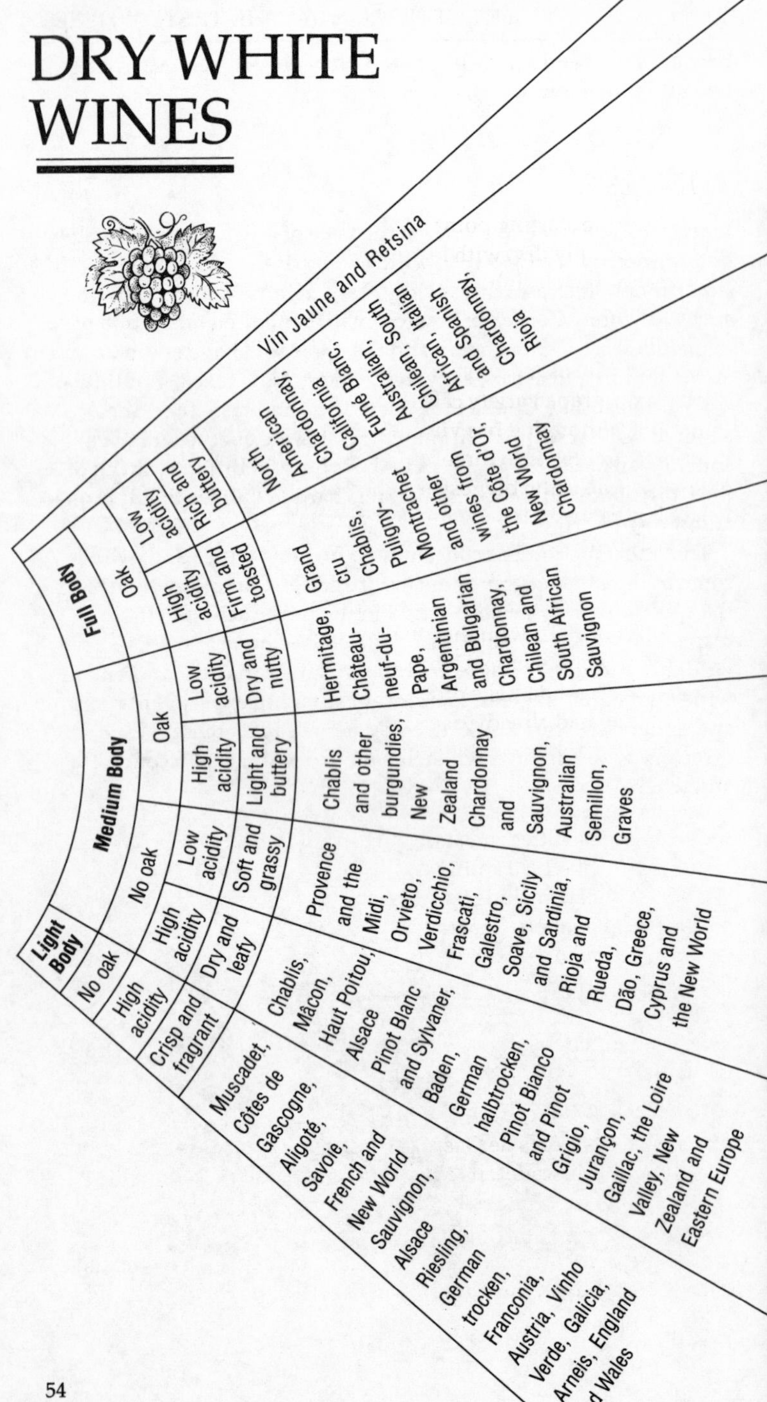

Light Body
No oak
High acidity
Crisp and fragrant
Muscadet, Côtes de Gascogne, Aligoté, Savoie, French and New World Sauvignon, Alsace Riesling, German trocken, Franconia, Austria, Vinho Verde, Galicia, Arneis, England and Wales
Medium Body
No oak
High acidity
Dry and leafy
Chablis, Mâcon, Haut Poitou, Alsace Pinot Blanc and Sylvaner, Baden, German halbtrocken, Pinot Bianco and Pinot Grigio, Jurançon, Gaillac, the Loire Valley, New Zealand and Eastern Europe
Low acidity
Soft and grassy
Provence and the Midi, Orvieto, Verdicchio, Frascati, Galestro, Soave, Sicily and Sardinia, Rioja and Rueda, Dão, Greece, Cyprus and the New World
Oak
High acidity
Light and buttery
Chablis and other burgundies, New Zealand Chardonnay and Sauvignon, Australian Semillon, Graves
Low acidity
Dry and nutty
Hermitage, Château-neuf-du-Pape, Argentinian and Bulgarian Chardonnay, Chilean and South African Sauvignon
Full Body
Oak
High acidity
Firm and toasted
Grand cru Chablis, Puligny-Montrachet and other wines from the Côte d'Or, the New World Chardonnay
Low acidity
Rich and buttery
North American Chardonnay, California Fumé Blanc, Australian, South African, Chilean, Italian and Spanish Chardonnay, Rioja
Vin Jaune and Retsina

CRISP AND FRAGRANT (LIGHT BODY, NO OAK, HIGH ACIDITY)

Muscadet

Muscadet is the starting point for this segment of the wheel. Good Muscadet is firmly dry, with lean steely acidity, stony fruit and a lively freshness. It is light in body and, indeed, is one of the rare appellations of France to have a maximum, rather than a minimum, alcohol level – 12.3 per cent – set down in its regulations. Muscadet comes from the Atlantic end of the Loire Valley from a grape variety called Muscadet (or Melon de Bourgogne, although it has virtually disappeared from Burgundy). The area is divided into three appellations, of which **Muscadet-de-Sèvre-et-Maine** is the biggest and the best. The words *sur lie* on the label indicate that the wine has been bottled off the fine lees or sediment of the fermentation, so that the merest prickle of carbon dioxide remains in the wine, providing extra freshness and zest.

The vineyards of Muscadet suffered dreadfully in the severe spring frosts of 1991, with the result that the vintage was tiny, only a third of the normal crop. Contrary to what might have been expected, the frost damage did not have any significant impact on prices, as they had already risen with the 1990 vintage, causing a certain disenchantment with Muscadet and an appropriate drop in sales. There were no spring frosts in 1992 and, at the time of writing, it looks set for a bumper crop. Although small, 1991 produced wines with good stony acidity and a better balance than in riper years, like 1990 and 1989.

Good producers include Sauvion at Château de Cléray (also with its Lauréat label), Château de Chasseloir, Chereau-Carré, Marquis de Goulaine, Métaireau, Domaine des Dorices, Château la Touche, Guy Brossard, Château la Noë and Donatien-Bahuaud.

The nearby VDQS of **Gros Plant du Pays Nantais** produces wines even greener and more acidic than Muscadet.

Côtes de Gascogne

Vin de pays des Côtes de Gascogne has some characteristics in common with Muscadet: it too is light, crisp and fragrant, with a slightly smoky, stony flavour. This is a wine born of the dramatic decline in sales of armagnac, made from grape varieties like Colombard, Folle Blanche and Ugni Blanc. It does not have terrific depth of taste but, at the right price, provides good everyday drinking. There has also been a little experimentation with Gros Manseng and oak-ageing for extra flavour.

Drink the youngest vintage available. Unfortunately, the 1991 crop suffered from bad spring frosts, but things should be better with the 1992 vintage. Hugh Ryman has made his mark here with numerous examples of Côtes de Gascogne: Domaine de Lian, Domaine du Biau, Domaine le Puts and Domaine Bordes, all of which are available in various supermarkets and high street shops. Other good estates include those of the pioneering Grassa family: Domaine du Tariquet, Domaine de Rieux, Domaine de la Jalousie and Domaine de Plantérieu. Domaine de San Guilhem is also good.

Bourgogne Aligoté

The appellation **Bourgogne Aligoté**, made from the Aligoté grape, fits into this section by virtue of the firm, stony acidity and crisp, dry flavour of the wine. Aligoté is often decried, but the problem is that it is usually planted in relatively unfavourable sites, resulting inevitably in less successful wine. The main exception to this is the appellation of **Bourgogne Aligoté de Bouzeron**, from the village in the Côte Chalonnaise that has made something of a speciality of Aligoté. Drink the youngest available, from Domaine Thévenot le Brun, de Villaine and Pierre Cogny.

Vin de Savoie

Vin de Savoie has a total of sixteen crus, scattered around the towns of Chambéry, Aix-les-Bains and Annecy. Most of them have little commercial significance outside of the holiday resorts of the French Alps, but the occasional one, such as Abymes or Apremont, makes an appearance on UK wine merchants' shelves. The main grape variety of the vineyards close to Chambéry is the little-known Jacquère, which makes some light, dry, rather stony, ethereal white wine, that is low in alcohol, with some firm acidity. Like most of the wines in this segment, there is nothing to be gained from extra maturity, so drink the youngest available. Alternatively, you may occasionally find the slightly fuller **Roussette de Savoie**, which can include a percentage of Chardonnay, or the appellation **Crépy**, with wines made from the Chasselas grape. The latter has more in common with the Swiss wines from the opposite shore of Lac Léman – it is made from the same grape variety, but like them, rarely travels.

French Sauvignon Blanc

And now back to western France, to the basic appellations of **Bordeaux Blanc** and **Entre-Deux-Mers**. Both are areas where vinification techniques have improved enormously in recent years, making them a much more appealing choice. Once they were oversulphured and often uncertain whether they were trying to be vaguely sweet or indecisively dry. Now Bordeaux Blanc and Entre-Deux-Mers are clean and fresh, positively dry, with some vibrant fruit. Sauvignon may well be the dominant grape variety, but sometimes some Sémillon is included to round out the wine a little. Oak-ageing is less likely for these humble appellations, although there are exceptions, which are mentioned further round the wheel.

Any dry wine produced in the Sauternais or any white wine from the Médoc is entitled only to the appellation Bordeaux Blanc, but if it comes from a leading estate it will be treated accordingly. There is a world of difference between Y, the dry wine of Château d'Yquem, and Château Thieuley, for example, not only in price but also in flavour. Generally, Bordeaux Blanc or Entre-Deux-Mers – sometimes sold as merchants' blends, such as Sirius from Peter Sichel or Maître d'Estournel – are intended for early consumption. The 1991 was badly affected by spring frosts, but there are still wines from the 1990 vintage around. Other good estates include Château Ducla, Château de Sours and Moulin de Launay.

The white wines of the South-West are based mostly on Sauvignon and Sémillon, which means that the white versions of appellations like **Bergerac**, **Côtes de Duras**, **Buzet** and **Côtes du Marmandais** are very similar in taste, and again have benefited from general improvements in vinification techniques. Buzet and Marmandais are dominated by regional co-operatives, while Hugh Ryman has made his mark on the Côtes de Duras, with Domaine de Colombet and Domaine de Malardeau. For Bergerac, look for recommended producers under red wine.

Other Sauvignons from France fit into this segment. The obvious example is **Sancerre**, as well as the adjoining white appellations of that part of the Loire Valley – Pouilly Fumé, Menetou-Salon, Reuilly and Quincy. Sancerre represents the Sauvignon grape at its most elegant and subtle, if indeed Sauvignon can ever be described as subtle. More often than not the pungent, somewhat brash flavours, reminiscent of gooseberries – perhaps with feline overtones – can intrude. However, good Sancerre, which is usually lighter in body than any

Bordelais counterparts, is refreshing and delicate with a stony flintiness. Inevitably, it is expensive, a phenomenon accentuated by the spring frost of 1991. There is little virtue in ageing it, so drink the youngest available, from producers like Vacheron, Gitton, Natter, Vatan, Bailly-Reverdy, Crochet, Cotat, Dézat and Thomas.

Pouilly Fumé is very similar to Sancerre in taste, some find the two virtually indistinguishable. Like Sancerre, Pouilly Fumé is best drunk in relative youth, from a vintage that was not too sun-soaked, otherwise the wine tends to be a little flabby, as in 1989. However, the star producer, Patrick de Ladoucette at Château du Nozet, argues the case for maturing Pouilly Fumé. His wines are generally considered the best of the appellation, but also the most expensive, especially his Baron de L. Also good, but more accessible in price, are Château de Tracey, Didier Dagueneau, Michel Redde, Jean-Claude Guyot and Guy Saget.

Menetou-Salon has been enjoying a revival in its fortunes and currently offers better-value drinking than either of its two more prestigious neighbours. The flavour is slightly less subtle, but none the worse for that. Henri Pellé and Jean Teiller are the best producers. **Reuilly** and **Quincy** are harder to find; virtually the sole representatives of the two appellations, Gérard Cordier and Denis Jaumier, feature on the list of the specialist Loire merchant, Yapp Bros.

Other comparable Sauvignons from France include **Sauvignon de Touraine**, which has some refreshingly pithy fruit. The successful co-operative of Oisly-et-Thésée is a key producer. **Sauvignon du Haut Poitou** is a touch fuller, with the regional co-operative the sole producer, while close to Chablis, the village of St-Bris-le-Vineux has a reputation for **Sauvignon de St-Bris**. Robert Defrance and Jean-Marc Brocard are good producers. All of these offer a price advantage over Sancerre and Pouilly Fumé, but do not have the same finesse.

New Zealand Sauvignon Blanc

New Zealand Sauvignon crosses the taste wheel, depending on its method of vinification – whether it has been fermented and/or aged in oak, or whether it is made in pristine stainless steel tanks. The most characteristic New Zealand Sauvignon, the wine that really brought the wines of the Antipodes to our notice, is Montana Marlborough Sauvignon. The first commercial vintage of this wine was as recent as 1980 and it quickly established a reputation for deliciously pungent, freshly vibrant Sauvignon fruit, with crisp acidity. It is eminently easy to drink, and inexpensive at around £5 a bottle. If there is a criticism to be made, the wine is perhaps a little one-dimensional, but that does not matter. Marlborough is on New Zealand's South Island and has established itself as the leading region for Sauvignon, to the extent that many of the wineries based outside Auckland either have vineyards in, or buy fruit from, Marlborough. The grapes are then either trucked to the North Island or, in a more recent development, vinified according to specifications in Marlborough by an independent winemaker.

The other key New Zealand Sauvignon is Cloudy Bay, which fits into a later taste segment, and which has partial barrel fermentation. Non-oaked New Zealand Sauvignons from Marlborough include Hunters, Matua Valley, Nobilo, Selaks, Stoneleigh, Vavasour, Jackson and Wairau River. The wines from the warmer North Island tend to be a little fuller and riper and, therefore, come into the next segment of the wheel.

Alsace Riesling

It may seem illogical to follow Sauvignon with Riesling, but there is a similarity in the fruit and balance of acidity in the two wines, making it possible to confuse the two when very young. **Riesling d'Alsace** is generally considered to be the finest, most subtle and most elegant of all the Alsace grape varieties, especially if it comes from a grand cru vineyard and a talented grower. Except in the case of Vendange Tardive and Sélection de Grains Nobles wines, Alsace Riesling is firmly dry, almost to the point of being lean and steely. Compared with German Riesling, it is much higher in alcohol as it is fermented until completely dry. Thus, it has more body and a steeliness which develops with bottle age. Wines from grand cru sites should also be a little more concentrated in flavour than a simple Vin d'Alsace.

Style varies from grower to grower; some, like Trimbach and Léon Beyer, make wines that are lean and understated, while those from Hugel are a little softer and more flowery. Riesling d'Alsace from a good vintage, such as 1990, 1989 and 1988, will age beautifully, developing slaty kerosene flavours, with considerable complexity.

Recommended producers include Trimbach (especially with Clos Ste-Hune and Cuvée Frédéric Emile), Hugel, Domaine Weinbach, Jos Meyer, Zind-Humbrecht, Domaine Ostertag, Marc Kreydenweiss, Schlumberger, Marcel Deiss, Rolly Gassmann, Léon Beyer and Kuentz-Bas.

Trocken wines from Germany

Trocken represents a broad generalisation of a relatively new and growing trend in German winemaking, and simply means dry. Some German producers have felt seriously disadvantaged by the underlying implication of sweetness in German wine, which they consider makes their wines unsuitable for drinking with food. They therefore ferment their wines until completely dry, leaving no residual sugar and ignoring the possibility of using Süssreserve. But, unless the grapes are fairly ripe in the first place, the result can be a rather unbalanced wine, with high acidity, low alcohol and very little body – in other words, a wine that is hollow and skeletal and decidedly unappealing compared to riper Spätlese and Auslese. However, with greater experience and expertise, some producers are making some successful trocken wines, especially those from the more southern vineyards of Germany, such as the Rheinpfalz, Rheinhessen and Baden. There the climate is warmer and the grapes are consequently riper, and the wines easily meet the criteria for Kabinett, Spätlese and even Auslese. They are better balanced, with more body, which could nudge them into the next segment of the wheel.

The taste of a trocken wine depends upon the grape variety. Usually it is firmly dry, quite light in body, slightly steely, with some austere, stony fruit. Recommended producers include Lingenfelder, Schloss Vollrads, Schloss Reinhartshausen, Schlossgut Diel, Georg Breuer and Karl Heinz Johner. These wines do not represent particularly good value. After all, there are so many other fine, dry white wines made all over the world that Germany would do better to maintain its originality by continuing with the elegantly honeyed Auslese and Spätlese that it makes so well, and which are not available elsewhere.

Franconia

The wines of **Franconia**, from vineyards in Northern Bavaria, around the town of Würzburg, fit into this segment. Traditionally, they have always been firmly dry, with some flinty fruit and they have never related quality to sweetness, as they do in the Mosel and the Rhine. Unusually, Müller-Thurgau and Silvaner, rather than Riesling, are the principal grape varieties. Franconian wines are always presented in the traditional dumpy flagons, called *bocksbeutel*, and are often referred to as Steinwein, after the most famous vineyard, Würzburger Stein. They are rarely available here, as they tend to be uncompetitive in price. The best producers are the Burgerspital, Juliusspital, Fürstlich Castell'sches Domanenamt and Weingut Hans Wirsching.

Austria

The most characteristic grape of Austria, Grüner Veltliner, fits into this category in its dry form. It crosses the border into Hungary and Czechoslovakia, but is grown nowhere else. In more commercial blends the wine sometimes has a trace of residual sugar, but it is usually firmly dry, with some fresh stony acidity and slightly smoky, slightly grassy fruit. It is usually light in body and is best drunk within a couple of years of the vintage. Occasionally, you may find it as a Spätlese, in which case it takes on a honeyed note, with some apricot fruit, but always has a dry finish. Recommended producers include Lenz Moser, Fritz Salomon and some of the supermarket own-label wines.

Vinho Verde and Bairrada

Vinho Verde, the green wine of Portugal, can be either white or red. In this instance, 'verde' means young (vinho maduro is mature wine). Although more red than white Vinho Verde is produced, it is the white that is exported. Good Vinho Verde is a crisp, dry white wine, although sometimes commercial blends have the sharp acidic edge of youth taken off them, so that they can taste very slightly sweet and rather soft.

The real thing has a crisp, pithy, lemony, stony acidity, sometimes with a hint of apples or apricots on the nose. It is very light in alcohol and can have a trace of carbon dioxide, to provide extra freshness and liveliness. In wines made from Alvarinho, the best grape variety for Vinho Verde, the apricot character is emphasised and they bear a resemblance to the wines of Galicia, just across the border in Spain.

Vinho Verde must be drunk as young and fresh as possible. For added interest, choose a single quinta or an estate wine, rather than a commercial brand, such as Solar das Bouças, Palacio da Brejoeira and Quinta da Aveleda, rather than plain Aveleda.

White **Bairrada** deserves a passing mention here. Although from slightly further south, it is still rather crisp and lemony in flavour, but perhaps slightly fuller than Vinho Verde. Most white Bairrada is sold under a supermarket own-label.

Spain

Rias Baixas, just across the border from Vinho Verde, is one of the four DOs of Galicia, in north-west Spain. Until a couple of years ago, these wines rarely travelled much outside their region, but they have recently begun to reach our wine shops. Albariño, with its slightly peachy character, is the grape which makes the best wines. They are light, fresh and delicate, low in alcohol with a gentle, refreshing, slightly peachy fragrance. Lagar de Cervera, Martin Codax and Bodegas Morgadio are the most widely exported.

The adjoining DO of **Ribeiro** includes red as well as white wines, but again it is the white wines that provide the more interesting and distinctive flavours, with Loureiro and Treixadura the main grape varieties. These wines have the same light body as Rias Baixas, but are perhaps more firmly dry, with a stonier flavour and finish. Unfortunately, most of the white wines of Galicia tend to be expensive compared with other Spanish whites, because they are sought after and can command high prices in Spain, so there is little need to export.

Viña Sol is taken as an example of the dry white wines of **Penedès**, as produced by Miguel Torres. This is characteristic of the improvement in winemaking that Torres has engineered, planting the native grape varieties of Penedès in the cooler, higher altitude vineyards of the region. Parellada is the main variety of Viña Sol, which lacks a distinctive flavour. The charm of Viña Sol lies in its dry, freshness and crisp finish, without any intrusive fruit flavour. Generally, it is a wine for drinking as young as possible. Gran Viña Sol and Gran Viña Sol Green Label feature in other segments of the wheel.

Piedmont

Arneis, an obscure Piedmontese grape variety that has been undergoing something of a revival, might also fit into this segment. The flavour is not so dissimilar from Rias Baixas. In the hands of Carlo Deltetto, for example, it has a delicate, lightly peachy flavour, with fresh fruit and a dry finish. Arneis is expensive, as is Favorita, another grape variety with a similar, but drier, flavour that is also enjoying something of a renewal of interest.

England and Wales

English wine is growing in importance as production approaches the 25,000 hectolitre mark, when some system of quality assessment, like the French appellation contrôlée, must be implemented by law. We are not yet there, but with a bumper harvest, unaffected by spring frosts, and with more vineyards coming into production each year, we are not far off. A Quality Wine Pilot Scheme is being introduced for the 1992 vintage. This presents one significant problem: some of the best-performing grape varieties in England and Wales, such as Seyval Blanc, Seyve-Villard and Madeleine Angevine, are not considered suitable for quality wine under EC law. Other grape varieties, mainly German crosses like Müller-Thurgau, Reichenstein, Schönburger, Kerner and Huxelrebe, are also grown. Although there are vineyards in all but eight of England's 46 counties, as well as a growing number in South Wales, the main concentration of viticulture lies firmly in the South-West, East Anglia and the Home Counties.

As yet there are few discernable regional differences, but an overall style of fragrant, flowery, slightly spicy, ethereal wines that are light in body and low in alcohol and often high in acidity. If the producer uses Süssreserve in the German manner, the wine will be slightly sweet. There is the occasional wine that has been in oak, and which therefore features in that segment of the wheel, as well as the occasional red or pink wine. Generally, though, English wine is white.

One possible confusion must be clarified. So-called British wine has nothing to do with English or Welsh wine, and hardly merits the name of wine, for it is a manufactured product, originating from reconstituted imported dehydrated grape juice. It should be avoided at all costs by any discerning reader of this Guide.

Wineries whose wines are currently showing well include Adgestone, Three Choirs, Tenterden, Carr Taylor, Staple St James, Biddenden, Elmham Park, Wootton, Pilton Manor, Mumfords, Nutbourne, Chiltern Valley, Barkham Manor, Penshurst, Breaky Bottom, Rock Lodge and a wine simply called English Vineyard, made at High Weald Winery. If in doubt, try your nearest local winery. The English Vineyards Association also awards each year a Seal of Excellence to wines which have attained the required standard: the black and gold seal on the bottle provides another guide to quality.

DRY AND LEAFY (MEDIUM BODY, NO OAK, HIGH ACID)

Chablis

Simple **Chablis** could be seen as the starting point for this section of the wheel – that is the basic village wine, or perhaps a young premier cru wine which has not seen any oak. Young Chablis, coming as it does from the most northern vineyards of Burgundy, should always have a lean streak of acidity, while the Chardonnay grape gives it a certain dry grassy character, with a touch of what the French call *pierre à fusil*, or gunflint. There is a firm stony quality to good Chablis, which will develop a little more complexity with age. However, Chablis does cross the taste wheel, depending on vinification methods and precise provenance, so a grand cru Chablis will have much more concentration than a basic Chablis. In riper vintages, such as 1990 and 1989, Chablis may be slightly lacking in acidity, while 1991 and 1988 have both made wines with a good balance of acidity; of these 1988 is the better vintage, with more concentration of flavour.

Of the good producers who do not use wood, Louis Michel is generally considered the best. Others include Bernard Légland, Adhémar Boudin, Olivier Savary, Jean-Marc Brocard, Alain Geoffroie, Domaine des Malandes, Jean Durup at Domaine de l'Eglantière and A. Régnard.

Mâcon and Haut Poitou

It is very easy to confuse a village Chablis with a **Mâcon Blanc** or **Mâcon-Villages**. The Mâcon should also be light and grassy, with the flavour of Chardonnay, usually vinified without any contact with oak. It should be a little fuller in the mouth, especially if it comes from one of the better villages like Lugny or Viré.

The village co-operatives work well in this region, such as Clessé, the aptly named Chardonnay, Lugny, Prissé and Viré, while good producers include Jean Thévenet at Domaine de la Bon Gran.

The adjoining appellations of **St-Véran**, **Pouilly-Vinzelles** and the rarely seen **Beaujolais Blanc** are similar in taste, though they may be a little fuller in body, while good Pouilly-Fuissé usually has some contact with oak.

Another comparable, but lighter, Chardonnay is **Chardonnay du Haut Poitou**, which offers good value for money, but lacks some complexity of flavour. Chardonnay from further south tends to fit into lower acidity segments of the wheel.

Alsace Pinot Blanc and Sylvaner

These tend to be considered the work horse grape varieties of **Alsace**. Sylvaner is declining in importance, tending to be replaced by Pinot Blanc, which makes some soft, undemanding, grassy wines. There should be nothing aggressive or hard in the flavour, just some soft fruit, without much depth. Sylvaner, too, is lightly grassy, with even less depth of flavour.

Pinot Blanc is usually drunk as an aperitif in Alsace. The occasional producer, such as Jean Meyer, gives it more serious attention, making wine from older vines on a grand cru site.

Others may age it in oak, but that is very much the exception to the rule. Drink the youngest available, from producers like Jos Meyer, Hugel, Trimbach and the Cave Vinicole de Turckheim.

Baden

In **Baden**, Pinot Blanc is called Weissburgunder and features significantly in the vineyards of Germany's most southerly wine region, along with Müller-Thurgau, and some Riesling, Silvaner, Gewürztraminer and Ruländer (the German synonym for Pinot Gris). Most examples of wine from Baden which reach our wine merchants' shelves are simply labelled Baden, without any further indication of provenance, although there are some noted vineyard sites, such as Ortenau, Kaiserstuhl and Markgärflerland. The region is dominated by growers' co-operatives, which in turn belong to an enormous central co-operative, the ZBW or Zentralkellerei Badischer Winzergenossenschaft.

Most Baden wine is dry or trocken, without any of the residual sweetness of the wines of northern Germany. A typical Baden Dry has a soft grassy flavour, or it may be drier and stonier, perhaps with a little spice, depending on the dominant grape variety. The wines tend to be fuller in body than those from further north, for Baden is significantly warmer than the Rhine or Mosel. They have more alcohol and are not so different from those of Alsace, its French neighbour across the Rhine.

German halbtrocken

Some of the **halbtrocken** wines of Germany could also fit into this segment of the wheel. Halbtrocken, or half-dry, wines are not as searingly acidic as some trocken wines, retaining a tiny amount of sweetness to soften the sharp edges of acidity. They are usually quite soft and fruity, with some underlying acidity and perhaps a hint of honey, and are fairly light in body and alcohol. The precise flavour depends upon the grape variety and Riesling gives the most elegant, steely flavour. Good producers include those who specialise in trocken wines, such as Lingenfelder, Bürklin-Wolf, Bassermann-Jordan, Schloss Reinhartshausen, Balthasar Ress and Schloss Vollrads.

Pinot Bianco and Pinot Grigio

Pinot Bianco and Pinot Grigio are the two most characteristic grape varieties of north-east Italy and are widely grown in the vineyards of the Alto Adige, Trentino and Friuli. There has been a certain amount of confusion between Chardonnay and Pinot

Bianco in north-east Italy, but this is the one region where Pinot Bianco takes precedence over Chardonnay, the more fashionable variety. You can find Pinot Bianco from the **Alto Adige** where, thanks to the historical accidents of boundaries and language, it is also called Südtiroler Weissburgunder, and also in the DOCs of **Trentino**, **Collio**, **Colli Orientali** and **Grave del Friuli**. The flavour is not unlike a Chardonnay, with a gentle buttery taste, light and creamy, with firm acidity, originating from a relatively cool climate. However, it does not have the potential weight of good Chardonnay and therefore is rarely, if ever, put into oak.

Good producers include the Abbazia di Rosazzo, Volpe Pasini and Ronco del Gnemiz in Friuli; Tiefenbrunner, Lageder, Hofstätter and Giorgio Grai in the Alto Adige; and Jermann and Pojer e Sandri in Trentino.

Pinot Grigio from northern Italy has much less character than Pinot Gris in Alsace. It tends to be somewhat nondescript, quite light with some fruit and acidity, and perhaps a hint of varietal spice. However, in Italy itself it is rated more highly than Pinot Bianco and there are the occasional producers who manage to extract a little extra flavour, such as Marco Schiopetto, Jermann and Lageder. Like Pinot Bianco, it grows extensively in **Trentino**, **Friuli** and the **Alto Adige**, while the DOCs of **Collio** and **Colli Orientali** make some of the more characterful wines.

Another grape variety also grown extensively in north-east Italy is Tocai Friuliano, also called Tocai Italico in the **Veneto**. Despite the similarity to the Alsace synonym for Pinot Gris (Tokay Pinot Gris), these two varieties are not related. However, the flavour is not dissimilar – fairly dry and neutral.

More flavour comes from the occasional example of Sauvignon which does feature in the various DOCs of north-east Italy, especially in **Collio** and **Colli Orientali**. Puiatti in Collio makes one of the best, with some pithy pungent fruit.

Jurançon and the Pyrenees

Now we go back to France, to **Jurançon**, the white wine of the Pyrenees, which can be either dry (sec) or sweet (moelleux). The moelleux version features further round the wheel. Dry Jurançon is made from the little-known Gros Manseng and Petit Manseng grapes, which provide some dry, pithy fruit, reminiscent of grapefruit, and which give it a mouth-filling flavour and some firm acidity on the finish. The best producer is Domaine Cauhapé; Château de Jolys is good too, and the regional co-operative is working well for the appellation.

Other wines of the South-West fit into this segment, with their combination of firm acidity and medium body. There is the nearby **Côtes de St-Mont**, where the regional co-operative has worked hard to put this little-known VDQS on the wine map of France. **Tursan** is another relatively obscure VDQS from the edge of the Landes, where the local co-operative has improved its vinification methods significantly in the last couple of years – making a clean fresh wine, with as much fruit as is possible from the decidedly nondescript Baroque grape. The new wines from Michel Guérard – Château de Bachen and Baron de Bachen – are both vinified in oak.

Gaillac

Gaillac, from vineyards around the town of Albi, is firm and dry, originating from a hotchpotch of different grape varieties, some of which – such as Mauzac and Loin de l'Oeil – are rarely seen outside the region. Others have a more international ring, like Sauvignon, Muscadelle and Sémillon. White Gaillac is usually made from Mauzac and Loin de l'Oeil and may retain a little carbon dioxide from the malolactic fermentation, in which case it is called Gaillac Perlé. The bubbles in the glass should look like tiny pearls, hence the name, and the wine tastes soft and dry, with hints of apples and almonds. Gaillac made with a greater proportion of Sauvignon may have more flavour, but there is no way of discerning this from the label.

The Loire Valley

The various dry white wines of the Loire Valley made from Chenin Blanc tend to have a little more body than those made from Sauvignon and therefore fit more comfortably into this segment than the previous one. **Anjou Blanc** and **Saumur Blanc**, the two basic appellations, are very similar in flavour. And while **Touraine Blanc** can be made from Chenin Blanc, the better wines are made from Sauvignon. Anjou Blanc may be dry or off-dry, with the acidity typical of Chenin Blanc. In ripe years there might be a little honey to provide some body and weight; on the other hand, in cool years, the wine can be exceedingly sour.

The star dry wine of the Loire is **Savennières**, with the smaller appellations of **Coulée de Serrant** and **Roche aux Moines**. These can be very much an acquired taste, wines to admire rather than enthuse over. There is no doubt that this is dry Chenin Blanc at its finest, always with firm acidity, but with a complex leafy flavour which develops more subtlety and depth with age. At a recent vertical tasting of Coulée de Serrant, the 1967 vintage was splendid, with innumerable nuances of flavour and a certain toasted, honeyed quality. The 1988 and 1989 were equally good vintages in the Loire Valley, and there is no reason why they too should not develop in the same way, given patience and time. While Coulée de Serrant and Roche aux Moines are single vineyards, good producers of Savennières include Domaine de la Bizolière, Château de Chamboureau and Domaine du Closel.

The remaining appellations of the Loire made from Chenin Blanc include **Vouvray** and **Montlouis** in their dry versions. Look for the word 'sec' on the label as a clue to flavour. Recommended producers of dry Vouvray include Gaston Huet, Foreau and Prince Poniatowski. Somehow Vouvray sec just does not have the stature and complexity of the more exciting sweet wines. In **Montlouis**, Berger is the name to go for, whilst in **Touraine Azay-le-Rideau** (a sub-appellation of Touraine), there is one producer of note, Gaston Pavy, with some dry, slightly grassy wines, with that characteristic Chenin Blanc wet dog nose. **Jasnières**, on the Loir, a tributary of the larger river, is another obscurity made from Chenin Blanc, with some potential to develop with age. The Loire specialist, Yapp Bros, is the source of many of these lesser-known Loire wines.

New Zealand

With the exception of some Sauvignon and Riesling, the dry unoaked white wines of New Zealand tend to come into this category. The cooler climate gives higher acidity levels than most of the other New World vineyards and some Sauvignons – especially those from the North Island – have a little more body than those in the previous segment, and therefore fit into the taste wheel here. Good North Island Sauvignons include Esk Valley, Collards Rothesay Sauvignon, Palliser, Morton Estate and Te Mata Castle Hill.

St Helena makes a delicious Pinot Blanc with some light grassy fruit, not unlike a good Chablis, and Collards is a winery which takes Chenin Blanc seriously – rather than putting it in a winebox. Its wine has some dry honeyed fruit, with balancing acidity.

Eastern Europe

One of the exciting new wines of the last vintage is a Hungarian Sauvignon, made by a team of Australian winemakers under the guidance of Hugh Ryman at the Gyöngyös estate. It has some vibrant juicy Sauvignon fruit, with fresh herbaceous acidity, and is extremely good value for money.

There are also examples of unoaked Chardonnay from Eastern Europe. From Bulgaria, the Controliran wines from Varna and Novi Pazar are made without any contact with oak, so that they are soft and grassy, with some light fruit. The best Hungarian Chardonnay is undisputably the Hugh Ryman wine from the Gyöngyös estate, with its light, buttery fruit.

SOFT AND GRASSY (MEDIUM BODY, NO OAK, LOW ACIDITY)

The difference between the wines in this segment and those of the previous segment is their acidity level. Most of the wines that follow come from a warmer climate, resulting in less obtrusive, lower acidity than in the wines of the previous segment. They may still be dry, but will lack that firm acidity that can provide backbone, so they are softer and more rounded in the mouth. Like many of the white wines on our merchants' shelves, these are all intended for early consumption, with little potential for ageing.

France

There are numerous appellations in the **Midi** which are better known for their red wines, but which also make some palatable white wines. In many instances there has been a significant improvement in quality in recent years, originating from a better control of fermentation temperatures and investment in new equipment. One such wine is Picpoul de Pinet. This is one of the crus of the **Coteaux du Languedoc**, made, as the name might imply, from Picpoul grapes in the village of Pinet, where the main producer is the local co-operative. The wine – marketed by Chantovent, one of the large merchant houses of the south, under its Contemporains label – is remarkable for its fruit and flavour.

The main problem with the white wines of the South is the uninspiring grape varieties that feature in the appellations. Ugni Blanc is decidedly low in flavour appeal and Macabeo and Bourboulenc are little better, so it is hardly surprising that the white versions of wines like **Corbières**, **Côtes du Roussillon** and

Minervois take second place to the reds. Even **Côtes-du-Rhône Blanc** is fairly limited in appeal. All these wines do is provide some dry refreshing whites that are at their best when well chilled.

Some examples of vins de pays made from grape varieties like Terret Blanc or Grenache Blanc can offer more flavour, while Sauvignon and Chardonnay may be better still. One of the more successful examples of Chardonnay from the Midi comes from the Australian-owned Domaine de la Baume. The merchant company Skalli is also achieving some success with its Fortant de France label. The Burgundy house, Louis Latour, makes an acceptable Chardonnay de l'Ardèche.

A little more flavour comes from **Provence**. Although the best white **Côtes de Provence** is Clos Mireille from Domaines Ott, which fits into the light and buttery section of the wheel, other white Côtes de Provence tend to be dry and fresh, with slight herbal hints, and the **Coteaux d'Aix-en-Provence** might provide a little more interest with wines like Domaine de Terres Blanches. Surprisingly, the appellation of **Cassis** stakes its reputation on white wine. The grape varieties are a blend of the ubiquitous Ugni Blanc, some Clairette and Marsanne (as in the Rhône Valley) for extra flavour, and perhaps a drop of Sauvignon for additional interest. However, it is expensive for what it is – a somewhat old-fashioned white wine, with solid, nutty flavours. It lacks the pithy acidity of modern winemaking techniques, but is none the worse for that in a world of growing Chardonnay-esque uniformity.

More flavoursome is white **Bellet**, a tiny and obscure appellation in the hinterland of the city of Nice. Rolle, the main grape variety, produces a dry, leafy wine with good fruit, but Bellet is expensive. So too is the white version of **Bandol**, which is generally dry and fresh, with some fruit, although again the grape varieties are fairly unexciting.

Across the water on **Corsica**, the main white grape is Vermentino, which may be related to the Rolle, and which makes wines with a nutty, slightly almond flavour. Domaine Peraldi is one of the few imported to Britain.

And Noah he often said to his wife when he sat down to dine, 'I don't care where the water goes if it doesn't get into the wine.'

G K Chesterton, *Water and Wine*

Tuscany

From Corsica, it is but a short hop to Tuscany. In the same way that the white wines of the Midi are dominated by Ugni Blanc, the whites of Tuscany, or for that matter most of Italy, rarely escape from the influence of Trebbiano, Ugni Blanc by another name. In one form or another, this grape variety crops up in wines all the way from Soave in the Veneto down to Alcamo in Sicily. The chief virtue of many Italian whites may be that they lack real positive punchy flavours, and are more subtle and delicate in their appeal. In a recent tasting of a range of white Italians from all over the country, the most forthright wines were those that had been aged in oak; the most typically Italian were good examples of Soave, Verdicchio and Vernaccia di San Gimignano, which were delicate with some subtle fruit, the kind of wines that offer delightfully uncomplicated drinking.

Vernaccia di San Gimignano is the most original wine of Tuscany, made, as its name implies, from Vernaccia, which produces a dry nutty wine, which is occasionally aged in oak, though the oak tends to swamp the elusive and delicate flavour of the grape. Good producers include Montenidoli, Falchini, Teruzzi e Puthod, Pietraserena and Pietrafitta.

A couple of other oases of individuality are to found in Tuscany. There is **Montecarlo**, a little known DOC, which includes such grape varieties as Pinot Grigio, Roussanne and Sauvignon, as well as Trebbiano. And the tiny DOC of **Pomino**, whose production is dominated by the large Chianti house, Frescobaldi, includes Pinot Bianco, Pinot Grigio and Chardonnay to make a wine with more character than is usual in Tuscany.

Otherwise, the indigenous white wines of Tuscany are firmly based on Trebbiano, with a drop of Malvasia. Most grew in importance following the glut of white grapes in central Tuscany when Chianti became a DOCG in 1984 and the percentage of white grapes was drastically reduced. **Galestro**, a relatively new wine created from that surplus, may include grape varieties other than Trebbiano, but it still seems to remain remarkably neutral in flavour – dry, but not acidic, light in alcohol, and best drunk well chilled. Wines like Bianco Val d'Arbia, Bianco Vergine Valdichiana and Bianco della Toscana, are very similar.

There are also numerous experimental wines, sometimes labelled **Predicato del Muschio** for Chardonnay-based wines, and **Predicato del Selvante** for those with a high percentage of Sauvignon. Wines made from Chardonnay, with the rare exceptions of Villa di Capezzana and Terre di Cortona from Avignonesi, generally fit into the oaky section, as do some Sauvignons. However, the best Tuscan Sauvignon, Poggio alle Gazze from the new estate of Ornellaia in Bolgheri, is made without oak.

In Umbria, **Orvieto** offers more flavour. Coming from vineyards around the attractive hilltop town, it is made from a mixture of grapes including Trebbiano, as well as Grechetto and Verdello, which provide a little more character. There is a growing trend for single-vineyard names – which the Italians call crus – which are generally the wines from the best sites that a producer owns, probably given some extra special treatment, with a price to match. Good dry Orvieto is slightly leafy, slightly nutty, with a hint of smokiness and a gentle fragrance. For Orvieto Abboccato see further round the wheel. Good producers include Bigi with its Torricella vineyard, Berberani and Decugnano dei Barbi. Antinori owns the magnificent medieval Castello della Sala, where it makes wines which do not conform to DOC regulations, for example, Cervaro della Sala from Chardonnay and Grechetto.

Nearby is the new DOCG of **Torgiano**, which really owes its existence to one family, Lungarotti, whose white wine, Torre di

Giano, made from a substantial proportion of Grechetto as well as Trebbiano, is quite full-flavoured.

Verdicchio, or to give its full name, **Verdicchio dei Castelli di Jesi**, comes from the hills of the Marche behind the port of Ancona. Verdicchio is also the name of the grape variety unique to this part of Italy. Verdicchio is always firmly dry, but not acidic. Indeed, it can be rather boring, with some fairly neutral flavours. However, along with so many other wine regions of Italy, it has been enjoying a certain revival, with more effort being made to improve vinification methods and extract flavour. There is an increasing emphasis on single-vineyard wines, such as Casal di Serra from Umani Ronchi, Le Moie from Fazi-Battaglia, Colle del Sole and il Pallio from Monte Schiavo. They may be more expensive than simple Verdicchio, but are generally worth the extra price. They usually come in the classic Bordeaux bottle, rather than the fancy amphora shape normally associated with Verdicchio.

Frascati, drunk by the Romans, is slightly fuller and fatter. Again, Trebbiano features in the grape mix, along with Malvasia, which does not contribute much. Frascati can be plain dull, epitomising some of the worst faults of Italian winemaking, but good Frascati can be quite mouth-filling, with a flavour reminiscent of bananas. As elsewhere in Italy, things are looking up and there are some interesting wines to be found. Colli di Catone (with the single vineyard Colle Gaio), Villa Simone and Fontana Candida (with the Santa Teresa vineyard, as well as its vino da tavola, Villa Fontana) are all recommended. The nearby DOC of **Marino** is very similar. As with virtually all white Italians, these are best drunk as young as possible as there is neither enough fruit nor adequate acidity to allow the wines to develop in the bottle.

There are a couple of pure Trebbiano wines which merit a mention for the sake of completeness. Trebbiano is grown extensively in the province of **Emilia-Romagna**, and performs a useful function in producing quantities of innocuously bland white wine which is served up as bianco della casa, or house white, in Italian trattorie all over the world, and which may have a hint of almonds with a trace of acidity and a whiff of fruit. The other white wine of Emilia-Romagna, the DOCG **Albana di Romagna**, rarely travels and certainly does not deserve its elevated status in the Italian wine world.

Trebbiano d'Abruzzo, on the other hand, does have a little more character. Take, for example, the leading producer Valentini, who produces a wine with some intensity and a full earthy flavour which could be described as something of an acquired taste.

Soave

Soave is such a well-known name – forming a trio in the Veneto with Bardolino and Valpolicella – that we may tend to take it for granted. In fact, good Soave has significantly more flavour than many other Italian white wines. Again Trebbiano features, but there is also Garganega for more fruit. Look for **Classico** on the label, which indicates that the wine comes from the heart of the vineyards around the eponymous village. **Superiore** denotes nine months' ageing as well as a minimum alcohol level of 11.5 per cent. However, it is the producer's name that is really the key to quality.

Good Soave has a delicate straw colour, with a subtle grassy nose, and is full and leafy with a slightly nutty finish on the palate. There is some acidity, but it is dry rather than crisp. Wines from named vineyards tend to have a greater concentration of flavour, standing out in a sea of insipid Soave – the result of excessive yields. Good producers include Pieropan and Anselmi, as well as Boscaini, Guerrieri-Rizzardi, Masi, Tedeschi, Zenato and Santi.

There are other northern whites that are not dissimilar, such as Lugana and Bianco di Custoza. Gavi dei Gavi from the Cortese grape is also soft and grassy, but has a reputation and price that are usually unjustified. La Scolca and la Giustiniana are the best producers there.

Sicily and Sardinia

Curiously, for a hot southern island, **Sicily** makes much better white wine than red. There is the DOC of **Bianco d'Alcamo**, where Rapitalà – the best and only producer of note – makes a delicate dry wine from a typically Sicilian grape, Catarratto, blended with a hefty dollop of the ubiquitous Trebbiano. However, most of the better Sicilian wines, red or white, do not fit into the DOC system, so the key to quality is the producer's name, rather than a DOC. The new star estate is Terre di Ginestra, which hit the limelight at the Vinitaly wine fair a couple of years ago and has demonstrated just how good Sicilian whites can be, with the sensible use of modern vinification methods, as well as restrained yields. Terrale is the second wine, a cheaper and slightly diluted version, but still providing agreeable drinking.

The best-known Sicilian wine, both red and white, is Corvo, which is the brand name of the Casa Vinicola Duca di Salaparuta. It gives a no more precise regional definition than Bianco di Sicilia, which indicates simply that grapes can be bought from all over the island. The most recent vintage tastes dry and fresh with a touch of almonds. The better-quality white, Columba Platina, has some light buttery fruit. In contrast, Bianco di Valguarnera tastes like an infusion of oak chippings in a fancy bottle.

Other respectable Sicilian whites include Cellaro, Settesoli, Regaleali and Donnafugata, all from leading estates or co-operatives.

The white wine of **Sardinia** which has made the most impact on the UK market is **Torbato di Alghero**. Torbato is another fairly neutral-flavoured grape variety, which makes some dry, quite refreshing but fairly nondescript white wine. Production is concentrated in the hands of village co-operatives and the large, competent producers of the island, Sella e Mosca.

Other Italians

Italy, south of Rome, is not renowned for its white wines, with a couple of honourable exceptions, **Fiano di Avellino** and **Greco di Tufo**. Both are made by the leading, and virtually only, Campania producer whose wines reach the UK, Mastroberardino. Greco is the principal white grape variety of the south and, as Greco di Tufo, is at its most flavoursome with some dry nutty fruit. Fiano, another grape variety, is more subtle and needs some bottle age. **Lacryma Christi del Vesuvio** is memorable for its name, but certainly not for the rather earthy white wines that occasionally find their way to these shores.

Spain

The majority of white **Rioja** fits into this segment of the taste wheel, for most of the large bodegas have given up ageing their white wines in oak, and now sell them as sin crianza (without oak). However, they simply do not have as much flavour as the oak-aged wines (see further round the wheel), as the main grape variety is Viura, which is rather lacking in flavour and acidity. At best, if drunk within a year or two of the vintage, white Rioja tastes young and fresh, sometimes with the boiled-sweets flavour that originates from very cool fermentation. The best wines are clean and fresh, but it is obvious why oak was favoured in the first place.

More intrinsic flavour comes from **Rueda** and, indeed, one of the leading Rioja bodegas, Marqués de Riscal, prefers to sell a white wine from Rueda rather than from Rioja. Rueda has been transformed in the last decade or so: where once it was an oxidised, fortified sherry-like wine, it has become, with the help of a new generation of winemakers and outside investment, a dry, nutty, grassy-flavoured wine. It is dry without being acidic, with a hint of almonds and a slight bitterness on the finish, and a stony freshness. Verdejo is the main grape variety, along with Viura and a drop of Sauvignon for extra pungency. **Superiore** on the label indicates a higher percentage of Verdejo. The best producers are Marqués de Riscal, Marqués de Griñon, Los Curros and Antonio Sanz.

Portugal

Across the border in Portugal, white **Dão** might fit into this segment, as it is quite full-flavoured with lemon and honey; it is fairly acidic in its youth, but that lessens as the wine matures and it becomes fatter and richer, with a certain nutty quality. There is often an old-fashioned feel to it. It must have six months' ageing before bottling, while **garrafeira** indicates a year's ageing in both bottle and vat.

One of the better Portuguese whites comes from the Douro – **Planalto Reserva**, which is made by the Mateus Rosé company of Sogrape. The expertise is apparent in this delicately fruity, soft grassy dry white wine.

Greece and Cyprus

The most characterful white wine of Greece – apart from Retsina, which merits a segment all to itself in the taste wheel – is **Robola of Cephalonia**, made from the Robola grape. It has a dry, nutty, old-fashioned flavour to it, as does white **Patras** from the Peloponnese. Demestica is a common brand of Greek wine, with a dry, rather undistinguished flavour.

Aphrodite, the white wine from the Keo co-operative on Cyprus, is very similar. It is dry and flat, with a slightly salty tang to the finish, the kind of wine that is delicious in the island sunshine, but does not have quite the same appeal under grey British skies.

The New World

Examples of Sauvignon from the warmer New World countries – California, South America, South Africa and Australia – fit into this section, for they tend to lack the acidity of their counterparts in New Zealand or the Loire Valley. The flavours tend to be a little broader and fatter, without the crisp pungency that can be so appealing in Sauvignon.

Chile Some Chilean Sauvignon is rather dull and flat, spoilt by the use of an inferior clone called Sauvignonasse, which lacks the pungency and zest of real Sauvignon. However, with plantings of better clones, reduced yields and investment in modern technology to control fermentation temperatures, flavours are improving. Torres, Santa Rita, Caliterra, Viña Carmen, Canepa and Undurraga are amongst the best producers. Torres, in fact, makes two Sauvignons, one without oak, and one with oak, called Bellaterra, which fits alongside South African Blanc Fumé further round the wheel. Chilean Sauvignon seems to fade very quickly once the wine is more than 18 months to two years old, so drink the youngest available.

South Africa If South African Sauvignon is aged in oak, it is usually labelled Blanc Fumé, while the unoaked wines are simply called Sauvignon. There are some good examples available, with soft, grassy, lightly pungent flavours. One of the most subtle comes from Klein Constantia, a winery that benefits from a winemaker who has worked in New Zealand. Thelema, Neil Ellis, Talana Hill, Boschendal and Villiera are also good. Usually, Sauvignon is much more successful than Chardonnay in South Africa. The other grape variety from the Cape which also fits into this segment is Chenin Blanc. South Africans tend to take it for granted as it is an easy, versatile grape variety. But, when vinified carefully, with grapes that are not diluted by excessive yields, it has some attractive fruit and flavour, medium-weight, with sufficient acidity and usually a hint of honey to make a soft, easy-to-drink, undemanding wine. The Simonsvlei co-operative makes a good, inexpensive example, generally sold under a supermarket own-label, as is Simonsig. (*See also our feature on South African wines on p. 27.*)

Australia Australia is not generally known for its Sauvignon: its Semillon and Chardonnay tend to be more exciting. However, one exception which does achieve some varietal pungency, comes from a new winery, Shaw and Smith, run by the talented team of Michael Hill Smith and Martin Shaw. Katnook Estate and Schinus Molle are fresh and vibrant too. Other examples tend to be oaked and fit into the next segment.

USA In California, the oaky Fumé Blanc style of Sauvignon is more popular. However, there are some Sauvignon producers who prefer to emphasise the tropical fruit flavours of ripe Sauvignon, such as Matanzas Creek. Quivira is crisp and pungent, as are Ojai, Carmenet and Konocti. Gallo is cheap, but rather fat and stewed.

Elsewhere, there is the occasional example of Sauvignon from Washington State, such as Columbia Crest and Latah Creek, and Cordier in Texas, which makes a soft, grassy Sauvignon.

LIGHT AND BUTTERY (MEDIUM BODY, OAK, HIGH ACIDITY)

Fermentation and maturation in oak add weight and stature to a wine. However, the wine must have sufficent structure and body in order to assimilate the oak in the first place. Sometimes, where oak ageing is tried as an experiment or as a way of adding additional interest to a wine which is less than exciting, it is not always successful. One particular example of this is Muscadet. The reasons for putting Muscadet in oak, to achieve more complex flavours, can be appreciated, and the tenacity of the producers in question admired, but the success is questionable. Melon de Bourgogne is a rather light ethereal grape, with little structure. What flavour it has is drowned by the overwhelming effect of new oak, and the wine tastes just like an infusion of oak chippings. On the other hand, some grape varieties, most notably Chardonnay, lend themselves perfectly to vinification and maturation in oak, again with the proviso that there is enough structure and body in the wine in the first place.

Chablis and other white burgundies

The above is amply illustrated by **Chablis**. One or two innovative young growers, namely Jean-Pierre Grossot and Bernard Légland, have experimented with what they call a *cuvée bois* for some of their village Chablis. It is one way of extending their range of wines and adding an extra dimension to their repertoire. But, at that level, the wood can overwhelm the flinty flavour of the Chablis, making the wine less attractive than the oak-free version. William Fèvre also uses oak for his village Chablis, Champs Royaux, producing quite a rich, buttery wine.

Up a rung in the appellation ladder are those growers who put their premier cru wines in wood: that produces quite a different flavour. Good premiers crus, especially from those vineyards on the same side of the valley as the grands crus, have the structure to benefit from the effect of oak ageing. The oak gives the wine a certain richness, but there should always be a firm backbone of balancing acidity. However, it must be said that in some of the ripest years, like 1989, acidity levels were fairly low. The 1990 is balanced, with a rich concentration of flavour, and the 1988 exemplifies the underlying steeliness that is characteristic of Chablis.

Growers who do put their wine in wood include Jean-Marie

Raveneau, René and Vincent Dauvissat, William Fèvre, Jean Collet, Jean-Paul Droin, and Michel Laroche (some of his wines).

Grand cru Chablis should be significantly richer than a premier cru and so belongs to the firm and toasted segment of the wheel, along with most of the principal appellations of the Côte d'Or. Possible exceptions might be the lesser ones, like St-Aubin and St-Romain, as well as the wines of the Côte Chalonnaise, and also Pouilly-Fuissé.

The white wines of the **Côte Chalonnaise**, namely Montagny and Rully, have a firm backbone of acidity and benefit particularly from some ageing in oak. Good producers include Noël-Bouton at Domaine de la Folie, Cogny, Dury, Faiveley, Jaffelin and Delorme. The 1990, 1989 and 1988 are all good vintages.

The appellation of **Pouilly-Fuissé** can produce some good wine, but lacks the depth of a good Rully or Montagny. As an object of fashion it has been beset by prices inflated completely out of proportion to its quality. However, good estates include Domaine Corsin and Vincent at the Château de Fuissé – especially the Cuvée Vieilles Vignes, a wine made from older than average vines, which have highly developed root systems to tap into deeper minerals and provide extra flavour and concentration.

New Zealand Chardonnay

As for Chardonnay from other regions, New Zealand belongs in this segment by virtue of both the relatively high acidity levels, originating in a coolish climate, and the customary oak treatment. Although some of the richer wines stray into the next segment of the wheel, the cooler New Zealand climate avoids some of the intense tropical fruit flavours found in Australian Chardonnay, and produces more subtle flavours. Chardonnay is treated seriously in New Zealand and is virtually always given some barrel maturation, even if it is not fermented in oak. The flavours may be rich, with the deliciously toasted taste originating from charred barrels, but there is always an underlying acidity and elegance.

Good producers of New Zealand Chardonnay include Te Mata's Elston, Martinborough Vineyards, Morton Estate, Kumeu River, Villa Maria, Matua Valley (especially with its Judd Estate), Hunters, Babich, Nobilo (particularly its Dixon Vineyard Reserve),

Once in the bottle a cork can last for decades but eventually it becomes brittle and crumbly with age.

Cloudy Bay, Neudorf, Redwood Valley and Collards. Good recent vintages include 1991, 1990, 1989 and 1987.

Canadian Chardonnay

The occasional example of Canadian Chardonnay should also feature here, by virtue of high acidity levels and oak treatment. Hillebrand tends to be over-oaked, while Inniskillin is a little more subtle and buttery, and Château des Charmes is quite burgundian.

New Zealand Sauvignon Blanc

Some New Zealand Sauvignon also fits into this segment. There is a distinct divergence in style, depending on whether the wine has spent time in oak or not, and the label may give some indication, with the words oak aged – but not always. Perhaps the epitome of this style of Sauvignon is Cloudy Bay, one of the great success stories of the New Zealand wine industry. It is amazing to realise that the first vintage of Cloudy Bay was as recent as 1985, and yet, in some circles, this wine is now synonymous with New Zealand Sauvignon. Demand far exceeds supply; the wine is sold on quota, and the price is significantly higher than that of other New Zealand Sauvignons. Only a part of the wine is barrel aged, which prevents the taste of oak from overwhelming the flavour of the grape. A tiny proportion of Semillon also fills out the wine, making it rounded and subtle, with gentle, understated flavours.

Other riper New Zealand Sauvignons include Brookfields, Waipara Springs, Rongopai and Matua Valley Reserve.

Australian Semillon

Australian Semillon fits into this category, but the acidity level is very much more apparent on the palate than in the average Australian Chardonnay. It is Semillon that really makes the most original and distinctive white wines of Australia. In Bordeaux it is rare to find a pure Semillon – usually it is blended with Sauvignon – but in Australia it is vinified as a pure varietal. The Hunter Valley is where Semillon performs best, enjoying the warm climate to yield wines that seem rather thin, if not lean and acidic, in their youth, but which develop into something complex and subtle with bottle ageing, more than repaying patience. There is a toasted nutty quality about mature Hunter Valley Semillon, with some underlying oily richness which makes a wine refreshingly original compared with jet-setting Chardonnay.

Good producers include Rothbury, Rosemount, Lindemans and

Penfolds. The best recent vintages include 1991, 1989, 1987, 1986 and 1985.

Occasionally, you can find blends of Semillon and Chardonnay – not only in Australia but also in New Zealand – as well as the traditional Bordeaux mix of Sauvignon and Semillon. However, in Australia it is pure Semillon that works best of all.

Graves and other oaked whites

Back to France and the Graves or, more precisely, the appellation of **Pessac-Léognan** which now includes the better properties of the reduced appellation of the Graves. This is the only appellation of significance in Bordeaux that is equally important in both red and white wine production. The white wines of the Graves can cover a whole range of flavours, depending on how they are made, on whether the producer has a modern approach to winemaking or not, and on whether or not oak is used. At their most basic, the white wines of the Graves are fuller, more solid versions of Bordeaux Blanc, while at the other end of the scale, amongst the more prestigious classed growths, the flavours are much more subtle and substantial and fit firmly into this segment of the wheel.

These are wines that generally benefit from the use of new oak and from ageing in bottle as well as in cask. There is a toasted character that is not dissimilar to Chardonnay, but with a different dimension of flavour. The use of Sémillon makes a flavour that seems leaner and less appealing, even a little dull, in its youth, but which develops into something broader and fuller. Sometimes, the oaky overtones can be a little overwhelming, but in good Graves the oak should be well integrated. Good performers currently are Fieuzal, Olivier, Couhins-Lurton, Clos Floridène (made by Denis Dubourdieu), Domaine de la Grave, Laville Haut Brion and Haut Brion, which makes a tiny amount of white wine. Also good are Carbonnieux, which has improved in the last few years, Domaine de Chevalier and Notre Dame de Landiras which, unusually, is a pure Sémillon. Good recent vintages are 1990, 1989, 1988, 1986, 1985, 1983 and 1982. As elsewhere in south-west France, 1991 suffered severely from spring frosts.

There are other examples of wines vinified in oak which are unusual for their appellation. In **Côtes de Provence**, there is Clos Mireille, the property of the Ott family. This is also a Sauvignon and Sémillon blend, which has something of the mature flavour of the Graves – an underlying nutty leafiness when given some bottle age. Unfortunately, but understandably, it is expensive, but delicious. Another Côtes de Provence estate, Domaine de la Courtade, made from a blend of Rolle and Sémillon, also uses oak for its white wines, which need bottle ageing for the oak to soften.

In **Tursan**, the new wines of Michel Guérard (of Eugenié-les-Bains fame), Château de Bachen, and the special cuvée, Baron de Bachen, are adding a new dimension to this overlooked VDQS on the edge of the pine forests of the Landes. Maturation in oak is a vital feature of the wine, and there is Sémillon, Sauvignon and Gros Manseng, as well as Baroque, in the blend.

A final postscript to this section is **England**, where enterprising vineyards are experimenting with oak. The most successful include Rock Lodge, Penshurst, Thames Valley, Tenterden, Lamberhurst, Chiltern Valley and Pilton Manor.

DRY AND NUTTY (MEDIUM BODY, OAK, LOW ACIDITY)

This segment covers wines made in warmer climates, such as the Rhône Valley, South America and Bulgaria, with lower acidity than in the previous segment. However, they do not quite have the weight and body of the wines further round the wheel.

The Rhône

Apart from the white wines based on Viognier, in the appellations of Condrieu and Château Grillet, and the lighter, one-dimensional Côtes-du-Rhône, other Rhône wines covered in this section are white Hermitage and neighbouring Crozes-Hermitage and St-Joseph in the northern Rhône, and Châteauneuf-du-Pape.

White **Hermitage** can age beautifully, especially when it is made by a talented grower like Gérard Chave and is given a few months' barrel ageing. It comes from two grape varieties, Roussanne and Marsanne and, in its youth, can seem a little dull and lifeless. However, it rewards patience by developing all kinds of wonderful flavours of honey and herbs, peaches and toasted nuts. In some ways it is not so different from a good white burgundy, but lacks the same acidity level or weight.

Some white Hermitage, such as Jaboulet's Chevalier de Stérimberg, is intended for earlier drinking and has a fresh lemony liveliness in its youth, but lacks the potential for further development. Good examples of traditional white Hermitage come from Chave and Sorrel. White St-Joseph and Crozes-Hermitage can at times be nothing more than slightly fuller versions of Côtes-du-Rhône, but happily this is not always so, with complex characterful wines coming from Clos de l'Arbalestrier in St-Joseph and Domaine des Remizières in Crozes-Hermitage.

White **Châteauneuf-du-Pape** can be made from Clairette, Bourboulenc, Picpoul, Picardin and Roussanne (but not Marsanne), and is not usually as flavoursome as Hermitage. Never the less, in the right hands, the taste can be distinctly leafy, with rich, herbal fruit and nutty overtones. The best producer is Château de Beaucastel.

(A **Californian** footnote to this segment is Le Sophiste from Bonny Doon, a Marsanne Roussanne blend, which is comparable both in flavour and price to white Hermitage.)

Argentina, Bulgaria and others

Both Argentinian and Bulgarian Chardonnay belong in this section as, with one or two exceptions, neither quite has the weight or body to fit into the next segment of the wheel. Chardonnay in **Argentina** is a relatively new grape variety. Like virtually every other wine-producing country, it too is joining the bandwagon of the world's most popular white grape variety, and one or two good examples are beginning to appear. The biggest producer, Trapiche, makes two Chardonnays: one, labelled Chardonnay Reserve, is without oak and is light and lemony; the other, a Chardonnay Oak Cask Reserve, has spent several months in new French oak. The price difference is quite significant: you pay about £1 (or 30 per cent) more for the oak. Trapiche is still learning about oak barrels and for the moment the wine tends to taste over-oaked. The situation will improve as the vines age and the winemakers learn to reduce the excessive yields resulting from liberal irrigation. Finca Flichman is the one other producer of Chardonnay available in the UK, with two wines, Flichman Claire Chardonnay and Caballero de la Cepa.

Bulgaria produces a range of different Chardonnays, as country wines, Controliran wines and Reserve wines. Some do not see any oak at all and fit into a previous segment of the wheel, while the Reserve wines must spend three years in wood, and the flavour is firmly oaky. The two Reserve wines are Varna and Khan Krum Chardonnay, while the Controliran Chardonnay from Preslav is also kept in new oak, and tastes of it. The value of these wines remains excellent for, despite the changes in the system, the Bulgarians are still aware of the need for foreign currency and price their wines advantageously.

In this section we should also include the occasional oaked Sauvignon from **Chile** – Miguel Torres Bellaterra Sauvignon, for example, with its firm, dry oaky flavours that rather overwhelm the fruit of the grape variety, as does Montes Fumé Blanc. The same could also be said of some of the Blanc Fumé wines from **South Africa**. They do not have the weight of New World Sauvignons from California or Australia, and the flavour of the grape is completely masked by the oak, with relatively low acidity.

FIRM AND TOASTED (FULL BODY, OAK, HIGH ACIDITY)

Grand cru Chablis

Grand cru Chablis is the epitome of this section. It has a richness and concentration of flavour which comes from the grape variety, Chardonnay, which is grown on the best hillsides of the village. This, combined with the backbone of firm acidity, is characteristic of all good Chablis. Grand cru Chablis, from one of seven named vineyards grouped together on the steep slopes above the river Serein, has weight, intensity and potential for ageing that is rarely seen in premier cru Chablis. Of the villages, the best known and largest is Les Clos; Grenouilles is the smallest. The others are

Blanchots, Vaudésir, Preuses, Bougros and Valmur. Several producers of grand cru Chablis ferment and age their wines in wood: William Fèvre at Domaine de la Maladière is the leading exponent of new wood, as well as the largest owner of grand cru vineyards, and his example has been followed by several others. More traditional growers like Dauvissat, Pinson and Raveneau have never abandoned their oak barriques, but have favoured a limited amount of new oak. Other exponents of oak in Chablis include Jean Paul-Droin, Michel Laroche, Jean Collet and Vocoret.

Amongst the 'no oak' contingent, Louis Michel remains supreme for steely grands crus that have never seen a stave of oak. The curious thing is that mature Chablis can, with bottle age, take on some of the nutty flavours that you would normally associate with oak maturation. However, Chablis that has spent some months in oak tends to be fuller in the mouth, with a greater concentration of flavour, particularly marked when it is young. With age, the differences fade.

Côte d'Or

The vineyards of the **Côte de Beaune** – there is virtually no white wine made on the Côte de Nuits – are about a hundred kilometres further south. The climate is that little bit warmer, making even richer, more concentrated flavours. Oak barrels are considered the norm here, even for the village wines of the Côte de Beaune. The classification is the same as in Chablis, with a division between grands crus, such as Le Montrachet, premiers crus, like Puligny-Montrachet, les Pucelles, Folatières or Combettes, and plain Puligny-Montrachet. A premier cru without a vineyard name is likely to be a blend from several vineyards.

Some of the village wines may not have the weight and body to justify their inclusion in this segment, but in general terms, the good wines, and certainly the great white wines of the Côte de Beaune fit in very firmly. They have complexity and richness, with a depth of flavour that develops with bottle age, and always have sufficient acidity, except, perhaps, in the very ripest years, like 1986. They are usually relatively high in alcohol, reaching 13.5 per cent, which makes them quite mouth-filling, but this should be balanced with acidity to retain the elegance that should be the hallmark of great white burgundy.

The principal white wine villages of the Côte de Beaune are **Puligny-Montrachet** (the subject of a fascinating insight into Burgundian village life by Simon Loftus in his book *Puligny-Montrachet,* published by Ebury Press), with neighbouring **Chassagne-Montrachet**, as well as **Aloxe-Corton** and **Meursault**.

These are the sources of some of the most evocative names of Burgundy – Bâtard-Montrachet, Corton-Charlemagne and others. These are the wines which the producers of the New World aspire to emulate, and some do indeed come close.

The name of the producer is the all-important key to quality in Burgundy, when several families own plots of the same vineyard. Names to seek out include Domaine Leflaive and Olivier Leflaive (from the same family); also Matrot, Charton et Trébuchet, Blain-Gagnard, Sauzet, Comte Lafon, François Jobard, Simon Bize, Jean-Noël Gagnard, Henri Jayer, Henri Germain, Coche-Dury, Michelot-Buisson and Bonneau du Martray.

As in Chablis, there has been a run of good vintages – 1990, 1989 and 1988 – with 1991 making less exciting wines. The 1990 is generally very highly considered, while the 1989 and 1986 may be slightly lacking in acidity. The other good vintages of the eighties were 1982, 1983 and 1985.

New Zealand Chardonnay

Among the wines of the New World, Chardonnays from California and Australia generally fit into the next section, while the richer New Zealand Chardonnays, with their higher acidity levels, come into this segment. Included here are wines with sufficient weight, like Te Mata's Elston, Kumeu River and Matua Valley's Judd Estate, which all have rich, toasted burgundian flavours.

RICH AND BUTTERY (FULL BODY, OAK, LOW ACIDITY)

Many of the Chardonnays produced in California, Australia, Chile and South Africa fit into this segment of the wheel because their natural acidity level is often lower than in fine white Burgundy. Admittedly, however, some of the best wines from Australia and California do come close to emulating their Burgundian peers.

California and other North American Chardonnays

California Chardonnay has moved towards wines that are a little leaner and understated, with a tight, dry, nutty flavour – that is to say, wines with greater subtlety, more suitable for drinking with a meal. They no longer leap out of the glass in the exuberant way that they used to. There are still wines that are ripe and opulent with the flavours of tropical fruit, pineapples and mangoes.

However, the understated wines are more rewarding, developing, rather than fading, with age.

As with all California wines, it is the winery name on the label that is the clue to quality. Robert Mondavi, Saintsbury, Simi, Au Bon Climat, Schug Cellars, Edna Valley, Sonoma Cutrer, Kistler, Long Vineyards, Qupé, Newton Vineyard, Kendall Jackson, Grgich Hills, Far Niente, Freemark Abbey and Rutherford Hill are amongst those making fine Chardonnay. The last ten years have seen some fine vintages in California; of recent years, 1991 and 1990 are very good, while 1986 and 1985 are drinking well now.

It is surprising to realise that Chardonnay is grown in as many as 42 other American states; however, very few of these wines actually cross the Atlantic. You may find examples from **Washington State** and **Oregon**, such as Covey Run, Blackwood Canyon, Eyrie Vineyard and Ponzi, and there are also some good Chardonnays from **New York State**, from the vineyards of Long Island and from Wagner in the Finger Lakes. **Texas** is an also-ran in the Chardonnay stakes, with Llano Estacado.

The wine that Californians term Fumé Blanc might also come into this segment. The name was coined by Robert Mondavi and others have followed his example, making a Sauvignon that may be blended with a little Semillon before being aged in oak barrels. The taste, a ripe mouthful of buttery fruit and overpowering oak with low acidity, has more to do with the oak barrels than with the grape variety, and for that reason the wine fits into this segment.

Australia

The obvious comparison with California is Australia. There is no wine region in this enormous continent that does not produce Chardonnay, and usually the flavours are ripe and buttery, with overtones of tropical fruit, lychees, pineapples and peaches. In contrast to burgundy, the taste is definitely fuller and riper, with lower acidity, usually not as elegant, and perhaps a little blowsy and overstated. Sometimes the wines can be spoilt by a slightly sharp citric finish, an indication that the acidity level has been adjusted. However, Chardonnay from some of the cooler regions of Australia – such as the Yarra Valley in Victoria and even cooler Tasmania – displays some elegance and the hallmarks of good varietal character, with the toasted nuances of oak maturation and good ageing potential.

The great advantage of Australian Chardonnay for the Chardonnay enthusiast is price: the large Australian wineries seem to have more modest aspirations about price than many of their Californian counterparts. While many California

Chardonnays demand a price that is comparable with good burgundy, Australians have appreciated the virtue of value for money. The choice of a good California Chardonnay for under £10 a bottle is rather limited, compared with what is available from Australia.

As with California, the winery name is an important key to quality and style. Names to look out for include Yarra Yering, Coldstream Hills, Pipers Brook, Petaluma, Tarrawarra, Moss Wood, Smith and Shaw, Rothbury, Rosemount, Schinus Molle, David Wynn, Cullen Wines and Lake's Folly. Good recent vintages include 1991, 1990, 1988 and 1987.

Chile

In comparison with Australia and California, Chilean Chardonnay still has quite a long way to go. The flavours may be somewhat heavy-handed and unsubtle, but even in the last three or four years, there has been a marked improvement as Chilean winemakers have begun to master the intricacies of barrel fermentation and maturation. Vineyard practices are changing and, in particular, excessive irrigation is being moderated, leading to an improvement in quality. However, for the moment the best Chardonnay from Chile does not yet have the subtlety of the best from either Australia or California. Names to look for include Villa Montes, Santa Rita, Errazuriz, and Concha y Toro amongst others.

South Africa

South Africa also has a long way to go with Chardonnay. It suffered from something of a false start when some smuggled Chardonnay vines turned out to be Pinot Auxerrois, but things have been sorted out since then; problems with quarantine regulations have been overcome and Chardonnay is being planted quite extensively. For the moment, most of the vines are still very young, and barrel fermentation and oak maturation are relatively new skills for South African winemakers, who have been cut off from the many technological advances of the last decade or so. Much South African Chardonnay is still spoilt by the heavy-handed use of oak and, in general, the wines have yet to acquire the understated elegance that is the hallmark of fine Chardonnay.

Some of the better South African Chardonnays, from the cooler vineyards of the Cape, include Hamilton-Russell, Klein Constantia, Thelema, Glen Carlou and Boschendal.

Chardonnay, then, is the white grape variety that every winemaker aspires to master, with the wines of Burgundy as their examples. Just about every wine-producing country grows Chardonnay somewhere, from Israel to Mexico, and there are numerous barrel-fermented, oak-aged examples. Often they are full-bodied, with ripe buttery oaky flavours; sometimes they can lack acidity. Chardonnay has been introduced not only to the New World vineyards, but also to regions where the indigenous white grape varieties do not have the same flavour and appeal.

Italy

There are numerous examples of Chardonnay from all over Italy. Chardonnay forms part of the innovative wave of experimentation in **Tuscany**. It is given some semblance of official recognition by Predicato del Muschio (a Tuscan classification for vino da tavola based on the proportion of Chardonnay), but is usually sold with a fantasy name like Le Grance from Caparzo, I Sistri from Felsina Berardenga or Il Marzocco from Avignonesi. These wines have varying success, depending on the producer's expertise and such factors as the age of the vines. They are usually expensive, presented in a designer bottle with a fancy label, which confirms the producer's aspirations and perception of his wine. In **Piedmont**, Angelo Gaja is the leading producer of Chardonnay, while Lungarotti in Umbria makes Chardonnay di Miraduolo.

Another Italian Chardonnay is Preludio No. 1 from **Puglia**, which is ripe and full-flavoured, and somewhat lacking in acidity, originating as it does from an even warmer climate.

Other comparable Tuscan wines which have been vinified and aged in oak include the oaked version of Pomino, Il Benefizio from Frescobaldi, made from a selection of grape varieties, with its ripe buttery oaky flavours which could be confused with Chardonnay. Another example is Terre di Tufo, from Teruzzi e Puthod, which is a barrel-fermented Vernaccia di San Gimignano.

Iberia

Across the Pyrenees in Spain, there are also examples of Chardonnay. Jean León, one of the leading winemakers of **Penedès**, pairs it with Cabernet Sauvignon, while that indefatigable innovator, Miguel Torres, has also planted it in Penedès. Torres Milmanda is a pure varietal wine, while Gran Viña Sol includes a substantial amount, along with Paralleda. Green Label Gran Viña Sol, which is a blend of Sauvignon and Parellada, also deserves a passing mention here, for it is aged in oak and is ripe and buttery in flavour. The Codorníu estate of Raimat, in the new DO of **Costers del Segre**, also produces oak-aged Chardonnay.

Portugal is beginning to consider Chardonnay too, with a recently introduced example from João Pires, Cova d'Orsa.

Rioja The final wine in this segment is the traditional, classic white Rioja, which is treated to the same ageing process as the red wine. Traditional white Rioja, made from grape varieties such as Viura, spends at least six months, if not longer, in wood and the result is firmly dry and nutty. Viura is not a particularly acidic grape variety, so the wine is low in acidity, but the flavour is firm and dry, marked by the wood, perhaps a little flat, but quite elegant. Good examples include Marqués de Murrieta, Viña Tondonia from Lopez de Heredia, and Monopole from CVNE.

VIN JAUNE

Vin Jaune needs a segment all of its own, as it is quite unlike any other table wine. The closest taste comparison is to fino sherry, which features in the fortified wine wheel, although Vin Jaune is not fortified.

This is one of the most original and distinctive wines of France, coming from the mountainous region of the Jura, bordering Switzerland. The method of vinification contradicts all the usual oenological practices: the wine is left in small oak barrels for a minimum of six years, during which time the barrels are not topped up, but are, instead, exposed to the summer and winter variations of temperature in a cellar which must not be completely below ground. During the ageing period a flor of yeast develops, as with fino sherry, and it is this flor which gives Vin Jaune its original flavour. The grape variety is the Savagnin which is unique to the Jura. After six years' ageing Vin Jaune has some distinctively nutty flavours, with a firm bite of acidity and an almost savoury, salty character, again like fino sherry. The best example comes from the tiny village of Château Chalon, and the other three appellations of the Jura – Arbois, l'Etoile and Côtes du Jura – all include Vin Jaune.

With small yields from the Savagnin grape and such a long ageing process, entailing a considerable evaporation and loss of wine, Vin Jaune is inevitably expensive. It is sold in the distinctive clavelin bottle of 62cl, the amount that 100cl reduces to in the course of six years. Château d'Arlay and Bourdy are the two examples available in Britain.

RETSINA

Retsina, most of which comes from Attica, is the best known of all Greek wines and the most individual. It maintains a centuries' old tradition of adding resin from the Aleppo pines to the fermenting wine, as a means of preserving it – a method which dates back to the days when little was understood about the damaging effects of temperature and oxidation.

Retsina has a wonderfully distinctive taste, which really has nothing at all to do with grapes, and it is the kind of wine you either love or hate. There is a sharp resinous taste, perhaps reminiscent of ginger (some might call it turpentine), which seems to complement rich Greek food. Good retsina should be light golden in colour, with a fresh lively attack of resin in the mouth. It should never be flat and lifeless and must be drunk fresh. Good producers include Kourtakis, Boutari and Tsantali.

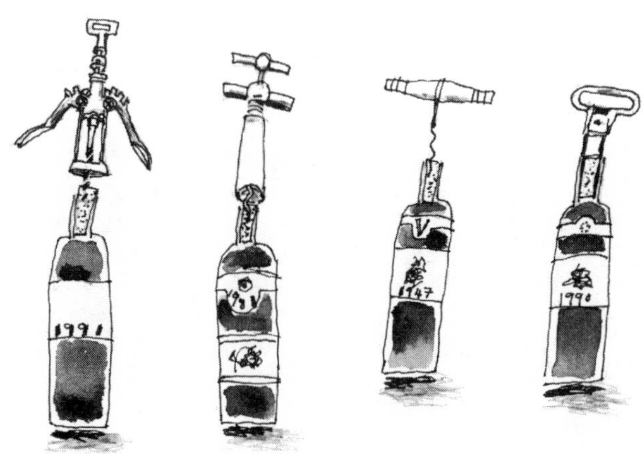

MEDIUM WHITE WINES

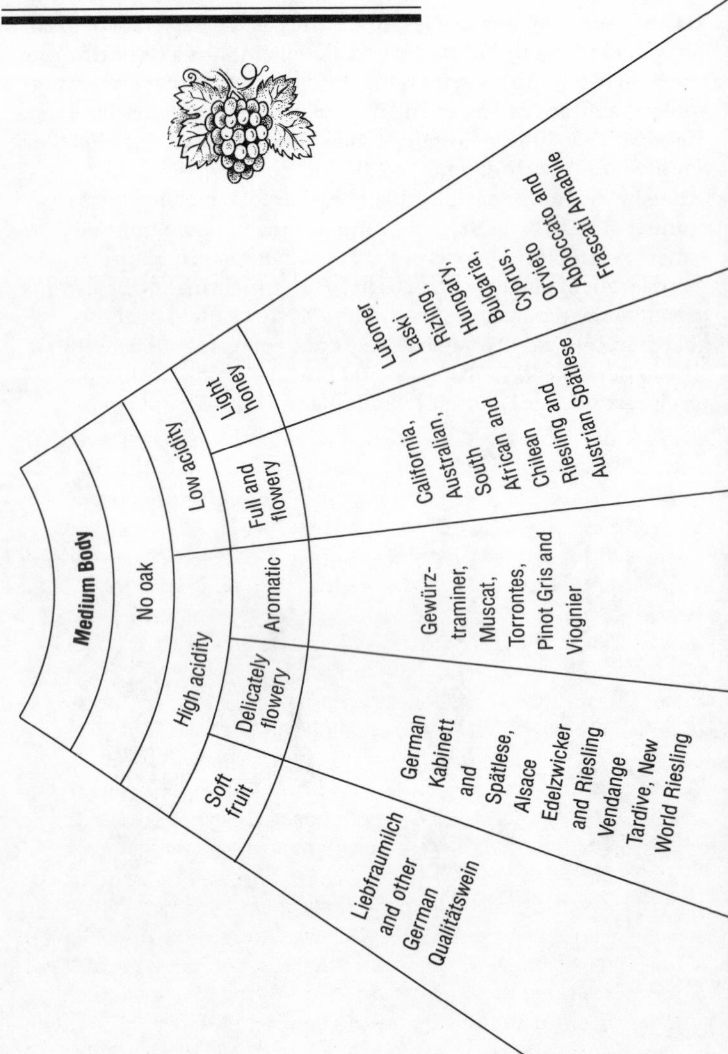
Medium Body
No oak
Low acidity
High acidity
Light honey
Full and flowery
Aromatic
Delicately flowery
Soft fruit
Lutomer Laski Rizling, Hungary, Bulgaria, Cyprus, Orvieto Abboccato and Frascati Amabile
California, Australian, South African and Chilean Riesling and Austrian Spätlese
Gewürz-traminer, Muscat, Torrontes, Pinot Gris and Viognier
German Kabinett and Spätlese, Alsace Edelzwicker and Riesling Vendange Tardive, New World Riesling
Liebfraumilch and other German Qualitätswein

In broad terms, medium whites encompass all those wines that are neither firmly dry nor intensely sweet. They are wines that may contain an element of residual sugar remaining from the fermentation, or they may have had some Süssreserve added to them, in order to give them a soft, rounded flavour and finish. Alternatively, the intrinsic flavour may give the impression of some aromatic richness, such as an Alsace Gewurztraminer, which is essentially dry, but does not really taste so because of the particular character of the grape variety.

SOFT FRUIT (MEDIUM BODY, NO OAK, HIGH ACIDITY)

Liebfraumilch

For a soft wine with high acidity, **Liebfraumilch** is the obvious starting point. This is the wine that dominates the German export market and accounts for a considerable percentage of Britain's wine consumption. Liebfraumilch from a respectable source is a perfectly acceptable wine. Its chief virtue is that it is innocuous: slightly sweet, soft and fruity, without any harsh edges, or indeed any distinctive regional characteristics. In the minefield of confusing German names it seems a safe and pronounceable choice. The well-known brand leaders, like Blue Nun and Black Tower, are subject to meticulous attention in their production, which entails the careful blending of several different wines from diverse vineyards and grape varieties, in order to achieve a consistent style, changing only with vintage variations. Liebfraumilch must be of Qualitätswein standard and must originate from the Rheinhessen, Rheinpfalz, Nahe or Rheingau. In practice, most Liebfraumilch comes from the first two regions.

Sadly, the enormous quantity of cheap and nasty Liebfraumilch that has flooded the British market has not only damaged the reputation of Liebfraumilch but has also brought the finer German wines into disrepute. It is no secret that the German wine market is in a sorry state: Riesling, which accounts for all fine German wine, is deemed an unfashionable grape, and the better quality German wines are undervalued and simply not appreciated. However, with an elegance and subtlety which is missing from Liebfraumilch, they do not fit into this particular segment of the wheel, but are scattered elsewhere.

Liebfraumilch is an easier way of asking for a standard German wine, like Niersteiner Gutes Domtal, or Rüdesheimer Rosengarten, or one of the innumerable Bereich or Grosslage names – that group several smaller vineyards, or Einzellagen – within a village. Without any mention of Prädikat or grape variety on the label, these are wines of basic Qualitätswein standard which have some regional characteristics. Wines from the Mosel, such as Bereich Bernkastel or Piesporter Goldtröpfchen, are lighter and a little more flowery, and may fit more comfortably into the next segment of the wheel, compared with those from the Rhine, such as Bereich Johannisberg or Oppenheimer Krötenbrunnen. Rhine wines are generally a little fuller and more honeyed and are made from grapes that have reached a certain level of ripeness, measured by the sugar level in the juice.

The grape variety is unlikely to be Riesling – more likely to be Müller-Thurgau, or perhaps a blend of some of the newer crosses, like Kerner, Huxelrebe or Scheurebe, developed for their greater ripening potential in the cooler climate of Germany's northern vineyards. The overall flavour is soft and easy, with a background of high acidity which is masked by the sweetness from the Süssreserve. These wines lack the elegance and refinement of good Riesling, but can make pleasant enough drinking if they come from a reputable source.

Germany had a run of three superb vintages with 1990, 1989 and 1988, while in 1991 things resumed a more average standard. For recommended producers, see under Spätlese in the next segment.

DELICATELY FLOWERY (MEDIUM BODY, NO OAK, HIGH ACIDITY)

Perhaps the term 'flowery' requires some explanation. It describes a wine that is not really dry, but is certainly not at all sweet. Quite simply, it evokes a certain scented character, that is neither cloying nor pungent, but gentle and fragrant.

Kabinett and Spätlese from the Mosel and Rhine

A Mosel Kabinett or Spätlese is the epitome of floweriness. A fine Mosel has a delicate flowery quality about it, but always with a steely backbone of acidity, originating from the relatively hard climate. There is also a slatey aspect to the wine which comes from the soil, and which is emphasised by the Riesling grape. Müller-Thurgau is widely planted in the Mosel, but the better wines are always made from Riesling and can be simply delicious. As they mature, they can develop a somewhat petrolly bouquet – some say kerosene – but they never lose that flowery and, in the sweeter wines, slightly honeyed, flavour.

To explain the origins of a wine take, for example, **Bereich Bernkastel**, the most basic wine, covering an extensive area of the Mittelmosel (as opposed to the two tributaries of the Mosel, the Saar and the Ruwer). From a reputable producer, a Bereich Bernkastel can provide a simple, refreshing glass of wine. Next up the scale come the Grosslagen, which are groups of vineyards. In the town of Bernkastel, the Grosslagen are Bernkasteler Badstube and Bernkasteler Kurfürstlay, and the best-known Einzellage – single-vineyard site – is Bernkasteler Doktor.

The quality scale of German wines is linked to the sugar content and ripeness of the grapes. At the bottom there is Tafelwein, which accounts for only a tiny proportion of Germany's wine production. Most of it fits into the Qualitätswein category, above which there is Qualitätswein mit Prädikat. In ascending order of sweetness or ripeness, the Prädikat are Kabinett, Spätlese, Auslese, Beerenauslese and Trockenbeerenauslese (the last three come into the sweet section of the wheel).

Although Kabinett is the driest of the Prädikat wines, unless it is labelled trocken it is unlikely to taste absolutely dry. There will usually be an underlying flowery, or perhaps a slightly honeyed, flavour, masking the firm backbone of acidity. Much depends upon the vintage; a riper vintage like 1990 will produce somewhat fuller wines, while a cooler vintage will result in fewer Prädikat wines, as the grapes will not be so ripe, and the wines themselves will not seem so rich.

The precise origin also affects the flavour. The Mosel produces the most delicate wines of Germany, with a combination of steely acidity tempered by flowery fruit, while the wines of the Rhine are a little fuller and richer. It is indisputable that the Rheingau makes the most elegant wines of the Rhine, while those from the Rheinhessen and Rheinpfalz are fuller and riper, coming as they do from a warmer climate. The Nahe, which adjoins the Mosel, Rheingau and Rheinhessen, has some of the characteristics of each.

Much depends too upon individual producers. As in Burgundy, what is ostensibly the same wine can be made by several different growers. For example, there are three owners of the reputed Doktor vineyard in Bernkastel. Leading estates in the Mosel include Lauerburg, Bert Simon, Deinhard, Dr Thanish, J J Prüm, Vereinigte Hospitien, von Hövel, Fritz Haag, Schloss Saarstein, Dr Fischer, Egon Müller, Höhe Domkirche, Bischöfliches Priesterseminar, Bischöfliches Konvikt, Friedrich Wilhelm Gymnasium, Weingut Klusserath, Max Ferdinand Richter and Dr

Loosen. Other good estates include: in the Rheingau, Schloss Johannisberg, Schloss Schönborn, Deinhard, Schloss Groenesteyn, State Domaine at Eltville, Schloss Reinhartshausen and Balthasar Ress; in the Nahe, State Domaine at Schlossböckelheim, Crusius and Anheuser; in the Rheinhessen, Louis Guntrum and Anton Balbach; in the Rheinpfalz, von Bühl, Bassermann-Jordan, Bürklin Wolf, Deinhard, Fitz Ritter and Lingenfelder.

The major stumbling block to the appreciation of German wines seems to be the nomenclature, and yet it is very logical. Take an example such as **Piesporter Goldtröpfchen Riesling Spätlese**. First comes the village name, then the vineyard, then the grape variety and, finally, the Prädikat. Not only is there some difficulty in the pronunciation, but there is no way of discerning whether a vineyard name is a large Grosslage or a small, individual Einzellage.

However, the German shippers Deinhard – who are also the owners of vineyards in three main regions – are among several working to surmount this problem with what they call their Estate Wine proposition, with which they have created a new identity for the various wines from all their different vineyards in the Mosel, Rheingau and Rheinpfalz. They will continue to make Prädikat wines from their very best vineyards – Bernkasteler Doktor, Wehlener Sonnenuhr, Rüdesheimer Berg Rottland and Forster Ungeheuer – as single vineyard wines, following the traditional German pattern. However, the wines from the various other vineyards will be blended to provide classic examples of the Mosel, Rheingau and Rheinpfalz, with a simplified name – Wegeler-Deinhard Riesling Kabinett or Spätlese, plus the area. The aim is to rationalise the multiplicity of vineyard names, building on their range of village wines that were launched some time ago as classic examples of Piesport, Nierstein, Bernkastel, Johannisberg, Deidesheim and Hochheim. For anyone confused by German wine labels, these offer an easier option from a reliable source.

Alsace

Across the Rhine and the border with France lies **Alsace**, with wines that do not quite belong to Germany, but which are not entirely French in style. With several different grape varieties, the wines of Alsace fit into different segments of the taste wheel. In this delicately flowery section comes one of the best, Riesling Vendange Tardive, and one of the most basic, Edelzwicker.

Take **Edelzwicker** first. This is the most basic of Alsace wines, a blend of grape varieties – rather than a single one, like all the other

Vins d'Alsace – making a flowery, and perhaps slightly spicy, fruity wine. It may be sold under a brand name, such as Hugel's Flambeau d'Alsace or under a supermarket or wine merchant's own label. In some ways, it may be seen as the Liebfraumilch of Alsace, but it is usually slightly drier and more aromatic. Essentially, it should be a cheerful, refreshing drink, with more alcohol and body than Liebfraumilch.

At the other end of the spectrum comes **Riesling Vendange Tardive** and also **Riesling Sélection de Grains Nobles**. In Alsace, Riesling is considered to be the finest, most characteristic and stylish grape variety, with a finesse and elegance lacking in Gewurztraminer. Normally, Riesling d'Alsace is bone dry (as discussed in the dry section of the wheel) but, in the best years, notably in the recent run of good vintages – 1990, 1989 and 1988 – some richer, more concentrated Vendange Tardive and Sélection de Grains Nobles wines are made. They are not sweet in the way that German Riesling Auslese or Beerenauslese might be, for in Alsace they always ferment their wines out as dry as possible. However, in years when the grapes have been affected by noble rot, some very rich wines will be made, with ripe fruit and concentration, but always with the steely acidity of good Riesling.

Producers of Vendange Tardive, and also Sélection de Grains Nobles Riesling include Hugel, Domaine Weinbach, Zind-Humbrecht, Rolly Gassmann, Marc Kreydenweiss and Marcel Deiss.

New World

Examples of Riesling from the New World (sometimes called Johannisberg, White or Rhine Riesling) may well fit more comfortably into this segment of the wheel, rather than alongside dry examples of Riesling d'Alsace in that segment. Most New World Rieslings have a ripeness and underlying sweetness, with a flowery, honeyed flavour that is neither German nor Alsatian. Indeed, these wines may even be slightly sweet or off-dry, even if they are not offered as late-harvest wines. They usually have an alcohol level comparable to those of Alsace, but with one or two exceptions, are lower in acidity.

However, the cool climate of **New Zealand** – particularly the South Island – is proving very successful for Riesling. Some of the best wines are late harvest, but Redwood Valley, Giesen and Dry River all make some delicious dry or off-dry Rieslings, which are elegantly fruity, with a relatively low alcohol level.

Cooler **Oregon** has a more suitable climate than California for producing the delicate Germanic style of Riesling, notably from

Knudsen Erath. **Washington State** also makes some good off-dry Rieslings, from Hogue Cellars and Snoqualmie.

AROMATIC (MEDIUM BODY, NO OAK, HIGH ACIDITY)

Aromatic is an adjective applied to wines made from grape varieties with a particularly characteristic aroma, wines which can be identified and enjoyed because of their bouquet, such as Muscat, Gewurztraminer or Viognier. The bouquet is not so much fruity and flowery, but pungently aromatic. They are not usually subtle wines, on either nose or palate (the one exception may be Viognier), but assail you with a powerful impact of flavour.

Gewurztraminer

Take Gewurztraminer first. This is the most typical, characteristic wine of Alsace. *Gewürz* means spice in German and the flavours of Gewurztraminer are just that, sometimes elegant, with a firm, structured backbone, but sometimes blowsy, with a vulgarly overpowering perfume. The wines can have a wealth of tropical fruit – some people mention lychees – or can be reminiscent of cold cream. Gewurztraminer is instantly recognisable and you either love it or hate it. The subtle, understated wines are best of all. In **Alsace** the wines are always fermented dry but, even so, with Gewurztraminer there is always an underlying richness, a characteristic oiliness, originating from a fairly high degree of alcohol, which packs a punch of rich flavour. Much can depend upon a producer's individual style: some enhance the opulent spiciness of Gewurztraminer, while others aim for something understated. Even then, Gewurztraminer can never really be described as elegant.

Gewurztraminer is one of the four grape varieties allowed in the grand cru vineyards of Alsace. The first 25 of these vineyards were only recognised as recently as 1983, as an addition to the basic appellation of Vin d'Alsace, and are some of the better vineyard sites in the main villages. Since then, more have been added and there are now 50 grand cru sites in all. Gewurztraminer can also be made as a Vendange Tardive or Sélection de Grains Nobles. While Sélection de Grains Nobles fits more comfortably into the sweet wine segment, Vendange Tardive is best here due to its concentrated spicy flavours, which are not actually sweet but rich. The recent vintages – 1990, 1989 and 1988 – produced some wonderful Vendange Tardive wines, while those from 1985 and

1983 are beginning to drink beautifully. Alsace wines, although rich in alcohol, always have a firm backbone of acidity which allows them to develop with bottle age.

Gewurztraminer grows in other parts of Europe and has travelled to the New World. In **Germany** a little is grown in the Rheinpfalz; one of the best examples is Weingut Fitz-Ritter's Dürkheimer Feuerberg Spätlese Trocken. **Austria** too has some Gewurztraminer in south and east Styria, close to what was the Yugoslav border.

Gewurztraminer is one of the grape varieties allowed in the DOC of the **Südtirol**, where it is called Traminer Aromatico. It is also allowed in **Friuli**, **Grave del Friuli** and **Collio**, for example. Gewurztraminer from northern Italy tends to favour the lighter, understated and more subtle style.

In **California**, Gewurztraminer has excited some interest, although certainly nowhere near as much as Chardonnay. Dry Gewurztraminer from California is sometimes spoilt by a bitter finish: it can be a difficult variety to vinify, requiring just the right balance of residual sweetness and alcohol, and the off-dry wines are more successful than those that are firmly dry.

New Zealand is probably the best source of Gewurztraminer from the New World, with some ripe spicy examples from Villa Maria, Vidal and Hunters. **South Africa** is also trying, with a full-flavoured wine from Weltevrede.

Although Gewurztraminer is grown quite extensively in **Australia**, exports to the UK seem to concentrate firmly on Chardonnay, with a few exceptions. There is a Gewurztraminer/Riesling blend in Hardys' Bird Series and Penfolds Bin 202 is another Gewurztraminer/Riesling mix.

Muscat

Muscat is the one grape variety that really does taste of the grape, those succulently juicy Italian Moscatel table grapes. There are, in fact, three main varieties of Muscat – Muscat d'Alexandrie, Muscat Blanc à Petits Grains and Muscat Ottonel – which between them account for the many and various Muscat wines of the world. Moscatel is another name for Muscat d'Alexandrie, while Muscat à Petits Grains has various synonyms, such as Muscat Canelli and Muscat de Frontignan. The methods of vinification and styles of wines can vary enormously, from a table wine like Muscat d'Alsace, to a fortified wine like Muscat de Beaumes-de-Venise, or an Australian Liqueur Muscat, or even a sparkling wine, like Asti Spumante. As a table wine it can be sweet or dry.

Muscat d'Alsace is the most characteristic example of a dry

Muscat. The bouquet really is reminiscent of the aroma of the grape, while the palate is drier, with a slightly pithy flavour, like bitter oranges. Muscat is one of the four grape varieties which can be grown on a grand cru site in Alsace and it is also occasionally made into Vendange Tardive or Sélection de Grains Nobles wines, but very much less frequently than either Gewurztraminer or Riesling. Muscat is best drunk as in Alsace, young, vibrantly fresh and as an aperitif. Good producers include Kreydenweiss, Zind-Humbrecht, Kuentz Bas, Becker, Trimbach, Léon Beyer, Domaine Weinbach and Muré.

Muscat grown in the warmer climate of the south tends to lack the pungent spiciness that you find in Muscat d'Alsace. Consequently, elsewhere in France the tendency is to turn Muscat into a fortified wine. One exception, however, is the growing amount of **vin de pays Catalan** or **vin de pays des Pyrénées-Orientales**, specifying 'cépage Muscat' on the label. The drop in sales of fortified Muscat de Rivesaltes has resulted in table wine being made instead.

In **Spain**, the closest comparison to the table wines is Torres Viña Esmeralda which is made from two parts Muscat to one part Gewurztraminer. It was an illustration of Miguel Torres' inquiring mind, and is now well established in his repertoire. In **Portugal**, the talented Peter Bright produces one of the freshest and most vibrant white Portuguese wines in Setúbal – João Pires dry Muscat – from grapes that might otherwise be used for Moscatel de Setúbal.

In north-east **Italy** the DOC of the Südtirol allows Goldmuskateller and pink Rosenmuskateller, with Tiefenbrunner the star producer. In Germany, Morio-Muscat is a variation on Muscat, grown in the Rheinpfalz to make a wine that is lighter in alcohol and a little sweeter than a Muscat d'Alsace. There are also occasional examples from Eastern Europe, notably a recent introduction from the Gyöngyös Estate in **Hungary**, where the vinification was carried out by an Australian team working with Hugh Ryman. They have succeeded in making an attractive off-dry wine, with some pithy Muscat fruit.

A diversion from **Czechoslovakia** comes in the form of a curious grape variety called Irsay Oliver, which is a crossing of Gewurztraminer and Muscat Ottonel, with a nose faintly reminiscent of cold cream, some Muscat and apricot fruit and firm acidity on the palate.

As for the New World, **North America** tends to favour late-harvest Muscat, as they do in **New Zealand**, while in **Australia**, Brown Brothers have a reputation for their Dry Muscat.

Torrontes

The closest that South America comes to Muscat is a grape variety called Torrontes which is grown in **Argentina**, in the vineyards of the province of Salta. Not only are they the country's most northerly vineyards, but they are also the highest, situated in the foothills of the Andes. Torrontes is not a direct import from Europe, but is said to be a mutation of Malvoisie, brought from the Canaries in the 1550s. It should be drunk as young as possible, when it has some of the aromatic qualities of Muscat, with some pithy orange flavours, tinged with a little sweetness. Bodegas Etchart, Michel Torino and Trapiche are the best producers.

Pinot Gris

Another **Alsace** grape, Pinot Gris, fits more comfortably into this segment than in the firmly dry white segment. Pinot Gris is traditionally called Tokay d'Alsace (but without any obvious connection with the Hungarian wine) and nowadays both names tend to appear on the label. It is one of the four grape varieties of Alsace that can be grown in a grand cru vineyard and is used for Vendange Tardive and Sélection de Grains Nobles. Pinot Gris has a certain spiciness that is not dissimilar to Gewurztraminer, except that the flavour is more subtle, and it complements food, particularly fish and game, very well. Like Gewurztraminer, it encaptures the quintessential flavours of Alsace. There is a similar weight and richness in the mouth and a bouquet of mushrooms, with the slightly musty smell of the undergrowth of damp woods, and perhaps a hint of apricots, or that wonderful French honey bread, pain d'épice. These flavours are emphasised all the more in the richer Vendange Tardive wines.

Alsace Pinot Gris ages splendidly; the best recent vintages are 1990, 1989, 1988, 1985, 1983 and the monumental 1976. Recommended producers include Domaine Weinbach, Muré, Schlumberger, Marc Kreydenweiss, Rolly Gassmann, Léon Beyer, Jos Meyer, Trimbach, Hugel and Zind-Humbrecht.

There are occasional examples of Pinot Gris from **Germany**, mostly from Baden, where it is called Ruländer. The slightly sweet **Hungarian** Badacsonyi Pinot Gris also fits into this segment, as does one example from **South Africa**, Van Loveren's ripe mushroomy Pinot Gris with a dry finish.

Viognier

The final aromatic grape variety in the segment is Viognier. The flavour of dried apricots is the key to the bouquet and palate, with some quite rich, in some instances almost unctuous, perfumed overtones. Viognier is a difficult, temperamental grape variety to grow. It is at its best in the tiny appellations of the northern **Rhône**, in Condrieu and adjoining Château Grillet. Both are expensive: Condrieu costs around £20 a bottle, while Château Grillet is nearer £35. It is questionable whether Château Grillet is really worth almost twice the price of Condrieu – Condrieu from a good producer like Pinchon, Georges Vernay, Château du Rozay and Dumazet certainly offers some original and appealing flavours.

Occasionally, you can find a **Côtes-du-Rhône** cépage Viognier. This may come from young vines not yet suitable for Condrieu, or simply from a grower who rises to the challenge of Viognier, such as Domaine Ste-Apollinaire. Viognier is also exciting some interest amongst the more innovative producers of the Midi. Skalli, for example, has just introduced a Viognier to its Fortant de France range. The flavour is not as intense as a Condrieu, but the wine is considerably cheaper.

Viognier has excited a little interest in **California**, amongst the band of so-called Rhône Rangers. To date, Calera is the only winery to produce a Viognier which holds its own alongside Condrieu.

FULL AND FLOWERY (MEDIUM BODY, NO OAK, LOW ACIDITY)

Most **New World Rieslings** fit into this category. They are often off-dry, but differ from Alsace and German Rieslings in their lower degree of acidity, originating from the warmer climates. That is particularly true of those from Australia, California, South America and South Africa, in contrast to those from New Zealand and Oregon, which have enough acidity and feature alongside Alsace and Germany in a previous segment of the wheel.

In California, good Riesling producers include Freemark Abbey, Joseph Phelps, Château St Jean, Firestone and Jekel. In Australia, the Barossa Valley of South Australia is generally deemed to be the best source of Riesling, with the influence of German immigrants from Silesia in the last century. Look out for Yalumba with its Pewsey Vale vineyard, Petaluma, Plantagenet in Western

Australia and Hill-Smith's Old Triangle Riesling, which offers some of the best value.

There are a couple of South African Rieslings available, notably De Wetshof and La Bri. These are clearly labelled Rhine Riesling, so as not to cause confusion with Cape Riesling or Paarl Riesling, which are Cruchen Blanc under other names.

In Chile, Torres makes a lone example of a South American Riesling, with some petrolly fruit and a sweet finish.

The other contender for this segment would be Austria, with Spätlese quality wines made from Riesling, Weissburgunder, Grüner Veltliner and other grapes. The climate is significantly warmer, giving wines with lower acidity levels. However, in practice, the Austrian wines actually available in this country seem to polarise between the rich and sweet Beerenauslese and Trockenbeerenauslese, or the firmly dry, steely Grüner Veltliner.

LIGHT HONEY (MEDIUM BODY, NO OAK, LOW ACIDITY)

Eastern Europe

It is quite extraordinary, given the phenomenal choice of wines available in Britain, that **Lutomer Laski Rizling** continues to head the list of top sellers. Laski Rizling comes largely from **Slovenia** which, as we write, has been unaffected by the turmoil in what was Yugoslavia. It is really Slovenia's answer to Liebfraumilch, soft, grassy and slightly sweet, with just enough acidity to stop it from cloying. There is nothing offensive about it, although it lacks character.

Laski Rizling is quite different from the Riesling of Germany. It lacks the depth of flavour and produces some light innocuous white wine, without much to distinguish it. It grows widely in Eastern Europe, as Welschriesling in Austria, Olasrizling in Hungary and Riesling Italico in Italy.

Comparable wines might include Austria's Welschriesling which is rarely exported, but has more fruit than its Slovenian counterpart. Hungary used to produce large quantities of a similar style of wine, but is now tending to concentrate on more Western varietals like Merlot, Cabernet Sauvignon, Chardonnay and Pinot Blanc. Bulgaria makes a basic blend of Riesling and Misket which is soft and slightly sweet, as is Thisbe from Cyprus, produced by the large co-operative, Keo.

Central Italy

The other contenders for this segment of the wheel are the slightly sweet wines of central Italy, such as **Orvieto abboccato** and **Frascati amabile**.

Abboccato means medium-sweet. Orvieto abboccato may be made occasionally from grapes affected by noble rot – in which case it fits into the sweet wine section of the wheel – but more often it comes simply from grapes that are riper than average, left on the vines that little bit longer. The acidity level will therefore be low and the taste gentle and honeyed, with some soft fruit.

Amabile is not quite as sweet as abboccato and is therefore nearer to medium-dry than medium-sweet in flavour, with some rather bland, nondescript fruit. Dry Frascati is more satisfying.

SWEET WHITE WINES

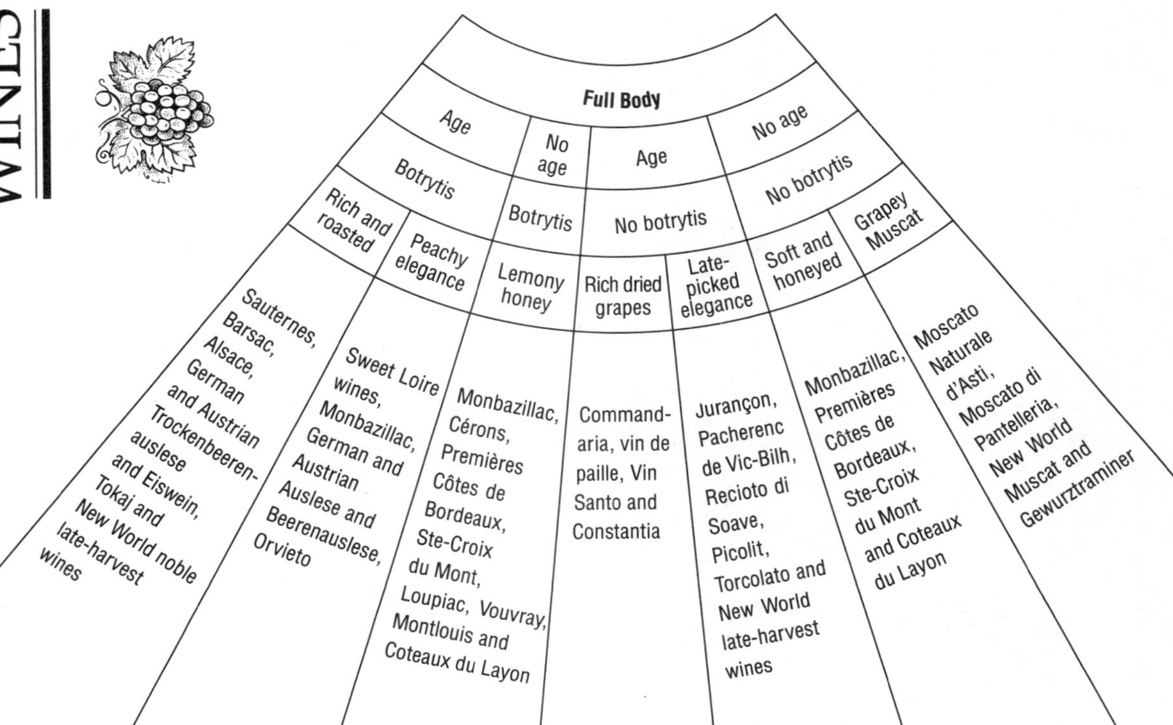

Full Body
Age
No age
Age
No age
Botrytis
Botrytis
No botrytis
No botrytis
Rich and roasted
Peachy elegance
Lemony honey
Rich dried grapes
Late-picked elegance
Soft and honeyed
Grapey Muscat
Sauternes, Barsac, Alsace, German and Austrian Trockenbeeren-auslese and Eiswein, Tokaj and New World noble late-harvest wines
Sweet Loire wines, Monbazillac, German and Austrian Auslese and Beerenauslese, Orvieto
Monbazillac, Cérons, Premières Côtes de Bordeaux, Ste-Croix du Mont, Loupiac, Vouvray, Montlouis and Coteaux du Layon
Commandaria, vin de paille, Vin Santo and Constantia
Jurançon, Pacherenc de Vic-Bilh, Recioto di Soave, Picolit, Torcolato and New World late-harvest wines
Monbazillac, Premières Côtes de Bordeaux, Ste-Croix du Mont and Coteaux du Layon
Moscato Naturale d'Asti, Moscato di Pantelleria, New World Muscat and Gewurztraminer

RICH AND ROASTED (FULL BODY, AGE, BOTRYTIS)

The phenomenon of *Botrytis cinerea* (*pourriture noble* or noble rot) has already been explained in the introduction to the taste wheels; suffice to say here that its development is essential to all the really great sweet wines of the world. Noble rot adds an extra dimension of complexity, making wines with considerable concentration, a combination of intense sweetness and balancing acidity, and the characteristic *gout de rôti*, or roasted, almost burnt, flavour of the botrytis. These are wines that will enjoy a long life; a sweet wine made without noble rot does not usually have the same potential for longevity.

Sauternes

Sauternes is the classic sweet white wine. It comes from a small part of the vineyards of Bordeaux, around the village of the same name. The neighbouring village of **Barsac** also gives its name to an appellation; however, while the wines from the village of Barsac may be called Sauternes, those from Sauternes may not be called Barsac. The weather at vintage time is crucial to the production of fine Sauternes: not only must the grapes be fully ripe, but the appropriate climatic conditions must prevail – dank misty mornings to encourage the growth of botrytis, followed by brilliantly sunny afternoons to dry the grapes. On average in a decade the right conditions probably occur only three or four times, and a potentially good vintage can be ruined at the very last moment by a heavy rainstorm. The run of three consecutive fine vintages which Sauternes has enjoyed with 1990, 1989 and 1988 is virtually unheard of, with all three making some simply wonderful, rich concentrated wine.

A careful selection of the grapes – Sauvignon, Sémillon and perhaps a little Muscadelle – is made in the vineyard, with successive meticulous pickings (a process called *triage*) selecting only those grapes affected by noble rot (sometimes as many as ten times at Yquem). In years when botrytis is not prevalent it is still possible to make some perfectly acceptable Sauternes if the grapes are ripe – the wine will be sweet, but it will lack that essential flavour of botrytis and complexity that are characteristic of great Sauternes. The botrytis gives the wine a firm bite and prevents it from tasting too sweet or cloying. There is a rich unctuous quality about good Sauternes, with ripe honeyed flavours, a hint of apricots and peaches, and perhaps toffee and cream and some tropical fruit. Good Sauternes is mouth-filling, for it is relatively high in alcohol – significantly higher than German wines of comparable sweetness – and also rich in glycerine.

Inevitably, good Sauternes is expensive given the unpredictability of its production. It is said that one vine accounts for one glass of wine at Château d'Yquem and, while a vine may provide more wine in other lesser châteaux, yields are still tiny. Estates that are currently performing well include Suduiraut, de Fargues, Lafaurie-Peyraguey, St-Amand (which is also called la Charteuse), Gilette and Bastor-Lamontagne. La Tour Blanche has improved significantly in recent vintages. The other good vintages of the last decade were 1986, 1983, 1981 and 1980.

The difference between Sauternes and Barsac is not easy to discern. The consensus is that Barsac is more elegant than Sauternes, perhaps more refined, with a delicacy and a delightful honeyed, lemony character which may nudge it into the next segment of the wheel. However, the taste is so similar that it fits just as comfortably into this segment.

Barsac has enjoyed the same good run of vintages as Sauternes. Good Barsac estates include Coutet, Climens, Caillou, Doisy-Daëne, Doisy-Védrines, Liot and Suau.

Burgundy

Burgundy would certainly not spring to mind as a source of *pourriture noble*. However, very occasionally, Jean Thévenet at Domaine de la Bon Gran in the Mâconnais makes a cuvée spéciale from botrytis-affected Chardonnay. The result is quite extraordinary and the wine is very expensive, with the 1983 vintage currently costing around £50 a bottle from Adnams of Southwold. Simon Loftus of Adnams describes it as 'renowned, very rare, nectar', so what more need be said?

Alsace

A first taste of Gewurztraminer, **Sélection de Grains Nobles**, alongside a Sauternes, may reveal striking similarities, not so much in the actual taste, but in the texture of the wine. Sélection de Grains Nobles can be made only from Riesling, Pinot Gris, Muscat or Gewurztraminer – and only in the best years, when the grapes are affected by botrytis – and it has a concentrated richness of flavour. Like Sauternes, it is also relatively high in alcohol and glycerine. A Muscat Sélection de Grains Nobles is rather rare; with Pinot Gris there is a full toasted flavour, while Riesling is a little more elegant and steely. With Gewurztraminer the flavours, especially from a year like 1988, 1989 or 1990, are rich and opulent, with the essential spiciness of Gewurztraminer, and will be even better with bottle age.

Hugel were the leaders in the production of late-harvest wines in Alsace. Other houses noted for their Sélections de Grains Nobles include Schlumberger, Léon Beyer, Paul Blanck, Domaine Weinbach, Muré, Rolly Gassmann and Zind-Humbrecht.

Germany

Across the Rhine in Germany, the Riesling grape makes some stunning sweet wines and it is the sugar readings in the grapes that determine the ultimate quality category (Prädikat) of the wine. While other grape varieties have been developed for their ability to attain high sugar levels, even in a relatively cool climate – such as Kerner, Optima and Huxelrebe – there is nothing to better a fine Riesling, with its elegance combined with a firm backbone of acidity, preventing the wine ever from cloying. Other grape varieties may attain greater ripeness, but they lack the essential breed and finesse that make **Riesling Trockenbeerenauslese** the great wine that it is. The German system of Prädikat has already been explained in the medium section of the wheel; suffice to say here that Trockenbeerenauslese and **Eiswein** (see opposite) are the two categories which fit into this segment of the wheel.

Trockenbeerenauslese, which means literally individually picked dried berries, is made only in exceptional years, such as 1988, 1989 and 1990 (another extraordinary run of three fine vintages). Even in the best vintages, Trockenbeerenauslese accounts for only a minute percentage of the production of an estate. Like Sauternes, it is made from grapes that are so affected by noble rot that they have become shrivelled and raisin-like but, in contrast to Sauternes, the alcohol level is very low, with an average of only 6 per cent compared to 15 per cent for Sauternes. It seems that the German yeast has less staying power than that of Sauternes, especially in the colder winters, and this accounts for the difference. Inevitably, with such a tiny and uncertain production, prices are high, comparable to some of the best Sauternes.

Austria

Austria has a similar quality system, based on the sugar readings, or oechsle levels, of the ripe grapes, with an additional category called **Ausbruch**, which comes between Trockenbeerenauslese and Beerenauslese. The village of Rust is particularly renowned for its Ausbruch wines. However, Austrian dessert wines generally tend to be heavier and less elegant than those of Germany, as the alcohol levels are higher – the result of the warmer Austrian climate. Riesling is less refined in Austria than in Germany; and other grape varieties such as Bouvier, Müller-Thurgau, Ruländer, and Welschriesling are also used for sweet wines. Austrian Trockbeerenauslese is amazingly good value, for example, less than £6 for a half bottle of Bouvier Trockenbeerenauslese.

Eiswein

Eiswein is more of a German, rather than Austrian, speciality, and there are also occasional examples from Canada and Washington State. Eiswein is something of a commercial gimmick. The grapes, having already attained Beerenauslese level, are left on the vines until well into winter, December or January, becoming even more shrivelled and dehydrated. The producer is waiting for the temperature to fall to below freezing point, so that the icy grapes can be quickly picked and pressed while their water content is still frozen. This means that the sugar and acidity are all the more concentrated and, in some ways, this makes a somewhat unbalanced wine, without the usual elegance of a Beerenauslese. There is an intense concentration of flavour, with searing acidity and powerful sweet flavours. Eiswein can be made in most good vintages and, with such an acidity level, will age for as many as 20 to 50 years.

Canada also makes some good examples of Eiswein, for the climate of Niagara, with its severe winters, lends itself to its production with relative ease. The only example to reach the UK market as yet comes from Inniskillin, with a hybrid variety Vidal. However, Inniskillin's Riesling ice wine is better, as is Château des Charmes late-harvest Riesling, although these are rarely imported. The Washington State winery, Covey Run, has made some successful Riesling ice wine.

Tokaj

Tokaj is not only Hungary's most individual wine, it is also one of the world's great dessert wines. The development of noble rot is a vital factor in the final flavour and there are various levels of sweetness. **Tokaj Szamorodni** (meaning 'as it comes', implying that nothing has been added to the wine) can be either dry or sweet, depending on whether or not the grapes have been affected by noble rot. Then there is **Tokaj Aszú**, the sweetness of which is measured in putts (meaning the number of puttonyos, or tubs, of very sweet wine added to the base wine). Three, four or five putts are usual, while six is exceptional and very rich. Then there is even sweeter **Tokaj Aszú Essencia** (generally the equivalent of 5 or 6 putts but aged longer – only the best wines are used) and finally, the sweetest of all, **Tokaj Essence** (drained from the aszú fruit at 45 to 65 per cent sugar level and fermented with great difficulty), which is very rare and precious and is even attributed with life-restorative powers.

Tokaj five putts is perhaps the standard wine which fits into this category, a deliciously concentrated dessert wine. It has the amber colour of amontillado sherry, with a taste of toffee-apples and burnt sugar along with a firm, balancing bite of acidity: a really mouth-filling wine. With such a concentration of sugar and acidity, the best Tokaj will age for many years, developing some delectable roasted toffee flavours.

Until the break-up of the communist system, production had been in the sole hands of the State Cellars, but now there have been moves towards privatisation, with initiatives being taken by individual producers, as well as investment and interest from abroad, notably Peter Vinding-Diers of Notre Dame de Landiras in the Graves, who is very excited by the potential of the area. The Royal Tokaj Wine Company has been created by a group of 68 producers, but for the moment it is too early to taste the results of their investment.

New World late-harvest wines

Sweet botrytis-affected wines form part of the repertoire of most of the New World producers, with examples from South Africa, California, Australia and New Zealand. Normally, the label will specify whether a wine is botrytis affected, or merely a **late-harvest** wine, made from over-ripe grapes. The use of the word 'noble' in conjunction with late harvest always implies botrytis. The botrytis-affected wines of the New World tend to come into this category of the wheel, as they are generally quite high in alcohol, with a rich concentration of flavour.

Unfortunately, EC regulations do not allow table wines over a potential alcohol level of 15 per cent to be imported, a regulation which affects most of the sweet wines of the New World, although a few do manage to slip through the bureaucratic net.

The best-known botrytis-affected wine of South Africa is **Edelkeur**, which was developed by Gunter Brözel, one of the leading winemakers of the Cape, for many years responsible for the wines of the Nederburg estate. Edelkeur, made from Chenin Blanc, was his flagship; it is concentrated in flavour, with the slightly burnt taste of botrytis but, sadly, is hard to find. A Weisser Riesling Noble late-harvest wine, from the recently renovated

Neethlingshof Estate, where Gunter Brözel is now winemaker, is about to be imported for the first time.

De Bortoli in the hot Murrumbidgee Irrigation Area of New South Wales, where the vines depend upon irrigation for survival, has established a reputation for botrytis-affected Semillon, making it the leader in this style of wine from **Australia**. The wine might have neither the concentration nor the balance of Sauternes, but it does have a lovely honeyed flavour with a tang of toffee-apples. Other Australian producers have followed De Bortoli's example: Petaluma with Botrytis Riesling and Yalumba with Botrytis Semillon.

In **New Zealand**, Rongopai makes something of a speciality of its botrytised wines, a blend of Chardonnay and Riesling, while Dry River Valley produces a delicious botrytis-affected Riesling, wonderfully rich and concentrated. Redwood Valley in Nelson also has a late-harvest Riesling that is sometimes affected by botrytis.

California too produces some botrytis-affected wines. Château St Jean has established a reputation for its noble late-harvest Rieslings, and Robert Mondavi makes the occasional noble late-harvest wine, mainly from Riesling, and occasionally from Sauvignon. Far Niente Dolce is a superb blend of one part Sauvignon to two parts Semillon, produced like a Sauternes, and with a distinct similarity of flavour. Also look out for botrytis-affected Sauvignon and Riesling from Renaissance.

PEACHY ELEGANCE (FULL BODY, AGE, BOTRYTIS)

Sweet Loire wines – Vouvray, Bonnezeaux, Coteaux du Layon and Quarts de Chaume

The Loire Valley rivals Sauternes and Barsac as the producer of the greatest sweet wines of France, though most agree that Sauternes has the edge – just. Although the best sweet wines of the Loire also depend on botrytis, there is a fundamental difference between the regions – the grape variety. In the Loire Valley Chenin Blanc is grown and, like Sémillon and Sauvignon in Bordeaux, is particularly susceptible to noble rot in the appropriate climatic conditions. Acidity is one of the dominant characteristics of Chenin Blanc, a feature which makes it so much more appealing as a sweet wine – with honey and botrytis to balance the acidity – and better than some of the dry white appellations of the Loire Valley. The acidity also gives it immense longevity: from a good vintage, a Vouvray or Bonnezeaux could live as long as 40 years.

Coteaux du Layon is the most basic sweet white wine of the Loire, from vineyards, as the name implies, on the banks of the River Layon, a tributary of the Loire. The appellation comprises six villages, the names of which may also appear on the label. **Chaume** is generally regarded as the best. Within the village of Chaume there is a tiny vineyard called **Quarts de Chaume**, with its own appellation which, in good years, makes some particularly fine sweet wines. Also in the same valley is the small appellation of **Bonnezeaux**, producing wines with an intensity lacking in Coteaux du Layon, and nearby is the little-known, but up-and-coming, appellation of the **Coteaux de l'Aubance**, with wines that are very similar to Coteaux du Layon.

Coteaux du Layon and the other adjoining appellations are always sweet. Even if there is no botrytis, the wine is made only from very ripe grapes or, in lesser years, the juice is chaptalised in order to obtain the right balance of sugar and alcohol. In contrast, **Vouvray** is something of a chameleon for, depending on the climatic conditions of the individual year, it may be anything from very dry to lusciously sweet. **Moelleux** and **doux** are the key words on the label, indicating a sweet wine. On the opposite bank is the village of **Montlouis** which produces very similar wines, but they lack the concentration of Vouvray in the very best years, and the appellation is smaller and less well known.

Bonnezeaux or Vouvray from a great vintage is wonderful. It is deliciously honeyed, with apricots and peaches and cream, but always there is the firm backbone of acidity which makes the wine long lived as well as complex. The Loire Valley has had a terrific run of good vintages in the last decade or so, with 1990, 1989, 1988, 1985, 1983, 1982, 1978, 1976 and 1975 all making some wonderful wines. These are wines which can be drunk when they are young and obviously honeyed, but they will also develop into magnificent bottles with age.

Recommended producers include in Vouvray, Huet, Foreau, Bernard Fouquet, Champelou and Pascale Delaleu; in Bonnezeaux, Château de Fesles; in Montlouis, Berger; in Coteaux du Layon, Domaine de Sauveroy, Vincent Ogereau and Baumard; in Quarts de Chaume, Château de Bellerive and Château de Suronde; and in Coteaux de l'Aubance, Domaine du Bablut, Domaine Richou and Domaine de Montgilet.

Monbazillac

Monbazillac is the sweet white wine of the Dordogne, coming from vineyards just south of the town of Bergerac. In the best years, the grapes are affected by noble rot – in the same way as Barsac or Bonnezeaux – for with its proximity to the river, there is the necessary humidity with autumnal mists. However, the years with noble rot tend to be the exception rather than the rule, and most Monbazillac fits more comfortably further round the wheel. But, when the grapes are affected by botrytis, Monbazillac makes a delicious and seriously under-priced dessert wine. Hugh Ryman has been making wine there with delicious results, in Château les Hébras and Château Monthaudes. Château Treuil de Nailhac is another excellent estate.

Germany and Austria – Beerenauslese and Auslese

Beerenauslese means literally 'a selection of berries' – in other words, berries affected by noble rot, which are dehydrated, with some concentrated sweet juice. Both Germany and Austria use this term. Austrian Beerenauslese is richer, with lower acidity and more alcohol, and may well fit more comfortably into the rich

segment of the wheel, while German Beerenauslese – especially if it is made with Riesling – will have a wonderful honeyed elegance, always balanced with some firm acidity that prevents a cloying finish. A good Beerenauslese will always be a perfect combination of elegance, flavour and acidity.

Auslese, which means 'selected harvest', is usually more delicate. The grapes may not necessarily be late-picked (as they are in a Beerenauslese) but the term implies a choice of the best bunches, which are particularly ripe and usually affected more than average by botrytis. The resulting wines are deliciously honeyed, not opulently luscious, but delicately sweet. The weight and body of a particular wine depends very much upon its provenance and grape variety. Riesling makes the most elegant wines, especially in the cooler Mosel valley, while wines from further south, from Rheinpfalz or Rheinhessen, may be a little heavier and fuller. If a grape variety like Scheurebe or Optima is used, the flavour will be less subtle and less elegant.

Italy

There are occasional examples of botrytised wines from Italy, which the Italians call *muffa nobile*. Antinori makes one on its Orvieto estate of Castello della Sala. Although, to all intents and purposes, the wine is a delicious **Orvieto** it can not be labelled as such: it is outside DOC regulations with the use of such grape varieties as Sauvignon, as well as Grechetto and Drupeggio, and is simply called Muffato della Sala. Other Orvieto producers also aspire to noble rot in the best vintages, most notably Decugnano dei Barbi.

LEMONY HONEY (FULL BODY, NO AGE, BOTRYTIS)

In practice, the dividing line between this segment and the previous one is very blurred. Ageing ability is the key distinction and most wines from a good vintage, made by a talented producer from botrytis-affected grapes which have sufficient acidity, have the ability to age. Those that come from lighter, lesser vintages are unlikely to be affected by botrytis and therefore may fit into the late-picked elegance segment of the wheel.

Monbazillac is an example of a wine that crosses three segments, depending on whether it has botrytis, and whether it comes from a light vintage or a more concentrated one. The best Monbazillac with botrytis, from a good vintage and a talented producer, will age for almost as long as a good Sauternes or Barsac. In lighter years, the grapes may only be partially affected by botrytis and the flavours will be less intense, with some gentle peachy honey, and the wine less suitable for ageing. The same may be said of the peripheral regions of Bordeaux such as **Premières Côtes de Bordeaux, Cérons, Ste-Croix du Mont** or **Loupiac**. In fact, more often than not these wines are not affected by botrytis.

From the Loire, a lighter, less intense **Vouvray, Montlouis** or **Coteaux du Layon** may fit into this section, although most of the sweet white Loire wines have an ability to age, with the firm acidity originating from the Chenin Blanc. Again, those less likely to age are without botrytis.

In other words, this segment of the wheel is a meeting point of wines that, for one reason or another, are misfits in other sections. When they are at their best, they fit more happily into other segments.

RICH DRIED GRAPES (FULL BODY, AGE, NO BOTRYTIS)

The process of drying grapes is a very simple way of increasing their sugar content. This is either done in the vineyard, with exposure to both sunshine and, more importantly, wind, or the grapes are picked and then left to dehydrate in a well-ventilated place. Whichever method is used, the grapes become raisin-like, with sweet, concentrated juice. The result is some rich, flavoursome wine, that may almost taste as though it is fortified, such are the concentration and weight.

Cyprus

Take **Commandaria**, which would not be out of place in the fortified taste wheel, alongside sweet sherry. It is the traditional dessert wine of the island of Cyprus, its name deiving from associations with the Knights Templar of the twelfth century. It is made from exotic and colourful-sounding grape varieties that are not found anywhere else, like Xynisteri, Mavron and Opthalmo. The ripe grapes are dried in the sunshine until they virtually turn into raisins, then they are pressed and the juice is slowly fermented. The resulting wine is rich and raisiny, somewhat reminiscent of Moscatel grapes, with some ripe walnuts and marmalade, but without the firm alcoholic bite of a fortified wine. However, Commandaria can be treated in exactly the same way as a cream sherry and can be drunk before or after a meal, depending upon your mood.

The main producers are the large co-operatives which dominate the wine production of Cyprus, and normally Commandaria is sold under a brand name, for example St Barnabas, Commandaria St John and Grand Commandaria.

Vin de paille

The practice of drying grapes is a very old one; often the grapes were laid on straw mats, giving rise to the term *vin de paille* in France or *Strohwein* in Germany. While Strohwein is no longer made, France still preserves the occasional pocket of tradition, with a little production of vin de paille, especially in the isolated region of the Jura mountains. While 100 kilos of grape would normally give about 70-75 litres of juice, for vin de paille the amount is drastically reduced to 20 or 25 litres. Fermentation is very slow, taking as long as four years in small barrels, and although red or white grapes can be used, the final colour of the wine is a rich brown with a taste of raisins and walnuts. This is a curiosity that rarely travels outside the region but is made by most of the growers for their family and friends.

Italy

The nearest Italian equivalent to vin de paille is **Vin Santo**, although it is not always comparable in taste. There are Vin Santi that are rich and sweet, but others that are almost shockingly dry. This uncertainty originates from the inexact, or indeed haphazard, method of production. The ripe grapes are left to dry for several weeks, with bunches either on straw mats or hanging from rafters in a well-ventilated barn. When the grapes are suitably *passiti* (dried), they are pressed and the resulting sweet juice is left to ferment in small oak barrels which are sealed, traditionally, with wax – but often more prosaically nowadays with concrete. The barrels are not completely filled, a factor which can determine the level of sweetness or not (the fuller, the sweeter). They are then left for a minimum of three years, but often longer, in an attic or somewhere that is subjected to both the summer heat and the winter cold. A considerable amount of evaporation takes place, as well as some gentle oxidation, and the resulting wine is wonderfully concentrated, with some sweet nutty flavours and a firm degree of acidity. Again, Vin Santo tastes as though it might be fortified, as the alcohol level is relatively high at 15 per cent, but genuine Vin Santo should never be fortified. Beware of any label that says Vino liquoroso, for that is not the genuine article.

Avignonesi is generally recognised as the best Vin Santo, but at a price to match. Other more accessible wines include Isole e Olena, Selvapiana, Capezzana, Antinori, Montagliari and Brolio. Although Tuscany is the most obvious source of Vin Santo, some is also made in Trentino, and a little in Umbria.

South Africa

South Africa's reputation as a wine-producing country was made with a wine called Constantia at the beginning of the nineteenth century. Today, the estate of Klein Constantia is trying to revive this old wine, but opinions vary as to whether the traditional Constantia was fortified or not. As nothing in the records of the estate says that it was fortified, the Muscat de Frontignan grapes remain on the vines until they are over-ripe. The wine is then left to age in 500-litre oak casks for a year until it turns golden amber in colour and tastes smooth and unctuous, with a flavour of orange marmalade. It is presented in an old-fashioned, irregularly shaped, 50-centilitre bottle. Avery's of Bristol is the sole importer, offering Vin de Constance at around £12 a bottle.

LATE-PICKED ELEGANCE (FULL BODY, AGE, NO BOTRYTIS)

The obvious contenders for this category are the various late-harvested wines which do not depend upon the development of *Botrytis cinerea* for sweetness and flavour. Some of the *passiti* wines of Italy may also come into this segment.

Jurançon

Jurançon, a white wine from the foothills of the Pyrenees, has already featured in the dry section of the wheel. However, the appellation also includes **Jurançon Moelleux**, which is made from grapes that have been left on the vines to dry, in a process called *passerillage* (botrytis occurs very rarely). This process relies upon the warm autumn winds – called the *froin* –that blow off the Pyrenees to keep the grapes healthy and free of rot. The grapes are usually picked some time in November and the wine is made in the classic way: a grower like Henri Ramonteu at Domaine Cauhapé ages his Jurançon Moelleux in oak barrels for a few months, and also makes a careful selection of the grapes, depending on variety and sugar levels. Like a fine Sauternes, a good Jurançon Moelleux (sometimes labelled Vendange Tardive) will develop more complex flavours with age. It can be a long-lived wine and has a significant price advantage over most Sauternes. Good recent vintages include 1990, 1989, 1988, 1986 and 1985. Reliable producers include Domaine Cauhapé, Château Jolys, Domaine Bellegard and the Co-operative de Gan, which is now working well for the appellation with its recently renovated flagship estate, Château Les Astous.

The nearby appellation of **Pacherenc de Vic Bilh** also includes moelleux, produced mainly by one grower, Alain Brumont at Château Boucassé. There are wines of three different levels of quality, named according to the month in which the grapes were picked, Octobre, Novembre and Décembre. A comparative tasting clearly illustrates that the longer the grapes stay on the vine, the sweeter and more concentrated the wine.

Italy

Recioto di Soave is made from grapes that could also be used for dry Soave but which are left instead to *appassire* (gently dehydrate), and are then vinified to make some deliciously elegant, honeyed sweet wine, with a concentration of fruit and balancing acidity which benefits from a little bottle age. The best producers are Anselmi and Pieropan.

Picolit was always presented as one of the great dessert wines of Italy, but it seems to have rested on its laurels, and does not now have the stature of some of its competitors. Picolit is the grape variety used, found mainly in the DOC of the Colli Orientali del Friuli. Production is tiny and demand in Friuli outstrips supply, which means that little is exported. The grapes are dried and the result is quite delicate.

Torcolato is a stylishly original Italian dessert wine, made by Maculan, the leading producers of the DOC **Breganze**. The main grape variety is the little known Vespaiolo, which may be blended with some Tocai, and again the grapes are dried out. Vinification entails some ageing in barriques to produce a lovely honeyed wine, which develops with five or six years' bottle age.

New World

The numerous late-harvest wines of the New World which depend not upon botrytis, but on the over-ripe grapes of a late harvest for their sweetness, fit into this segment of the wheel. Again, the availability is affected by the EC regulation limiting the potential alcoholic strength of these wines to 15 per cent.

California Grapes may be left on the vine in the hope of attracting botrytis in California, but if that fails to happen, a straightforward, sweet late-harvest wine is made. Riesling is the most usual grape variety, sometimes called White or Johannisberg Riesling: Firestone, Joseph Phelps, Château St Jean and Renaissance are names to look out for, while Mark West produces a Late-Harvest Gewurztraminer, which is ripe and spicy. However, in such a warm climate there is always the danger of a loss of acidity if the grapes are left on the vine for too long.

Washington State Riesling is generally more successful in cooler Washington State than in California. Not only is some steely dry Riesling produced, but also some lovely late-harvest wines, which usually have a better acidity balance and more elegance than those from the Golden State. Examples include Select Late-Harvest Riesling from Arbor Crest Wine Cellars and Stewart Vineyards Late-Harvest White Riesling – both of which are imported by Windrush Wines, who were pioneers of this part of the so-called Pacific North-West.

Australia and New Zealand Muscat seems to be the most popular grape variety for late-harvest wines from Australia, which feature further round the wheel. New Zealand too favours late-harvest Muscat, but there are also some delicious examples of late-harvest Riesling, occasionally affected by botrytis, with elegant Riesling fruit and balancing acidity; good examples come from Redwood Valley and Montana.

SOFT AND HONEYED (FULL BODY, NO AGE, NO BOTRYTIS)

One of the pleasures of sweet wines is that they have an instant appeal when they are young. Most will develop greater complexity with bottle age, but lighter wines from less prestigious appellations can offer some immediate enjoyment within a couple of years of the vintage.

Monbazillac

Monbazillac is an example of a wine that crosses two, if not three, taste segments. While the best examples of Monbazillac benefit from botrytis- affected grapes and improve with bottle age to last for some considerable time, in lighter years it is drinkable in its early youth, but may not necessarily develop.

In the past, Monbazillac had been the victim of bad winemaking, spoilt by excesses of sulphur and chaptalisation, but things are looking up, with some good producers making some lovely light honeyed, peachy wine. It may never have the subtlety of good Barsac or Sauternes, but it does offer a considerable price advantage. That roving winemaker of the south-west, the English-born, Australian-trained Hugh Ryman, has achieved great things with two estates, Château les Hébras and Château Monthaudes. Other good estates include Château Treuil de Nailhac, Château le Fage and Château Boudigand.

Some of the peripheral sweet appellations of Bordeaux are very similar to Monbazillac. The grape varieties are the same – Sauvignon, Sémillon and a drop of Muscadelle. In the finest years they may also have noble rot, but more often than not they are made from very ripe grapes and, in unripe years, may well depend upon chaptalisation for the right balance of alcohol and sufficient sweetness. However, in the better vintages, wines like **Loupiac**, **Ste-Croix du Mont** (look out for Château des Coulinats and Château Roustit), **Cadillac** and **Premières Côtes de Bordeaux** can offer some enjoyable and good-value drinking. There is also Château St-Georges in the Graves, with vineyards immediately adjoining those of Sauternes, which, contrary to the expectations of the appellation, makes a sweet honeyed wine.

The Loire

Some of the sweet wines of the Loire Valley from lighter vintages also fit into this segment. Take a wine like **Coteaux du Layon** – under ideal conditions the grapes are heavily affected by botrytis; in less than perfect conditions they are not and the producers will hope merely for ripe grapes with enough sugar to make an elegantly sweet wine, preferably without having to resort to chaptalisation. Unlike Vouvray, which is everything from very dry to very sweet depending on the condition of the grapes, Coteaux du Layon and the adjacent appellations are always sweet. For recommended producers, see the peachy elegance segment.

GRAPEY MUSCAT (FULL BODY, NO AGE, NO BOTRYTIS)

There is no doubt that the **Muscat** grape makes some delicious sweet wines; sometimes these are fortified but, in table wines, the natural sugar left in the grape emphasises the rich, perfumed flavour of the grape itself.

Italy

Asti Spumante is described in the sparkling wine wheel. The still wine of the region is **Moscato Naturale d'Asti**, refreshingly low in alcohol, at only 5·5 per cent, taking its sweetness from the grape sugar remaining after the fermentation has been stopped. It can be delicious, light, delicately refreshing and grapey. Good producers include the Viticoltori dell'Acquese, Ascheri and Chiar. Drink the youngest and freshest available.

The island of Pantelleria produces **Moscato di Pantelleria**, which can fit into two different wheels – sometimes it is fortified and sometimes not. **Moscato Passito di Pantelleria Bukkuram**, from the leading producer, Marco de Bartoli, is not fortified and is wonderfully opulent in flavour.

New World

There are numerous sweet Muscats produced in the New World, from California, Washington State, New Zealand and Australia.

In California, Robert Mondavi's **Moscato d'Oro** is the leading example, with some ripe honeyed Muscat fruit. From Washington State there is **Muscat Canelli** (which is the same grape as Muscat de Frontignan, or Muscat à Petits Grains) from the Cascade Estate Winery in the Yakima Valley, with apricots and acidity, and Château Ste Michelle, with a lovely Muscat and peach flavour.

In Australia, Brown Brothers have made a name for themselves with their Late-Picked Muscat, which has some wonderful ripe fruit (see also the Liqueur Muscats in the fortified wine wheel); while in New Zealand the best late-harvest Muscat comes from Matua Valley. A new technique called cryoextraction is applied, which concentrates the juice in the grapes, reducing the water content to make a very sweet, ripe, luscious wine.

While late-harvest Rieslings or Semillons might fit into a previous segment of the wheel, wines made from Gewurztraminer, with its spicy flavours, are more comfortable in this section. Examples include Matua Valley Late-Harvest Gewurztraminer from New Zealand, and from California, Mark West's Late-Harvest Gewurztraminer. Perhaps the flavour is not so different from a Sélection de Grains Nobles Gewurztraminer from Alsace, but it lacks the effect of the botrytis and has a lower acidity level.

ROSÉ WINES

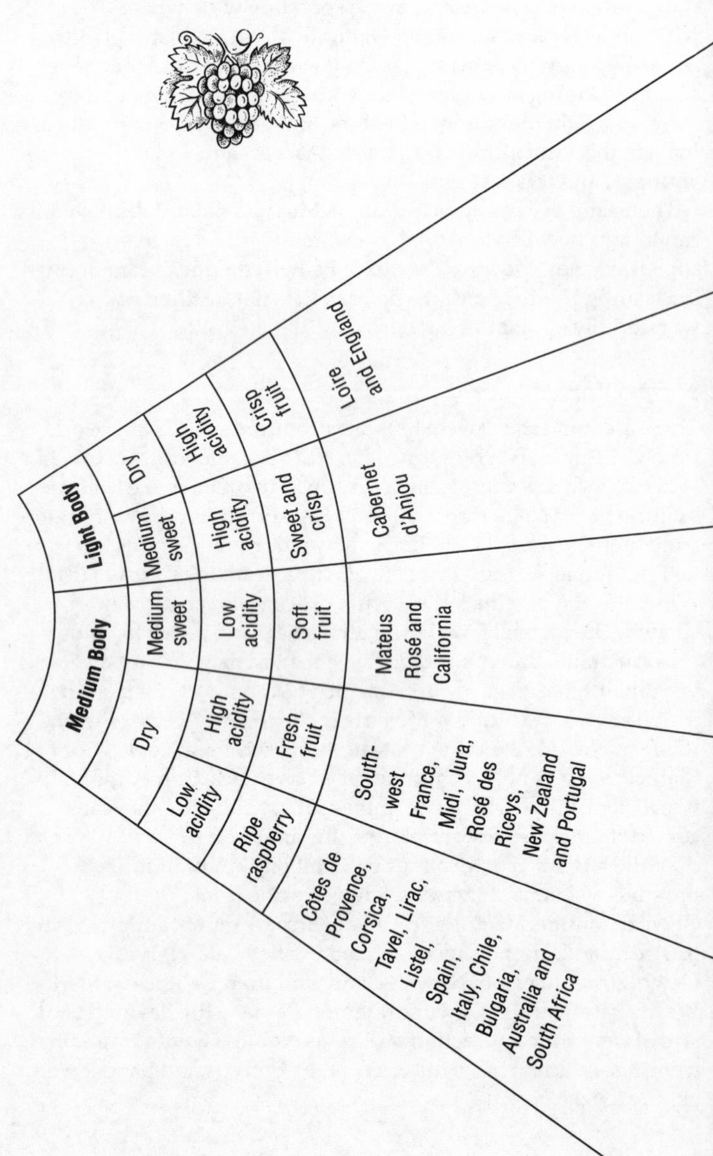

Light Body
Medium Body
Dry
Medium sweet
Medium sweet
Dry
High acidity
High acidity
Low acidity
High acidity
Low acidity
Crisp fruit
Sweet and crisp
Soft fruit
Fresh fruit
Ripe raspberry
Loire and England
Cabernet d'Anjou
Mateus Rosé and California
South-west France, Midi, Jura, Rosé des Riceys, New Zealand and Portugal
Côtes de Provence, Corsica, Tavel, Lirac, Listel, Spain, Italy, Chile, Bulgaria, Australia and South Africa

Rosé wines are often seen as a compromise; when we are uncertain whether to drink red or white we may opt for pink instead. Essentially, the taste range of rosé is more akin to white than to red wine, though without the complexity or broad spectrum of flavours of either. Tannin and oak do not really feature and, although the best rosés are dry and fresh, there are some that are slightly sweetened; none are lusciously sweet. Acidity and body are the two main components of the pink segment of the taste wheel. Rosés are best drunk when they are young and fresh, within a year to three years of the vintage; there is nothing at all to be achieved by laying down rosés for further bottle age. Generally, light-bodied wines with high acidity come from cooler climates, while fuller-bodied wines with lower acidity originate from hotter countries.

It is rarely appreciated how difficult it actually is to make good rosé. The colour comes from contact with the grape skins: still rosé wine is never a blend of red and white wine. The key element, therefore, is in deciding how long to leave the juice in contact with the skins; the timing must be just right or the wine will be unbalanced. The visual aspect of a pretty pink in the glass is part of the charm of good rosé; too long and the colour will be too deep; not long enough and it will look pale and insipid.

Most rosés are made by what the French quite graphically call the *saignée* method of production; literally, this means that the tank of juice is bled. The red grapes are gently crushed and fermentation starts, with the juice taking on some colour until, after a few hours when it has absorbed sufficient colour, the juice is run off the skins. Fermentation then continues in the same way as for white wines, at a cool temperature. The poetic expression *vin d'une nuit* originates from the juice remaining on the skins over one night. The remaining skins are then usually added to the producer's red wine for extra colour and tannin. Alternatively, the skins may be given a gentle pressing after the juice has been run off.

> *'Have some wine,' the March Hare said in an encouraging tone. Alice looked all round the table, but there was nothing on it but tea. 'I don't see any wine,' she remarked. 'There isn't any,' said the March Hare.*
>
> Lewis Carroll, *Alice's Adventures in Wonderland*

MEDIUM BODY, DRY WITH LOW ACIDITY

Wines in this category originate from a warm climate, so are usually quite high in alcohol, and therefore taste quite full and rounded in the mouth. They have relatively low acidity – enough to give the wine structure, but not so much as to be obtrusive in the mouth.

Côtes de Provence and some of the other pink wines of the south of France are the obvious examples in this category. The appellation Côtes de Provence can cover white, pink or red wines. In fact, very little white is actually made and, although the red is growing in interest and quality, the most common is the pink wine, which is produced extensively in the hinterland of St-Tropez and Toulon. It is quite a full-flavoured wine, dry but not acidic, with some substantial fruit flavours, including raspberries, which makes it a good accompaniment to fish and picnics. However, the youngest available should be drunk, for it can quickly lose its freshness and charm, turn tired, flabby and a little stewed.

Domaines Ott at Château de Selle are leading producers of the appellation; but although well-made, the rosé is rather over-priced. The wines of the Vignerons du Presqu'Ile de St-Tropez are good examples of the appellation.

Neighbouring **Provençal** appellations include rosés which are very similar in flavour, coming from the same grape varieties: a mixture of Grenache, Cinsaut, Carignan, and perhaps some Syrah and other lesser known Midi varieties. In the Coteaux d'Aix-en-Provence, Château Fonscolombe makes some acceptable rosé, while within the tiny appellation of Palette, rosé accounts for only a small part of the production of the virtually sole estate of Château Simone. Likewise, Château Val-Joanis in the Côtes du Lubéron makes a wine that is full and fresh, with ripe raspberry fruit, benefiting from technical expertise and high-tech equipment. Rosé also features in the appellation of Bandol, but in tiny quantities, and also in the small VDQS of Coteaux Varois.

The island of **Corsica** also offers the occasional pink, notably from an indigenous grape variety called Sciacarello, that is grown particularly around the towns of Ajaccio and Sartène. Domaine de Peraldi is the leading Ajaccio estate, with some refreshing pink wine that is reminiscent of the herbs of the Corsican *maquis*.

The best appellation of the **Rhône Valley** for rosé is Tavel which, unlike its neighbour Lirac, is an appellation for rosé alone. It seems strange that Tavel has established a reputation for its rosé wines because the region is so much better suited to the production of gutsy reds. It lies north-west of Avignon, close to Châteauneuf-du-Pape. The rather alcoholic Grenache is the main grape variety used, so the wine tends to be quite heavy and alcoholic, lacking some of the freshness and elegance that is really desirable in a pink; it is best drunk within a year of the vintage. Reputable producers include Aqueria, Genestière, Trinquevedel, Vieux-Moulin and Forcadière.

In Lirac, which is very similar in taste, Assémat is the best producer, and Château Bouchassy is also good. Côtes-du-Rhône may also be pink, usually produced by a village co-operative; so too may Gigondas.

The other leading wine of the south of France that fits into this segment is the biggest seller from the Salins du Midi, Listel Gris de Gris, which has recently been renamed Grains de Gris. This is quite a full-flavoured fruity rosé, from a large producer that has led the way with technical developments in the cellar and virtually organic treatments in the vineyard. Grains de Gris is a vin de pays des Sables du Golfe du Lion, from phylloxera-free vineyards on the sand-dunes of the Camargue.

If we move outside France we find there are some full-bodied pink wines produced in **Spain**. Rioja rosado can be full and fruity, from producers like Marqués de Cáceres, but it is rarely aged in oak these days. The one exception here is Marqués de Murrieta, with the dry, tarry, slightly herbal flavours of traditional oak-aged Rioja. Any rosé from Navarra and Penedès is likely to be very similar to pink Rioja: Torres Casta Rosada is the most typical example. Pink wines from further south, from Jumilla, for example, which includes pink in its DO, tend to be rather heavy and over-alcoholic.

In **Italy**, the occasional DOC includes a rosato. In Bardolino, Bardolino Chiaretto is made, a lighter version of the already pale red wine. Further south, Cerasuolo d'Abruzzo makes full-flavoured, fairly alcoholic wine from the Montepulciano grape, and most of the main Sicilian producers include a pink wine in their range. Cellaro Rosato is a pleasantly quaffable pink.

One of the better Italian pinks comes from Carmignano, a wine that is poetically called Vin Ruspo, or more prosaically Carmignano Rosato. Vin Ruspo literally means stolen wine, and the name originates from the days when the peasant farmers used to keep the juice from the last picking of grapes, which were not delivered to the landowner's cellar until the following morning. The resulting wine, fermented off the skins, was pink. The occasional Chianti estate produces a rosato, which shows how suitable Sangiovese can be for pink wine, producing some fresh fruit flavours; Rosa dell'Erta from San Polo in Rosso is a good example.

Bulgarian Vintners have introduced a **Bulgarian rosé** from the Burgas region, made from Cabernet Sauvignon, which is quite full in flavour, with the merest hint of residual sugar (which could almost push it into the next segment); it is clean and fresh, and firmly eschews the idea of a blush wine.

One of the most successful pinks from outside Europe comes from **Chile**. It has a European connection: the producer is Miguel Torres of Penedès fame. His Santa Digna rosé, made from Cabernet Sauvignon, is a wonderfully fresh, but quite full, ripe raspberry-flavoured wine.

A couple of examples from **Australia** are ripe and fruity: Mount Hurtle, made from Grenache and 10 per cent Shiraz, has a ripe strawberry nose, and is reminiscent of strawberry-flavoured boiled sweets. Schinus Molle rosé is lighter and drier, with less obvious raspberry flavours.

South Africa also includes the odd rosé in its repertoire; there is a fresh Blanc de Noir from Boschendal, made from a mixture of Cabernet Sauvignon, Shiraz, Merlot and Tinta Barocca, as well as some dry, fruity rosé, made under the Fleur du Cap and Culemborg labels.

MEDIUM BODY, DRY WITH HIGH ACIDITY

Numerous appellations of France include rosé, but it is often of minimal significance and can be seen as simply a useful way of disposing of excessive juice when making red wine. This process of running off surplus juice is, to all intent and purposes, the same as the *saignée* method. Examples include Irancy rosé, Chinon rosé, Beaujolais rosé, each of which usually account for only a very small part of the appellation, but with an accordingly larger production in years of more generous yields.

Wines from the moderate climate of **south-west France** tend to have some body and weight, while retaining quite a high level of acidity. They are always firmly dry, although they may have a richness that verges on sweet, originating from the flavour of ripe fruit. The little-known appellation of the Gironde, Bordeaux Clairet, is epitomised by Château Thieuley, whose wines have some lovely raspberry fruit. Simple Bordeaux Rosé is also possible, as at Château de Sours, again with some wonderfully ripe fresh fruit.

The adjoining appellation of Bergerac also includes rosé, but only in small quantities. Château la Jaubertie makes a pleasing example, which has a surprisingly deep colour. Côtes de Gascogne rosé from Château le Puts is also good.

Rosé du Cabernet du Haut-Poitou, from the excellent regional co-operative outside Poitiers, is a well-made fruity pink, from both Cabernet Sauvignon and Cabernet Franc.

Further south, the little-known appellation of Béarn owes its initial creation to the prevalence of Rosé de Béarn, made from Cabernet and Tannat. However, its appeal is limited outside the foothills of the Pyrenees. Better flavours from the same grapes come from the co-operative of Plaimont in the form of pink Côtes de St-Mont, a small VDQS around the tiny hamlet of St-Mont which is just north of the appellation of Madiran. Fresh, fruity acidity and easy drinkability are the keynotes of this wine.

Among the wines of the **Midi**, an effort is made to retain some acidity by picking the grapes before they are truly ripe, so that a refreshing crispness is part of the character of the wine. Some very successful rosé vins de pays have been produced because the producers have given the pink wines as much care and attention as their red and white wines. A pink vin de pays des Coteaux de Bessilles (one of the newer vins de pays from close to Pézenas, from a dynamic producer at Domaine St-Martin de la Garrigue) is deliciously fresh and fruity, encapsulating the essence of good rosé. So, too, Domaine de Limbardié, an innovative estate in the vin de pays des Coteaux de Murviel, produces some good rosé. Another good rosé is a vin de pays d'Oc cépage Syrah, under Skalli's Fortant de France label.

In the **Jura**, on the other side of France, close to the Swiss border, rosé is included in the appellation Côtes du Jura. In fact, neither Poulsard nor Trousseau, the two indigenous red grapes of this isolated hilly region, provides much colour – nor, for that matter, does the third red grape allowed in the appellation, Pinot Noir. The dividing line between red and pink can be somewhat blurred, with wines that are either deep pink or light red, both with quite full-bodied flavours. However, these wines tend not to travel too far from the region and so are rarely seen.

The obscure Champenois appellation of **Rosé des Riceys** also fits into this category. This is a pink wine made from Pinot Noir in the village of les Riceys in the department of the Aube. Good Rosé des Riceys is surprisingly deep in colour and full in body for such a northern climate, with ripe raspberry fruit that, in its best years, can have some of the chocolatey character of Pinot Noir. However, as far as value is concerned, it is an expensive curiosity.

Most **Portuguese rosé** is slightly sweet, but there is now one exception: from Bairrada comes Nobilis – made by Sogrape, the people who created Mateus Rosé. It may be seen as an attempt to upgrade the image of Mateus, and move away from its lightly sweet, fizzy associations. The 1990 vintage is crisp and fruity, with good acidity and some fresh strawberry fruit.

There is one lone example from **New Zealand**, a rosé made by Esk Valley in Hawkes Bay from Merlot and Cabernet Franc, which is quite rounded and mouth-filling with good acidity on the finish.

MEDIUM BODY, MEDIUM-SWEET WITH LOW ACIDITY

The obvious example in this category is Mateus Rosé, a light pink, slightly sparkling, slightly sweet wine. Perhaps it should be included in the sparkling wheel, but as it is far from fully fizzy (some carbon dioxide is merely injected into the wine, and evaporates quickly once the bottle is opened), it can feature just as happily here. Mateus Rosé was one of the wine trade's great success stories, with world sales once standing at a million bottles a week. The eye-catching, instantly recognisable dumpy bottle, with a picture of the Mateus palace on the label, has probably introduced thousands of people to wine. The other key Portuguese pink wine is Lancers, made by the large company of J M da Fonseca. Both are really quite uncharacteristic of the real flavour of Portuguese wine.

Another marketing success story, though not as long-lasting or eye-catching as that of Mateus, was the ploy of renaming pink or rosé wine as blush. For some reason, this seemed to capture the consumer's imagination and it became fashionable to drink blush wine. California led the way, with numerous blush wines made from its surplus Zinfandel. White Zinfandel therefore indicates a pink wine, usually with the full, soft, slightly sweet flavour of California. The giant producers, E & J Gallo, owe their chief success in the British market to White Grenache, again a soft pink wine, with full body and low acidity.

LIGHT BODY, MEDIUM-SWEET WITH HIGH ACIDITY

Rosé is the tiniest section of the wheel, indicative of the scant attention paid to it by most British wine merchants; Simon Loftus of Adnams of Southwold is the rare exception of a wine merchant who actively enthuses about rosé, even to the extent of including it in tastings. The fact remains that pink wines represent a tiny 5 per cent of the British wine market, chiefly accounted for by Mateus Rosé, and the lightly sweet wine from the Loire Valley, Cabernet d'Anjou. The latter is made from Cabernet Franc and, less often, Cabernet Sauvignon, and is grown in vineyards around the town of Angers. It may be firmly dry, but is usually slightly sweet, over-sulphured and generally uninspiring; the dry version is usually a more interesting glass of wine. Serious producers in Anjou tend to concentrate on red wine, motivated by the relatively recent creation of the appellation Anjou Villages for the better red wines of the area.

Occasionally you may find a mature Cabernet d'Anjou, such as the 1961 Domaine de Bablut, stocked by Adnams, which has some mature herbal flavours and a hint of toffee on the finish. It is something of a rarity, not to mention a curiosity.

LIGHT BODY, DRY WITH HIGH ACIDITY

The other dry wines of the **Loire Valley** are not unlike dry Cabernet d'Anjou in flavour, but they allow a wider range of grape varieties to be used, including Groslot and Gamay, as well as both Cabernets and Pinot Noir. The appellations here are simple: Anjou Rosé is always dry; Saumur Rosé and Touraine Rosé are very similar to one another. A curiosity called Noble Joué Touraine – made from a blend of Pinot Meunier, Pinot Gris and Pinot Noir – is made by Clos de la Dorée, and is redolent of fresh raspberries, quite full on the palate with some crisp acidity on the finish. Rosé de la Loire and Chinon Rosé are two other appellations for light dry pinks. Sadly, many Loire pinks can be rather flat and dull, spoilt by an excess of sulphur.

Further east, **Sancerre** includes rosé in its appellation, as does nearby Reuilly. Both tend to be very pale in colour, the lightest of pink, and are very delicate on the palate, but usually with some crisp acidity. Beurdin in Reuilly and Vacheron in Sancerre are worth trying. However, these wines are not cheap, tending to be similar in price to the red wines of their appellation.

Across the Channel, you can find the occasional pink wine from our own **English** vineyards; Conghurst, Denbies and Tenterden rosés are the best, with fresh raspberry fruit and crisp acidity.

RED WINES

Body	Age	Tannin / acidity	Style	Wines
Light Body	No age	Acidity	Fruity acidity	Beaujolais and other Gamays, Bardolino, Valpolicella, Dolcetto and Barbera, Alto Adige, Germany, Austria and Hungary
Medium Body	No age	Light tannin	Soft fruit	Basic burgundy, Jura, Rouge d'Alsace, Loire, Côtes du Fronton, Costières de Nîmes, Corsica, sin crianza Rioja, north Italy, Switzerland and Germany
Medium Body	No age	Medium tannin	Fruit and tannin	Bordeaux Rouge, south-west France, Chile, Argentina, Bulgaria, vin de pays, Chianti and light Tuscans, Patrimonio and Pinotage
Medium Body	Age	Medium tannin	Medium structure	Claret, Cahors, Madiran, New World Cabernet Sauvignon, Loire, Beaujolais crus, Tuscany, Umbria and Piedmont, Bairrada, Dão and
Medium Body	Age	Medium tannin	Oak and vanilla	Rioja, Costers del Segre, Ribera del Duero, Penedès, good burgundy and New World Pinot Noir
Full Body	No age	Medium tannin	Southern warmth	Côtes-du-Rhône, Provence, Languedoc-Roussillon, Sardinia, Sicily and southern Italy, Spain, Portugal, Lebanon, Greece, Cyprus, Yugoslavia and
Full Body	Age	High tannin	Rich and spicy	Rhône, California Syrah and Zinfandel, Australian Shiraz, Valpolicella
Full Body	Age	Structured heavy weights		Classed-growth clarets, California and Australian Cabernet Sauvignon, Super Tuscans, Brunello di Montalcino, Barolo and Barbaresco

FRUITY ACIDITY (LIGHT BODY, NO AGE, ACIDITY)

Young red wines are often dominated by acidity rather than tannin. They are light in body and are not destined for much ageing, but are best drunk within one or two years. Their immediate appeal is their fruit and easy drinkability, combined with a lack of harsh edges.

Beaujolais and the Gamay grape

Beaujolais is made from the Gamay grape and is sometimes vinified in a particular way called carbonic maceration (see introduction): whole bunches of grapes are put into a vat full of carbon dioxide, a process which brings out the youthful fruity character of the wine by emphasising the fruit flavours and reducing the tannin content. A variation on this, called semi-carbonic maceration, is more commonly used in Beaujolais: no extra carbon dioxide is added to the vat, but is retained from the fermentation. The effect is very similar, making some wonderfully fresh, lively wines, with some acidity and stacks of fruit, often reminiscent of ripe cherries. Beaujolais-Villages, a superior appellation originating from the better villages of the region, tends to have a little more body, but is still a wine for relatively early drinking.

The essential wine for early drinking is, of course, **Beaujolais Nouveau**, but this has lost some of its frivolous, popular appeal. However, it still accounts for something like half the production of the Beaujolais region, with wines that are delightfully fruity in a ripe vintage, but mean and acidic in a poorer vintage. In practice, Beaujolais Nouveau is often very much better at Christmas, or even Easter, than on its release date of the third Thursday of November.

Beaujolais Nouveau has had its imitators, inspired by its apparent success. In France there is **Gaillac Nouveau**, also made from Gamay; as well as **Côtes-du-Rhône Nouveau**, and the nouveaux wines among the vins de pays of the Midi, which can be released a month earlier than Beaujolais. As they originate from a warmer climate, they are often riper and more fruity. Italy has not escaped the craze for *vini novelli*, with Banfi's Santa Constanza, Antinori's San Giocondo and Gaja's Vinòt.

The 1991 is a superb Beaujolais vintage, producing some really ripe fruity wines, with a little more staying power than usual. For wines with more structure, see Beaujolais crus in a later segment.

Good producers of Beaujolais include the range of growers in the Eventail des Vignerons Producteurs, a marketing group of such people as André Depardon, Guy Patissier, Louis Genillon and others. Georges Duboeuf is a reliable name, and so too are Loron and Chanut. The village co-operatives are also important, accounting for around 40 per cent of the production of the region. Cellier des Samsons in Fleurie is particularly fine.

The 1990 and 1989 are also good vintages in Beaujolais but, for basic Beaujolais, drink a younger vintage, and look for the crus in older vintages.

The Gamay grape rarely produces wines with any staying power. The sole exceptions are the ten Beaujolais crus, and even then, perhaps not all of them. Elsewhere in eastern France, Gamay makes deliciously accessible wines for early drinking. The nearby **Coteaux Lyonnais**, which adjoins the vineyards of Beaujolais in the south, is one of those overlooked appellations which makes an agreeable alternative to Beaujolais. Georges Duboeuf is the most easily available producer.

Other Gamay-producing regions Mâcon, which adjoins Beaujolais, also produces a red wine made predominantly from Gamay. However, it rarely seems to have the vibrant fruitiness of good Beaujolais; the white wines of the Mâconnais are better. Gamay is also grown in the upper reaches of the Loire, and production in the **Côtes du Forez** is dominated by one of France's most modern and efficient co-operatives, the Cave Co-opérative des Vignobles Foreziens, which produces a range of wines based on Gamay, all lively and fruity and ideal for early drinking. The wine of nearby **Côte Roannaise** is very similar, though perhaps with a little more body.

Saint-Pourçain, a fairly obscure VDQS of central France, makes a red wine that is usually a blend of Pinot Noir and Gamay, in other words a type of Passe-Tout-Grain (the Burgundian appellation for wines which are a blend of Gamay and, at least a third, Pinot Noir), with some fruity acidity and light body. The wines of the local co-operative are imported by that intrepid Loire specialist, Robin Yapp of Yapp Bros, but there are numerous small producers whose wines rarely travel.

Gamay also grows along the Loire Valley in the form of **Gamay de Touraine**, as well as in the regional **vin de pays du Jardin de la France**. There is also an occasional Gamay from the **Fiefs Vendéens**, down on the Atlantic coast near the Sables d'Olonne, which is generally light and fruity, with a little more acidity and less actual fruit than good Beaujolais. **Gamay du Haut-Poitou**, from the high-performance regional co-operative, has a little more structure. A more substantial Gamay from close to the Rhône Valley, is **Gamay de l'Ardèche**, again produced by a local co-operative.

Pinot Noir

Other northern French wines have the similar characteristics of fruit and acidity, but have little tannin. There are various wines made from Pinot Noir in the vineyards of Champagne, northern Burgundy and the Loire Valley, which are comparable in flavour. Pinot Noir, in a cool climate, produces some refreshing raspberry fruit, balanced with lively acidity, rather than tannin. It is only in the very ripest years that wines like Bouzy and Sancerre have much tannin and staying power and lose their fresh acidity.

Irancy, the best-known red wine appellation of the Yonne, from a village close to Chablis, usually has enough body to push it into the next segment of the wheel. Nearby **Coulanges-la-Vineuse** tends to produce wines which have a softer flavour, with some of the vegetal character of Pinot Noir; while the wines of **Epineuil**, from the third red wine-producing village of the Yonne, are fruity with a slight earthiness.

The central vineyards of the Loire Valley, Sancerre, Menetou-Salon and Reuilly, are only about 80 miles from the Yonne, so there are distinct similarities, with the same disadvantages of growing red grapes in marginal vineyards. Red **Sancerre** – like Menetou-Salon and Reuilly – is light and fruity, with acidity rather than tannin, except in very ripe years, when it might be given a little oak maturation. Generally, however, these red Loire wines are best destined for early drinking.

Bouzy, the appropriately named still red wine of Champagne, is proof that the wines of that area are so much better with bubbles, without the need to have sufficiently ripe grapes to provide enough colour for red wine. Acidity is certainly the dominant, usually excessive, taste element, with insufficient balancing fruit. Worth trying are Laurent-Perrier's red Coteaux Champenois and Bollinger's red Ay la Côte aux Enfants.

Italy

Northern Italy is the source of some light, easy-to-drink fruity reds. **Bardolino** is a pretty village on the shores of Lake Garda which produces light red and pink wine, from a mixture of grape varieties. The word '**classico**' on the label indicates that the wine comes from the heart of the vineyard area; '**superiore**' denotes a year's ageing, which does not usually improve the quality of the wine, as Bardolino is best drunk as young as possible. It is light in colour and light in body too, with some sour cherry fruit and an indefinable Italian flavour. **Chiaretto** is the pink version of the DOC, which also allows for Bardolino Novello, if you want a change from Beaujolais Nouveau.

Closest to Bardolino is **Valpolicella**, from vineyards to the north of the enchanting city of Verona, near Lake Garda. Valpolicella covers a distressingly wide quality range, resulting from an over-extension of the production area and an excessive increase in the permitted yields. However, attempts are now being made to tighten up the regulations, hopefully to some effect. Wines labelled 'classico' should have some ripe cherry fruit and should be drunk as young as possible. There is also a technique called *ripasso*, which gives fuller, richer wines, with some tannin, which places them in the rich and spicy segment of the wheel. Unfortunately for the consumer, there is rarely any indication of this on the label. Good Valpolicella producers include Allegrini, Masi, Quintarelli, Boscaini, Zenato, Tedeschi and Guerrieri-Rizzardi.

In north-west Italy, **Piedmont** – although known above all for its firmly structured wines – also makes some deliciously accessible and easy-to-drink reds from the Dolcetto and Barbera grape varieties. Dolcetto accounts for seven DOCs; Dolcetto d'Ovado, Dolcetto d'Acqui, Dolcetto d'Asti, Dolcetto di Dogliano, Dolcetto di Diano d'Alba, Dolcetto delle Langhe Monregalesi and Dolcetto d'Alba. This last one is the wine you see most often, with the highest concentration of good producers, partly because they also produce Barolo and Barbaresco. The great advantage of the Dolcetto grape is that it ripens early, and can be picked before the autumn rains.

The essence of good **Dolcetto** is ripe berry fruit, which is always balanced with some lively acidity, resulting in a deliciously refreshing bitter-sweet wine. It is rarely heavy or tannic, thus making it the most accessible of all the Piemontese reds. The key producers of the region complement their range with it, such as Altare, Giuseppe Mascarello, Aldo Conterno, Giacomo Conterno, Cavallotto, Prunotto and Rinaldi.

Barbera also fits most happily into this segment, as the key to the taste of Barbera is acidity, rather than tannin. It is a grape variety that is grown all over Italy, both in the north and the south, but which really comes into its own in Piedmont, with three DOCs – Barbera d'Alba, Barbera d'Asti and Barbera di Monferrato. There is a quintessentially Italian flavour to Barbera, with its bitter-sweet fruit – sour cherries and plums – and a refreshingly astringent and acidic finish. Barbera d'Alba is considered the most substantial of the three DOCs, while Barbera de Monferrato is the lightest and easiest to drink. Barbera should be drunk when it is young and fresh and never more than four years old. As far as producers go, there is no-one who really specialises in Barbera; it forms part of the repertoire of most of the key Piedmontese estates.

There are other Italian DOCs whose key characteristics are soft ripe fruit, balanced with acidity. One is **Lagrein Dunkel**, from the Alto Adige or Südtirol, hence the Germanic ring to the name. Lagrein is the name of the grape used (dunkel means dark), which produces wines with masses of ripe, soft fruit, without any aggressive edges of tannin, and so is best drunk in early youth. Good producers include Grai, Lageder and Tiefenbrunner. There is a pink version too, called Lagrein Kretzer

Lago di Caldaro, or Kalterersee, is another wine from the Alto Adige. The best classico version comes from vineyards immediately around the lake of the same name, while the DOC spreads over a large area of the Alto Adige, from north of Bolzano down to Trentino. Light red fruit is its key characteristic, but with a smoky hint. Superiore indicates a half degree more alcohol, and you may see 'scelto' on the label too, which implies that the producer has made a special selection of the grapes. Good producers include Hofstätter, Schloss Schwanburg, Lageder and Tiefenbrunner.

Mountain vineyards seem to lend themselves to soft fruity reds. **Santa Maddalena** is one wine from the Alto Adige, made in exhilaratingly steep terraced vineyards outside the town of Bolzano. Schiava is the main grape variety used to make this light red wine, which has some strawberry fruit and which is for soft, easy drinking, the younger the better. Good producers include Grai, Hofstätter and Lageder.

Germany

German reds cross the boundary between the fruity acidity and soft fruit segments. Traditional German reds have the same quality categories as white wines, with the same sweetness levels. Thus, a red Spätburgunder Spätlese could be sweet, but confusingly, and happily, is not always so. A new wave of German winemakers are taking their red wines much more seriously and giving them some oak-ageing, with the aim of making wines with more stature and structure. In this instance, a Spätburgunder Spätlese would have the same level of ripeness as the sweet white wine, but would be fermented out until firmly dry; the label will indicate this with the word 'trocken'. Consequently, an increasing number of German wines fit into the following soft fruit segment.

Czechoslovakia

Czechoslovakian, or more precisely, Slovakian wines are beginning to make an appearance in Britain. One example which fits into this segment is a light, fruity red wine from an indigenous grape called Frankovka, which has fresh berry flavours.

Austria and Hungary

Red wine does not seem to be Austria's strength. However, there are some singularly Eastern European grapes in its repertoire, such as Blauer Zweigelt, which makes a soft fruity wine, with little body. Blaufrankisch is also grown, mistakenly believed to be the Gamay of Beaujolais. It is not the same grape, but there may be a similarity in taste, with wines which have some light fruity acidity and minimal tannin. In Hungary, the same wine is called Kékfrankos, and in Germany, Lemberger. Examples of any of these are pretty rare on British wine merchants' shelves.

SOFT FRUIT (MEDIUM BODY, NO AGE, LIGHT TANNIN)

Soft, ripe, juicy fruit is the key to this segment, but always with the backbone of a light streak of tannin. These are wines to drink in relative youth; they may age a little but that would be the exception to the rule.

Burgundy

First comes the basic category of red burgundy, or **Bourgogne Rouge**, which is made from Pinot Noir all over the region, from the Yonne down to the limits of Beaujolais. In the northernmost vineyards it tends to be light, with raspberry fruit and acidity, but acquires more substance the further south you go. In the **Côte d'Or**, Bourgogne Rouge comes from the less-favoured slopes: neither grands crus, premiers crus, nor part of a village appellation. However, in the hands of a good producer, Bourgogne Rouge can make for an agreeable glass of wine. The grapes may come from younger vines, which have insufficient structure for a better appellation. The wine may even be given a little barrel ageing for extra backbone and weight, though that is unlikely. Usually, Bourgogne Rouge is the result of standard red-wine vinification in a steel or cement vat, with a few days' maceration on the skins.

Pinot Noir is a sulky grape variety, both temperamental in the vineyard and difficult to vinify in the cellar. It depends very much on the conditions of the vintage; Burgundy has been blessed with an excellent run of vintages in 1988, 1989 and 1990, all of which are currently available. They are ripe fruity wines, with a little more body than is sometimes the case. This means that wines like Irancy and Coulanges-la-Vineuse (featured in the previous segment) may also have a little more structure than usual. Irancy, made from Pinot Noir and, occasionally, a very tiny amount of César and Tressot for extra body, tends to be a little sturdier than neighbouring Coulanges.

Good producers of Bourgogne Rouge include the Cave de Buxy in the Côte Chalonnaise and almost any top burgundy producer.

Further south, the new appellation of **Bourgogne Côte Chalonnaise** has been created to distinguish the vineyards of the Côte Chalonnaise, which do not fit into the village appellations of Rully, Givry, Montagny and Mercurey, from Bourgogne Rouge produced elsewhere. Previously, the only clue to the more precise origins of the wine was the postal code of the producer. Generally, at this level, the red wine of the Côte Chalonnaise is very similar to, but a little lighter in body than, that of the Côte d'Or. All over Burgundy the key to quality is the producer's name on the label. Good producers of Bourgogne Côte Chalonnaise include the dynamic Cave de Buxy, as well as Michel Goubard, Michel Juillot and Roger Narjoux.

The hinterland of the Côte d'Or is the source of two lesser, but increasingly popular, Burgundian appellations, **Hautes Côtes de Beaune** and **Hautes Côtes de Nuits**. As their names imply, the vineyards are on the upper plateau, behind the main slope of the Côte d'Or, where the climate is distinctly cooler. The wines tend to be lighter, with a little more acidity, and have some stalky tannin. In warmer years they should also have some refreshing raspberry fruit.

Bourgogne Passe-Tout-Grain is a blend of Pinot Noir and Gamay (usually in the proportion of two to one), and can be attractively fruity, with a bit of acidity and tannin. The other lesser appellation of Burgundy, **Bourgogne Grand Ordinaire**, is anything but grand. It is decidedly ordinary, usually made from Gamay, and perhaps a little Pinot Noir, and is best forgotten.

Jura

The red wines of the Jura are covered by two appellations: **Arbois**, which includes the vineyards around the town (its one claim to fame is that it is the birthplace of Louis Pasteur), and the broader appellation of **Côtes du Jura**. The grape varieties used for red wine include Pinot Noir, as well as the indigenous Trousseau and Poulsard, both of which are peculiar to the Jura. Wines may be a blend of all three, or you may find pure Pinot Noir or Trousseau – but there will be little indication given on the label. They have a soft ripeness that can be reminiscent of light burgundy and, when they are made from Pinot Noir, they take on some of the soft vegetal characteristics, as well as the ripe fruity flavours, of that grape variety.

Unfortunately, the wines of the Jura are not widely available in Britain. Worth trying, if you can find them, are those from the Château d'Arlay, Christian Bourdy, Rollet Frères, and also those from Henri Maire's four different estates.

Rouge d'Alsace

Pinot Noir is the sole red grape variety of Alsace. Sometimes it makes a wine that is more pink than red, for in cooler years it suffers from the difficulties of ripening in relatively northern vineyards. Until recently, it had not really been treated seriously, with insufficient maceration to extract colour, nor any barrel-ageing to add structure. The general aim was a soft, light, fruity, easy-to-drink wine that was not sure whether it was trying to be pale red or deep rosé. Now, amongst some producers – such as Hugel, the Cave de Turckheim, Ostertag, Zind-Humbrecht and Muré – there is a trend towards producing a more structured **Rouge d'Alsace**, but it will always be a fairly light wine, with a light streak of tannin at the most, and some soft raspberry fruit. The recent run of fine vintages, notably 1988, 1989 and 1990, has helped produce some good wines. Occasionally an older wine turns up tasting remarkably like a lesser burgundy.

Chinon, Bourgueil and the wines of the Loire

Chinon and **Bourgueil**, the two key red appellations of the Loire Valley, could cross the taste segments and fit into two categories. They may have light tannin and need no maturation or, depending on the vintage, produce a more structured wine that does need ageing. The soil also determines the style of wine: gravel, close to the river bank, makes light fruity wines; while a mixture of clay and flint gives wines structure and tannin. The grape variety used is Cabernet Franc and, while Cabernet Sauvignon is included in the appellations, in practice it is rarely used. The problem is that on the label there is little indication of the style of wine: you have to know the right grower and vintage, and both can change. Both 1990 and 1989 were good vintages; 1990 made rich, fruity wines, whilst those of 1989 are sturdier, with more staying power. Good Chinon producers include Couly-Dutheil, Charles Joguet, Bernard Baudry, Domaine de la Perrière and Clos du Saut au Loup.

Bourgueil, and the small enclave of **St-Nicolas de Bourgueil**, may fit more easily into the medium structure segment, but **Anjou Rouge** and the slightly more robust **Anjou Rouge Villages** come into this eminently fruity segment. They should have a little tannin, and ripe cherry and plum fruit should dominate the taste – what the French call *fruits rouges*, or red fruits, an all-embracing term for summer fruits, or a glorious summer pudding. Anjou Rouge is rarely worth keeping, except in the very ripest and hottest years. Similarly, **Saumur Rouge**, which is a lighter version of Anjou Rouge, from vineyards around the town of Saumur, rarely warrants keeping. However, the small enclave of **Saumur-Champigny** sometimes has a little more weight and body in riper years. Good producers include Domaine Richou, Château du Breuil and the Château de Chamboureau in Anjou; and Filliatreau and the Château de Targy in Saumur-Champigny. Amongst noted Bourgueil producers are Caslot-Galbrun and Lamé-Delille-Boucard, with Taluau and Jean-Claude Mabilleau in St-Nicolas de Bourgueil.

Côtes du Frontonnais

The **Côtes du Fronton** is one of the appellations of south-west France. It is not completely overshadowed by Bordeaux, but has some original flavour of its own, coming from the Négrette grape, which must account for a minimum 50 per cent of a wine, along with Cabernet Franc, Cabernet Sauvignon and Merlot, among others. Négrette is distinguished by its lack of tannin; this means that it produces deliciously easy-to-drink soft fruit, but needs blending with other grapes to give the wine body. Côtes du Fronton has a soft immediate appeal, in wines like Château Bellevue-la-Forêt, which is the largest estate. Other producers include Château Baudare, Château Flotis and the Cave de Fronton.

Costières de Nîmes

This is one of the newest appellations of the Midi, created in 1986. It was originally called Costières du Gard, but the name was changed in 1989 to avoid any possible confusion with vin de pays du Gard. The grape varieties are the usual Midi mixture – Carignan, Cinsaut, Grenache, as well as some improving Mourvèdre and Syrah – but the wines are very much lighter and easier than elsewhere in the south. There is an attractive spiciness, with a hint of southern warmth, but not much body. Village co-operatives dominate the appellation, but there are some good individual estates too, such as Château de la Tuilerie.

Corsica

There are three strands to Corsican viticulture: the grape varieties of North Africa and the Midi – Grenache, Cinsaut and Carignan – brought to the island by the *pieds noirs* leaving Algeria; the more recently introduced varieties like Cabernet Sauvignon and the white grapes, Chardonnay and Chenin Blanc; and, most colourful of all, the indigenous Corsican grape varieties, such as Nielluccio and Sciacarello. Nielluccio may be related to Sangiovese, and has some structure and backbone, while Sciacarello produces some wonderfully soft spicy, herbal fruit. In wines like Ajaccio, and some of the crus of **Vin de Corse** (such as Sartène, Calvi and Porto Vecchio), or in some of the **vins de pays de l'Ile de Beauté** (the evocative vin de pays that covers the whole island), Sciacarello is blended with Nielluccio and Grenache and can provide some delightfully spicy, original flavours, reminiscent of the Corsican countryside. These Corsican wines are rarely heavy or structured, but have a light, fruity character, with enough tannin to provide backbone, but no ageing potential.

Rioja

Rioja is the wine that put Spain on the world wine map. It comes from northern Spain, from vineyards around the town of Logroño, situated on the river Ebro. The wines divide into three distinct areas of production, with different soil and climatic conditions, namely, Rioja Alta, Rioja Baja and Rioja Alavesa. Most Rioja is a blend of two, if not all three, areas. The grape varieties are a mixture too: Tempranillo (in other regions largely responsible for some of Spain's best red wines) blended with Grenache, or Garnacha, as well as some Mazuelo, (otherwise known as Cariñena or Carignano) and perhaps a drop of Graciano.

There are four categories of Rioja, three of which benefit from oak ageing and one that does not. The latter is the wine that concerns us here, namely **sin crianza Rioja**, as opposed to crianza, reserva and gran reserva. Whereas the others come into the oak and vanilla segment of the wheel, sin crianza Rioja (which literally means 'without nursing', or in other words, ageing) depends upon the fruit flavour of the grapes for its taste and so fits in here. In fact, it does not have a very strong personality; it is a youthful fruity wine, with a touch of spice, but without any great individuality.

For information on producers and vintages look under gran reserva Rioja.

Other northern Spanish reds that have not been aged in wood have a similar flavour. As the nearby DO of **Navarra** produces wines from the same grape varieties, the flavours are comparable. **Toro**, which is further south on the Duero river, is made mainly from Tinto de Toro (otherwise known as Tempranillo), as well as Garnacha, so that the sin crianza version is not unlike a young Rioja. Bodegas Fariña is the best producer.

Italy

Cabernet, both Sauvignon and Franc, is widely grown all over north-east Italy. Usually, where Cabernet is included in a DOC, the label simply says Cabernet without specifying which one, and more often than not the wine is a blend of both. The taste is generally ripe and fruity, soft and plummy, with a little tannin to allow for two or three years' ageing, and occasionally it has the slightly herbaceous character that you can find in Cabernets from the Loire Valley.

Other north Italian reds have a similar fruity character, with a little tannin. One example is **Franciacorta Rosso** from Lombardy, which comes mainly from Cabernet Franc, with some Cabernet Sauvignon and Merlot, and which has some ripe berry fruit flavours, with a little tannin. **Teroldego Rotaliano**, a curious grape variety from Trentino, with its own DOC, produces ripe cherry fruit flavours, with a little tannin; Gaierhof is one of the few such wines to leave the country.

Switzerland

Swiss wines make a very occasional appearance on our shelves. Most of them are drunk by the thirsty Swiss themselves and the few wines that are available represent seriously bad value for money. More white than red wine is produced in Switzerland; the reds that we may find go under the name of **Dôle**, or may simply be labelled as Gamay or Pinot Noir. Generally, the colour tends to lack depth, and the palate definition, though they may have some of the vegetal flavour and raspberry fruit of Pinot Noir.

Germany

The better red German wines come into this segment of the wheel. The principal grape varieties are Pinot Noir (otherwise known as Spätburgunder) as well as Trollinger, Lemberger and Dornfelder. The Ahr Valley is considered to be the prime source of red German wines, but Baden and Württemberg are also important. The wines that we see most often are likely to come from Baden, or the Ahr Valley, with the occasional example from Rheinpfalz. Tesco, for instance, has introduced a Baden Red to partner its Baden White, which is a light, fruity, slightly jammy Pinot Noir, with some raspberry fruit and acidity.

The more serious red German wines are given some oak ageing, but although this may not be obvious on the palate, the oak does provide more structure and backbone. The intrinsic taste, however, is the soft, vegetal flavour of Pinot Noir. Lingenfelder in Rheinpfalz makes some good Pinot Noir, with some ripe vegetal fruit and just enough tannin; Kessler in the Rheingau produces a slightly more austere Pinot Noir, while Weingut Meyer Nakel makes a Pinot Noir with some sweet fruit. Wines made from the Dornfelder grape tend to be a little drier and more solid, but with some ripe berry fruit. This is a relatively new German crossing that is becoming more popular, especially in southern Germany. It shows potential, both in the vineyard, where it is easy to grow, and in the bottle, with some good flavours.

FRUIT AND TANNIN (MEDIUM BODY, NO AGE, MEDIUM TANNIN)

If there is a grape variety that dominates this section, it must be Cabernet Sauvignon, blended perhaps with some Cabernet Franc and Merlot. Some grape varieties naturally produce more tannin from their skins than others, irrespective of whether they are then aged in oak, and assimilate more tannin from the wood – Cabernet Sauvignon is one of those. Although the tannin may be more obvious than in wines featured in the previous segment, it must always be balanced by sufficient fruit to make a harmonious wine. A backbone of tannin is an intrinsic part of the character of the wine; there is no virtue in keeping it on the assumption that the tannin will fade. It may well do, but so will the fruit, and then the wine is dead.

Bordeaux Rouge

Bordeaux Rouge is the most basic appellation of the Gironde, along with **Bordeaux Supérieur**, which simply denotes an extra half degree of alcohol and therefore a little more body. It covers all the vineyards outside of the better village and area appellations and is claret at its simplest and most accessible. Bordeaux Rouge is the house claret or own-label claret of wine merchants and supermarkets. The wines inevitably vary with the vintage, but are generally ready for drinking within one to three years. There has been a run of good vintages in Bordeaux: Bordeaux Rouge from 1988, 1989 and 1990 is drinking well, with plenty of ripe blackcurrant fruit. A good Bordeaux Rouge has all the characteristics of a greater wine from the region, but less so. The blend of grape varieties, Cabernet Sauvignon, Cabernet Franc, Merlot (and perhaps Malbec, depending on the vineyard) makes a wine with some cassis fruit, perhaps a hint of spinach (the slight vegetal character of Merlot, which is not the same as the rotting vegetation of Pinot Noir), with a sturdy streak of tannin to provide some backbone.

There is not so much difference between a good Bordeaux Rouge and the wines of some of the peripheral areas of Bordeaux, such as **Premières Côtes de Bordeaux**, **Côtes de Castillon**, **Côtes de Bourg** or **Côtes de Blaye**. Those that adjoin St-Emilion, such as **Canon Fronsac** and the up-and-coming **Côtes de Francs**, have more affinities with St-Emilion, with a little more flesh and richness; while those that face the Médoc across the estuary of the Gironde have a lean, sturdier character.

Oak rarely features in the vinification of these wines. The economics of production simply do not permit such an indulgence; oak barrels are expensive and the price that Bordeaux Rouge fetches certainly does not warrant the outlay. Concrete or steel vats, lined with epoxy resin – not even stainless steel – are usual. Some Bordeaux Rouge is produced by a *négociant* who has bought wine, must or grapes from numerous small growers; if it comes under a château name, the so-called château will be a simple farmhouse, with a shed for the winemaking, and certainly not a handsome edifice, complete with *chai*. Much Bordeaux Rouge comes from the vineyards of Entre-Deux-Mers, which only have a specific appellation for white wine, although both colours are produced.

In Britain, much Bordeaux Rouge is sold under a wine merchant's own label such as The Society's Claret, Tanners' Claret, Harvey's No. 1 Claret, or under a brand name like Mouton Cadet, or the substantially better Sirius Rouge.

Amongst the so-called petits châteaux, the lesser estates that provide the basis of any good claret list, try de Sours, Bonnet, Thieuley, Méaume, de Tourtigeac, la Gardéra, all with the appellation Bordeaux or Bordeaux Supérieur.

From more precise appellations try: in Canon-Fronsac, Moulin Pey Labrie and Canon-Moueix; in the Côtes de Bourg, de Barbe, du Bousquet, la Croix-Millorit; in Fronsac, la Rivière, la Vieille Cure, Richotey; in the Côtes de Francs, Puyguéraud; in Côtes de

Castillon, Pitray; in Premières Côtes de Blaye, Haut-Sociondo; and in Premières Côtes de Bordeaux, du Juge, Reynon, Cayla and Tanesse.

South-west France

The appellations of south-west France have close affinities with Bordeaux. Until the region of Bordeaux was delimited in 1911, much of the wine from Bergerac, Duras and Buzet was simply blended with that of the Gironde. The grape varieties are the same, with Cabernet Sauvignon, Cabernet Franc and Merlot forming the basis. It is only as you travel further from Bordeaux that there are distinct changes, notably in Cahors and Madiran, but they come into the next segment. It is the wines of the appellations closest to Bordeaux that are generally ready for drinking within one to three years of the vintage.

The appellation of **Bergerac** was certainly overshadowed by Bordeaux for many years and only in the last decade has it really striven to create a separate identity. The vineyards on the western edge of the appellation touch those of St-Emilion and there are certain affinities of taste between the two. **Côtes de Bergerac** covers the same area, but indicates an extra degree of alcohol, while **Pécharmant** is a small enclave to the east of the town of Bergerac, where the wines are a little more structured and sturdy.

Co-operatives are important in Bergerac, and there are also some good individual estates. Best known is Château La Jaubertie, which has benefited from some Australian influence in the wine-making techniques, with the result that the wines are a little fuller and richer than others in the appellation. Other good estates include Château la Raz, Château Belingard and Château Court-les-Mûts. Try also Château Tiregand in Pécharmant.

The vineyards of the **Côtes de Duras** are separated from Entre-Deux-Mers simply by the departmental boundary. The differences between Bordeaux Rouge from Entre-Deux-Mers and red Côtes de Duras are therefore negligible; climate, soil and vinification methods are similar and the flavours are comparable. Two large co-operatives dominate the production of the Côtes de Duras, one of which is actually within Entre-Deux-Mers and makes both appellations. The other is outside the town of Duras. There are numerous small estates too, such as Domaine la Grave-Béchade, Domaine de Ferrant and Château de Conti.

A little further south are the **Côtes du Marmandais**, situated around the town of Marmande, which is better known in France for its tomatoes than for its wine. Flavours again are similar to Bordeaux Rouge, with similar weight, but with a streak of originality in the inclusion of the Abouriou grape, which can add an extra dimension of perfume. In practice, however, it is usually overwhelmed by Cabernet and Merlot, so that Côtes du Marmandais tastes very similar to a young Bordeaux. Two co-operatives account for almost the total production of the area.

The final Bordeaux Rouge taste-alike of the south-west is **Buzet**, formerly Côtes du Buzet. Once again, the grape varieties are Cabernet Sauvignon, Cabernet Franc and Merlot. A large and efficient co-operative dominates the appellation, unusual in having its own cooperage, so that the better wines of Buzet are all given some oak ageing. However, this is not obvious on the palate and merely provides the wines with the subtle addition of some tannin, as well as some gentle oxidation. The best wines from the co-operative go under the châteaux of individual members, namely Château de Gueyze and Château de Padère. Vintages in this part of France follow those of basic Bordeaux very closely, so that the wines of 1988, 1989 and 1990 are all good vintages in the south-west, with wines that are already beginning to drink well.

Gaillac, the appellation with vineyards around the Toulouse-Lautrec city of Albi, has improved the quality of its wines steadily over the last few years. However, it does suffer from something of an identity crisis in its red wines, for the regulations allow a considerable mixture of grape varieties. There are those of Bordeaux, as well as Gamay, Duras (no connection with the appellation), Fer Servadou, Négrette and Syrah, with various restrictions as to minimum and maximum percentages in the blend. The veritable hotchpotch of flavours produced makes it very difficult to define the quintessence of Gaillac, but it seems that Duras is the most characteristic grape variety, and most Gaillac Rouge includes a significant proportion. If it is blended with the Bordeaux grape varieties, the result is a red wine with some of the characteristics of the Médoc, with some tannin as well as fruit. However, if Syrah and Fer Servadou are used, the result is a little more spicy. Co-operatives dominate the production of Gaillac, notably Labastide-de-Lévis, whose wines have improved considerably in recent vintages, as well as the Cave de Técou. There are some good individual producers too, such as Château Clément Termes.

The flavours of the south-west meet those of the Midi in the twin VDQS of **Côtes de la Malepère** and **Cabardès**, which are situated on either side of the city of Carcassonne. The vineyards are a melting pot of grape varieties; those of the Midi mingle with those of Bordeaux to produce some original flavours which owe something to Bordeaux and something to the Languedoc. However, they retain a structure and a degree of leanness that has more in common with Aquitaine than with the Midi, so they fit quite happily into this taste segment. In the search for good value, it is the lesser-known regions of France that are coming into their own and there is no doubt that the value offered by a Côtes de la Malepère or Cabardès is far greater than a comparable petit château. Producers include Château Ventenac, Château de Rayssac, Château Troncin-Capdevila and Château de Pennautier in Cabardès, and Château de Routier and Château de Malviès in the Côtes de la Malepère.

Another lost area of the south-west is the **Côtes de St-Mont**, a small VDQS lying in the foothills of the Pyrenees, to the north of the appellation of Madiran. The local Plaimont co-operative is one of the best in France, in terms of equipment, expertise and motivation, and has worked hard for its place on the wine map of France. Red Côtes de St-Mont has a sturdy flavour, originating from the local Tannat grape, which is softened by some Cabernet and Fer Servadou. It generally provides good-value drinking.

Chilean Cabernet Sauvignon

Chile continues to make an impact. After the first flush of enthusiasm, when it was hailed as the next exciting discovery of the wine world, things have settled down somewhat, but there has been a steady improvement in both vineyard and cellar techniques. Chile does not yet produce a Cabernet Sauvignon to compete with a classed-growth claret – good cru bourgeois is about as near as it comes – but there is plenty of sound Chilean Cabernet Sauvignon which makes a very acceptable alternative to a Bordeaux Rouge or an unknown petit château.

There is no reason why Chile should not be able to produce ripe healthy grapes. The country has the major advantage of being phylloxera-free – how fortunate it was that the first vine cuttings from France crossed the Andes before phylloxera had reached Europe. The climate is superb for viticulture and there are virtually no problems with rot or disease. Irrigation is essential, with water supplied by the melted snows of the Andes. In the past there has been a tendency to over-irrigate in order to encourage generous yields; now they are learning to control growth in the vineyard and reduced yields will undoubtedly make for more concentrated flavours.

Some better Chilean Cabernet Sauvignons, such as Santa Rita Medalla Real and Errazuriz Don Maximiano, may fit more comfortably into the medium structure segment of the wheel, but basic Chilean Cabernet Sauvignon, often sold under a supermarket own label, makes an original diversion from Bordeaux Rouge.

Argentina

Argentina has lagged behind Chile, but is trying hard to catch up. It is one of the big producers in the world league table, but most of the wine produced, from the insipid Criolla grape, is destined for its own domestic market. There are European grape varieties, such as Chardonnay and Cabernet Sauvignon, but so far they represent a minute percentage of the total production. The majority of the vineyards of Argentina are on the sandy soils of the province of Mendoza where again irrigation is essential and, although there is phylloxera, it does not pose a threat in such sandy soil, so the vines remain ungrafted. Yields in Argentina have been rather excessive in the past, but they are being reduced, with the result that the occasional good Cabernet is beginning to appear, notably from Trapiche. As yet, they are without the depth of flavour of the best of the Chileans. Merlot and Syrah from Trapiche are good too, and the wines of Finca Flichman, Etchart and Michel Torino are also worth a try.

Bulgaria

Bulgaria is the one country of Eastern Europe that has successfully adapted its wines to western taste and commercial demands. The state-controlled wine industry was subsidised so that it could offer competitive prices and thereby earn much sought-after foreign currency. Bulgarian Cabernet Sauvignon was one of the great success stories of the 1980s and it continues to represent very good-value drinking, despite problems within Bulgaria, originating from the dismantling of the systems of the Communist era. Somehow, the taste of Bulgarian Cabernet Sauvignon will never be very refined for it has a certain rustic earthiness about it. The country's vineyards are divided up into *controliran* regions which, more or less, equate to appellations. The best for Cabernet Sauvignon are **Svischtov**, **Yantra Valley** and **Oriachovitza**. The word 'reserve' on the label indicates three years' ageing in wood, including a short time in new American oak and a longer period in large Slavonik oak casks, with Reserve Cabernet Sauvignon from Suhindol and Oriachovitza showing well. Sometimes Cabernet Sauvignon is blended with Merlot. Stambolovo Merlot is also good. Production is generally in the hands of large anonymous co-operatives.

Two indigenous Bulgarian grape varieties also fit into this section, namely Melnik and Mavrud. Both are fairly sturdy, rugged varieties. Assenovgrad is the best area for Mavrud, while Melnik comes from the village of the same name. With some oak ageing it can have more body and substance than Mavrud.

And after this meander around the comparable Cabernet Sauvignons of the world, it is back to France, for vin de pays.

Vin de pays

There are vins de pays all over viticultural France, covering a multitude of flavours. The greatest concentration is in the Midi, particularly in the four departments of the **Gard**, **Hérault**, **Aude** and **Pyrénées-Orientales**. Vins de pays were created about twenty years ago, as a category below appellation contrôlée and VDQS, in order to give some kind of identity to the lake of anonymous vin de table – or plonk – that was produced in the south of France. Regulations are not as strict as for an appellation, allowing a much greater flexibility of grape varieties, and thus a considerable range of quality. There are vins de pays that compete with, or even out-perform, their neighbouring appellations, and there are others that are really no better than ordinary plonk and do nothing more than continue to contribute to the diminishing wine lake of the Midi.

The charm of the vins de pays is that they provide an outlet for creativity for the imaginative experimental producer. A producer is not compelled to plant the grape varieties of an appellation but can experiment pretty freely. It is true that there are regulations as to what can be planted, but if a grape variety is planted which is not authorised but which proves to be successful, the chances are that a blind eye will be turned. The most basic vins de pays come from Carignan and Cinsaut, and perhaps from crossings like Aramon and Alicante Bouschet, which were developed in the last century with the sole aim of boosting the colour in high-yielding vineyards. Syrah and Mourvèdre are increasingly planted, as are the grape varieties of Bordeaux, the Cabernets and Merlot, with some success. A winemaker may not put Merlot in his Minervois, but there is nothing to stop him experimenting with Merlot in his vin de pays.

Unlike appellations, all the vins de pays (with one exception, vin de pays des Sables du Golfe du Lion) depend upon administrative geography for their delimitation, usually in the form of a department (such as vin de pays de l'Aude), or a zone within a department covering several villages (such as vin de pays de la Vallée du Paradis). The Sables du Golfe du Lion are limited by the sand dunes of the Camargue, while there are four other larger vins de pays that cover several departments. The relevant one for the Midi is vin de pays d'Oc, covering Languedoc-Roussillon. The Comté Toloson accounts for a large part of south-west France, while the Comté Rhodaniens relates to the northern part of the Rhône Valley and the Jardin de la France covers the whole of the Loire Valley. This last vin de pays is usually a white wine; the others fit quite happily into this taste segment.

The Midi is one of the most exciting regions of France, for a wind of experimentation has blown through the region at near gale force and continues to do so. There are constant changes, new developments, innovative techniques and new producers coming to the fore. Outside interest has been excited, not just from other parts of France but from other continents. Hardys, the large Australian company, has established a super new winery at Béziers and is encouraging local growers to plant more Cabernet Sauvignon, Sauvignon Blanc and Chardonnay, to which Australian vinification techniques are being applied. Domaine de la Baume from the Chais Baumière is the result.

Skalli, a long established *négociant* in the port of Sète, realised the changing role of the local merchants and has created a series of varietal wines under the Fortant de France label, mainly for Cabernet Sauvignon and Chardonnay, but for other grape varieties as well, such as Syrah, Merlot and Viognier.

There are numerous estates with imaginative, far-sighted owners who are seeking to achieve the best from their vineyards. They are pulling up their old Carignan and Aramon vines and replacing them with Syrah and Cabernet. The older generation is giving up its vines, in which its children have no interest, so that many of the old vineyards on the plains of the Midi are gradually being abandoned. Village co-operatives account for a considerable part of the production of the south; some are good, some are bad. Amongst individual estates worth seeking out are Domaine de St-Martin de la Garrigue, Domaine de l'Arjolle, Mas Jullien, Domaine de l'Abbaye de Valmagne, Domaine de Limbardié, Domaine Anthéa, Mas Chichet and Domaine Pech de Celeyran.

All of the above make good sturdy vins de pays, with a good balance of fruit and tannin. Sometimes the wines may benefit from a little bottle age, but, generally, vins de pays are best drunk at most within three to four years of the vintage. The main exception to this rule is Mas de Daumas Gassac, which fits more comfortably into the structured heavyweights segment of the wheel. Generally, however, most vins de pays – whether they are based on Cabernet, Carignan or Syrah – fit into this segment.

Chianti and other Tuscan reds

The epitome of Tuscany is Chianti, from vineyards covering a large part of the region. The DOCG of Chianti breaks down into several sub-zones. The most important is **Chianti Classico**, between the two cities of Siena and Florence. Then there is **Rufina**, the tiniest zone, which lies in a small valley north-east of Florence. **Montalbano** comes from the slopes of the Monte Albano, to the west of Florence (adjoining the more structured wine of Carmignano). **Colli Fiorentini** lies to the south and west of Florence; the **Colli Senesi** is a large area, encompassing the vineyards of Montalcino, Montepulciano and San Gimignano. The vineyards of the **Colli Aretini** are mixed up with suburbs of Arezzo and the **Colline Pisane** are contained in a small group of hills south-east of Pisa.

Essentially, there are two styles of Chianti, Chianti normale and Chianti riserva. The normale is for early drinking, while the riserva is not sold until it is at least three years old, and therefore comes in the next segment of the wheel. It is **Chianti normale** that concerns us here. The Chianti Classico Consorzio has gradually extended the ageing period of Chianti Classico normale; previously it was available in the June following the vintage, but this has now been extended a further seven months so that the 1992 vintage, for instance, will not be available until January 1994. In contrast, most other Chianti normale is available in the March following the vintage. The motives behind this lie in the Consorzio's attempt to make Chianti Classico appear a more serious, structured wine than light-hearted simple Chianti. It aims to cast off the image of frivolity attached to Chianti, along with the dumpy straw-covered bottle, and to demonstrate that Chianti deserves more serious attention. It also wants to distinguish Chianti Classico from the other Chiantis, in anticipation of Chianti Classico being given its own separate superior DOCG. Apparently all that is needed is the appropriate signature on the decree.

There are other differences between Chianti Classico and the other zones: for example, yields are lower and the required proportion of white grapes is smaller. None the less, Chianti normale, Classico or otherwise, is a delicious wine for relatively early drinking. The mainstay of Chianti, and all the wines of central Italy, is Sangiovese. Basically, there is good and bad Sangiovese, originating from a variety of different clones. Chianti has suffered from an influx of the wrong clones and some unfortunate plantings, but things are now looking much brighter, with considerable improvements, not only in the vineyard, but also in the cellar. As well as Sangiovese, a small percentage of a lighter grape, Canaiolo, is included, along with the statutory percentage of white grapes, Trebbiano and Malvasia, often ignored by the better producers.

Good Chianti Classico normale does have more structure than the other Chianti normale. It can age, but the general aim is to produce a wine for earlier drinking. Sangiovese produces a firm streak of tannin and an element of astringency that simply demands wonderful Tuscan olive oil to balance it. If the wine and food of a region are the natural complement to each other, then this is the perfect example. The flavour of Chianti Classico is of ripe but sour cherries, whereas Chianti from the other areas, with the possible exception of Rufina, tends to be lighter, a little softer, with less body, but none the worse for that. Drinkability is its essence and it does not merit much ageing.

Vintages do vary quite considerably in Tuscany. The 1990 was one of the great Chianti vintages, a year in which everything went right and some first-class wines were produced. The 1988 was also an excellent vintage; the 1985 and 1986 were good too, while the 1987, 1989 and 1991 were lighter. (For recommended producers see under Chianti riserva.)

There are other Tuscan wines in the style of Chianti. In the wake of the creation of the DOCGs of **Vino Nobile di Montepulciano** and **Brunello di Montalcino** came two new DOCs, **Rosso di Montepulciano** and **Rosso di Montalcino**. These are from the same vineyards as the finer wines, but are lighter, without the ability to age. Rosso di Montepulciano is available in the April following the vintage while Rosso di Montalcino can be bottled a year afterwards. With Sangiovese the principal, or indeed only, grape variety in the case of Rosso di Montalcino, there is a distinct similarity with young Chianti, especially Chianti Classico, which has a moderate amount of tannin to provide sufficient structure, but which lacks the depth and body for long ageing. Rosso di Montalcino offers particularly good-value drinking, and is a very acceptable and much more accessible alternative to the often overpriced Brunello di Montalcino.

Morellino di Scansano is another Tuscan wine that is based on Sangiovese. Quite simply, Morellino is the local name for Sangiovese, in the town of Scansano in the heart of the Maremma in southern Tuscany. The mix of grape varieties is similar to that of Chianti – allowing Canaiolo, and also Malvasia Nera and some Ciliegiolo – and the taste is similar. You can also find a riserva version, which may even have been kept in *barriques* for a few months, in which case it would fit into the next segment. That is particularly true of the wines of Erik Banti. Le Pupille and Montelassi are two other good estates.

Brief mention can also be made of the small estate of **La Parrina**, which is virtually synonymous with the DOC of the same name. It is situated on the hills near the town of Orbitello and, with similar grape varieties to Chianti, is fairly alike in taste, with some sour cherry fruit and the typical Tuscan bite of astringency. The Italian specialists, Winecellars, are the sole importers.

Patrimonio

It is but a short hop across the water from Tuscany to Corsica, to a grape variety called Nielluccio which is the mainstay of **Patrimonio**, and which is said to be related to Sangiovese. As Corsica belonged to the city state of Pisa from the eleventh to the thirteenth century, this may well be true. Certainly there is a similarity in the wines: Patrimonio has an underlying astringency and a firm streak of tannin that is indeed not unlike Sangiovese in flavour, but it lacks the aromatic perfume of the lighter wines of the island, featured in the previous segment. However, it rarely travels; nor does it have much ageing potential. It does bear a slight resemblance to some of the wines of the south of France, such as those from Coteaux du Languedoc or from Minervois, which come under the southern warmth segment.

South Africa

Pinotage is the most individual of all the South African wines. A cross between Pinot Noir and Cinsaut, created in the 1920s by a Professor Perold from Stellenbosch University, it has been seen as the red workhorse grape variety of the vineyards of the Cape. It is easy to cultivate and to vinify, generous in its yields and adaptable in the cellar. It can produce light red, blush, or even sparkling, wine, but is at its best when given a serious red wine vinification, with grapes from low-yielding vines. Then, it has some structure and tannin and a balancing amount of fruit; it may even benefit from a little ageing in large, rather than small, oak barrels, but that should not be apparent on the palate. It is not usually a wine for ageing, but is best drunk in relative youth. Sometimes it can be spoilt by rather rubbery overtones. Good producers include Simonsig, Kanonkop and Vriesenhof (with a second label, Paradise Vale).

MEDIUM STRUCTURE (MEDIUM BODY, AGE, MEDIUM TANNIN)

Again Bordeaux is the starting point for this segment of the wheel, but with wines that are the next rung up the quality ladder.

Bordeaux

This is a broad section that excludes only the basic claret of the previous section and the very best clarets, which feature in the structured heavyweights segment. It does include the crus bourgeois and lighter classed growths of the Médoc, with the communes of Listrac and Moulis. It also includes some Graves, many of the wines of St-Emilion and its satellites, and Pomerol.

To a certain extent, the 1855 classification still holds good today. There have been changes: one or two châteaux have disappeared, their vineyards absorbed into other estates. Mouton-Rothschild is the only property to have achieved an actual change in status, while other châteaux are generally acknowledged to be in the wrong category. Quality is never static; winemakers come and go; châteaux change hands; vines are replanted; vinification methods alter; all of these affect the ultimate quality of the wine in the glass. The best classed growths fit into the structured, heavyweights segment, and the lighter wines, perhaps the fourth or fifth growths, come into this segment.

These are wines with good structure as well as a considerable amount of tannin, which enables them to age for a few years. They will probably have been kept in oak for some months before bottling, but this should not be too obtrusive on the palate.

In the hierarchy of the **Médoc** châteaux, the **crus bourgeois** is the category below the classed growths, although some of the better ones, such as Chasse-Spleen and Fourcas-Hosten, are generally considered to be of classed-growth quality. A syndicate of crus bourgeois lays down certain quality criteria which must be satisfied in order to meet the membership requirements.

The wines of the Médoc are the most elegant of Bordeaux, perhaps the leanest, with more austerity than those of Graves. Certainly, they are not as fleshy as those of St-Emilion and Pomerol: the generally high proportion of Cabernet Sauvignon and the gravelly soil are the reasons for this difference.

St-Emilion and **Pomerol** both contain a much larger proportion of Merlot, as well as more Cabernet Franc, rather than Cabernet Sauvignon. This makes richer, fleshier wines, which could be confused with burgundy, except for the firm streak of tannin which gives them a certain structure. However, although Merlot has a youthful plummy character, it can develop deceptive vegetal overtones as it matures, especially in lighter-bodied wines.

Pomerol, which was a rural backwater until the Moueix family of Pétrus fame established it firmly on the world's wine map, does not have any form of classification. St-Emilion, on the other hand, has a plethora of grands crus classés, perhaps too many to have any real meaning. The most significant part of the classification system of St-Emilion is premier grand cru, with two châteaux, Ausone and Cheval Blanc in category A, and another nine estates in category B, representing some of the better wines of St-Emilion, which might fit better into the structured heavyweights segment of the wheel.

Graves, or **Pessac-Léognan**, comes between the previous two in style and character. Good Graves is typified by a *goût de terroir*, a certain smoky character which is said to originate from the soil, from the gravel pebbles of the appellation. Even good Graves generally has neither the richness of St-Emilion, nor the elegance of the Médoc. Again the better wines of the Graves come into the structured heavyweights segment.

In this category are wines of medium structure and medium ageing ability, such as Magence, Landiras, Domaine la Grave, Domaine de Gaillat, Chicane, de Chantegrive, Montalivet, Rahoul and de Roquetaillade-la-Grange. They all offer good medium-term drinking and several of them bear the mark of two leading winemakers of the region, Peter Vinding-Diers and Pierre Coste.

South-west France

Two of the wines of the south-west have some capacity for ageing: Madiran and Cahors. Both can be compared to Bordeaux.

The appellation of **Cahors** is centred on vineyards in the Lot Valley close to the medieval town of the same name. It is an area that has evolved considerably over the last decade or so, with major investment by growers and *négociants*, and vineyards planted on the arid plateau above the valley. The principal grape variety is Auxerrois, which is the rather insignificant Malbec in Bordeaux. In Cahors it makes lean, sturdy wine, with a rugged quality, softened by some Merlot, while extra structure is added by Tannat which, as the name implies, is thick-skinned and tannic. Surprisingly, perhaps, Cahors does not contain a drop of Cabernet Sauvignon.

The wine of Cahors can vary in style; traditionally it was the black wine of the last century, so thick and tannic that it was barely drinkable. Today, it has become significantly more accessible, to the extent that some Cahors is made for fairly early drinking, although wines from good estates repay some bottle-ageing. There is a sturdy fruitiness to the wine, a certain stalky character which comes from the harshness of the Auxerrois. Some oak ageing softens this, but only in the best estates are the barrels new, and only for the best wines from those estates, such as Clos Triguedina's Prince Probus. Other serious estates include Château de Chambert, Rigal, Prieuré de Cenac, Domaine de Gaudou, Domaine d'Eugénie, Château de Cayrou and Clos la Coutale. The regional co-operative works well for its appellation, making sound wine under the label of les Côtes d'Olt, and also under several individual châteaux names.

Madiran is the red wine of the Pyrenees, from vineyards around the sleepy village of the same name, north of Pau. The dominant grape variety is Tannat, which, as mentioned earlier, makes wines that are deep-coloured and firmly tannic; it can be softened with some Merlot and Cabernet Franc and perhaps some Cabernet Sauvignon. Madiran needs ageing, in vat or in wood, depending on the means and wishes of the producer. Good Madiran will have spent a few months in oak, perhaps even in new oak, and the result is a structured wine, with more flesh and weight than Cahors. It repays keeping. Vintages generally follow those of Bordeaux.

Good producers include Château Montus and Domaine du Boucassé from Alain Brumont, and also Domaine Teston, Château d'Aydie and Château Arricau-Bordes.

Cabernet Sauvignon from North America

Cabernet Sauvignon is generally considered to be the most successful red grape variety of **California**. It is treated in the same way as in Bordeaux, except that it is not always blended with Merlot or Cabernet Franc. The varietal name on the label implies a minimum of 75 per cent, but it may well be 100 per cent. Merlot is the grape variety that is usually added; Cabernet Franc is a much more recent and experimental innovation. California Cabernet Sauvignon has a more immediate impact than the somewhat reticent wines of Bordeaux: it tends to leap out of the glass, reeking of blackcurrants, with instant appeal. Recently, however, its producers have begun to aspire to some subtlety as well, making wines with rich, ripe cassis fruit, tannin, and occasionally some herbal minty hints.

The better California Cabernet Sauvignons fit into the structured heavyweights segment. More accessible wines, which need only four or five years' ageing, such as Mondavi's Woodbridge label, Sebastiani, Konocti and Sutter Home, are included here. There are some good Merlots, too, such as Newton and Rutherford Hill, but they very much take second place to Cabernet Sauvignon.

Washington State is making respectable Cabernet Sauvignon and Merlot – perhaps lacking the depth of the best California wineries, but good none the less. Arbor Crest and Chinook Merlot, and Cabernet Sauvignon from Hogue Cellars and Columbia Crest, are all wines to look out for.

Perhaps this is the place to mention the red wines of **Long Island**, which is now deemed to be the best viticultural region of New York State, even though the first vines were planted on the island as recently as twenty years ago. Perhaps the reason is that the climatic conditions of the North Fork of Long Island are very similar to those of Bordeaux, with a mild maritime influence. Merlot may be marginally more successful than Cabernet Sauvignon, but there are some excellent results as the vines grow older and the winemakers gain experience. Hargrave, Palmer and Bridgehampton are the leading wineries.

Australian Cabernet Sauvignon

Cabernet Sauvignon grows successfully all over the viticultural regions of this vast continent, from the Hunter Valley and Mudgee in New South Wales to the Margaret and Swan rivers of Western Australia, and even in the vineyards of Château Hornsby in the semi-desert of Alice Springs. However, it is indisputably at its best in the vineyards of **Coonawarra** in South Australia, where the famous iron-rich terra rossa soil produces the most complex examples. As with California, ripe blackcurrant fruit is the theme. The wines are full and ripe, sometimes with minty, eucalyptus flavours, as well as a sweetness that you do not find in Bordeaux. There is usually enough tannin to allow the wines to age for a few years, although the acidity is usually lower than in a claret.

Cabernet Sauvignon may be blended with Merlot, but Shiraz (the Australian name for Syrah), is the more common choice and adds a little extra spice to the wine. Again, the best wines fit into the structured heavyweights segment of the wheel. The easier to drink styles of Australian Cabernet Sauvignon include Brown Brothers Koombahla label, Wolf Blass Yellow Label, Hill-Smith and Yalumba.

New Zealand Cabernet Sauvignon

New Zealand Cabernet Sauvignon is coming of age. Until very recently it was very much an also-ran in the mammoth annual New Zealand tasting, but the emphasis has gradually shifted. White wines will always dominate the New Zealand wine scene, but there is now an ever-growing number of serious red wines. New Zealand Cabernet is sometimes spoilt by a vegetal, herbaceous character, which is a defect of the cool climate, but when it is good, it can be very good indeed, to the extent that it may also fit into the next segment. A notable example is Te Mata's Coleraine Cabernet Sauvignon, which has a firm impact of tannin, making a wine that will age for several years.

The better New Zealand Cabernets, such as the wines from Villa Maria, Vidal, Pask and Vavasour, contain a moderate amount of tannin, balanced with some attractive fruit. They have enough structure to enable them to age for three or four years, but are medium, rather than full-bodied. However, the cooler climate of New Zealand, with its long ripening season, makes more elegant wines than California and Australia. Vintages inevitably vary, but 1991, 1990 and 1989 have all produced some good wines.

South Africa

Cabernet Sauvignon is quite widely planted in South Africa, especially in the cooler Coastal Region that includes Stellenbosch and Paarl. Sometimes it is a pure varietal, although the varietal name on the label indicates a minimum of 75 per cent. The quality is not yet very consistent; there are some good South African Cabernet Sauvignons with cedarwood and blackcurrant fruit, but sometimes the wines can be just a little too high in alcohol and are spoilt by earthy, rubbery flavours, and by watery fruit. A recent tasting left an impression that high yields, stemming from excessive irrigation, had simply diluted the fruit.

Things can only improve and there is no doubt that South African winemakers are working hard to bring their wines back into the mainstream. The Bordeaux blends of Cabernet Sauvignon, Cabernet Franc and Merlot generally seem much more successful. The addition of Merlot and Cabernet Franc rounds out the fruit and gives the Cabernet Sauvignon more flesh. Often these wines are sold under fantasy names, like Paul Sauer, Trilogy, Rustenberg Gold. There is much less vintage variation in the Cape than in northern Europe. Good producers include Rustenberg, Warwick Farm, Overgaauw, Klein Contantia, Simonsig and Vriesenhof.

Chinon, Bourgueil and St-Nicolas de Bourgueil

Chinon and **Bourgueil**, two **Loire** appellations, feature largely in the soft fruit segment, but there are exceptions to every rule, and this is one of them. Depending on the soil in the vineyard and the conditions of the vintage, as well as the winemaker's particular philosophy and method, Chinon and Bourgueil, and even more so, the smaller appellation of **St-Nicolas de Bourgueil**, will age. With the right climatic conditions, most recently in 1989, these appellations produce wines that are structured, with a firm backbone of tannin, that benefit considerably from some bottle age. This was amply illustrated by bottles of 1964 and 1955 Chinon from Couly Dutheil: in the summer of 1991 they were both delicious glasses of wine, with elegant cedarwood flavours, more reminiscent perhaps of a classed-growth claret, and quite belying the view that all red Loires are made for drinking young.

The Beaujolais crus.

Again, **Beaujolais** may not be an obvious choice for inclusion in this taste segment, but when it is made in the traditional way, with a classic red wine vinification, rather than by carbonic maceration, it has more tannin, body and guts and can indeed age very successfully. Of the ten crus, some are distinctly lighter than others. The newest, Régnié, has yet to prove that it is really any better than a Beaujolais-Villages, while others, notably Moulin-à-Vent and Morgon, develop more complexity in better vintages, such as 1991. They start life with a tannic streak, with some ripe plum and cherry fruit, and develop considerable finesse with age. Ironically, mature Beaujolais behaves like a vinous chameleon. taking on the vegetal character of Pinot Noir, with a flavour that quite belies its origins.

Beaujolais has suffered in the past year or two from excessively inflated prices, but these have now returned to a more reasonable level, making cru Beaujolais relatively good value for money. Like much of France, Beaujolais enjoyed a run of good vintages; 1990, 1989 and 1988 were good, while 1991 was a very much better vintage in Beaujolais than elsewhere in France. Good producers include Georges Duboeuf, Château de Chénas, Château du Moulin-à-Vent, Brac de la Perrière, Geoffray and members of the Eventail des Vignerons Producteurs.

Chianti Riserva

Many **Tuscan** wines come into this segment. The first, Chianti, crosses two segments of the wheel: Chianti normale has some tannin but is not really intended for ageing, while a **Chianti riserva**, especially a **Chianti Classico riserva**, is kept for three years before it is released for sale. A riserva is only produced in better vintages, from the better wines of an estate. Very little will have been made in the rather patchy vintages of 1991 and 1989, but plenty in the excellent years of 1990 and 1988, with their rich, structured wines. The decision is generally made in the vineyard; the producers know which vineyards are more likely to produce riper grapes and more concentrated wine. They follow the evolution of the wine in barrel, ensuring that it will be able to sustain maturation, not only in cask, but also in bottle.

Some Chianti riserva might be criticised for being prematurely mature and dilute in flavour. There has, however, been a considerable improvement in the quality of Chianti, with Chianti Classico in particular proving its ability to age, perhaps as much as eight or ten years. A good Chianti riserva has a firm backbone of tannin and structure, with enough balancing fruit to develop into a fine bottle with age. The sharp reduction in the percentage of white grapes included in Chianti, following its elevation to DOCG status, brought about a considerable change in its personality, gradually turning it into a wine that merits serious attention.

The current vintages of Chianti riservas generally available are 1988, 1986 and 1985. All three are good, but 1988 is deemed to be the best. The wines from the good estates will never be cheap, but they will reward patience with some delicious bottles. There are numerous producers to recommend: Felsina Berardenga, Volpaia, San Polo in Rosso, Fontodi, Fonterutoli, Selvapiana, Vecchie Terre di Montefili, Ama, Villa Cafaggio, Le Masse, Badia a Coltibuono, Montagliari, Pagliarese, Il Palazzino, San Giusto a Rentennano, Riecine, Rampolla and Vicchiomaggio. While Isole e Olena does not make a Chianti riserva as such, Cepparello, labelled a vino da tavola because it is pure Sangiovese, is similar in style and quality.

Vino Nobile di Montepulciano

Vino Nobile has been criticised for being little more than a superior Chianti, and in some instances it was doubtful whether it was even that. The grape varieties are virtually identical to Chianti: Sangiovese is the mainstay, with a particular clone called Prugnolo in Montepulciano. There is Canaiolo too, perhaps Mammola, and a maximum ten per cent of white grapes. However, there is no minimum percentage, so the most serious producers have omitted the white grapes altogether from their wines. Two years' ageing is mandatory, while three years denotes a riserva quality. Generally, the wines are richer than Chianti normale, and more comparable to Chianti riserva.

Vino Nobile di Montepulciano has benefited from the dramatic improvement in winemaking all over Tuscany. The pacesetters were two estates, Avignonesi and Poliziano, but others have followed in their wake. Good Vino Nobile has a firm structured texture, with some ripe plummy fruit, good tannin, and the firm streak of astringency from Sangiovese that gives it backbone. Other good estates include Boscarelli, le Casalte and Il Cerro.

Brunello di Montalcino

Brunello di Montalcino is generally considered to be the Tuscan wine with the most stature. The Biondi Santi family placed it firmly on the wine map of Italy and created a red wine that was a hundred years ahead of its time, by making it from just one grape variety alone, the Brunello (which was their particular clone of Sangiovese), rather than from the customary mish-mash of grapes used all over Tuscany. Thus, they preceded the vogue of the Super Tuscans and established the potential for pure Sangiovese. Three years' ageing in large wood (what the Italians call *botti*) forms part of the production regulations. Small Bordeaux *barriques* cannot be used as they give a flavour that is quite foreign to Brunello. Originally, the statutory ageing period was four, then three and a half years, now reduced to three years in recognition of the fact that an excessively long period of wood ageing can sometimes destroy the fruit flavour of the wine.

Young Brunello has the sour cherry fruit of Sangiovese, which develops with bottle age, acquiring much greater complexity and a flavour that is sometimes reminiscent of the cedarwood of St-Julien. Sometimes it has a hint of herbs and perhaps some spice and smoky overtones, but always with a firm backbone of tannin. Good Brunello is beautifully balanced and elegant. It may be very tannic in its early youth, in which case it fits more happily into the structured heavyweights section, in the same way that the young, better classed-growth clarets do. Some producers, the so-called 'new school', aim to make their wines ready for drinking earlier, while other, more traditional producers aim for considerable longevity.

Good producers include Altesino, Caparzo, Il Poggione, Talenti, Col d'Orcia, Lisini and Banfi. Biondi Santi is expensive.

Carmignano

Carmignano is the newcomer to the line-up of Tuscan DOCGs. At first it was lost in a sea of Chianti, but then – thanks to the efforts of one family, the Bonacossis of Villa di Capezzana – it was awarded its own DOC, with the distinguishing feature of an obligatory percentage of Cabernet Sauvignon. It is thought that Cabernet Sauvignon was first brought to these hills west of Florence by the Medici, when they were dukes of Florence. This means that Cabernet Sauvignon is no upstart newcomer, as in other parts of Tuscany, but has long-standing credentials. However, Sangiovese still remains the principal grape variety, with some complementary Canaiolo and the usual drop of white wine.

With DOCG status, the proportion of Cabernet Sauvignon was increased from 10 to 15 per cent in order to distinguish Carmignano still more from Chianti. The ageing period is two years, and three for a riserva. The best-known producer is Villa di Capezzana, while Villa di Trefiano belongs to Vittorio, the son of the family. Fattoria di Ambra is another tiny, but highly recommended estate. The taste of Carmignano is a little softer and richer than Vino Nobile, and is a little more accessible than Brunello di Montalcino.

Torgiano

The other new DOCG of central Italy is **Torgiano**, which was essentially the creation of one man, Giorgio Lungarotti, whose family controls virtually the entire production of the vineyards surrounding this small Umbrian village. His red wine, made principally from Sangiovese, is sold under the name of Rubesco, while Rubesco riserva, cru Monticchio, is a stylish wine, capable of considerable longevity.

North-west Italy

Barolo and Barbaresco are the two great red wines of Piedmont, but there are numerous other Nebbiolo-based reds which have fruit and tannin, but which do not quite have the same stature or potential for longevity. **Gattinara** is a new DOCG, in some ways the least deserving amongst the Piedmontese wines. There are two good producers, Travaglini and Antoniolo, but other neighbouring wines, such as **Roero** and **Carema**, often offer more exciting flavours. The co-operative of Carema works well and Luigi Ferrando is a good private producer.

In nearby Lombardy, **Valtellina**, which borders Switzerland, produces wines which are also based on Nebbiolo. The DOC is simply Valtellina or, for better wines, **Valtellina Superiore**, which has four sub-divisions with the evocative names of Inferno, Grumello, Vargella and Sassella. Nino Negri and Rainoldi are the best producers here.

Portugal – Bairrada

Bairrada was seen as a rising star amongst Portuguese wines, but the question must be asked: has it fullfilled its promise? It comes from vineyards in central Portugal, south of the city of Oporto. While it can be red, white or sparkling, red accounts for the largest part of the production and this is the wine most usually found outside Portugal.

The main grape variety of red Bairrada is Baga, a tough-skinned variety that can make unyielding, astringent, tannic red wines, which require several years' ageing in both barrel and bottle. However, changes in vinification methods have made the wine more approachable; destalking the grapes before fermentation softens the tannin; experiments with new oak have improved the flavour, allied with a better understanding of the effects of oxygenation, as opposed to fruit-destroying oxidation. This softer style of Bairrada is ready to drink early – in a year, say.

Good Bairrada, that is not dried-out and tired, has a backbone of tannin, with a certain spiciness – a cross between a claret and a Côtes-du-Rhône, with some pepperiness and blackcurrant. In youth it has the stalky taste of young claret, but will develop more mellow flavours with age.

Good producers include Luis Pato, Caves São João, Sogrape and Caves Alianças.

Dão

Dão, Portugal's best-known red table wine, has undergone some of the same changes as Bairrada. It comes from northern Portugal, from hillsides around the town of Viseu, to the south of the Douro river. It too can be either red or white, but is more commonly red, made from a hotchpotch mixture of indigenous grape varieties, with quite unmemorable names.

Red Dão requires a minimum of 18 months' ageing, while **garrafeira** wines, those which the producer deems to be his very best, must spend at least two years in vat and one in bottle. Often it is longer, and sometimes too long: the tendency has been to keep Dão in wood for so long that the fruit has disappeared long before it ever reaches the bottle. Dão is firmly tannic and certainly needs some ageing, but not too much. Mature Dão is medium-weight, with a rugged, dry, peppery character but it never quite loses that rough, puckering edge of tannin. Sogrape's Grão Vasco is one of the best currently available examples.

Other parts of Portugal produce table wines that are growing in importance. It is debatable whether they always have enough ageing potential to fit into this segment, or whether they belong to the previous segment, or in the category of southern warmth. **Arruda**, from one successful village co-operative in the Estremadura, is a combination of fruit and tannin, but lacks the staying power of either Bairrada or Dão. However, at a competitive price, it is a good introduction to the flavours of Portugal. The better table wines of the Douro, those not used for port, are well worth trying; they have fruit and tannin, with a hint of the liquorice overtones of port. The best and most expensive is Barca Velha, produced by the port house Ferreira, while Quinto do Côtto is also good.

Other Portuguese garrafeira wines also come into this segment, such as Romeira Garrafeira, as well as some of the wines of the leading Setúbal company, J M da Fonseca. Periquita, the name of the grape, but also meaning parrot in Portuguese, combines tannin with a certain indefinable Portuguese flavour. Quinta da Camarate, which includes some Cabernet with Periquita, is also distinctly Portuguese in flavour, while Quinta da Bacalhão, made from Cabernet Sauvignon by the talented Australian, Peter Bright, at João Pires, has some New World blackcurrant fruit, balanced with tannin.

Israel

An unexpected postscript to this section might be Cabernet Sauvignon from Israel. Yarden from the Golan Heights produces Merlot, but the Cabernet Sauvignon is better. With some attractive cassis fruit, it is a well-made wine of medium staying power.

OAK AND VANILLA (MEDIUM BODY, AGE, MEDIUM TANNIN)

As explained in the introduction, countless wines benefit from the effects of oak maturation, but the taste should not always be apparent in the mouth; wines that have an obvious oaky flavour in their youth, mellow with age, so that the strong taste of new oak disappears, leaving fruit and tannin. One wine in which the taste of oak is especially noticeable, forming a vital component of the flavour, is Rioja, which gets its distinctive vanilla overtones from American oak. Rioja wines, therefore, dominate this section, and other northern Spanish wines are included as they are very similar, also benefiting from the influence of American oak.

It may seem illogical, contradictory or perverse also to include fine red burgundy and good Pinot Noir from elsewhere but, although the use of oak should be less marked in these wines, there is a similarity of taste, a certain sweetness, with some ripe flavours that is not so unlike a good Rioja.

Rioja

Rioja is the wine that first put Spain on the international wine map, preparing the way for other Spanish wines. It comes from northern Spain, from vineyards around the town of Logroño. There are three distinct areas of production, with differences in soil and climate: the Rioja Alta, the Rioja Baja and, the one which is considered to be best of all, Rioja Alavesa. Most Rioja is a blend from all three areas, or at least from two. The concept of a single-vineyard Rioja was unknown in the area, but there is now a handful of estates making wine from their own grapes, namely

Contino, Remélluri, Baron de Ley and Amezoladella Mora. The large bodegas that dominate the production of Rioja may own vineyards in the different areas and also buy in a large proportion of grapes from numerous small farmers.

Rioja is the first Spanish wine to be given a higher qualification than DO; as from 1991 it is DOCa (Denominación de Origen Calificada), which entails stricter controls – including bottling at source – for all Rioja. Although the Denominación covers all three colours, Rioja is known primarily for its red wines. There are four different categories, beginning with **sin crianza**, without any wood ageing, which features in an earlier segment. Then there are **con crianza, reserva** and **gran reserva**, all of which entail some time in oak – from twelve months for a crianza wine to a minimum of two years for a gran reserva, or perhaps longer, depending on the individual bodega style. In any case, a gran reserva must be aged for a total of five years altogether before sale, and a reserva for a minimum of three years, of which at least one must be in cask. Crianza Rioja also requires one year's ageing in cask, but only a further year of ageing in tank or bottle before release.

Tempranillo is the key grape variety which gives Rioja its fruit and flavour, as well as featuring in many of the better DOs of northern Spain. There may be a link with Pinot Noir, but that remains unproven. Grenache or Garnacha is the other important variety, as well as Mazuelo, and a drop of Graciano, which is currently enjoying something of a revival in the vineyards.

Oak maturation for Rioja is always done in small American oak barrels of 225 litres, the same size as the classic Bordeaux *barrique*. Oak, therefore, is a dominant feature of the taste of Rioja and it is only wines with a sufficient inherent structure in the first place that can cope with a long period in wood. Otherwise, the smoky fruit of the Tempranillo grape is lost. Leading producers include Marqués de Riscal, CVNE, Contino, Remélluri, Marqués de Cáceres, Olarra, La Rioja Alta, Bodegas Riojanas, Berberana, Olarra and Muga.

Costers del Segre

Raimat is a remarkable estate in the province of Lérida in northern Spain, which belongs to the Raventos family of Codorníu fame (see sparkling section). As well as white grapes for cava, there are plantings of Tempranillo, Cabernet Sauvignon and Merlot, in semi-desert land where the vines depend upon irrigation for survival. The energy of the company was responsible for the creation of a new DO, **Costers del Segre**, to cover the wines of the Raimat estate. These include three reds: a Tempranillo, a Cabernet

Sauvignon and Abadia, which is a blend of Cabernet Sauvignon and Merlot. Although the grape varieties of the last wine may be French in origin, there is something distinctly Spanish about the flavour, with the pronounced influence of American oak, some rich spicy fruit and a soft velvet finish.

Ribera del Duero

Ribera del Duero became a DO as recently as 1982. Until then there was just one estate of any note in the region, namely Vega Sicilia, whose wines are fabulous, both by reputation and in price. As well as Tempranillo, which they call Tinto Fino, the Bordeaux grape varieties, Cabernet Sauvignon, Merlot and Malbec, are grown. The resulting wines are known for their considerable richness and longevity, and ageing in both French and American oak is an important part of the production process. In the case of Vega Sicilia Unico, the key wine of the estate, made from the oldest vines, ageing could be for as long as ten years. There is also an extraordinary Reserva Especial, which is a blend of old vintages, some from the 1950s. While the 1980 vintage of Vega Sicilia Unico costs around £40 from Spanish specialists Laymont & Shaw, the Reserva Especial costs roughly twice as much. There are also two slightly more accessible wines from the same estate, called Valbuena, released in the third and fifth years of maturation, which have some wonderful complex flavours, equating to fine Rioja.

Apart from Vega Sicilia, the production of Ribera del Duero (literally, the banks of Duero, better known in Portugal as the Douro) was, until recently, dominated by co-operatives. That was until the wines of Pesquera, made by Alejandro Fernandez, hit the limelight after their discovery by an American wine merchant. Other bodegas have caught the public eye, following in the wake of Pesquera – Viña Pedrosa and Bodegas Mauro, for example. Unfortunately, prices have escalated, following the demands of fashion. Tinto Fino remains the principal grape variety used and, given some ageing in small barrels, makes some wonderfully rich, complex, smoky wines.

Penedès

Penedès is known, above all, for cava (see the sparkling wine wheel). However, still wines are made too and production is dominated by one family – Torres – who have put their region and their own name firmly on the world wine map. Miguel Torres was the first to plant grape varieties that are not Spanish, and to experiment with Cabernet Sauvignon, Merlot and Pinot Noir. He has done the same with white grape varieties too. The range of Torres wines continues to expand, with a rich plummy Merlot called Las Planas, and Mas Borras, which is a single-vineyard Pinot Noir. Other stalwarts include Tres Torres and Gran Sangredetoro, both made from Grenache and Carignan; Coronas, made from Tempranillo; Gran Coronas, which includes some Cabernet Sauvignon along with the Tempranillo; Mas La Plana, which replaces the former Gran Coronas Black Label, made from pure Cabernet Sauvignon; and Viña Magdala, a blend of Pinot Noir and Tempranillo. The flavours produced are a combination of the fruit of the grape, whether it is the blackcurrants of Cabernet Sauvignon or the vegetal overtones of Pinot Noir, with the Spanish influence of American oak barrels. These are wines that may mislead us as to their origins.

There are other producers of still wines in Penedès, such as Masia Bach, now part of the Codorníu group, who produces some serious red wines, including Cabernet Sauvignon.

The other star of Penedès is Jean León, known for his Cabernet Sauvignon as well as his Chardonnay (see further round the wheel). The Cabernet Sauvignon is rich and oaky, blended with a little Cabernet Franc and Merlot, and has plenty of ripe fruit. The oak places it in this segment of the wheel, but with its firm tannin, it could also fit into the previous section.

Another Spanish Cabernet Sauvignon comes from the Marqués de Griñon, Carlos Falco, who had the imagination to replant the vineyards of his family estate near Toledo with Cabernet and Merlot, rather than the ubiquitous Airén of the Spanish plains. A good Marqués de Griñon red can be rich in blackcurrant fruit and oak, but is generally not a long-lived wine.

This is also the place to include the wines of an up-and-coming DO in Aragon, namely Somontano, which literally means under the mountain. The wines of a new company, Covisa, with the brand name Viñas del Vero are worth seeking out. The Duque de Azura crianza, made from Moristel and Tempranillo, and aged for a few months in American oak, has some spicy vanilla flavours and a backbone of tannin. The basic Tinto, with its plummy fruit, as well as tannin, fits more comfortably into the fruit and tannin section, while the Val de Uga, made from Pinot Noir with some sweet vanilla fruit, bridges the gap between Spain and Burgundy.

Burgundy

When Pinot Noir is great it is sublime, and there is nowhere it performs as well as on the best sites of the **Côte d'Or**, in the grand cru vineyards of the best villages of the **Côte de Beaune** and the

Côte de Nuits. There is an initial sweet oaky flavour in Pinot Noir when it is young, mixed with some raspberry fruit. In some years the fruit will taste ripe; in leaner years, there may be a stalky overtone to the wine. In the best vintages, the oak and tannin will fade, leaving some ripe vegetal fruit, as should happen in the unparalleled run of good vintages in 1988, 1989 and 1990. The 1988 vintage was the best since 1985, with wines that are quite firm and tannic. In contrast, 1989 produced ripe, fleshy wines, which may lack structure. The best of the three is undoubtedly 1990, with both tannin and body and, better still, prices are lower than the 1989 level. These are wines that will undoubtedly age into great bottles, especially from leading producers like Joseph Roty, Domaine Dujac, Armand Rousseau, Trapet and Marquis d'Angerville.

The wines of the **Côte Chalonnaise**, especially from Rully, Givry and Mercurey, are similar to those of the Côte d'Or, but lighter in style and less elegant. They lack the refinement of the best red burgundies, but if there are bargains to be had anywhere in Burgundy, the Côte Chalonnaise may provide one. Good producers include Noël-Bouton at Domaine de la Folie, Cogny, Dury and Delorme.

New World Pinot Noir

Pinot Noir is the Holy Grail of the New World; Chardonnay and Cabernet Sauvignon have proved fairly easy to master, there are good Merlots and Rieslings too, but the essential quality of Pinot Noir has proved infuriatingly elusive. It is a temperamental grape that hitherto has only performed well on one small hillside in northern France. Things, however, have begun to change, with a growing feeling that the New World growers might just be on to a winning streak.

California There has been an enormous improvement in California Pinot Noir. There have been more plantings of better clones in the cooler parts of the State, notably at the southern end of the Napa and Sonoma Valleys in Carneros, where temperatures are moderated by the maritime influence of the Pacific Ocean. Pinot Noir needs a long, cool growing season; it does not like to ripen quickly. There are numerous different clones – some good, some distinctly inferior – and there is still much to be learnt about them. The other problem is that Californians have tended to make Pinot Noir in the same way that they make Cabernet Sauvignon, with some unhappy results. Now that they have realised that it needs completely different treatment, things are definitely looking up, and there are some good California Pinot Noirs around.

Successful producers include Robert Mondavi, Saintsbury, Au Bon Climat and Kent Rasmussen. The flavours may not yet be as subtle as the best red burgundies, but at about £10 a bottle the price is distinctly attractive.

Oregon Further north, in cooler Oregon, Pinot Noir may have even greater potential than in California, and it is certainly proving more successful there than Cabernet Sauvignon. David Lett first set the pace at Knudsen-Erath. After a period of excitement, things fell into the doldrums, but are now looking up again, with interest excited by the first vintage from Robert Drouhin's estate. Other good estates that have captured something of the elusive qualities of Pinot Noir include Ponzi, Eyrie Vineyard and Bethel Heights.

New Zealand New Zealand boasts of the advantages of its cool climate and Pinot may well provide the next success story of the Antipodes. St Helena, a winery outside Christchurch, on the South Island, first caught the limelight with its 1986 Pinot Noir. About the same time, Pinot Noir was being planted in the Wairarapa, north of Wellington, around the village of Martinborough. The first vintage of Martinborough Vineyards was a Pinot Noir, made by a Pinot Noir fanatic, Larry McKenna, and it met with instant acclaim. Others have followed his example: Ata Rangi, Dry River and Te Kairanga.

Back on the cooler South Island, Pinot Noir is planted as far south as the 45th parallel, at Rippon Vineyards on Lake Wanaka in Central Otago. St Helena, after a hiccup or two, is continuing its initial success, along with Waipara Springs and Omihi Hills, from two more Pinot Noir enthusiasts, Mark Rattray and Danny Schuster. In the tiny area of Nelson, Tim and Judy Finn at Neudorf Vineyards, and Hermann and Agnes Seifried from Redwood Valley, are also achieving some exciting flavours. Perhaps New Zealand Pinot Noir does not quite have the subtlety of the best burgundies, but a consistency of flavour and quality is beginning to develop – something you do not always find in burgundy – and there is a distinct price advantage to boot.

Australia Much of Australia is simply too hot for Pinot Noir. Murray Tyrrell, in the Hunter Valley of New South Wales, was the first to produce some rather jammy Pinot, but it is now generally agreed that the best areas for it are the coolest – the hills south of Adelaide, the Yarra Valley of Victoria, and Tasmania, the most temperate of all the Australian Vineyards. Pipers Brook is achieving good things in Tasmania, while James Halliday, a lawyer-turned-wine-writer and now winemaker, has made some successful Pinot Noir at Coldstream Hills. Mountadam in south Australia and Dromana Estate in Victoria are good too.

South Africa South Africa has tended to concentrate on Pinotage and Cabernet Sauvignon. However, there is some growing interest in Pinot Noir, which in any case was a parent of Pinotage. Tim Hamilton-Russell, of Hamilton-Russell Vineyards in Hermanus, was the first to take Pinot Noir seriously; he looked long and hard for suitably cool conditions where he could plant it and now makes one of the most successful wines from the Cape, with some lovely vegetal fruit and rich flavours.

His ex-winemaker, Peter Finlayson, has recently joined forces with Paul Bouchard, and together they have planted vineyards close to the Hamilton-Russell Vineyards, which are not yet in production. However, Bouchard-Finlayson will be a name to watch out for. Meanwhile, Peter's brother, Walter, is responsible for Glen Carlou, which produces another stylishly oaky Pinot Noir. Meerlust is another estate to make a commendable example; with some ripe but elegant vegetal fruit and good oaky flavours.

Italy, Austria and Romania There are occasional examples of Pinot Noir from Italy. So far, the best one to come out of Tuscany is Ruffino's Tondo del Nero. Although Pinot Noir is one of the permitted grape varieties of the DOCs of the Alto Adige, Trentino and Friuli, the wines produced are rarely exciting.

In Austria, George Stiegelmar is almost alone in making an oaky raspberry-flavoured Pinot Noir, while in Romania the Pinot produced is rather hot and jammy, with the merest hint of farmyards.

SOUTHERN WARMTH (FULL BODY, NO AGE, MEDIUM TANNIN)

Perhaps the idea of southern warmth needs some explanation: it is a term which should conjure up thoughts of wines that are born in warm sunshine, which are redolent of the scents and herbs of the Midi and the flavours of the Mezzogiorno of Italy. Generally, these wines are full-bodied, for sunshine produces sugar and thereby alcohol. Usually, they have some structure and a backbone of tannin, but not enough to merit a lengthy amount of ageing; they are usually best drunk within three to four years of the vintage but, as with any well-made red wine, especially if from a good vintage and a talented producer, there are always exceptions that last longer.

Côtes-du-Rhône

The **Côtes-du-Rhône** is a good starting point; this is the basic appellation of the Rhône Valley, with the greatest concentration of vineyards in the south, around Avignon. Although Côtes-du-Rhône can be white and pink, the best wines are red. **Côtes-du-Rhône-Villages**, usually with the name of one of the 17 villages on the label – Chusclan, Beaumes-de-Venise or Sablet, for example – has stricter production regulations, making wines with a little more substance and body. Where no village name is given, the wine is generally a blend of wines from more than one of these villages.

A good Côtes-du-Rhône tastes of the south, providing a warm mouthful, scented with herbs of the Midi, lavender, thyme and rosemary, as well as a touch of spice and liquorice. A mixture of different grape varieties is allowed, with Grenache, Syrah, Mourvèdre, Cinsaut and Carignan the most common. Grenache is the most important, making wine that is quite high in alcohol, full-bodied and mouth-filling. Sadly, modern trends have sometimes lightened Côtes-du-Rhône, turning it into a feeble shadow of its former self. However, a wine like the 1988 Côtes-du-Rhône from Guigal is a superb example of the appellation.

Other good producers include Pascal, Jaboulet (especially with Parallèle 45), Château du Grand Moulas, Cru du Coudoulet, Chapoutier, Domaine St-Gayan and Château Ste-Estève. The recent vintages of 1988, 1989 and 1990 offer some delicious drinking.

Vacqueyras was once a Côtes-du-Rhône-Villages, but it now has an appellation in its own right. The grape varieties are the same, the flavours warm and fruity, with perhaps a little more body. The nearby **Côtes du Ventoux** also compares with Côtes-du-Rhône, but is a little lighter; again, southern warmth prevails with a large helping of Grenache in the grape mix. For Côtes du Ventoux, try Domaine des Anges; whilst Jaboulet and Pascal both make good Vacqueyras, as does the village co-operative.

Gigondas, with vineyards dominated by the dramatic skyline of the Dentelles de Montmirail, is a lighter version of a Châteauneuf-du-Pape, with some warm, southern fruit. Domaine du Grand Montmirail and Domaine St-Gayan are reputable estates.

Côtes de Provence

Contrary to what its name might imply, this appellation covers a relatively small part of Provence, but with vineyards scattered over quite a wide area. They are mostly in the department of the Var, including the coastal region south of the Massif des Maures and a large area to the north of the mountains. On the west side, the **Côtes de Provence** are limited by the **Coteaux Varois**, a relatively recently created VDQS. Although pink wine accounts for a larger percentage of the appellation, red Côtes de Provence is an infinitely more interesting wine.

There have been moves to improve the blend of grape varieties allowed for both pink and red wine. The high-yielding Carignan used to be the principal variety, making some singularly dull and uninspiring wine. Nor did lengthy ageing in old oak barrels improve matters. The percentage of Carignan has now been significantly reduced, and replaced by Grenache, which makes some warm, fruity, full-bodied wine. However, it is Syrah and Cabernet Sauvignon that have attracted the most interest in the vineyards, with their role as improving grape varieties, although neither must exceed 30 per cent in the wine. Serious producers are adamant that they do not want to make a Provençal claret, but there is no doubt that a little Cabernet Sauvignon does wonders for the aroma, and provides backbone in a wine that has sometimes lacked structure. Syrah, although more commonly associated with the vineyards of the northern Rhône, is encroaching on the south and undeniably provides fruit and flavour, without detracting from the true character of the appellation.

All over the south of France, vinification methods are improving significantly – and Provence is no exception. Carbonic maceration is generally considered to have a beneficial effect on Carignan; it extracts fruit without too much tannin, and gives some warm vibrant flavours. Small oak barrels, as opposed to large casks, are another fashionable trend, and certainly benefit the wine, provided that care is taken that the oak does not dominate.

A good Côtes de Provence is not so different from a Côtes-du-Rhône. It may be a little meatier in character, but it has the same full-bodied warmth of the south. Good producers include the Vignerons du Presqu'Ile de St-Tropez, with their flagship estate, Château Pamplonne; Domaines Ott; a new up-and-coming estate; Domaine de la Courtade, on the island of Porquerolles; also Domaine de St-Baillon, Domaine Richeaume and Château Rimauresq.

Coteaux d'Aix-en-Provence

The nearby appellation of **Coteaux d'Aix-en-Provence**, with the sub-region of the **Coteaux des Baux**, is a more serious red wine appellation than Côtes de Provence. Its advantage, which seemed rather a slight at the time, was not to be made an appellation at the same time as the Côtes de Provence, in 1977. This, however, provoked a considerable improvement in the quality of the wines, with greater concentration on red wines – rewarded with an appellation in 1985. Indeed, the wines of the better producers of the area fit more comfortably into the next segment of the wheel.

As with Côtes de Provence, a considerable mixture of grape varieties is allowed – including Carignan, Cinsaut, Counoise, Grenache, Syrah, Mourvèdre and Cabernet Sauvignon. The maximum allowance of Carignan will be reduced to 30 per cent by 1995, while 40 per cent is the maximum for the other red varieties. However, not everyone conforms to the regulations. Indisputably, the best Coteaux d'Aix-en-Provence comes from vineyards at the foot of the Alpilles of les Baux, at Domaine de Trévallon, where Eloi Dürrbach obstinately refuses to plant any Grenache, but continues to make his wine from Cabernet Sauvignon and Syrah alone. The results are majestic, and the wine fits into the next segment. The wines of his neighbours around the Alpilles are softer and fruitier, with a higher percentage of Grenache and with the wonderful warm herbs of the south; wines like Mas de la Dame, Domaine des Terres Blanches, Domaine du Gourgonnier. Organic viticulture is widely practised here; the growers have a considerable advantage over colleagues from more northern climates, for the drying winds of the Mistral provide a wonderful anti-rot treatment.

Other good estates in the appellation include Château du Fonscolombe, whereas the estate that was once seen as the flagship of the appellation, Château du Vignelaure, has been through an unsatisfactory period, with changes of ownership. However, it has recently been bought by the Shivdasani family, which also owns Domaine du Galoupet in the the Côtes de Provence, so things may look up.

Other appellations of Provence provide winter-warming wines, although the red version of Cassis is not better than a rather undistinguished Côtes de Provence. The **Côtes du Lubéron**, produced from vineyards on the foothills of the Montagne du Lubéron, became an appellation in 1987 and is an area where tradition and innovation lie side by side. The Chancel family at Château Val Joanis made a considerable investment in its new estate, redesigning the contours of the landscape with bulldozers and diggers, replanting vineyards with experimental as well as traditional varieties, and installing the latest technology in the cellar. The wines are widely available, not only under the name of Château Val Joanis, but also as Domaine Chancel and Domaine des Blancs.

In contrast, the wines of Château la Canorgue are made on a much smaller scale, with more elementary equipment but with some good results. The Côtes du Lubéron adjoins the Côtes-du-Rhône, but the wines are a little lighter and more aromatic, but with the same southern warmth.

Côtes du Roussillon

On the other side of the French Mediterranean coast are the vineyards of **Côtes du Roussillon** and **Côtes du Roussillon-Villages**, with two named villages – Caramany and the poetic-sounding Latour de France. The reason that these two were singled out had more to do with commercial clout than quality. As throughout the Midi, the principal grape varieties are Carignan, Cinsaut and Grenache, with more recent plantings of Syrah and Mourvèdre. Carignan does better here in the sun-soaked arid hills of Roussillon than anywhere else in the Midi. None the less, it is generally accepted that it needs an additional boost of flavour from Syrah and Mourvèdre. There is not the same interest in Cabernet Sauvignon here as elsewhere in the Midi. Village co-operatives dominate the production of the appellation and their wines are usually marketed by one of the large growers' unions, such as the Vignerons Catalans.

There are some individual estates setting the pace in the appellation, such as Château de Jau, which has done good things, replanting vineyards and modernising equipment. Château de Corneilla is another leading estate whose wines are worth seeking out for their warm flavoursome fruit. Cazes Frères is another company working well for the appellation.

Fitou

The oldest appellation of this part of France is **Fitou**, dating back to 1948. Again, co-operatives dominate the production, although two individual estates of note are Château de Nouvelles and Château l'Espigne. The Vignerons du Val d'Orbieu had considerable success with their Madame Claude Parmentier label, which resulted in shortages and price rises, but things have now stabilised. The flavour of Fitou is solidly warm and rustic. The co-operative des Producteurs de Mont Tauch is one of the more innovative, making not only good Fitou, but also Corbières and Rivesaltes, with various levels of quality.

Nearby **Collioure**, with vineyards that are adjacent to those of Banyuls, also offers some warm southern fruit. In the hands of a meticulous producer like Alan Parcé it is indeed a serious wine with some stature as well as warm spice.

Corbières and Minervois

Further north, the twin appellations of **Corbières** and **Minervois** are enjoying renovations in vineyard and cellar. Both became appellations in 1985 and the grape varieties for each are similar, with Carignan, Cinsaut and Grenache forming the backbone of the wine. Some Syrah and possibly Mourvèdre may be added to give an extra injection of flavour as *cépages améliorateurs* (improving grape varieties). Growers who have Cabernet and Merlot in their vineyards here, use them, in theory, for vin de pays, but perhaps not always in practice.

The vineyards of Corbières lie on the first foothills of the Pyrenees, while those of Minervois are on the north side of the valley of the Aude, on the very first foothills of the Massif Central. Much depends on individual producers here. There are those who are making a great effort to improve the quality of their wine, reducing their yields, planting better grape varieties, and improving vinification methods in efficiently equipped cellars. There has been investment and interest from Bordeaux, from Peter Sichel in Domaine du Révérend and Bernadette Villars of Château Chasse-Spleen in the Château de Cabriac.

Both appellations cover quite large areas and there are moves towards further sub-divisions to recognise differences in microclimate and soil. However, in choosing the wine in the glass, it is the producer's name that counts. Good Corbières producers include Château les Ollieux, Château de Caraguilhes, Domaine de Fontsainte, Château de Cabriac, Domaine du Révérend, Château St-Auriol and Château de Lastours. For Minervois, try Domaine de Ste-Eulalie, Château de Paraza, Domaine Maris and Château de Gourgazaud. Although expensive, best of all is Clos Centeilles, which is stocked by Corney & Barrow and Adnams of Southwold.

Coteaux du Languedoc

Further east, the wines become progressively lighter until you reach Côtes-du-Rhône and Coteaux d'Aix-en-Provence. However, the **Coteaux du Languedoc** fits more happily into this segment than anywhere else. The wines may not quite have the weight of some of the others of the Midi, but the best do have a certain southern warmth. Several crus are included in the appellation – the best are **St-Chinian** and **Faugères**. Originally, they were appellations in their own right, but have since been incorporated into the larger appellation. There are both individual producers and co-operatives working well for their area, such as Cave de Berlou with its brand name Schisteil, Château Coujan, Gérard Alquier and the Château de Haut Fabrègues.

The other crus include **St-Georges d'Orques**, which is mainly produced by one go-ahead co-operative. Other good individual producers include the Prieuré de St-Jean de Bébian, just outside Pézenas, where Alain Roux grows all thirteen grape varieties of the appellation of Châteauneuf-du-Pape, as he claims that the soil in his vineyards is identical.

Italy

The islands and the south dominate Italy's input into this section.

Sardinia What the French call Grenache the Italians call Cannonau – grown, above all, in Sardinia, as **Cannonau di Sardegna**. Sometimes it is used to make a port-like dessert wine, but as a table wine it has some southern warmth and fruit, with a dry finish. Sella e Mosca are leading producers.

Sicily Sicily provides some sturdy warm flavours, not only from the widely available Corvo – which is the trading name of the Casa Vinicola Duca di Salaparuta – but also from other producers such as Rapitalà, Regaleali, COS (who make the DOC wine Cerasuola di Vittoria) and Donnafugata. The newest claim to fame in Sicily is Terre di Ginestra, which makes more exciting whites than reds. Its reds fit a little uneasily into this segment as they are relatively light, with a little spice and tannin. Corvo's latest introduction, Duca Enrico, is over-oaked and over-priced to match. Surprisingly, for a southern island, Sicily makes much better white than red wine.

Mezzogiorno On mainland Italy, many of the wines of the southern part of the country fit into this category. **Montepulciano d'Abruzzo** is a warm, rather earthy wine made from the Montepulciano grape, and has nothing to do with Vino Nobile. The leading producers are Valentini, Cornacchia, Illuminati, Casal Thaulero and Tollo.

Cirò, the principal DOC of Calabria, is a pretty hefty red wine, made from a little-known grape variety called Gaglioppo. It has the warmth and herbs of the south, with a rather dry earthy finish and alcoholic body; Librandi is the key producer.

Spain

Many of the red table wines of southern Spain fit into this segment too. The warm sunshine makes heady, alcoholic wines, which are then aged in large oak barrels for several months or longer. Take **Jumilla**, for example: a full-bodied alcoholic red wine from vineyards in the arid hills behind the town of Alicante in south-east Spain, made mainly from the grape variety Monastrell. Old-style Jumilla was kept for several months, if not years, in large oak vats, with the result that the fruit flavours tended to disappear and a rather dry, tarry, even oxidising, red wine was left. High alcohol was its dominant characteristic. But there has now been a gradual change in the winemaking, so that Jumilla has become just a little lighter in body, with a little more fruit, while still retaining its southern warmth.

Good producers include Ascensio Carcelén, Bodegas Juvinsa, Señorio del Condestable and the San Isidro co-operative. Vintages are of little significance. Other wines from the south of Spain also appear occasionally on our shelves, such as the adjoining DOs of **Yecla, Almansa, Utiel Requeña**, as well as **Valdepeñas**, which is a hilly enclave in the vast plains of La Mancha. The red wine of the latter has improved considerably over the last few years, benefiting from better winemaking techniques. The main grape variety is Cencibel (the Tempranillo of Rioja); when aged in oak for a few months, it provides some ripe flavours, with a hint of southern warmth and a mellow fruitiness. Thus, Valdepeñas straddles two segments of the taste wheel. The leading producer is Bodegas Felix Solis, under the brand name Viña Albali, a wine which offers some delicious good-value drinking.

Two other Spanish wines fit into this segment. The first is **Priorato** in southern Catalonia, a full-bodied gutsy red wine made from Cariñena and Garnacha, with some liquorice spice and an alcoholic finish. Masia Barril is the estate to follow. The other wine to look out for is **Lar de Barros**, from Tierra de Barros, an aspiring DO to the west of La Mancha, which has some warm fruit, a hint of vanilla and some gamey overtones.

Portugal

Some of the table wines of Portugal have a warmth about them that brings them into this category. Mention has already been made of Arruda and the Douro, as well as leading producers, such as J M da Fonseca and João Pires, in the medium structure segment. However, some of these wines could also fit equally well into this segment. Periquita, for example, has both structure and warmth, while Tinta da Anfora from João Pires is a warm, rugged red. Other wines from southern Portugal are beginning to appear. The co-operative of Borba in the Alentejo has begun to improve winemaking techniques significantly and now produces some acceptable wines. In some instances the winemaking leaves much to be desired, but at best there are some warm, spicy flavours.

Lebanon

Château Musar is virtually the only estate of the war-damaged Lebanon. The wine is produced with considerable determination by Serge Hochar, who trained at Bordeaux university and planted Cabernet Sauvignon as the main grape variety of his vineyards. Vinification methods follow those of Bordeaux, with ageing in small barrels, and yet the wines have a warmth and spiciness that has more in common with the south of France than with Bordeaux. The Cabernet is blended with some Syrah and Cinsaut, but not too much, and results in some warm, meaty flavours. Musar tends to release its wines when they are ready for drinking; the 1983 is the current vintage, which is drinking beautifully.

Greece

Although the Greek wine scene is still dominated by Retsina, there are a growing number of wineries producing wines with flavour and individuality. Domaine Carras, made from the indigenous Limnio grape, is warm and spicy, with a Rhônish quality to it; while Château Carras, made in the Côtes de Meliton from a Bordeaux blend, based on Cabernet Sauvignon, has established a reputation for its red wines and would fit more comfortably into the medium structure segment of the taste wheel. But it is the exception among Greek wines. Semeli, another up-and-coming estate, makes red Nemea, with some warm, raisiny fruit from the Agiorgitiko grape. Another full-bodied Greek wine is Naoussa, from the Xynomavro grape.

Cyprus

Othello is the standard Cypriot red wine that UK buyers are most likely to encounter. It is produced by Keo, one of the large co-operatives that dominate the island's wine production. The grapes are a blend of indigenous island varieties like Mavron and Ophthalmo, grown in the arid foothills of the Troodos mountains. In summer, temperatures can be searingly hot and this can be tasted in the wine, with its dry, tarry flavour and warm alcoholic finish.

Other wines from Cyprus include the brands from other co-operatives, like Afames, Domaine d'Ahéra and one private estate, Laona, where efforts are being made to improve vinification methods, especially on a smaller, more individual scale. Vintage variations are insignificant.

Macedonia

At the time of writing, the country that was once Yugoslavia is currently beset by civil strife, with trade sanctions in force against Serbia. However, its best-known wine, Lutomer Laski Rizling, comes from Slovenia, which remains unaffected by the unrest. Macedonia, too, is untroubled, and that is one of the sources of **Vranac**, which is sold as a varietal wine and provides originality. Vranac makes full-bodied, warm, robust red wine that is quite high in alcohol, with some southern warmth, which is characteristic of the southern Rhône. Sometimes there is a slight bitterness on the finish, not unlike some of the southern Italian reds. Vintages do not vary.

There are also examples of French grape varieties, like Merlot and Cabernet Sauvignon, from Slovenia. Otherwise, some of the more individual grapes and flavours, like Postup, Prosek and Dingac, come from the Dalmatian coast and are currently unobtainable.

Mexico

A postscript to this section is a newcomer to our wine shelves, **Petite Sirah** from Mexico. It is no relation at all to Syrah, but is the little-known Durif of France, although it has virtually disappeared from French vineyards. However, in California it is grown quite extensively as Petite Sirah and has travelled south into Mexico. An example from L A Cetto provides some ripe brambly fruit, with a hint of spice, some tannin and a warm finish.

RICH AND SPICY (FULL BODY, AGE, HIGH TANNIN)

This section covers full-bodied, rich spicy wines with tannin and ageing potential, wines like the 1990 **Rhônes**, which epitomise, above all, the characteristics of this segment of the wheel. This is especially true of the northern Rhônes – the appellations of Côte Rôtie, Hermitage and Cornas, whose wines are made from the Syrah grape, which is redolent of spice. Young Syrah is deep-coloured, rich and peppery, intense and full-bodied, with the ability to age into more elegant wines; the blackcurrant gums and peppery aromas of its youth develop into more meaty flavours with maturity. The Rhône Valley has been blessed with an incredible run of vintages – 1988, 1989, 1990 – and even 1991, decried in most other parts of France, has produced some superlative wines.

Côte Rôtie

The most northern of the Rhône appellations is **Côte Rôtie**, which literally means the roasted slope. The vines are grown on steeply terraced hillsides behind the town of Vienne, but recently have also been allowed to spread on to the less favourable plateau behind. Syrah is the main grape variety, but it is sometimes softened by a little Viognier, 10 per cent at the most. The flavours, from the best growers, are always rich and concentrated, demanding several years of bottle ageing and, although the wines spend several months in cask in the cellar, oak is not immediately apparent to the taste buds.

1990 was a difficult year in Côte Rôtie; many of the vines suffered from problems linked to the extensive drought, so a careful selection is essential. Some growers, such as Jamet, have made truly great wine. The 1989 is also very good, with more consistent quality. Other good producers include Chapoutier, Jaboulet, Guigal, Barge, Champet, Gentaz and Jasmin.

Hermitage

Hermitage is the next red appellation down the valley. It too is made from Syrah, which in this instance can be softened with a little Rousanne and Marsanne. Tightly knit, concentrated blackcurrant is the key to Syrah – not the ripe juicy fruit of Cabernet Sauvignon, but the rubbery flavour of fruit gums, with masses of pepper and tannin. Young Hermitage is a solid mouth-puckering wine that requires several years of ageing, at least five for a light vintage and a minimum of ten for a good vintage, to soften it out into a wonderfully spicy bottle, with liquorice fruit and herbs.

Gérard Chave remains the star of the appellation, producing serious and long-lasting wines. He is, however, challenged by others, such as Sorrel and Grippat, as well as two *négociants*, Jaboulet (with Hermitage la Chapelle) and Chapoutier. Vintages to lay down include 1990, 1989 and 1988, while 1986 and 1983 are just beginning to drink well. 1985 is still too young.

Sadly, the peripheral appellation of **Crozes-Hermitage** is often no more than a shadow of the main appellation, for the vineyard area has been extended to include land that is not really worthy of the appellation. At worst it is barely distinguishable from a Côtes-du-Rhône, but at best – and there are some good wines – it can provide satisfyingly spicy fruit, and in a more accessible form than Hermitage itself. The wines are softer, with less stature, but still with enough tannin in their youth to merit ageing. For example, Jaboulet's 1983 Domaine Thalabert was just reaching its peak in the summer of 1992. Other good producers include Desmeure, Pochon at Château de Curson, Fayolle, Graillot and Chapoutier.

St-Joseph

St-Joseph is another northern Rhône appellation that can vary considerably in quality. Sometimes it has little more depth than a Côtes-du-Rhône, but in the hands of a producer like Dr Emile Florentin from Clos de l'Arbalestrier, it takes on a different stature. This is winemaking at its most traditional and meticulous. The

1990 vintage is packed with flavour and will not be ready for drinking for years. Other reliable producers include Chapoutier, Grippat and Coursodin.

Cornas

Cornas is the other great red appellation of the northern Rhône. In some respects it is very similar to nearby Hermitage, with vineyards of Syrah on steep, granite hillsides. There is the same rich, blackcurrant gum fruit in early youth which will develop into complex, elegant, meaty bottles with maturity. Thierry Allemande is a young grower in the appellation, with just two hectares in the best sites. His 1990 Vieilles Vignes can only be described as monumental, with intense fruit and considerable structure. Noël Verset is another serious producer, as are Auguste Clape, de Barjac, Juge, Michel and Voge.

Châteauneuf-du-Pape

Châteauneuf-du-Pape is the principal appellation of the southern Rhône. Unlike the northern half of the valley, with its concentration on just one grape variety, here there may be as many as thirteen used, but in practice the most common varieties are Syrah (as in the north), as well as Grenache and Mourvèdre. While Syrah gives spice, and Mourvèdre weight and backbone, Grenache provides ripe fruit and alcohol. Indeed, the minimum alcohol level is a heady 12.5 per cent (sometimes significantly higher). You only have to see the huge stones in the vineyards in the heart of the appellation – that reflect heat on the ripening grapes in the height of summer, and retain warmth during the cooler nights – to appreciate how Châteauneuf-du-Pape can be as rich and full-bodied as it is. However, as Grenache does not have the staying power of Syrah and Mourvèdre, the wines soften earlier than those of the north.

There is a perfumed scent in good Châteauneuf-du-Pape, with wines redolent of the herbs and spices of the south – the thyme, lavender and rosemary that defined the original vineyard area. Sadly, there have been less than conscientious producers who have been content to dilute the flavours of their wine, making anaemic Châteauneuf-du-Pape that is not worthy of the appellation. But, in the right hands, it is a rich, full-flavoured wine with tannin, requiring some years of bottle age to reach maturity, especially in good vintages like the 1990 (truly great in the southern Rhône), which is comparable to the fabulous 1961.

Leading estates include Château de Beaucastel, Clos des Papes, Château Rayas, Vieux Télégraphe and Château Fortia. The vintages of the mid-eighties, 1986, 1985 and 1983, are drinking well now.

Bandol

Bandol is a rich spicy red wine from the terraced vineyards behind the eponymous Mediterranean port. Serious Bandol is red (there are white and pink Bandol too, but they are of infinitely less significance). It has something in common with the southern Rhône, a certain warmth as well as a distinctly meaty quality, from the Mourvèdre grape, which must account for a considerable percentage of the wine. The appellation laws dictate a minimum of 50 per cent, but serious growers are using even more. Eighteen months' oak-ageing in large oak casks is mandatory and the result is some wonderful rich wine, with meaty complex flavours, animal overtones and a firm backbone of tannin.

Domaine Tempier is the star producer, for its owner, Lucien Peyraud, did much to resurrect a flagging appellation. Domaine du Pibarnon is serious in stature, while other slightly softer, more accessible wines include those of the Bunan family at Mas de la Rouvière and Moulin des Costes, as well as Domaine de Terrebrune and Château Vannières. Vintages tend to follow those of the southern Rhône.

Palette

The tiny appellation of **Palette** deserves a passing mention in this segment. This is one of the smallest appellations of France, situated just outside the enchanting town of Aix-en-Provence. There is just one serious producer, Château Simone, whose red wines are made from an extraordinary mixture of grape varieties – the classic Mourvèdre, Grenache and Cinsaut, as well as other relatively unknown Provençal varieties. Methods here are firmly traditional, resulting in some structured, meaty wines, with the spices of the south, that merit some bottle age.

Coteaux d'Aix-en-Provence

Undeniably, the best red wine of the appellation of **Coteaux d'Aix-en-Provence** fits firmly into this segment, rather than with the wines of the rest of the appellation. Eloi Dürrbach at Domaine de Trévallon breaks the rules by refusing to plant the necessary small percentage of Grenache that is required to make his wine a true Coteaux d'Aix-en-Provence. He persists with a highly successful blend of Cabernet Sauvignon and Syrah, which is aged in small oak barrels, to make one of the most individual wines of Provence.

California Syrah

Syrah, or Shiraz, from other parts of the world also fits into this segment. Over the last few years California has seen an increasing trend of growers intent on trying to perfect Syrah and Mourvèdre: Cabernet Sauvignon is deemed to be boring; everyone else is growing it all over the world, so Syrah (not to be confused with the Californian grape Petite Sirah) and Mourvèdre present a much more exciting challenge. The group of wineries in question have been dubbed the Rhône Rangers; Qupé, Jade Mountain, Ojai and Bonny Doon are the leaders in the British market. They follow the vinification methods of the Rhône Valley, with long maceration periods and oak-ageing. Bonny Doon is known for using flamboyant names: Le Cigar Volant – the French for flying saucer – refers to an occasion in 1954 when the village council of Châteauneuf-du-Pape issued an ordinance to forbid the landing of flying saucers in the vineyards of the village. The back label tells all and, appropriately, the wine is a classic Châteauneuf-du-Pape blend of more or less equal parts of Grenache and Mourvèdre, with a little Syrah, while Ca' del Solo Big House Red has different proportions of the same grape varieties and is a little lighter in body. Jade Mountain makes pure Mourvèdre, while Qupé Syrah, from the Central Coast, has good blackcurrant gum spice, as does Ojai, with some sturdy fruit.

California Zinfandel

Zinfandel is the one California grape variety that is not obviously borrowed from the Old World. It may be the Primitivo of southern Italy – cuttings of which were brought to north America by Agoston Haraszthy, the Hungarian nobleman who did so much for the blossoming wine industry – but this theory is unsubstantiated. A hundred or so years later, Zinfandel has acquired its own individuality.

Zinfandel is eminently versatile. It can make all manner of wines, from pink blush, often labelled White Zinfandel, through light, fruity Beaujolais taste-alikes and jug wines to medium-bodied reds and more heady, alcoholic and tannic wines. It can even be used for fortified wine, with pretensions towards ruby port. It is an easy grape to grow and a generally undemanding vine in the vineyard, although it can ripen unevenly; in the cellar, versatility is the name of the game. As a result, it is often taken for granted and rarely given the serious treatment it deserves.

However, when Zinfandel is given due consideration, with low yields from a coolish vineyard, careful vinification and some oak-ageing, the resulting wine is rich and individual. At its best, Zinfandel has ripe berry flavours, with a substantial amount of tannin and some meaty, liquorice and spicy fruit that is not so different from Syrah. Good Zinfandel is mouth-filling, with weight and concentration.

Ridge is generally considered to make the best Zinfandel, with individual vineyard names like Paso Robles and Geyserville. Other good producers include Frog's Leap Wine Cellars, Lytton Springs and Sutter Home.

Outside California, there is the odd example: notably in Australia, from David Hohnen at Cape Mentelle in Western Australia, as well as the occasional Zinfandel from South Africa. However, neither travels much as yet and so our perception of Zinfandel remains firmly Californian.

Australian Shiraz

What the French call Syrah is called Shiraz in Australia. The grape variety is identical and the taste can be very similar too. Shiraz grows all over the continent, from the warm vineyards of the Hunter Valley of New South Wales, to the cooler regions of Victoria and South Australia. Like Zinfandel in California, it can be exceedingly versatile in flavour, ranging from the light fruity wines that are more like young Beaujolais, to substantial, full-bodied wines with depth and flavour. The best of these is indisputably Grange – formerly called Grange Hermitage – which was created by the talented Max Schubert, the winemaker of Penfolds, back in the 1950s. Grange demonstrates just how good an Australian Shiraz can be. It is a wine that is comparable in stature, if not exactly in flavour, to some of the great Syrahs of Hermitage.

Young Shiraz has the characteristic nose and palate of blackcurrant gums, the hallmark of all good Shiraz; sometimes there is an almost sweet, minty eucalyptus taste that is typical of some New World Shiraz. A good example will be deep in colour, with masses of fruit and tannin, really packing a punch of flavour, with a long finish.

Cabernet Sauvignon is sometimes blended with Shiraz, or vice versa, and the Cabernet generally adds some elegance and more subtle blackcurrant fruit. Much, however, depends upon the producer's individual style.

Grange is expensive, but deserves to be. Luckily, Penfolds produces other good, but more price-friendly Shiraz, such as Kalimna Shiraz Bin 28. Other serious producers of Shiraz include

David Wynn, Bannockburn Vineyards, Henschke, Peppertree Vineyard, Plantagenet, Rouge Homme, Rothbury, Montrose, Kies Estate and Cape Mentelle.

Italy

The sole example of **Syrah** in central Italy is from Paolo de Marchi of the Chianti estate, Isole e Olena. He originally planted vine cuttings, obtained from Guigal, as an alternative to Cabernet Sauvignon, to boost the flavour of his Chianti. He now makes a pure varietal, under the Collezzione dei Marchi label, with some ripe spicy fruit; it is good, but expensive.

Another Italian oddity which may just fit into this category is **Sagrantino di Montefalco**, and the even more individual **Sagrantino passito**. Sagrantino is a peculiarly Umbrian grape variety, grown particularly around the village of Montefalco, which has a spicy, bitter-sweet, berry fruit flavour. Alternatively, the grapes are dried, in a process that the Italians call *passito*, to make a richer, port-like wine that is usually drunk as a dessert wine. It is an interesting curiosity.

Valpolicella

Italy's best-known red wine, after Chianti, features at both ends of the taste spectrum. Everyday **Valpolicella** is light and fruity, while serious Valpolicella is quite a different animal. There are two vinification processes that transform its flavour and character. Look for **Recioto** or **Amarone** on the label. Recioto means that the wine has been made from grapes that are left to dry and dehydrate so that the juice becomes rich and concentrated. If the subsequent fermentation is stopped before all the sugar has turned to alcohol, the wine will be sweet and rich. If, on the other hand, it is fermented until it is completely dry, it takes on an entirely different stature, with a rich, concentrated flavour, reminiscent of sour cherries and plums with meaty, smoky overtones. In this instance it is called Amarone de la Valpolicella.

Another way of obtaining additional flavour in Valpolicella is a technique called *ripasso*, where the fermenting juice is put into a vat containing the lees of the previous year's Recioto. This adds fruit and intensity to the young wine, as well as structure and tannin. A ripasso wine is quite different from everyday Valpolicella – it has a deep colour, a ripe nose of plums and cherries with, on the palate, tannin and plenty of rich cherry fruit, as well as spice. The taste is rich rather than sweet. Unfortunately, the bureaucrats of the EC forbid the use of the word ripasso on a DOC wine, though not on a vino da tavola, with the result that it is impossible to identify a ripasso Valpolicella. Masi's Campo Fiorin is the best-known example, for it is labelled as a table wine.

Try also Allegrini, Le Ragose, Quintarelli (who makes some of the most individual wines of the DOC), Serego Alighieri, and Tedeschi's Capitel San Rocco (which is another table wine), plus Boscaini's Le Canne, Santi's Castello d'Illasi and Bolla's Jago. The price is considerably higher than basic Valpolicella, but that is more than compensated for by additional flavour. Particularly good recent vintages in the Veneto were 1990 and 1988.

STRUCTURED HEAVYWEIGHTS (FULL BODY, AGE, HIGH TANNIN)

This segment covers the very biggest wines, mainly from France, Australia, California and Italy. We begin with Bordeaux.

Claret

The best **classed-growth claret** is the epitome of this segment. The blending of Cabernet Sauvignon, Cabernet Franc and Merlot in varying proportions –perhaps with a little Malbec and Petit Verdot – makes wines of great distinction and style. It is these wines that winemakers all over the world aspire to emulate with their own Cabernet Sauvignon and Bordeaux blends, and now do so with increasing success. However, there is a certain indefinable quality to fine claret which makes it arguably the greatest of all red wines. Advocates of red burgundy will disagree, for it is true that when red burgundy is great, it is truly sublime, but top-quality Bordeaux has a very much lower disappointment rate than supposedly fine burgundy. Claret in its youth is rich and intense in fruit, flavour and tannin. It requires at least 18 months in small oak barrels, probably a high proportion of them new oak – if not entirely new oak in the most prestigious châteaux – to soften the tannins, followed by several years of bottle age before the wine becomes an enjoyable drink.

Cabernet Sauvignon always makes a deep-coloured wine, which allows for development with maturity so that it gradually acquires a delicate brick-orange rim. Blackcurrant is the main aroma, often tempered with the vanilla or the toasted character of new oak. In its youth, a good claret is mouth-puckeringly tannic: it needs to be if it is to develop in the bottle for 20 years, or perhaps more. There is some intense blackcurrant fruit on the palate, which mellows into softer fruit flavours and more elegant cedarwood subtlety.

The differences between the various village appellations of Bordeaux can be hard to define; perhaps **St-Estèphe** may be more austere, **Pauillac** more opulent, **St-Julien** more elegant, while **Margaux** comes somewhere between. **Pomerol** and **St-Emilion** are richer and plummier, with a higher percentage of Merlot and Cabernet Franc, while the **Graves** has the distinctive *goût de terroir* of the appellation.

As we go to press in the summer of 1992, the Bordeaux market is not in a happy state. Whereas previous years have seen a flood of *en primeur* offers, with excitement at the opening prices of the big names, this year things have been decidedly quiet. The first growths have announced their opening prices for the 1991 vintage at 30 per cent below the 1990 average; after a run of three good vintages in Bordeaux, 1991 is a difficult year. Spring frosts caused considerable damage and conditions were generally problematic throughout the summer, with rain during the vintage.

While 1989 was seen as a great vintage almost before the grapes were picked, 1990 enjoyed less hype and is now being re-evaluated as perhaps a potentially finer vintage than 1989. *En primeur* prices were lower for 1990 than 1989, and these may well increase as the economic situation improves. For those wishing to buy claret for laying down, 1990 would be the choice. However, for a relatively inexpensive, enjoyable glass of wine for current drinking, the wines of the 1987 vintage from St-Emilion and Pomerol are the ones to consider. The 1987 vintage was a better year for Merlot, while Cabernet Sauvignon in the Médoc was rather diluted. The 1983s are more forward than 1982s and are beginning to make enjoyable bottles, as are the 1985s from lighter châteaux. Generally, 1985s are better in St-Emilion and Pomerol, while 1986s are more successful in the Médoc.

It is difficult to recommend estates in this category. There are the great names of the 1855 classification, which have the prestige of fine claret. But there are other estates which, for one reason or another, are not included and deserve to be, such as d'Angludet and Chasse-Spleen. Reputations come and go: currently Montrose is improving; so is Baron Pichon-Lalande, after some considerable investment by its new owners. Rausan-Ségla has also been enjoying a revival in its fortunes. Other good wines from the Médoc include Palmer, Beychevelle, Grand-Puy-Lacoste, Léoville-Las Cases, Léoville-Barton, Langoa-Barton, Ducru-Beaucaillou and Lynch-Bages, and on the right bank, Pavie, Trottevieille, Figeac and Magdeleine.

Mas de Daumas Gassac

The other French example appropriate to this segment is a unique vin de pays from the Hérault, **Mas de Daumas Gassac**, which has excited over the years an enormous amount of interest and has been given such epithets as the Lafite of the Languedoc. That may be rather far-fetched, but there is no doubt that, for a mere vin de pays, it has a stature and weight quite outside its class. The principal grape variety is Cabernet Sauvignon, grown in unusual glacial soil; the renowned Professor Peynaud advised on vinification methods and his advice has been strictly followed. The result is undeniably very bordelais in character, a wine that improves both in the bottle, and with every vintage, as the vines themselves age. The current available vintage is the 1989 and, at around £15 a bottle, the price has more in common with classed-growth claret than a vin de pays.

Australia and California

Winemakers in Australia and California see classed-growth claret as the standard towards which they strive with their Cabernet Sauvignon. Some are near to success. Cabernet Sauvignon grows easily all over Australia, from the warm vineyards of the Hunter Valley and Mudgee to Western Australia. However, it is in cooler Coonawarra, with its famous terra rossa – the iron-red soil – that Cabernet Sauvignon really excels. The wines have a richness, but with perhaps less elegance than Bordeaux, with plenty of soft tannins to allow for ageing, although probably not for as long as the finest clarets.

Great **Australian** producers of Cabernet Sauvignon include Wynns with the John Riddoch label, Katnook Estate, Lindemans St-George, Rouge Homme and Petaluma in Coonawarra, while the best of recent vintages are 1990, 1988 and 1986. From elsewhere on this vast continent try Henschke, Yarra Yering, Cape Mentelle, Montrose Wines, Tim Knappstein, Hungerford Hill, Rothbury, Rosemount, Penfolds, Chittering Estate and Parker Estate.

The trend in **California** is now towards more subtle flavours. Where once California Cabernet Sauvignon had instant appeal, leaping out of the glass to greet you, it is now more reticent in its approach. The climate is generally warmer than in Bordeaux, which produces some rich, ripe blackcurrant fruit, with plenty of tannin, and sometimes some herbaceous minty overtones, as in Joseph Heitz Martha's Vineyard.

One of the main differences from Bordeaux, and this applies to Australia too, is that less attention is paid to the precise provenance of the grapes: wineries in both California and Australia think nothing of trucking grapes across states in refrigerated containers to blend them with grapes from other vineyards. While California does have the elements of an appellation system, in the form of the Authorised Vineyard Areas or AVAs – of which there are now close to a hundred – this is purely an indication of provenance, with no quality tag attached to it. The choice of a wine depends very much upon the winery name on the label.

The Rutherford Bench, in the Napa Valley, is generally deemed to produce some of the best California Cabernet Sauvignons. It includes wineries which have established a particular reputation for that grape variety, notably Robert Mondavi, Heitz, Joseph Phelps and Freemark Abbey. Opus One is the result of a joint venture between Robert Mondavi and Baron Philippe of Château Mouton-Rothschild, while Dominus takes advantage of the expertise of Christian Moueix of Pétrus fame. Clos du Val, Simi, Beaulieu Vineyards, Stag's Leap and Newton are other names to look for.

Italy

The one other place where Cabernet Sauvignon really excels, and where wines of comparable stature to classed-growth claret are made, is Tuscany – but more often than not it is blended with that very Tuscan grape variety, Sangiovese.

Sassicaia and Tignanello were the pacesetters here. The Marchese Niccolò Incisa della Rochetta planted Cabernet Sauvignon, with a little Cabernet Franc, on his estate in Bolgheri, close to the Tuscan coast, for no other reason than that he liked the taste of claret and wanted to make his own. For several years **Sassicaia** was produced by Giacomo Tachis, the talented oenologist from Antinori, who thereby gained the experience of the first small Bordeaux *barriques* to be used in Tuscany. At the end of the 1960s, Tuscan viticulture was in a sorry state, without reputation or standing. Antinori, among others, decided that something had to be done and **Tignanello** was created, intended as a wine with international appeal, but with a Tuscan flavour. The main grape variety is Sangiovese, but with a fluctuating percentage of Cabernet Sauvignon, and the method is that of Bordeaux, with ageing in small oak barrels, which are regularly replaced. The impact was immediate, following in the wake of the success of the 1968 Sassicaia which brought the wine to the attention of the world's wine connoisseurs. However, it was Tignanello that really showed just what could be achieved with

Sangiovese if it was vinified properly, with Cabernet Sauvignon used to add a little extra body and structure.

Numerous others have followed the example. Tuscany is now awash with expensive designer bottles, adorned with appropriate labels. Sometimes the contents are superb; sometimes they leave much to be desired. It is not enough to put an indifferent wine into new oak barrels for a few months in the hope of turning it into something exceptional – you have to start in the vineyard and that is what the better Tuscan producers have realised. A man like Paolo de Marchi at Isole e Olena is working hard on improving the overall quality of his Sangiovese, seen at its best in his vino da tavola Cepparello (see also the medium structure segment). This wine takes the place of a riserva Chianti, but cannot be called Chianti because it breaks the rules by being pure Sangiovese. De Marchi is working on Cabernet Sauvignon, too, but it is Sangiovese which excites him most.

The Italian wine law is such that these wines, many of them the best that an estate produces, do not conform to the regulations so must remain classed as supposedly inferior vini da tavola, or what are sometimes called Super Tuscans or alternative wines. The Predicato system, which has been developed by a handful of the larger companies, attempts to give them some form of order, but in fact has a very limited acceptance. To read a Tuscan wine list, you virtually need a specialised glossary.

However, among the vini da tavola which fit into this segment, try Sassicaia, Tignanello, Ornellaia, Balifico, Cepparello, Coltassala, Elegia, Fontalloro, Montesodi, Le Pergole Torte, Rancia, Sammarco and Vinattieri. They may include some Cabernet Sauvignon or not. None are cheap, but they are amongst the best that Tuscany has to offer.

There are plantings of Cabernet Sauvignon in other parts of Italy too, with the quality attaining the same level as some of the Super Tuscans. Angelo Gaja, of Barbaresco fame, is achieving successful flavours with Darmagi. As an illustration of the idiosyncrasy of nomenclature of these alternative wines in Italy, Darmagi (what a shame!) was his father's comment on seeing one of the better vineyard sites of the family estate planted with Cabernet Sauvignon rather than Nebbiolo. The wine is, however, impressive, with an impressive price to match.

Brunello di Montalcino Brunello di Montalcino has been discussed in some detail under the medium structure segment but, in fact, it is a borderline wine and several of the better Brunellos di Montalcino come within the structured high tannic category. Sometimes there is little difference between a Brunello and a pure Sangiovese vino da tavola, possibly only in the ageing process. Usually the vino da tavola has been in small new Bordeaux *barriques*, while the Brunello must spend three years in the traditonal large *botti* of Slavonic oak. The difference is apparent on the palate. Depending on the producer, the body varies between medium and full; usually a good Brunello di Montalcino is quite full-bodied in its youth, but matures into a wine with more elegance, sometimes something akin to a St-Julien.

Barolo Barolo is the great red wine of northern Italy. It is produced in vineyards around the village of the same name in the Langhe hills, south-east of the town of Alba. The tough-skinned Nebbiolo grape is the sole variety, producing wines that are high in tannin, extract and acidity. In the right hands, the results can be amongst the best that Italy has to offer, but Nebbiolo is not always easy to vinify. Long fermentation, adding even more extract and tannin, means that the wine requires a long ageing period in wood even to begin to soften. This is the traditional style of Barolo, with maturation in large Slavonic oak barrels which may even be 100 years old. The modern trend, however, is towards something softer and more accessible, with subtle changes in vinification, a short period of maceration and more bottle- rather than barrel-ageing. None the less, Barolo is still required by DOCG regulations to spend a minimum of two years in wood, plus another one in vat before sale. Riserva on the label indicates four years of ageing, and riserva speciale five years.

In its youth, Barolo is tough and unyielding, a sturdy, structured wine with masses of colour, tannin, acidity and extract. The harsh tannin is tempered by some fruit, liquorice and prunes, but still leaves an underlying austerity, with a dry tarry finish. However, this initially unapproachable quality is what turns Barolo into great wine when it is ten, if not twenty, years old. With age, it mellows, developing a rich nose that is reminiscent of Christmas cake, with a wonderful fruity, cinnamon and nutmeg taste on the palate. Some associate it with truffles, for Piedmont is the home of some of the finest white truffles; others talk of violets. There is no doubt that it is a serious, attention-demanding glass of wine. Great Barolo can be sublime, but to some it is very definitely an acquired taste.

Good producers include Aldo Conterno, Giacomo Conterno, Mascarello, Altare, Cavalotto, Ceretto, Pio Cesare, Ratti, Prunotto, Vietti. The best recent vintages include 1990, 1989, 1988, 1986, 1985 and 1982.

Barbaresco In comparison with Barolo, Barbaresco, the second long-standing DOCG wine of Piedmont, is more accessible. It too is made purely from Nebbiolo, grown in vineyards around the village of the same name. The clue to the difference lies in the soil, which is much lighter than that of Barolo and makes a less substantial wine. Consequently, Barbaresco requires a shorter ageing period – two years in barrels and bottle, three years for a riserva and four for a riserva speciale.

Like Barolo, Barbaresco is tough and unyielding in its youth, though it is perhaps the less aggressively tannic of the two. The wine is still intense, with plenty of extract. With ageing it develops some lovely aromas of rich fruit-cake, liquorice, prunes and raspberries and, with increasing maturity, it can take on almost burgundian overtones, some vegetal sweetness, but never loses the firm tannic backbone.

Like Barolo, Barbaresco has enjoyed a similar run of good vintages. The key producers are Gaja, making good, but expensive, wine, Marchesi de Gresy, Bruno Giacosa, and some of the leading Barolo producers, such as Pio Cesare, Rinaldi, Ceretto, Oddero and Mascarello.

There are a handful of wines from southern Italy that have the same tannic, sturdy character, with structure and backbone. Aglianico is the grape variety responsible, sometimes described as the Nebbiolo of the south, with a similar tannic character, as well as acidity and extract. It is at its best in the dramatic-sounding wine of the Basilicata, **Aglianico del Vulture**, the Vulture being an extinct volcano. This is a DOC of growing interest, as vinification methods improve. Fratelli d'Angelo is the best producer, followed by Paternoster and Sasso.

Aglianico is also the grape variety of **Taurasi**, a DOC from Campania, produced mainly by the leaders of the region, Mastroberardino. Like young Barolo and Barbaresco, young Taurasi can disappoint: bottles should be stored away and forgotten about for at least five, if not ten, years.

Portugal

Some sturdy, tannic examples of Dão and Bairrada could also creep into this segment of the wheel, but have been discussed at greater length under the medium structure segment, which is where they sit most comfortably.

FORTIFIED WINES

All the wines in this wheel (see inside back cover) have one thing in common: the addition of grape brandy has featured at some stage during the production process. Although the precise moment when the brandy is added may vary from wine to wine, its use always accounts for the higher level of alcohol, taking the wine above the 15 per cent that generally constitutes the highest alcohol level in a table wine.

The range of flavours of fortified wines is as rich and varied as with table wines, from light and elegant to rich and luscious, and everything in between. Some are aged, in some instances for many years; others are best drunk in early youth. The appropriate moment to drink them varies too: some make excellent aperitifs; others are very much better after a meal, or make delicious pudding wines.

DRY AND LIGHT

Fino sherry

Fino sherry is a highly underrated aperitif in Britain. Its austere tang is the perfect foil for the mouth-watering range of tapas eaten in its native Spain – olives, roasted almonds, chorizo sausage and other more exotic flavours. One of the reasons for the immense drinkability of fino sherry on its home ground may be that it is not fortified to the same extent for consumption in Spain itself, so that it is only marginally more alcoholic than a table wine. Also, it may well be much fresher and therefore more appealing – the problem with fino is that it begins to lose its freshness the moment it is bottled, and the time-lag between bottling in Jerez and consumption in Britain may amount to several weeks, if not months. The only solution is to be sure to buy your fino from a wine shop with a fast turnover, not from an emporium where it has gathered dust on the shelves. Consider, too, the advantage of a half-bottle, which provides a generous glass, and maybe a top-up, for three or four people at one time.

Good fino sherry should be pale in colour and light in body, absolutely bone dry, with a firm, almost austerely dry finish. It should never be heavy or clumsy. The flavour depends upon the development in cask of a film of yeast, called flor, which looks rather like a veil of cotton wool and accounts for the distinctive taste. Contrary to most winemaking practice, oxidation through contact with the air plays an essential part in the development of a good fino. As with all sherry, a period of ageing in a *solera* system is an important part of the production process. A *solera* consists of a series of tiers, or scales, of sherry barrels containing the same wine, with each tier being younger than the one below. As the wine is drawn off from the oldest barrels for bottling they are refreshed with a slightly younger wine, and so on up the tiers, and the youngest tier is replenished by a wine that has not yet been aged at all. The *solera* system depends upon the fact that the younger wine takes on the characteristics of the older wines.

Most fino sherry is sold by the large sherry bodegas under brand names like Garvey's San Patricio, Gonzalez Byass' Tio Pepe and Domecq's La Ina. Finos from Lustau and Don Zoilo are good, and look out too for Waitrose's own-label fino in half-bottles.

Manzanilla

Manzanilla is very similar to fino sherry, but with an extra distinctive nuance of flavour, a firm salty tang, that is not found in fino. This salty characteristic is said to originate from its maturation by the sea; it is matured in barrels in the warehouses of the port of Sanlúcar de Barrameda. Good manzanillas, from the large sherry bodegas, include Hidalgo's La Gitana, Barbadillo and Don Zoilo. Sainsbury's own-label manzanilla is available in half-bottles.

Montilla

Montilla also comes from southern Spain, not far from Jerez de la Frontera, but it has acquired something of a tarnished reputation as a poor man's sherry. The term amontillado literally means 'in the style of montilla' but generally it is montilla which is the less exciting and cheaper drink. The grapes tend to be riper, making wine that is low in acidity, as well as higher in alcohol and therefore needing less fortification. The final alcoholic strength is slightly lower than that of sherry, which makes it cheaper on the shelf. Also, montilla undergoes a shorter ageing period than amontillado. It tends to be rather soft and rarely has the firm dry backbone of good fino – indeed, virtually all montilla imported into Britain is not fortified at all. What would be a fino montilla in Spain is sold as montilla dry in Britain. Bodegas Alvear is the best producer, but most montilla is sold under a supermarket's or merchant's own label.

Madeira: sercial

Sercial is the driest style of all the wines from Madeira, the Portuguese island that is closer to Africa than to Europe, and it has an original taste all of its own. The production of all madeira involves a process of heating the wine in what is called an *estufa*, which may be a tank or a heated warehouse. This 'cooking' of the wine is said to imitate the days when Madeira was the last port of call for ships crossing the Atlantic, or rounding the Cape of Good Hope on their way to India. The wine was taken on as ballast, and as such was literally cooked in the hold of the ship during the long sea voyage; amazingly, it was found to be much improved in flavour on its arrival at its destination.

Sercial takes its name from the grape used, although until very recently it was made predominantly from Tinta Negra Mole, as were most other madeiras. However, as EC regulations now require a wine to contain 85 per cent of any grape mentioned on the label, the Portuguese have had to conform. Sercial is generally not quite as bone dry as fino sherry, although, like all madeira, it has a very high acidity level and has a certain fullness in the mouth which can be likened to a cheesy character. The Madeira Wine Co. dominates the island's production, controlling many of the famous old names like Cossart Gordon, Rutherford & Miles, Leacock and Blandys. The handful of other producers includes Barbeito and Henriques & Henriques. Sercial is very rarely sold as a vintage wine; more often it has an indication of age, such as 5-year-old or 10-year-old. Even better, and more expensive, is Cossart Gordon's Duo Centenary Celebration. Very occasionally you may find a *solera* madeira.

MEDIUM-SWEET

Pale cream sherry

It seems appropriate to include **pale cream sherry** under the medium section, for it is nothing more than fino sweetened with cane sugar, and therefore does not have the weight of a standard cream sherry. Basically, it panders to the snobbery of wanting to be seen to drink dry, while actually drinking sweet. The colour is that of deep fino, but the flavour is somewhere between an amontillado and a cream sherry, although it lacks the body of either. A handful of pale cream sherries are marketed as commercial brands, of which Croft Original Pale Cream is the brand leader.

Amontillado sherry

Amontillado is the term commonly used to describe medium-sweet sherry, but the truth is that as such it is a complete travesty of the real thing (discussed later under 'dry and heavy'). Commercial amontillado is quite soft and sweetish, with some body and alcohol and a dryish finish. Like all sherry it has gone through the *solera* system of ageing, but it is then blended with some sweetening agent, usually concentrated Pedro Ximénez, to bring the wine to the required specification of sweetness. It is undemanding and fairly undistinguished and is sold under numerous shippers' brand names, such as Dry Fly, Dry Sack, Harvey's Club Amontillado. These are the wines that have done little to enhance the declining fortunes of the sherry trade. For real sherry, turn to the dry segments of the wheel.

Cyprus and South Africa

Cyprus and South Africa both produce medium-sweet sherry-style wines, but have a price advantage over Spanish sherry. South Africa now has a very small share of the market, and brand names are used, like Cavendish Cape Medium Dry. Illogically, Cyprus is still allowed to use the term sherry, but the wines bear little relationship to the real thing, and lack alcohol and bite. Mosaic and Emva are the two main brands.

Montilla

Montilla, which gave its name to amontillado sherry, also has a medium-sweet, amontillado category. As with the fino or dry style, it is paler and lighter than sherry with less bite and generally labelled medium-dry.

Verdelho

After sercial, **verdelho** is the next step up the madeira sweetness ladder. It is fuller and richer than sercial, with more body and, like all madeira, it has a firm backbone of acidity. It benefits from ageing in cask for an absolute minimum of eighteen months and usually for considerably longer. This makes a medium-bodied wine with a nutty flavour and a trace of sweetness or, more accurately, richness. The members of the Madeira Wine Co. are the principal names to look out for on the label.

All madeira has a wonderful capacity for ageing: the exceptionally high level of acidity, not to mention the heating of the wine during the production process, makes it virtually indestructible. Madeira never seems to oxidise once a bottle has been opened and old bottles of madeira can be bought without any fear of deterioration.

The occasional bottle of Rainwater, another medium-dry style, and Terrantez, made from a less common grape variety, also fit into this taste category. Rainwater is not really as poetic as it sounds. There are various stories on the origin of its name – most common is that the contents of some caskets of madeira were diluted with rain and that the result became a popular style of madeira in America in the eighteenth century. Today it is a commercial blend of different grapes, and varies from shipper to shipper in weight and flavour.

Port: white, ruby, tawny, colheita, single quinta, late-bottled vintage, crusted and vintage-character

'Port' covers a multitude of qualities: most is medium-sweet, but with variations in depth of flavour, richness, nuttiness and staying power (or length in the mouth). It is aged in either bottle or cask and the best bottle-aged port is vintage port, which comes into the rich and heavy segment of the taste wheel. All other styles of port fit more or less into the medium-sweet segment of the taste wheel – or should it really be medium-dry? The distinction is rather blurred. In any case, the sweetness of port comes from the natural sugar in the grape juice, which remains in the wine because the fermentation is stopped at the appropriate moment by the addition of grape spirit.

Take **white port** first of all – this accounts for a minuscule proportion of the port trade, to the extent that some houses do not bother to produce it at all. The vinification process is the same as for standard ruby port and the taste is dryish rather than bone dry, with a softness, a hint of liquorice and a lightly mouth-filling flavour. Taylor's Chip Dry is the best known; and Delaforce and Cockburns also produce white ports. It provides an original aperitif, but lacks the finesse of an elegant fino or manzanilla.

Moving on, **ruby port** describes a young wine that is sold after two or three years' ageing in wood. It is deep in colour, with the typical liquorice fruit flavour of port, but with a rather spirity, alcoholic burn to the finish, as the brandy is not properly integrated into the taste. Cheap **tawny**, which is generally a blend of white and ruby, is lighter in colour and body, but not dissimilar in taste.

However, **mature tawny** port is quite another story. It has been aged for ten, twenty or maybe as long as forty years in cask, so the colour has turned tawny-red as part of the natural process of maturation. The taste is mellow and nutty, redolent of liquid walnuts, with an underlying elegance and sweetness. A newcomer to the British market is a 10-year-old tawny from Quinta da Ervamoira, an estate which belongs to Ramos Pinto, and in which Louis Roederer now has a controlling interest

While a 20-year-old tawny, for example, gives only an indication of the average age, a **colheita** port is a single vintage tawny, that is, a wine that is treated in the same way as a blended tawny but comes from only one vintage. It must be aged in cask for a minimum of seven years and, in practice, often for much longer. The label gives not only a vintage date but also a bottling date. Colheitas seem to be the preserve of the Portuguese port houses and have been neglected by the English shippers like, for example, Taylors or Cockburns; while Cálem, a leading Portuguese house, makes something of a speciality of its Colheitas, as does Niepoort; Souza is another name to look out for. The taste, depending on the vintage, is not unlike that of a 10- or 20-year-old tawny, with similar nutty overtones. Pricewise they compare with tawny ports of a similar age.

There is a growing trend for port shippers to produce what they call a **single quinta** port, which is a wine from their best estate or vineyards, in years in which a port vintage is not generally declared (otherwise this wine would be used for the vintage port). Generally, it is a lighter version of vintage port, with some ripe liquorice fruit and an underlying sweetness and richness, but without the body of a vintage port. Wines like Taylor's Quinta de Vargellas, Graham's Quinta do Malvedos, Delaforce's Quinta da Corte all provide a vintage-style wine, at a much more affordable price than a true vintage port. Usually, a single quinta is sold at the moment that it is ready for drinking so, for instance, 1979 Quinta do Malvedos is on sale at about £15 a bottle at the moment, while the currently most accessible vintage port from Grahams, the 1975, costs about £24 a bottle, a good deal more expensive.

A newcomer to the ranks of port producers is Quinta la Rosa, from a small family estate, launched with the 1988 vintage. It has potential, with some ripe liquorice fruit but, needless to say, it needs some bottle age before it will make an enjoyable drink.

Interesting, but of less depth of character, are the **late-bottled vintage** wines, LBV for short. As the name implies, this is the wine of a single vintage, which is bottled later than is normal for a true vintage port (between four and a half and six years, instead of eighteen months or so after the vintage). The idea behind the concept is that the wine, from a lighter year than a true vintage, ages more quickly in cask than in bottle. In theory there is some trace of vintage style, although the wines are somewhat lighter, albeit with some liquorice fruit. Late-bottled vintage wines are generally ready for drinking once they are bottled, with little to be gained from giving them further ageing in bottle. Taylors were the trendsetters here, while others, such as Warre, Sandeman, Graham, Fonseca and Dow, have followed suit.

Wines labelled **vintage-character** are really only one step up from basic ruby, with little real aspiration to emulate vintage port. **Crusted**, or crusting, port, on the other hand, which is produced only for the British market, is a blend of wines from two or three quite good – but not great – years, which are aged in cask for three or four years before bottling. The result can be quite flavoursome and also presents some good-value drinking.

New World tawny and ruby

Not so long ago the wine industries of Australia and South Africa concentrated on dessert wines, mainly port and sherry lookalikes and, although there has been a definite shift of emphasis towards table wines in the last ten or twenty years, fortified wines are still produced in some quarters. Sometimes the grape varieties are the same as for European wines, sometimes quite different. In California, ruby styles are made with Zinfandel and Cabernet Sauvignon. In Australia, the traditional Portuguese port varieties, such as Touriga Nacional and Bastardo, are sometimes used.

Australia produces some remarkably good port-style wines. Of course, the export label must not mention the word port, but the terms tawny and ruby are permitted. Yalumba's Galway Pipe is a delicious old tawny, with some rich, sweet walnut fruit. Seppelt's Mount Rufus Finest Old Tawny is a little drier, but with a similar walnut flavour. In California, Quady makes a joke of the fact that it cannot mention the word port on the label by calling its ruby-style wine Starboard. It is rather sweet, with a taste of raisins, rather than the more classic liquorice flavour of ruby port.

In South Africa, Allesverloren makes some of the best port styles with some ripe liquorice fruit, albeit a trifle coarse, but these wines are not yet available in Britain.

Vin doux naturel from Rivesaltes, Banyuls, Maury and Rasteau

The **vins doux naturels** feature amongst France's undiscovered vinous delights, although those made from Muscat (see next segment) are well-known. Other wines which are based on Grenache and other red grapes are aged in large oak casks and then left for six months or more in glass demijohns outside in all weathers, giving them a distinctive individuality. The term vin doux naturel is something of a misnomer. What it really means is that the sweetness in the wine is natural, originating from the grape, not from sacks of sugar, and that sweetness is retained in the wine by the addition of brandy at the appropriate moment during vinification to stop further fermentation. With some lengthy ageing in cask the wines take on rich, nutty flavours, redolent of walnuts, liquorice and prunes. Walk into a cellar of old casks in Rivesaltes and there is the wonderfully enticing aroma of fruitcake.

Rivesaltes is the most important vin doux naturel of the Midi in terms of volume. The vineyards cover a wide area around the town of the same name and intermingle with those of the Côtes-du-Roussillon. Moving on, **Banyuls** is a small village almost on the Mediterranean border with Spain, and its vineyards are the same ones that make the gutsy red wine Collioure. The third name to look out for, **Maury**, is made in one tiny village in the heart of Roussillon. Mas Amiel is the only producer of any importance and a 15-year-old Maury is certainly worth seeking out.

The village of **Rasteau** is in the Rhône valley and is better-known for being a part of the appellation of Côtes-du-Rhône-Villages. Its Grenache-based fortified wine forms a pair with Beaumes-de-Venise's Muscat, from another village of the Côtes-du-Rhône-Villages.

There is an element of obscurity in all these wines: they have suffered with the fall from fashion of sweet aperitif wines. However, they can make delicious after-dinner drinks in place of the more conventional port, and have the added advantage of being a little lighter in alcohol.

Recommended producers include Cazes Frères with their Vieux Rivesaltes, which makes a wonderful alternative to tawny port; the competent Rasteau village co-operative and the leading Banyuls producer, Domaine du Mas Blanc.

SWEET MUSCAT

Muscat-based vin doux naturel from Beaumes-de-Venise, Frontignan and Rivesaltes

Muscat de Beaumes-de-Venise, from one of the Côtes-du-Rhône-Villages, established the popularity of Muscat-based vin doux naturel as a delicious dessert wine, the essence of which is the fresh, ripe flavour of the Muscat grape. The skill in the vinification is judging the exact moment to stop the fermentation by the addition of grape brandy: too soon and the wine is sweet and heavy; too late and some of the fresh fruit flavour is lost. Producers even sleep in their cellars at night in order not to miss the vital moment.

Good producers include Domaine de Durban, Domaine de Coyeux and the village co-operative. The wine should be drunk as young as possible, within a year or two of the vintage, before its fresh grapey flavour fades. There are other Muscat-based vins doux naturels in France that are similar in taste, but they are less popular and therefore offer better value. For example, **Muscat de Frontignan** comes from the town of Frontignan on the Mediterranean coast, where Château la Peyrade makes the most delicate wine.

Muscat de Rivesaltes, from the large appellation in the foothills of the Pyrenees behind the town of Perpignan, is just beginning to re-emerge from a period in the doldrums, with a handful of producers struggling to make their wines better known. It has the characteristic taste of Muscat, with lemon and honey flavours, and hints of ripe apricots and pithy oranges. Domaine de Sarda-Malet, Cazes Frères, and the Arnaud de Villeneuve label are all worth trying.

A handful of other little-known Muscat-based vins doux naturels occasionally find their way across the Channel, for example **Muscat de Lunel** (a tiny appellation near Montpellier), **Muscat de Mireval** (the next-door appellation to Muscat de Frontignan) and **Muscat de St-Jean-de-Minervois** (from one village within the appellation of Minervois). Sainsbury's has the imagination to sell Muscat de St-Jean-de-Minervois in half-bottles.

In addition, there is the occasional vin doux naturel which does not have an appellation, such as the José Sala label, which originates from somewhere near Pézenas and which offers unrefined and cheerful good value.

Valencia, Málaga, Samos and Pantelleria

Parts of southern Spain also grow Muscat, or Moscatel as they call it, and it is treated in much the same way as when making the vins doux naturels of the Midi. **Moscatel de Valencia** is a cheap and cheerful fortified Muscat made in vineyards behind one of the largest cities of Spain, a city which is generally better known for the production of large quantities of increasingly quaffable but undistinguished table wine. It is heavier and infinitely less elegant than its French counterparts, but has some ripe, grapey fruit, offers excellent value for money and can stand up to rich sweets, even mince pies.

Málaga wine, from southern Spain, comes in many guises, and one of the forms it takes is a **Moscatel de Málaga**. Scholtz is the leading Málaga producer, and Sainsbury's sells an own-label wine in half-bottles.

The Greek island of Samos is also known for its fortified Muscat wines, as are Patras and Lemnos; these wines are similar in flavour.

Southern Italy, or more precisely the tiny island of Pantelleria, lost in the Mediterranean between Sicily and Tunisia, produces a **Moscato di Pantelleria**. Depending on the producer it may or may not be fortified. The best wines are not generally fortified and therefore feature in the sweet section of the table wine wheel. However, the Marsala producers Florio have recently begun to take an interest in the island and have introduced a new fortified Moscato di Pantelleria called Morse di Luce.

USA and South Africa

Most sweet Muscats from California tend to be unfortified, late-harvest wines, which fit into the sweet segment of the table wine wheel. The one exception comes from Quady, a small Californian winery, which makes a speciality of fortified wines and whose Essensia Orange Muscat has the pithy orange fruit of the Muscat grape.

Some of the early traditions of South Africa are based on fortified wines from Moscatel. Often the sweet grape juice was simply fortified to prevent any fermentation. However, Muscat de Montac is made in the same way as the vins doux naturels of the south of France, with a little fermentation prior to fortification, thus retaining the grapey flavour.

Neither Australia nor New Zealand ever seems to have vinified Muscat in this way. Both countries make some deliciously grapey late-harvest Muscats, which feature in the sweet segment of the table wine wheel, and Australia also boasts some wonderful Muscat-based fortified wines, in the form of Liqueur Muscat, which is described below.

RICH AND HEAVY

Australian liqueur Muscat and tokay

Liqueur Muscat must be Australia's most original wine. It is produced around the town of Rutherglen in the north-east corner of the state of Victoria. It is made from Muscat grapes that are left on the vines until they are over-ripe and raisin-like; the fermentation is stopped by the addition of brandy and the wine is then matured in oak barrels, often for several years and sometimes even in a *solera* system, like sherry. The result is magnificent, rich and luscious, the essence of liquid walnuts and orange marmalade; older wines become more toffee-like, losing some of the orange flavour of the Muscat grapes. Colours range from amber-orange to mahogany-brown.

The best producers include Chambers, Campbells, Stanton & Killeen, All Saints, Seppelts and Baileys. Sadly – but inevitably – these wines are expensive, given the small yields and long periods of maturation, but they are well worth it, making a dessert wine or after-dinner drink with a taste of Australian individuality. They partner Christmas pudding and chocolate triumphantly.

Baileys also produces what it calls Founder Liqueur Tokay, which is very similar to Liqueur Muscat in taste, wonderfully smooth and unctuous, with a flavour of marmalade and cinnamon. The method of production is virtually identical, using very ripe grapes, and extensive maturation in old oak barrels, with the main difference in taste coming from the grape variety, which is Muscadelle. The price is comparable too.

Cream sherry

Cream sherry or sweet oloroso sherry covers a multitude of flavours. Not to put too fine a point on it, there are cream sherries that are rich and luscious and simply delicious whilst others – commercial blends, well-laced with sweet grape concentrate – are of little distinction. However, there is nothing better than a real cream sherry on a cold winter's night by an open log fire, wonderful to sip with a bowl of walnuts. The best-known commercial brand may be Harvey's Bristol Cream, but there are many wines with infinitely more depth of flavour and character. Look out for Gonzalez Byass Matusalem, Lustau's Old East India and Sandeman's Royal Corregidor. (For dry oloroso see under the dry and heavy segment.)

The use of the name sherry is now controlled on labels with increasing severity. South Africa may no longer use the term, while Cyprus may, and, for some nonsensical reason, although British wine is not even acceptable as real wine because it is based on reconstituted grape juice, the term British sherry is still permissible. From Spain, Montilla cream is not dissimilar to a commercial cream sherry, nor is cream Cyprus sherry, usually sold under a brand name like Mosaic. The same style of wine from

South Africa is sold simply as cream under a brand name such as Cavendish Cape and Ouzerust.

Moscatel de Setúbal

The Setúbal peninsula, south of Lisbon, is a source of some delicious Moscatel-based wines, as well as greater quantities of table wine. The grapes used (a blend in which Moscatel is the most important but does not always amount to the 85 per cent necessary for it to feature on the label) are fermented and grape brandy is added at the appropriate moment. The grape skins are then left to macerate in the young fortified wine until the following spring, in order to extract even more aroma and flavour. Then the wine is kept in first large, then small, wooden barrels. Sometimes the wine has a vintage, sometimes merely an indication of age.

The best **Moscatels de Setúbal** are those that have been aged for several years, perhaps as many as 20 or 25, so that they take on rich toffee-like flavours, reminiscent of fruitcake, nuts and treacle. Alternatively, the younger wines, usually sold when they are about four years old, are fresh and grapey, with a somewhat spirity finish, and have more in common with Muscats from the Midi or Spain.

Vintage port

Vintage port stands apart from other ports, for in early youth it is very rich and concentrated, with mouth-filling flavours of liquorice, prunes, tannin and spirit, none of which have quite blended together yet. It needs several years in the bottle before it is ready to be enjoyed. The idea of laying down vintage port for the coming of age of a child demonstrates that 21, or at least 18, years is an appropriate period of maturation.

As it ages, vintage port mellows, becoming smooth and elegant, losing any rough spirity edges and developing some complex flavours of prunes and spice, with an underlying rich sweetness. It will always have more body, concentration and colour than a tawny port of similar age.

Vintage port is not made every year. The decision to declare a vintage depends not only on the quality of the grapes, but on the economic health of the port trade. An extreme example was when the depression of the 1930s stopped every shipper but Noval from declaring the fabulous 1931 vintage. Similarly, only three shippers declared the good 1987 vintage, as it followed too closely after the 1985. The decision belongs to each house individually; some years are declared almost universally and others not. Sometimes, when there are two comparable years side by side, the shippers may be almost equally divided between the two, for example, in 1982 and 1983. In fact, 1983 is now generally considered to be the better year of the two.

The most recent generally declared vintage was 1985, while high expectations are placed on 1991. Port shippers, like champagne houses, have a house style that is individual to them, so personal taste should be a guide when reading our recommendations. A generalisation which is not totally founded is that the Portuguese houses, such as Ferreira, Niepoort and Cálem, make wines that are a little lighter in style, while the wines from the English shippers are richer and more full-bodied. This may be something to do with the indisputable fact that a lighter tawny is an infinitely more attractive drink in the hotter climate of Portugal than a full-bodied vintage wine, which is more appealing in a colder northern clime.

Among currently available vintages 1966 and 1970 are drinking well; the underrated 1980 is also beginning to show well; 1975 is not really fulfilling its promise, while 1977 should be kept for a few years more, as can 1963. After madeira, vintage port is the most long-lived fortified wine, as a sip of Taylors 1865, offered recently on the occasion of the company's 300th anniversary, well demonstrated.

Madeira: bual and malmsey

Bual is the next stage up the sweetness scale after verdelho. It is fairly sweet and nutty, with the slightly cooked flavour of all madeira. The older it is, the better. Compare Cossart Gordon's Good Company Bual, which is positively cheesy on the palate, with its 5-Year-Old Reserve which is sweeter and nuttier, and then with the Duo Centenary Celebration Bual which is smooth and rich, with a dry caramel nose, a firm bite of acidity and a rich powerful mouthful of flavour.

Malmsey, as the fourth wine on the sweetness scale, is so rich and sweet that it is positively unctuous, with rich burnt caramel flavours, nuts and fruit, and a firm bite of acidity to counter-balance the sweetness. Good madeira will never be cheap, but it deserves greater attention than it is generally given. It is the most long-lived of all wines, with the added and unique advantage that an open bottle does not deteriorate.

Málaga

At the height of the Victorian era, Málaga was eminently fashionable; today the name tends to conjure up images of sun-soaked package holidays. The grape varieties grown in the vineyards behind the town in southern Spain are Pedro Ximénez and Moscatel. A wide range of styles is possible, from seco to dulce (dry, sweet) and, sometimes classified by colour, from blanco, to dorado, rojo-dorado, oscuro and negro (white, golden, tawny, dark and black). However, there are three styles that are worth seeking out; first is the Moscatel de Málaga, mentioned earlier under fortified Muscat.

Next is **Lágrima**, a wonderful, rich dessert wine, made only from free-run juice, matured in wood for several years. It has an intense dark chocolate colour, with hints of Bovril on the nose and a rich and concentrated taste. The wine is so unctuously thick that you could almost stand a teaspoon in it, but it is wonderfully soothing to the throat and has a dry finish so it does not cloy.

More common is a Málaga which is aged in a *solera*, like sherry. The most popular is Solera Scholtz 1885 (1885 refers to the year in which that particular *solera* was started, so that the wine may contain only the tiniest drop of wine from 1885), which is deep brown in colour, with rich moscatel flavours, as well as walnuts. It is smooth with a firm finish: with wines like these, Málaga deserves a return to popularity.

DRY AND HEAVY

Sherry: oloroso, amontillado and Palo Cortado

British tastebuds are so attuned to expect sherry to be sweet (unless it is fino or manzanilla) that we forget that in Spain all sherry begins life as a dry wine, and more often than not stays that way. We glibly equate oloroso to cream sherry, but the word oloroso actually means fragrant, so that an oloroso sherry is usually a rich, aromatic wine. **Oloroso seco** is a firmly, sometimes searingly, dry wine, with a concentration of flavour reminiscent of nuts and prunes. It is fortified to a higher degree than either fino or amontillado, to 18 or 20 per cent, and is aged for several years in a *solera* system. Real olorosos include Gonzalez Byass Apostoles, which is very slightly sweetened; Williams & Humbert's Dos Cortados Old Dry Oloroso; Rio Viejo from Domecq and the olorosos in Lustau's Almacenista range. The words seco (dry) and muy viejo (very old) are the clue to quality.

Authentic **amontillados**, rather than the commercial variety, are wines that were once finos, but have lost their flor character and developed with age. They are fortified to a higher degree than fino but they do not quite have the weight of an oloroso, and so are more delicate, dry and nutty. Good examples include Garvey's Tio

Guillermo, Gonzalez Byass Amontillado del Duque, Principe from Barbadillo and Napoleon from Hidalgo.

Palo Cortado is something of an anomaly, coming somewhere between amontillado and oloroso in style. Like oloroso, it does not develop flor, and it is possibly best described as an elegant oloroso. Genuine Palo Cortado is rare and tends to be quite expensive; take Harvey's 1796 as an example, which costs around £10.

Also worth seeking out are the **almacenista** sherries, which are the particular speciality of Emilio Lustau. The term almacenista describes a small amount of a particularly fine unblended sherry purchased from a small stockholder.

With wines like these, dry olorosos and aged amontillados, sherry takes on another dimension of flavour and quality. Inevitably these wines seem expensive compared to commercial blends, for the years of maturation in a lengthy *solera* system have to be sustained. But in reality they represent exceptional value for money in terms of flavour and quality.

The sherry industry is not without its problems. It faces the prospect of pulling up large tracts of vineyards in an effort to solve the problems of over-production which stem from the sharp decline in sales over recent years. On top of that, the 1991 vintage was severely affected by striking pickers and cellar workers. Yet despite all this, sherry remains one of the great wines in a world that is increasingly polarised between Chardonnay and Cabernet Sauvignon.

Marsala

Last in this wheel is **marsala**, which crosses taste bands from sweet to dry and traverses the quality range from fairly dire to sublimely delicious. Once upon a time it held its place amongst the great fortified wines of the world, proudly taking its position alongside sherry, port and madeira. But then the decline set in. You could find marsala flavoured with egg, coffee, even bananas, designed for making zabaglione. Happily these travesties of the real thing have now been relegated to the category of cremova. The classification of marsala is far from simple and is determined by wood-ageing – a minimum of one year for fine and two for a superiore (up to ten years old or more). Colour represents another possible category of classification: oro, ambra or rubino. Then there is sweetness, or otherwise, to consider; dry, semi-dry and sweet. Vergine marsala with five years' ageing is dry, and depends upon small amounts of older wine for its character.

The best marsalas are firmly dry. Take as a guideline the

distinctive and individual wines of Marco de Bartoli, who has done more than any other producer to restore the tarnished reputation of marsala. Often his wines do not conform to the DOC regulations, but that does not affect the taste. De Bartoli's 10-year-old Vecchio Samperi is not, in fact, fortified, which means that technically it is not marsala at all, but it comes from the two key grape varieties of marsala – Grillo and Inzolia – and has a wonderful dry nutty flavour with great depth of flavour and complexity. Other marsala producers of note include Curatolo, Rallo and Florio.

SPARKLING WINES

Champagne (see the wheel on the inside of the back cover) is the pacesetter: the sparkling wine that all the others aspire to emulate, if not actually to imitate. There is no doubt that a really good champagne is sublime, an incomparable drink full of bubbles and festivity, but in reality not all champagne is so good. It is also expensive and, consequently, there are a growing number of equally (if not more) enjoyable, and certainly more affordable, alternatives. These may take champagne as their bench mark, but the individual taste of each is adapted to the specific conditions of the region of production, particularly taking into account climate and grape varieties.

Champagne at its best is undeniably unique. The particular method of making sparkling wine in Champagne has evolved through years, if not centuries, of experience and is unquestionably accepted to be the best way of making sparkling wine. The second fermentation, which takes place in the bottle, gives the wine greater finesse, with a finer, lighter mousse and more staying power, as well as a greater depth of flavour, originating particularly from the contact of the wine with the lees of the second fermentation. This allows for yeast autolysis, where the wine takes on more complex flavours (which can be described as yeasty, or bready) from the dead yeast remaining from the second fermentation.

A blind monk, Dom Pérignon, the renowned cellarmaster of the Abbey of Hautvillers outside Epernay, was the first to appreciate the art and skill of blending wines from different vineyards. Aided by the development of cork as a bottle-stopper and the new possibility of producing glass bottles strong enough to withstand pressure, he worked out how to retain the bubbles of carbon dioxide. Then Madame Veuve Clicquot, one of the great ladies of champagne, invented the technique of *remuage*, or riddling, in order to remove from the bottle the sediment resulting from the second fermentation. This has subsequently been refined by the use of modern machinery, automatic giropalettes, which consist of a metal frame in which the bottles are placed neck downwards and rotated daily, manually or mechanically, or even by computer programme. Meanwhile, Moët & Chandon are working on more sophisticated techniques, which will completely remove the need for *remuage*.

The grape varieties used in champagne production are Chardonnay, Pinot Noir and Pinot Meunier. Chardonnay generally provides delicacy and elegance, while Pinot Noir contributes body and backbone. Pinot Meunier lacks the finesse of the other two, but contributes some flavour; it has the disadvantage of ageing faster than either Chardonnay or Pinot Noir, but this, on the other hand, could benefit someone aiming to make a young champagne taste more mature. Pinot Meunier has not travelled much outside the Champagne area, while Pinot Noir and Chardonnay are grown extensively for sparkling wine, especially in the New World.

What singles out champagne from other sparkling wines is the soil, a type of chalk called *Belimnita quadrata* that is found extensively in the land around Reims and Epernay. Climate also plays a part, for the vineyards of Champagne – with the exception of those of the little known Côtes de Toul – are the most northerly in France and are subject to all the climatic vagaries which that entails. This results in wines with lean steely acidity. If you have ever tasted the *vin clair*, or base wine, of champagne, it is obvious why bubbles are essential to render it palatable. The same might also be said of the occasional bottle of still Coteaux Champenois produced in the region.

The **champagne method** is used all over the world for making any sparkling wine with pretensions to quality. It is used elsewhere in France, in such appellations as Blanquette de Limoux and Crémant d'Alsace; for cava in Spain; in Italy; in the New World; and even in England. The Champenois are very anxious to protect their name from pale imitations, with the result that the use of the words 'méthode champenoise', or similar, is banned as of September 1993. Alternative terms such as 'méthode traditionnelle', or 'metodo classico', or 'second fermentation in *this* bottle' will be used instead.

For cheaper sparkling wine, the most common method of production is variously called '**cuve close**', 'the Charmat method', after the man who invented it, or 'the tank method'. The essential difference from the champagne method is that the second fermentation takes place not in a bottle, but in a tank. The wine is then filtered and bottled under pressure. The resulting mousse is infinitely less subtle, with larger bubbles and less staying power; with a far greater volume of wine in contact with the lees, there is less effect of yeast autolysis. In addition, the wine generally has contact with the lees for a much shorter period of time, a matter of weeks rather than months, or even years. However, for cheerful bubbles, this is a perfectly acceptable way of making sparkling wine.

Somewhere between the champagne and Charmat methods comes what is called the **transfer method**, or *transvasage*, where the second fermentation takes place in a bottle, but the wine is then emptied into a tank under pressure before filtration and subsequent rebottling. This avoids the labour-intensive processes of *remuage* and *dégorgement* (ejection of sediment).

Another variation in method is to stop the first fermentation and then allow it to take off again, but this time retain the bubbles of carbon dioxide, as in the case of Asti Spumante, where a quantity of unfermented grape sugar enhances the lusciously sweet flavour of the wine.

Finally, the cheapest method of all for making sparkling wine is to inject bubbles of carbon dioxide into the finished wine. This could be termed the bicycle pump method, for the technique is somewhat similar to pumping up a bicycle tyre. The bubbles have no staying power at all and are large and coarse. Needless to say, this is used only for cheap wines which are not usually fully sparkling.

CHAMPAGNE

Champagne is the world's greatest sparkling wine. However hard its competitors may try to emulate it, there is a certain indefinable quality about champagne that ensures that they never quite succeed. They may come very close; they may even make better wines than some champagne. Yet when champagne is great, it is very great indeed. This is not to say that there are no poor champagnes; unfortunately there are. And there are times when an alternative to champagne is the preferable choice – when the occasion does not justify the price or when quantity rather than quality may be a consideration – but when the best is what is needed, champagne is the only choice.

Champagne sales in Britain have dropped significantly in the last year or so, in some measure a result of the unhappy inflationary economic climate, but also in response to the excessive price increases demanded by the Champenois and the growing range of alternatives to champagne, with wines that are so close to the real thing as to be nearly indistinguishable.

Dosage is an essential part of the process of champagne production. When the *liqueur d'expédition* is added after *dégorgement*, the champagne can be sweetened according to taste. Most non-vintage champagne is **brut** which contains no more than

15 grammes of sugar per litre, and allows for a certain flexibility to show a house style; an **extra sec** contains between 12 and 20 grammes of sugar per litre; and the very rare **doux** more than 50 grammes per litre. There has been a certain vogue for ultra-dry champagnes without any dosage. These can be so steely and austere that it is immediately apparent why champagne benefits from a gentle dosage. For some austerely dry bubbles, look for names like Brut Zéro, Brut Sauvage and Ultra Brut. The best come from Besserat de Bellefon, Laurent Perrier and Piper Heidsieck.

Non-vintage

The most basic category of champagne is the standard **non-vintage brut** wine, which demands a minimum of 12 months' ageing on the lees of the second fermentation. This is the wine which illustrates the particular house style of the producer, and upon which reputations are based. There should be no difference in taste from one year to the next, with the maintenance of a consistency of style. The large champagne houses, or *grandes marques*, hold reserves of wine of previous years which enable them to blend the still wines, the *vins clairs*, taking annual differences into account, balancing wines with low acidity with some of an earlier year with higher acidity, or fuller wines with leaner wines. A non-vintage champagne will certainly contain a dozen or so different wines and perhaps as many as 50, from different villages and vineyards scattered over the appellation, mainly from the Montagne de Reims, the Côte des Blancs and the valley of the Marne, and perhaps the outlying vineyards of the Aube. A permutation of grape varieties is possible too, with greater or smaller percentages of white or red grapes.

The great advantage of the large champagne houses is the wide choice that they have in the provenance of their wines. Although most own some vineyards, these supply only a small proportion of their needs and so they buy grapes from growers. Until 1990 the price of a kilo of grapes was set each year, according to the quality and size of the vintage. Now a free market prevails, with individual agreements between growers and merchants, which may prove better for the region in the long term.

Some smaller growers have been encouraged to make their own champagne, rather than sell their grapes to a large house. This gives rise to a much wider choice of relatively unknown and potentially good-value names. Some are very good, but have one big disadvantage – a small grower relies upon the grapes from his own vineyards and therefore does not have the resources or reserves to maintain the same consistency of style. He is much more at the mercy of the climatic vagaries of the region. Good small growers include Vilmart and Alain Cossins.

The choice of a non-vintage champagne, therefore, depends upon preferred style; some are lighter and creamier, with a higher percentage of Chardonnay; others include more Pinot Noir and are heavier with more body and weight. Bollinger, Roederer and Veuve Clicquot tend towards the richer style, while Charles Heidsieck, Laurent Perrier, Pol Roger and Deutz all favour the lighter style.

Choice also depends upon the price that you are prepared to pay. A non-vintage *grande marque* champagne from one of the prestigious names of the area can cost approximately twice as much as an unknown name, perhaps a small grower or a BOB – Buyer's Own Brand champagne. A wine merchant or supermarket goes to one of the large houses or co-operatives in Champagne and chooses the wine it would like to go under its own label. Sometimes it is difficult to tell what is what, but a judicious look at the small print on the label can help, for each producer must be registered, with a number and a category: NM, CM, RM or MA. NM is a *négociant manipulant*, a merchant who makes and sells champagne under his own name; CM is a co-operative; RM is a *récoltant manipulant*, a grower who produces and sells his own champagne; while MA is a *marque auxiliaire*, in other words, a secondary brand name.

Numerous factors determine the final cost of a bottle of champagne. The vineyards and villages are graded in what is called the *échelle des crus*, including grand cru at 100 per cent and premier cru from 90 to 99 per cent. Ratings are according to the quality of the grapes produced, so the wine of a producer who uses only grands crus and premiers crus will be significantly more expensive than a wine from vineyards with a lower rating, as their grapes will have cost more in the first place; you do occasionally see the terms grand cru and premier cru on a bottle. There are other differences in price: a wine that has spent longer on the lees of the second fermentation is likely to be more expensive and taste better than one which has had the barest minimum of 12 months. Houses that maintain large stocks of reserve wines have to finance them; manual *remuage* is more costly in manpower than mechanical *remuage*. Basically, you tend to get what you pay for. Although a cheap champagne may prove to be a delicious bargain, it could well turn out to be a decidedly disappointing experience, and you could have had infinitely more drinking pleasure from a comparably priced bottle of bubbles from elsewhere in the world.

Bottle age also affects the taste of a champagne quite

significantly. All champagne improves with some bottle age, be it only six months or so, so that the flavours mellow and develop. While champagne needs a fairly neutral base wine with firm acidity, its true flavour comes from the second fermentation, with the effects of yeast autolysis creating a delicately nutty, creamy, yeasty – some call it bready – flavour. However, when a young champagne is first disgorged, it can still taste quite lean and acidic. A few months of bottle age can change the taste quite dramatically, allowing the flavour to fill out and the acidity to tone down. Some champagne houses give their wines some bottle age before they leave the cellars; others do not.

Vintage

Vintage champagne, the wine of a particular year and that year alone, requires a minimum of three years on the lees before disgorgement. While at one time vintage champagne was made only in exceptional years, it now seems to be produced in most years. The decision depends upon individual houses but 1984 is the one rare exception of the last decade and, in the 1970s, only 1972 was missed completely. A vintage champagne accentuates the characteristics of the year. The current vintage that is generally available is 1985, which is a fine vintage that yielded wines with good fruit and balance; 1986 will follow shortly, but at the time of writing was not generally available for tasting; 1982 and 1983, both big vintages, producing some good wines, can still be found. Of the last two, acidity levels were slightly higher in 1983, which might make the wines longer lived, while the 1982 may have a greater concentration of flavour. Inevitably, they will always be compared to one another, while 1979 stands alone and is drinking beautifully. Again, vintage champagne often benefits from some bottle maturation, depending on the character of the vintage.

Blanc de Blancs and Blanc de Noirs

Champagne is the one wine where the over-used term **Blanc de Blancs** has any real meaning. When it appears on a white table wine it is nonsensical, for a white table wine is always made from white grapes, unless it happens to be a blush wine, coming from red grapes. However, as it is possible to make champagne from both red and white grapes, the term Blanc de Blancs does indeed describe a wine that comes from Chardonnay alone. The taste is usually delicate and creamy, light and flavoursome and, with age, a good Blanc de Blancs develops some of the rich, nutty aromas of mature Chardonnay. Good examples include Ruinart, Taittinger, Pol Roger, Salon, Jacquart, Joseph Perrier and Mumm de Cramant, which was formerly Crémant de Cramant, but has been renamed in response to the change of regulations, limiting the use of the term Crémant to the other sparkling wine appellations of France.

In contrast, **Blanc de Noirs**, which is quite rare, is made from Pinot Noir and Pinot Meunier, without a drop of Chardonnay. This makes a wine with backbone and body and with more substance and weight than a Blanc de Blancs or even a straight non-vintage champagne. Good examples include Bollinger and Bruno Paillard.

Cuvée de prestige

The most expensive of all champagnes are the so-called **cuvées de prestige** or de-luxe champagnes. These are the absolute flagships of the champagne houses, to which are attached glamour and prestige. Generally, these wines come from the very best vineyards and from the very best vintages; they are always vintage wines. They are made in small quantities and are appropriately expensive, usually double the price of a vintage champagne.

Amongst the leading cuvées de prestige feature Dom Pérignon and Roederer Cristal (in its unusual clear bottle, intended to imitate the crystal bottle that was produced for the Tsarist court). Bollinger makes what it calls Bollinger RD, a mature wine that has been recently disgorged – the current vintage is 1982. Its Vieilles Vignes, from two tiny vineyards of pre-phylloxera vines in the villages of Ay and Bouzy, might also be considered a de-luxe cuvée; Dom Ruinart Blanc de Blancs is wonderfully rich and full; Perrier Jouët's Belle Epoque comes in the bottle of the period; and look out too for La Grande Dame, as well as Salon le Mesnil; the latter is only made in good vintages – 1982 is currently on sale.

In general

The flavours of champagne cover a wide spectrum of the taste wheel, with variations according to house style, amount of dosage, blend of grape varieties and the age of the wine. However, a broad generalisation can be made between wines that are delicate and creamy, and those that are fuller-bodied and richer with nuttier and more yeasty, bready flavours. Bottle age, as well as house style, certainly plays a part in this.

Young champagne should have a lightly creamy, delicately bready nose, but nothing too pronounced and rich. Try Pol Roger, Perrier Jouët, Deutz, Billecart-Salmon, Henri Abelé and Canard Duchêne.

More mature wines have developed richer, fuller flavours. A mature Dom Ruinart is a fine example, for, as a Blanc de Blancs, it has the ripe nutty flavour of mature Chardonnay, with considerable depth of flavour. A few suggestions for good, rich, full-flavoured wines include Bollinger, Krug, Salon, Roederer, Joseph Perrier and Alfred Gratien.

COMPETITORS TO THE REAL THING

Sparkling wine producers all over the world aspire to emulate champagne, and there are several sparklers which are more than acceptable alternatives, with flavours near enough to be confused with the real thing. The key grape varieties, Pinot Noir and Chardonnay, have travelled the world with some success. When they are grown in a cool climate, they produce base wines without too much positive flavour and with fairly high acidity – essential to the production of good sparkling wine. The techniques of the champagne method have been perfected, with Champenois acting as consultants in various parts of the world.

Moët & Chandon were the first to spread their wings outside Champagne. Their activities include the production of sparkling wine in many parts of the world, as diverse as South America, Austria, Australia, Germany and California. Domaine Chandon in **California** is the wine that has made the most impact; it is destined for the domestic market, and is not intended to be an imitation of champagne. However, the grape varieties and method are identical and, but for a fullness of flavour that is absent in champagne, it could be seen as a competitor. The same may be said for some of the other sparkling wines produced by subsidiaries of champagne houses in the Golden State, such as Mumm's Cuvée Napa, Roederer Estate, Maison Deutz and Piper Sonoma. Most of these have vineyards in Carneros, at the coolest end of the Sonoma and Napa valleys.

However, California has a distinct disadvantage over northern France in that the climate is usually much too warm to make the base wines with the almost searing acidity necessary for champagne. The one country in the New World that comes closest is **New Zealand**. A joint effort between Montana, one of the two giants of the New Zealand wine industry, who provided money, equipment and grapes, and Champagne Deutz, who contributed expertise, has produced Cuvée Deutz from Marlborough, on the cooler South Island. The result is a stylish, elegant, creamy sparkling wine, with finesse and flavour, at approximately half the price of a *grande marque* champagne. Production for the moment is small, while larger quantities are made of a lesser cuvée, Lindauer, which has sound, flavoursome bubbles, but is without the elegance of the Cuvée Deutz.

Another name to look out for from New Zealand is Daniel le Brun, who originally came from Champagne. Now he is applying his expertise in Marlborough, with Pinot Noir, Chardonnay and, unusually for the New World, Pinot Meunier. The range includes a non-vintage Brut, as well as the current 1988 vintage, and a 1989 Blanc de Noirs.

The closest contender to champagne to come out of **Australia** is generally considered to be Croser, named after its creator, the talented Brian Croser, who benefits from an input from Bollinger at his Petaluma winery. The grape varieties used are Chardonnay and Pinot Noir and the flavour is definitely elegant, lightly yeasty, fresh and very stylish. However, Croser may well have a contender for its prime position with the recent launch of Green Point from Domaine Chandon. The first release comprises a 59 per cent Chardonnay and 41 per cent Pinot Noir blend from the cool Yarra Valley and it certainly has that imperceptible, indefinable something that makes champagne the wine that it is, with a light nutty flavour and a hint of attractive yeastiness.

Seppelt Sallinger benefits from a high altitude and cool climate provenance, with some elegant, dry nutty fruit. Yalumba D also has a touch of class, with some lemony acidity and just a hint of yeasty fruit.

The most obvious champagne look-alike from France is **Crémant de Bourgogne**. After all, the vineyards are closest to Champagne, so the climate is similar; the grape varieties, mainly Pinot Noir and Chardonnay, are original to the area and the method did not have far to travel. Good Crémants de Bourgogne compare favourably with cheaper champagnes.

LIGHT AND CREAMY

Light and creamy describes a category of sparkling wine that comes close to emulating champagne, but which lacks the richness of some champagnes. These are wines with a delicacy of flavour, a certain yeasty creaminess that usually, but not always, originates from the Chardonnay grape. The champagne method is an essential part of the quality, as is some firm acidity to give the wine bite and backbone.

Crémant de Bourgogne is the most obvious example in this category, although it also fits into the competitors-to-the-real-thing segment. Chardonnay is often the dominant grape variety, blended sometimes with Pinot Noir, to make some creamy, fruity, sparkling wines. Sparkling burgundy is produced all over the region, from near Chablis right down to the Mâconnais. One producer, the Cave de Bailly, dominates production in the Yonne with both white and pink wines, sold under the brand name of Meurgis. Nuits-St-Georges is the historic centre for sparkling wine in the Côte d'Or, as is Rully in the Côte Chalonnaise. In addition, some of the co-operatives of the Mâconnais, such as Viré and Lugny, produce some good-value sparklers, with some creamy fruit and yeasty, bready overtones.

The Jura may not be an obvious source of sparkling wine, although the appellation **Côtes du Jura** does include mousseux made by the champagne method. Chardonnay is the usual grape variety and there are some good producers, such as Hubert Clavelin. Although Henri Maire is the largest and best-known producer of the Jura, his mass-produced Vin Fou is not at all the same thing, but a branded wine of indefinite origins. Other curiosities from France are the sparkling wines of **Gaillac**, based on Mauzac and usually made according to the champagne method by the occasional producer, such as Jean Cros and Robert Plageoles.

Crémant d'Alsace is a relatively recent appellation, created in 1976, although the history of sparkling wine in Alsace is much older. The main grape variety here is Pinot Blanc, while others such as Riesling, Pinot Noir and Tokay Pinot Gris can also be used. Riesling can make some elegant, stylish wines, with a slatey finish, while Pinot Blanc produces some soft creamy wines, with good fruit. Dopff 'au Moulin' is the leader in the market with Cuvée Julien, and other producers of note include Dopff & Irion and the village co-operatives of Turckheim and Eguisheim. For the moment, Crémant d'Alsace enjoys more success in France than it does in Britain.

A much newer appellation is **Crémant de Bordeaux**, made from the white grapes of the Gironde. That of Patrick Boudon at Domaine du Bourdieu is a blend of Sémillon and Ugni Blanc, with some attractive creamy fruit.

NEUTRAL

Neutrality in sparkling wine fulfils a purpose if you are looking for a drink that is innocuously festive, with clean, fresh bubbles. It is cheap and cheerful but has no real flavour, which makes it an ideal foil for orange juice or cassis liqueur – or indeed other flavours like blackberry or peach. There are numerous sparkling wines without any specific regional definition; their virtue is a clean but anonymous flavour. Sometimes the grapes are grown in one place and the base wine turned into sparkling wine elsewhere: for example, Henkel in Germany buys a lot of wine from Corovin, a large co-operative in Emilia Romagna. Sparkling wine of this nature is considered to be a manufactured industrial product rather than the result of a combination of grape varieties, soil, climate and technical expertise.

The second fermentation takes place in a tank, which is ideal for mass-production. The base wine should be clean and fresh with some acidity, but with as little intrinsic flavour as possible. High-yielding, low-acidity grapes like Ugni Blanc often provide the backbone. These wines have no regional denomination or appellation; the clue to the place of production may lie in the postal code, but generally there is nothing more precise than the country of origin on the label. Veuve du Vernay, produced in Bordeaux and Kriter from Burgundy are the two most obvious examples on the British market. Cavalier from Wissembourg, north of Strasbourg, is better than average; it is a cheap and refreshing wine, which is all it sets out to be. Flutelle, a mousseux from south-west France, has a hint more flavour and body, as does Blanc de Chardonnay made from grapes grown in Corsica and turned into sparkling wine in Salon de Provence by Auran.

Some **Sekt** may also come into this neutral category, especially where the wine is bought from another country, such as Henkel Trocken. Essentially, this segment of the taste wheel is filled by various branded sparkling wines, sold under fantasy names.

DUSTY, LEMON AND HONEY FLAVOURS

Low acidity

Various wines fit into this segment because they lack a certain acidity.

Blanquette de Limoux Blanquette de Limoux claims a history even older than that of champagne. The wine was first made by the monks of the Benedictine monastery of St-Hilaire, near the city of Carcassonne, perhaps as early as the sixteenth century. Blanquette is the local name for a somewhat dull grape variety called Mauzac, which can be enlivened with some Chenin Blanc and Chardonnay. A new appellation, **Crémant de Limoux**, created in 1990, denotes an even higher percentage of these two additional grape varieties, namely a maximum of 40 per cent rather than the 30 per cent maximum in Blanquette de Limoux. But here lies the problem with the sparkling wines of Limoux – Mauzac can lack charm; it makes rather flat, dry, even slightly bitter, white wine. While it is true that the base wine for a sparkling wine must not be too characterful, it does help if there is some elegance and fruit. Coming as it does from the south of France, Blanquette de Limoux can also be quite low in acidity. It can have a soft southern dustiness about it, while the addition of Chenin Blanc and Chardonnay provides a definite touch of creaminess and fruit.

The co-operative of Limoux is the main producer, using high-tech equipment for efficient production by the champagne method (although it does not say so on the label, the appellation automatically implies the use of the champagne method). The wines are available under various brand names, such as Aimery and Sieur d'Arques. In addition, there are a handful of individual estates, such as Domaine des Martinolles and Domaine de Froin.

Cava Most Spanish cava fits into this segment of the taste wheel, for it too can lack a certain acidity, and the grape varieties used in its production are not the most exciting. The base is provided by Parellada, Macabeo and Xarel-lo, while one or two more of the innovative estates are growing Chardonnay in the search for additional flavour and elegance. The DO of cava automatically implies that the champagne method is used. Geographically, it covers a large part of northern Spain, mostly Catalonia, with the centre of the cava industry in the town of San Sadurní da Noya, as well as in villages in areas as far apart as Rioja, Cariñena, Costers del Segre and Tarragona.

The principal grape varieties are rather flat and bland. More significantly, they can lack acidity and, consequently, tend not to age well – sometimes even the minimum nine months on the lees can seem too long. This can produce a somewhat earthy or dusty flavour, with a hint of pepperiness. More exciting are the occasional cavas made from Chardonnay, notably from Raimat and Codorníu, which have quite ripe, full, buttery flavours and fit into the fuller-flavoured segment of the taste wheel. The charm of the better cavas can be their soft, slightly flowery, lightly honeyed flavours. They are also significantly cheaper than any champagne, not to mention some of the French or Italian alternatives. Amongst more traditional cava producers, Codorníu is the biggest, with some sound, reliable wines; Freixenet's Cordon Negro is an innocuously pleasant drink, undemanding with refreshing bubbles. In addition, Cavas Hill, Ferret i Mateu, Juvé y Camps and Marqués de Monistrol are all worth trying. Sometimes a vintage wine or better cuvée offers more interest, such as the recently introduced Cuvée DS from Freixenet, which has more complexity after four years on the lees, with some creamy fruit and a yeasty finish.

Russia Sparkling wine has a long tradition in the former Soviet Union; Tsarist Russia was a big consumer of champagne in the nineteenth century. The republics bordering the Black Sea, namely Russia itself, the Ukraine and Moldavia, all produce wine. André Roederer, of the champagne family, even built a winery in Odessa in 1896. Today, Russian sparkling wine is made, not by the champagne method, but on a much more economical variation of the cuve close method involving a series of tanks that turn the base wine into a sparkling wine within a month. Two Russian sparkling wines are available here: St Petersburg, made from a mixture of different grape varieties, quite full and almost sweet, although supposedly dry; and Grand Duchess Brut, made mainly from Aligoté, and rather lemony and yeasty. Do not expect either to be very distinguished.

High acidity

Crémant de Loire, Saumur, Vouvray and other wines from the Loire Valley The Loire Valley has the ideal conditions for the production of sparkling wine, so much so that Saumur has been an important centre for wine production since the beginning of the last century. The tufa rocks provide ideal cellar conditions, like the chalk cellars of Champagne. But the principal difference between champagne and the sparkling wines of the Loire lies with the grape variety – in the Loire Valley Chenin Blanc predominates rather than Pinot Noir and Chardonnay. Chenin produces a base wine with the firm acidity essential for good sparkling wine but, unfortunately, when Chenin is not fully ripe, it displays the somewhat unattractive overtones of wet dogs or wet wool. This is more noticeable in still wine, but can also feature in the sparkling wine. Good sparkling Loire wine, be it Crémant de Loire, Saumur or Anjou, should have some delicate honey and yeasty flavours with firm acidity.

The appellations of the Loire can all be grouped together within this same taste segment. They include **Crémant de Loire**, which covers the whole valley and which has stricter production regulations than either Saumur or Anjou; **Saumur**, from the vineyards around the town of the same name, where most of the large producers are based; and **Anjou**, which is really only distinguished from Saumur by geography. In addition, sparkling **Vouvray** is made in years when the Chenin Blanc grapes have not ripened fully, when to produce sweet Vouvray would be an impossibility. **Montlouis**, across the river, is similar, but not so well known.

Good Loire fizz producers include some of the big names like Gratien & Meyer (who own the champagne house of Alfred Gratien), Bouvet-Ladubay and Langlois-Château (who both belong to champagne houses), as well as Marc Brédif and Gaston Huet in Vouvray and the Château de Chenonceaux.

Savoie On the other side of France, the town of Seyssel, which straddles the Rhône, is a centre for sparkling wine, notably with the company of Varichon et Clerc. Its Seyssel Mousseux is a blend of two peculiarly Savoyard grape varieties, Molette and Roussette, with firm acidity and some light dusty, lemony fruit.

In the Rhône Valley, the small appellation of **St Péray** includes sparkling, as well as still, wine from a blend of Rousanne and Marsanne. However, it is rarely seen outside the region.

England The occasional sparkling wines of England fit into this segment by virtue of their high acidity. David Carr Taylor, of Carr Taylor vineyards outside Hastings, is a pioneer who uses the champagne method. Others have followed his example; one of the most successful is Rock Lodge in Sussex with Impresario.

German Sekt To be blunt, Sekt rarely excites. Until quite recently the base wine for what was labelled 'Deutscher Sekt' did not even have to come from Germany, but was more often than not a dull white wine imported from central Italy, to be turned into Sekt in Germany. It was the production process, not the grapes, that was German. Now plain Sekt indicates this dual country origin, while **Deutscher Sekt** is purely Germanic. The best examples are made from Riesling, but are generally made by the transfer method, with the second fermentation taking place in a bottle, but not in *the* bottle in which the wine is subsequently sold. If more specific details of origin are given, this indicates a more serious wine, such as Deinhard Lila Imperial Riesling. Although the most common Sekt, Henkel, comes into the neutral segment of the wheel, with grapes grown in such a northerly clime, there will always be a firm acidity in German Sekt. There may be a hint of honey too, especially if the base is ripe Riesling, but more often than not there is a none-too-inspiring dusty quality about the wine.

FULLER FLAVOURED

One of the keys to the elegance of champagne is the acidity in the base wine. Wines coming from warmer regions are automatically handicapped without the natural advantage of the Champagne region. Their producers may use the same grape varieties as champagne; they may believe the soil to be similar to that of Champagne and the production method identical – perhaps even performed by Champenois who have learnt their skills in Reims and Epernay – but the flavour will not be the same, for the one thing that is different is the climate. Longer hours of sunshine make riper grapes, with lower acidity and richer flavours, all of which translate into a wine with fuller, riper flavours. These producers may try to compensate by picking the grapes before they are fully ripe or by seeking out particularly cool vineyard sites, often at higher altitudes, with sharp contrasts between day and night-time temperatures. Some are successful, others not. Perhaps the dividing line between this segment and competitors to the real thing is somewhat blurred, for the origins of both may be the same.

There is no doubt that acidity is a key flavour factor. The fuller-flavoured wines tend to be lower in acidity and lack the intrinsic elegance that should be present in good champagne. But this does not mean that they are not worthwhile drinks in their own right, and they sometimes have a significant price advantage.

Italy

Asti Spumante and Lambrusco may be Italy's best-known sparkling wines, but there are numerous examples of dry sparkling wines, especially in the north-eastern part of the country. Sometimes the grape varieties are indigenous, like Prosecco; sometimes they are more recent introductions, like Chardonnay or Pinot Noir. The method is usually, but not always, that of Champagne, which the Italians call metodo classico. Sometimes these wines come from a region where there is a long tradition of sparkling wine; sometimes they are the result of an attempt to diversify within a DOC, alongside a still wine, such as Verdicchio; and sometimes they provide yet another challenge or source of experimentation to satisfy the curiosity of an eager winemaker.

The main DOCs for sparkling wine, apart from Lambrusco and Asti Spumante, are **Oltrepò Pavese, Trentino, Prosecco di Conegliano di Valdobbiadene**, which tends to be lightly sparkling or frizzante, as opposed to fully spumante, and **Franciacorta Spumante** (as opposed to the still wines), but more often than not it is simply the producer's name on the label that provides the clue to choice and quality, for much spumante is made without any reference to regional DOC regulations. Names to watch for include Berlucchi, Ca'del Bosco and Bellavista from Franciacorta, Carpené Malvolti from Conegliano and Ferrari and Equipe 5 from Trentino.

Cava

Although **cava** comes into another taste segment, there is one exception, namely the occasional cava made from Chardonnay rather than the indigenous grape varieties of Penedès. Wines like Raimat's and Codorníu's Chardonnay have a rich, full-flavoured taste. They are ripe and buttery and can be blowsy and overblown, but what they may lack in elegance, they make up for in flavour, compared with the average, traditional cava.

Australia

There is no doubt that **Australia** is one of the best sources of good-value quaffable bubbles. Take a wine like Yalumba's Angas Brut or Penfold's Killawarra Brut: they may not be subtle and refined, but they are fresh and well made. Angas Brut, based on Semillon and made by the transfer method, is a reliable and inexpensive glass of bubbles; it is full of flavour, slightly biscuity, low in acidity and eminently drinkable.

Other Australian bubbles have more pretensions to finesse. Some succeed, while others remain in the full-flavoured category, lacking that indefinable touch of elegance that puts them above the others. Wines that remain firmly in this segment of the wheel include Seppelt's Imperial Brut, Orlando's Carrington with its ripe easy-to-drink fruit, Seaview Brut and Rosemount Brut, all with fresh, well-made bubbles, some weight and flavour.

California

Just about every **California** sparkling wine that crosses the Atlantic aspires to emulate champagne, usually not only in flavour but also in price. Some succeed better than others. However, in general, they all tend to have a richness and lack of acidity that separates them from champagne; there is a full-flavoured biscuity character that detracts from their elegance, but they may on occasion be infinitely more appealing than a lean, acidic champagne.

Schramsberg is the winery that set the pace in California. Older established houses like Hans Kornell and Korbel had made little impact outside the domestic market until, in 1965, Jack and Jamie Davies bought the historic Napa Valley winery which has links with Robert Louis Stevenson. They planted Chardonnay and Pinot Noir and quickly established a reputation for excellent champagne-method sparkling wine.

About the same time, Domaine Chandon was set up in the Napa Valley, representing the first investment in California by a champagne house. In the past 15 years numerous others have followed their example, namely Roederer, Mumm, Deutz, Piper Heidsieck, Taittinger, as well as a couple of cava producers, Codorníu and Freixenet.

Iron Horse has also come on the scene as another true California sparkling wine, as well as Schaffenberg, which has a link with Lanson. There is no doubting the expertise, with so many wines master-minded by champagne houses, but many of them lack that indefinable something that separates them from champagne. They are richer and fuller, with less acidity, riper more biscuity flavours – they may even verge on the clumsy. The better ones, however, do offer an alternative to the real thing.

South Africa

Like Australia and California, South African sparkling wine appears in various segments of the wheel. The better wines, such as Charles de la Fère from the Villiera Wine Estate, have some fresh, lightly yeasty fruit, while others are not as distinguished, and suffer from the disadvantage of a warm climate.

India

India is a highly unlikely source of sparkling wine, or any wine, for that matter. However, high in the hills of the Maharashtra region near Bombay, vineyards of Chardonnay, Pinot Blanc and Ugni Blanc have been planted, and sparkling wine is produced under the guidance of a former winemaker of Piper Heidsieck. The resulting wine, Omar Khayyam, is remarkably good under the circumstances, with some ripe fruit and fat yeasty flavours. The quality can be a little inconsistent, but it makes up for that in curiosity value.

> Once in the bottle a cork can last for decades but eventually it becomes brittle and crumbly with age.

SWEET WINE

Asti Spumante

Good **Asti Spumante** is wonderfully luscious and fresh. It is made from Muscat grapes and should really taste of the grape. As with all good Muscat wines, it is the flavour of the grape itself that gives the wine its intrinsic appeal. With no aspirations whatsoever to imitate champagne, unlike most other Italian sparklers, Asti (from vineyards around the eponymous town, near Turin, in Piedmont) is the most individual of all Italian spumante. It is unashamedly sweet, but it should never be cloying and must always be drunk as young and fresh as possible – within a year or two at the most. It has the advantage of being low in alcohol, for no sugar or yeast are added to induce the second fermentation. Instead, the first fermentation is stopped, leaving some sugar in the wine, and the carbon dioxide from the first fermentation is retained in the tank, as a variation on the cuve close method.

Good producers include the Viticoltori dell'Acquese who makes some perfectly delicous Asti. Fontanafredda is good too, while some of the big vermouth houses (Turin is the vermouth capital of Italy) also make respectable Asti, namely Gancia, Martini & Rossi and Cinzano. Freshness and youth are the keys to enjoyment, along with the right balance of grapiness and sweetness.

Moscato d'Asti is similar, but not quite as fizzy. Sparkling **Moscadello di Montalcino**, from producers like Banfi and Col d'Orcia, also has the same appealing grapiness.

Lambrusco

White **Lambrusco** fits into the sweet, low acidity, cuve close segment of the wheel. However, its charm is pale compared to Asti. The wine lacks the real luscious depth of flavour of Asti, for it is made from red Lambrusco grapes and vinified off the skins so that no colour is retained in the wine. Fermentation takes place in a tank, and the sweetness comes from the judicious addition of grape concentrate. The result is pretty bland, quite sweet and fairly neutral, with low acidity. It is easy to drink if well chilled, and then instantly forgettable.

The other sweet Italian sparkler comes from **Soave**. Although Soave is known principally as a dry white wine, a traditional technique of drying the grapes makes sweet **Recioto di Soave**, which may be either still or sparkling. Usually it is still, but the occasional sparkling version is quite full and flavoursome, with some richness.

Clairette de Die Tradition

This wine comes from a tiny appellation situated on a tributary of the Rhône. The rather neutral Clairette is the principal grape variety, but the addition of a small amount of Muscat changes the flavour into a fresh, lightly grapey sweet wine, with a fresh juicy vitality. The method is that of champagne, producing more alcohol than Asti and a mousse with longer staying power. The key here is the word 'tradition' on the label; otherwise the wine is made from Clairette alone, and so will have infinitely less individuality. Virtually the sole producer is the village co-operative.

Champagne

We are so accustomed to drinking dry **champagne** (usually labelled brut) that we tend to overlook the fact that the need to add the dosage to champagne allows the level of sweetness or otherwise to be significantly altered. The wording on the label, at first glance, has little bearing on the actual taste in the bottle for, while brut may indeed mean very dry, confusingly it is drier than extra dry, and sec is medium-dry and demi-sec positively sweet. Doux is very sweet, indeed intensely so, but is rarely made these days. Most sweet champagne is likely to be labelled demi-sec, and in reality it represents only a tiny percentage of the champagne market and is hardly ever seen, except occasionally in France served with dessert, or in Eastern Europe where people generally have a sweeter tooth.

PINK WINE

Champagne

Pink champagne is underrated, for it is fiendishly difficult to make. Great skill lies in obtaining just the desired depth of colour: not too pale or the wine will seem wishy-washy, and not too dark or it will be heavy and clumsy. There are two ways to make pink champagne; either you leave the juice in contact with the grape skins long enough for it to absorb the required amount of colour; or you can blend a tiny proportion of still red wine into the white base wine. This is one of the very rare instances when it is permitted to blend red and white wine together in order to make pink wine and it is the more common way to make pink champagne because it provides a closer control of the colour. Even so, account must be taken of the effect of the second fermentation on the depth of colour, for some colour is generally lost during the fermentation.

Most of the major houses include a pink champagne in their repertoire, and occasionally even a pink vintage wine, but some take it more seriously than others. Names to look out for are Alfred Gratien, Louis Roederer, Bruno Paillard, Laurent Perrier and Billecart-Salmon. Pink champagne is always more expensive than the non-vintage brut from the same house, for the simple reason that it is more difficult and therefore more expensive to produce.

As for taste, pink champagne should have a delicate flavour of raspberries, with the dry yeasty tang which is characteristic of champagne. The extra dollop of red grapes in the blend provides backbone and body, but it should not be heavy or coarse. Instead, it should be subtle and flavoursome, though sometimes with a little more weight than a normal champagne.

Champagne method

The **Loire Valley** is the major source of pink sparkling wine in France. All the main producers, such as Gratien & Meyer, Bouvet-Ladubay and Langlois-Château include it in their ranges. The grape varieties may include Pinot Noir (but not Pinot Meunier) and, more likely, Cabernet Franc and Gamay, and perhaps Cabernet Sauvignon and Groslot. Rather than blending red and white juice, the colour tends to come from a limited period of skin contact. The two principal appellations are **Saumur** and **Crémant de Loire**, and the wines are generally crisp and fresh, with good acidity and delicate raspberry or strawberry fruit, and are perhaps even firmer and fuller bodied than pink champagne. Prices are distinctly competitive with champagne.

The appellation **Crémant de Bourgogne** also encompasses rosé, originating in this instance from Pinot Noir or Gamay. The main centres of sparkling wine production in Burgundy include Nuits-St-Georges, the tiny hamlet of Bailly, just outside the appellation of Chablis, and Rully in the Côte Chalonnaise. Pink Crémant de Bourgogne is the closest alternative in taste to pink champagne because of some similarity in grape variety, but it never quite has the finesse and elegance of good pink champagne. Good examples come from the Cave de Bailly, sometimes under the brand name Meurgis, and also from André Delorme in Rully. There is also the occasional **Crémant d'Alsace** rosé.

Across the Pyrenees, a small amount of pink **cava** is made by blending Garnacha Tinta and Monastrell with the usual cava grapes, Parellada, Macabeo and Xarel-lo. The flavour is slightly dusty, heavier and less acidic than anything from France.

Northern **Italy** has a flourishing sparkling wine industry, with producers like Berlucchi in Franciacorta making some very acceptable pink spumante. Other names to look out for include Bellavista, Ca' del Bosco, also in Franciacorta, as well as Equipe 5 from Trentino and Monsupello from Oltrepò Pavese. Again the champagne method is used and the resulting wine is quite full and fruity, with less acidity than French counterparts, but usually with a little more elegance than Spanish cava.

There is the odd example of pink bubbles made by the champagne method from the **New World**, such as California's Cuvée de Pinot from Schramsberg, which has some soft raspberry fruit, and Mumm's Cuvée Napa Rosé . However, the most popular Australian pink sparkler is Yalumba's Angas Brut which is made *not* by the champagne method but by the transfer method. The result is a wine that is full-bodied, with soft, ripe raspberry fruit, and which is excellent value for money. It may lack acidity and elegance, but proves immensely quaffable when well chilled. Killawarra Rosé from Penfolds is comparable in flavour and price, as is Orlando Carrington Brut Rosé, while Taltarni Brut Taché is a little drier and crisper. From New Zealand, Montana makes a pink version of its Lindauer sparkling wine which is dry and fresh.

England, too, makes some pink sparkling wine: Tenterden produces a sparkling rosé with some raspberry fruit and fresh acidity.

Cuve close

Traditionally, **Lambrusco** is a sparkling red wine. However, with the extension of its commercial popularity, the colour range has been widened to include pink Lambrusco, made by the cuve close method from the same Lambrusco grapes that are used for the red wine, but with minimal skin contact. Often it is lightly sweet and lacking in acidity. Its chief virtue is that it is innocuous.

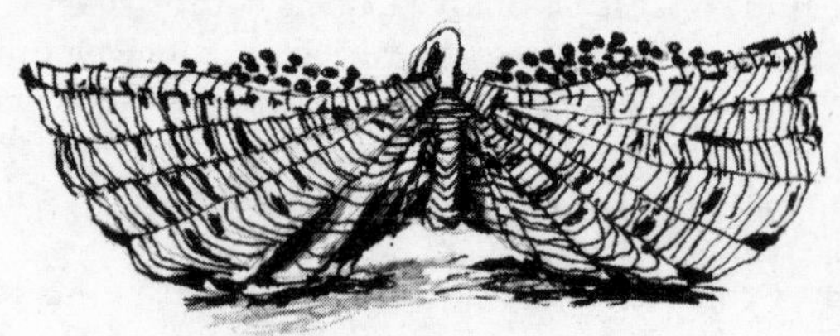

RED WINE

Cuve close

Red bubbles are a pretty unusual, not to mention an acquired, taste. The most obvious example is **Lambrusco**, which is considered a bit of a joke, partly because the true traditional Lambrusco has been distorted to include pink or blush, as well as white. In addition, some producers have pandered to commercial taste and have turned Lambrusco into a sweet wine, when traditionally the real thing is garnet-red and firmly dry.

Lambrusco takes its name from the grape of the same name, which is grown in the region of Emilia-Romagna. A variety of different Lambruscos are produced, some that are DOC, and some that are not. It can all be rather confusing – the best Lambrusco is Lambrusco de Sorbara, Sorbara being both a sub-variety of the grape and also the name of the particular area in the centre of the province of Modena where it is grown. It has perfumed cherry fruit, fresh acidity and a firm, bitter finish which goes remarkably well with the rich regional cuisine of Bologna and Modena. Good producers include Cavicchioli, Chiarli and Giacobazzi. Other good examples are Lambrusco Grasparossa di Castelvetro and Lambrusco Salamino di Santa Croce, and you can also find Lambrusco di Modena and Lambrusco Reggiano, or just plain red Lambrusco, which is probably best avoided. Lambrusco is not fully frothy, but gently fizzy, and above all it must be young and fresh.

Champagne method

A tiny amount of sparkling red **burgundy** is still produced from Pinot Noir and Gamay, and it tends to be rather dry and heavy. The same goes for red **Crémant de Loire** and **Saumur**, made from Cabernet Franc, Cabernet Sauvignon, Gamay and Groslot. These are definitely of minority interest, with some cherry fruit and acidity and more body than is usually appealing in a sparkling wine. Gratien & Meyer's Noir de Noirs Cardinal goes particularly well with a bowl of strawberries.

Australia is an unexpected source of red bubbles, but Seppelt has indeed added a sparkling Shiraz to its range which is distinctive and original in flavour, reminiscent of blackcurrant fruit gums and frothy blackcurrant juice – which is perhaps something of an acquired taste (but as a talking point...).

Part III

Where to buy wine

Symbols

Denotes generally low prices and/or a large range of modestly priced wines.

A merchant given this symbol offers exceptionally good service. We rely on readers' reports in allocating service symbols; this means that there may be merchants offering first-class service who appear here with no symbol, because such distinction has gone unreported. Readers, please report!

A merchant awarded this symbol makes a special effort to train staff to a high standard in wine knowledge, so advice from behind the counter should be particularly reliable. Other merchants without this symbol may also offer good advice – please report.

Indicates high-quality wines across the range.

This award is given for a wide range of wines from around the world.

Best buys

These are the Editor's choice of four out of a group of wines selected by the merchant in question as being distinguished in terms of value for money, or offering very fine quality regardless of price. In most instances, two wines at under £5 and two at over £5 have been selected. A very few merchants were unwilling to nominate any wines as their best buys and so the recommendations here may be restricted.

A & A Wines

Smithbrook Kilns, nr Cranleigh, Surrey GU6 8JJ
Tel (0483) 274666

Case sales only **Open** Mon–Fri 9.30–5.30; Sat 10–2 **Closed** Sun, public holidays **Credit cards** Access, Visa; personal and business accounts **Discounts** On 6–19 cases and 20+ cases **Delivery** Free to Surrey, Sussex, Hampshire, Middlesex; London (min 5 case order); mail order available **Glass hire** Free; breakages charged for **Tastings and talks** 2 large wine tastings in June and Oct/Nov; 6 smaller tutored tastings; themed months featuring a particular country or region **Cellarage** £2.50 per case per year

With walls six feet thick and no natural daylight, the old brick kilns at Cranleigh are ideal for wine storage. The kilns are home to A & A Wines, run by Andrew Connor and Andrew Bickerton. Regular tastings are held in these fairly unusual surroundings, often hosted by winemakers.

Most wine areas of the world are represented on the list, but the main emphasis is on Spain. Ten bodegas, including Riojanas and AGE, provide a range of red and white Riojas; Penedès wines are from Torres and the small family-owned Bodega Alsina & Sarda. A clutch of wines from Gutierrez in Valladolid provides interesting and good-value drinking.

Italy and Germany have reasonable selections, although the pattern does not seem to change much from year to year. A collection of vintages from Cissac looks interesting in the Bordeaux section; burgundies are mainly from small producers. Australian wines come from two big yet good producers – Seppelt and Wyndham – and South Africans now include a range from the Avontuur Estate as well as the usual KWV wines.

A & A also arranges annual trips to the vineyards.

Best buys

Artesa Rioja 1990, Bodegas Ontanon, Spain, £
Moyston Semillon/Chardonnay, 1991 South-East Australia, £
Rioja Campo Viejo Reserva 1982, Spain, ££
Frank Phélan 1986, second wine of Ch. Phélan-Ségur, ££

Best buys
£ denotes a bottle costing under £5
££ denotes a bottle costing over £5

Abbey Cellars

The Abbey, Preston Road, Yeovil, Somerset BA21 3AR *Tel* (0935) 76228

Case sales only **Open** Tue, Wed, Fri 11.30–6; Sat 10–3 **Closed** Sun and Mon; Thur by appointment only; public holidays **Credit cards** Access, Visa **Discounts** Available depending on quantity **Delivery** Free within 20-mile radius of Yeovil and west central London (min order 1 case); £5 per case outside van area **Glass hire** Free **Tastings and talks** Tastings held twice a year; in-store tastings throughout the year **Cellarage** Not available

There is a small but well-chosen collection from Abbey Cellars in Yeovil, with the emphasis on getting good flavour for your money. Wines rarely stray over £10 and only then with good reason. Clarets are represented by an impressive selection of petits châteaux, including the well-made Ch. La Tour St-Bonnet from Haut-Médoc. The high notes are given by Amiral de Beychevelle 1984 and Ch. La Rose Trintaudon 1983 (which only just tip over the £10 mark). Burgundies provide enough choice to sample the flavour of the area; the Rhônes include La Vieille Ferme from the Côtes du Ventoux; and among the Loires is Tinel-Blondelet's excellent Pouilly Fumé. French country wines look worth spending some time on, none of them costing over £5. There is little excitement from Spain and Italy despite a reasonable choice of wines from both. The New World includes a sound selection from Australia: Seaview, Seppelt, Penfolds and Plantagenet. New to the list this year are four South African wines from Hamilton-Russell and Bovlei.

For all its good wines and good prices, the range is very limited. Perhaps the planned retail outlet might encourage a little more adventure at the Abbey.

Best buys

Cuvée Jean Paul house wines, £
Señorio de Los Llanos Reserva 1984, Valdepeñas, £
Bew Cabernet Sauvignon 1983, Weinert, Argentina, ££
Plantagenet Chardonnay 1990, Western Australia, ££

Ad Hoc World of Wine

363 Clapham Road, London SW9 9BT *Tel* 071-326 1799

Open Mon–Fri 9–7.30; Sat 10–7.30 **Closed** Sun, public holidays **Credit cards** Access, Visa; personal and business accounts **Discounts** Quantity discounts available **Delivery** Free within M25 **Glass hire** Free (deposit required) **Tastings and talks** Monthly in-store tastings; to wine clubs by arrangement; Bulgarian evenings organised **Cellarage** Not available

There is a strong Bulgarian theme at this wine warehouse in Clapham, which is not surprising as it is owned by Bulgarian Vintners. From the cheap but good country wines right up to special reserves, the whole range is available. And if you really want to appreciate the flavour of Bulgaria, Ad Hoc devotes monthly tastings to the area. But this is just a tiny part of the range and there is a tremendous selection from the rest of the world.

From the non-classic regions of France Ad Hoc brings you 50 or so wines for under £5. Vins de pays, Minervois, Hérault, Roussillon and Madiran crowd the shelves of the warehouse and provide endless good-value drinking. There is a fine choice of clarets, most of them priced below £10, and the range includes Domaine la Grave 1986 made by Peter Vinding-Diers. The upper price bands are occupied by a few second wines from top-flight châteaux, such as a Carruades de Lafite Rothschild and Forts de Latour, plus a smattering of cru classé wines including Haut-Brion 1982.

Burgundy drinkers are well provided for, and the Rhône includes plenty of solid flavour from Chapoutier, among others. The Italian section is well chosen: only a few super-priced Super Tuscans here, the rest are traditional wines made by good producers. Similar enthusiasm exists about Spain, with a clutch of good Riojas and a sprinkling of Torres and Jean León.

Sampling the tremendous New World range should keep the residents of Clapham busy and, apart from the Grange Hermitage, only a few Californians stray over the £10 price mark.

Ad Hoc looks and sounds like a warehouse but has a retail licence which allows you to buy single bottles as well as by the case.

Best buys

Côtes-du-Rhône-Villages 1990, Lastours-Clocher, £
Domaine St-Jean 1990, Vin de Pays de l'Hérault, £
Chablis St-Martin 1990, Vieilles Vignes, Domaine Laroche, ££
Jamieson's Run 1989, Coonawarra, Australia, ££

Adnams Wine Merchants

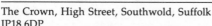

The Crown, High Street, Southwold, Suffolk IP18 6DP — *Tel* (0502) 724222

The Cellar & Kitchen Store, Victoria Street, Southwold, Suffolk IP18 6DP — *Tel* (0502) 724222

The Grapevine, Cellar & Kitchen Store, 109 Unthank Road, Norfolk, Norwich NR2 2PE — *Tel* (0603) 613998

Open (The Crown) Mon–Fri 9–5; (Cellar & Kitchen Store) Mon–Sat 10–6 (Southwold), 9–9 (Norwich) **Closed** Sun, public holidays **Credit cards** Access, Visa; personal and business accounts **Discounts** 5% on 12 cases **Delivery** Free on UK mainland (min 2 cases); otherwise £5 (1 case); mail order available **Glass hire** Free **Tastings and talks** To groups on request; 3 public tastings a year (London and Suffolk in May, Norwich in autumn) at £7.50 per person (£5 refundable against purchase); up to 40 bottles always available in Southwold store **Cellarage** £5 per case per year

Not only is Adnams interested in what we drink but it has our sartorial elegance at heart, too. The latest addition to the list is a range of exuberant ties and waistcoats with a grapes and vine leaves design. In colours that are a shade more violent than most club ties, these will nevertheless distinguish you as a member of a widespread and well-informed wine-drinking fraternity.

Adnams has shops in Southwold and Norwich as well as a pub and a hotel, but most of its customers know the company via the list which thuds on to the doormat every May. It is a user-friendly list packed with information about vintages, winemakers and wines, all written about in the enthusiastic style of Adnams' director and buyer, Simon Loftus. It is the kind of list that whets the appetite and encourages you to try the many new additions to the range. Who could resist trying the Remelluri Rioja 1989 once they have heard how it was prised away from the producer, or Charlie Melton's Nine Popes with its odd but apposite name?

However, nothing gains its place on this list just by having the right name on the label. Each wine has been selected by Simon Loftus and his team for character and style. They sell wines they like to drink themselves and while this can leave some areas rather bare – such as Eastern Europe (apart from Tokay) – their obvious enthusiasm for other regions brings dividends.

The South of France section has grown – each wine is described in typical Loftus style, with tasting notes like lime blossom, wild pears, chocolate, tar and brambles conjuring up flavours on the page. Burgundy has expanded this year with a wonderful collection of wines from individual growers. The huge choice of Puligny-Montrachets accompanies the launch of the latest Loftus book about that village. Italy shows a particular passion for wines with distinctly different flavours, while the Australian section has expanded so much that a special supplement is planned. Half-bottles and magnums are a speciality, as are mixed 'sample' cases from each of the regions.

If your only contact with Adnams is by phone, help and advice are always available, but if you should decide to head off for some bracing east coast sea air, the tasting room at the Cellar & Kitchen store has a huge collection of wines open and ready for tasting.

Best buys

Ozidoc Sauvignon 1991, Vin de Pays d'Oc, £
Vinho Verde Tinto 1991, Cooperativa da Ponte da Lima, Portugal, £
Sauvignon 1991, Ojai Vineyards, Napa, California, ££
Remelluri Rioja 1989, ££

David Alexander

69 Queen Street, Maidenhead, Berkshire SL6 1LT — *Tel* (0628) 30295

Open Mon 10–7; Tue–Thur 10–8.30; Fri–Sat 10–9; Sun 12–2 **Closed** Public holidays **Credit cards** All accepted; personal and business accounts **Discounts** 5% on 1 case **Delivery** Free in Maidenhead and M4 corridor to west London (min 1 case order) **Glass hire** Free with order **Tastings and talks** In-store tastings once every three months; to groups on request **Cellarage** Available (charges on request)

This well-stocked shop in Maidenhead offers something from everywhere, with the focus on quality and individuality. From France, the range of clarets is surprisingly wide – there are good petits châteaux, a few second wines and some older vintages from the 1970s. Burgundies are from a variety of growers and *négociants*; the Rhône selection is impressive, with an extensive range from Delas, including the Marquise de la Tourette Hermitage, at fairly reasonable prices. Elsewhere in France there is plenty of choice, and it is encouraging to see a few unusual wines, such as a Pinot Noir from Jura and half-bottles of Vin Jaune.

Germany provides mainly estate wines, Italy a tasty selection, and Spain is popular, with La Rioja Alta wines, Ochoa Navarras and two vintages of Vega Sicilia. Australia is another favourite area: Peter Lehmann, Pikes, Pirramimma and Petaluma produce wines with bags of flavour for your money. With more wines from the USA, Canada, Chile and South Africa, it is not surprising that the shelves and racks of this shop are stuffed full. The two partners, David Wright and John Leech, claim to have the hottest delivery service on two cylinders – we presume they mean speed not temperature – and with one case delivered free along the M4 corridor from Reading to west London they are not only hot but diligent, too.

Best buys

St Pourçain Chardonnay 1990, Jutier et Serra, £
Vin de Pays des Côteaux de l'Ardèche, Cabernet Sauvignon 1990, Caves Co-operatives de Montfleury Mirabelle, £
Riesling Trocken 1990, Dr Loosen, Mosel, ££
Campbells Rutherglen Shiraz 1988, Victoria, Australia, ££

Ameys Wines

83 Melford Road, Sudbury, Suffolk CO10 6JT *Tel* (0787) 77144

Open Tue–Sat 10–7 **Closed** Sun, Mon, public holidays **Credit cards** Access, Visa **Discounts** 5% on 1 case **Delivery** Free delivery within 20-mile radius of Sudbury (min order £50+) **Glass hire** Free **Tastings and talks** Free tastings most Saturdays **Cellarage** Not available

High business rates drove Ameys out of Colchester three years ago, but what was Colchester's loss was definitely Sudbury's gain. This retail shop has a wide, well-structured range which could keep the local populace supplied for quite some time. New additions arrive as Peter Amey finds room for them.

Australian wines seem to do well in this part of East Anglia, and the choice of over 50 includes not only the big names of Rosemount, Seppelt and Hardy but also some small producers such as Schinus Molle and Coldstream Hills. There is even an organic Tasmanian wine from Buchanan. Other New World areas, such as California and Chile, are represented by a small but good selection including the super Montes wines from Chile. South Africa is strangely absent from this cosmopolitan collection. Italy has seen some recent additions, with Chiantis from Felsina Berardenga and Fattoria di Vetrice and the super Barco Reale from Villa Capezzana. Spain's contribution consists of quality wines from Torres and Berberana. The French section covers all the regions well – a reasonable choice of petits châteaux wines, with a few classed growths for when the occasion demands. Rhônes include the good-value La Vieille Ferme made by the Perrins of Ch. de Beaucastel fame and there are two organic burgundies from Jean Musso. Wines from south-west France and Languedoc-Roussillon provide further choice for under £5.

Free tastings are held in the shop most Saturdays, which seems like a pleasant way to avoid doing the family shopping.

Best buys

Eden Ridge Dry White 1991, David and Adam Wynn, South Australia, £
Villa Montes Cabernet Sauvignon 1989, Curicó, Chile, £
Cabernet Sauvignon/Merlot 1988, Dromana Estate, Victoria, Australia, ££
Elston Chardonnay 1989, Te Mata, New Zealand, ££

Les Amis du Vin

(Mail order only)
430 High Road, London NW10 2HA *Tel* 081-459 8011
Shops
The Winery, 4 Clifton Road, London W9 1SS *Tel* 071-286 6475
Les Amis du Vin, 51 Chiltern Street, London W1M 1HQ *Tel* 071-487 3419

Open Mon–Fri 10.30–8.30, Sat 10–6.30 (W9); Mon–Fri 10.30–7, Sat 10.30–5 (W1); Mon–Fri 9.15–5.15 (office) **Closed** Sun, public holidays **Credit cards** All accepted; personal and business accounts **Discounts** 5% per bottle, 10% per unmixed case for wine club members; 5% per unmixed case for non-club members **Delivery** Free on UK mainland (min 3 cases); otherwise £3.95 to Greater London, £5.50 elsewhere on UK mainland, £10 to Scottish Highlands and offshore UK deliveries **Glass hire** Free with order **Tastings and talks** Regular tastings through Les Amis du Vin Wine Club; to groups on request **Cellarage** Available

Les Amis du Vin has joined forces with the Wine Growers Association and now both companies operate from the same address and the same joint list, called the Wine Portfolio.

The Wine Growers Association is a straightforward mail-order business with a 5 per cent discount on unmixed cases and free delivery on three cases or more. Les Amis du Vin operates like a club, with a £15 subscription (for life membership) which entitles you to a 5 per cent discount on all Portfolio prices and 10 per cent on unmixed cases. Les Amis Club members also get discount at the two London shops. This confusing situation is probably a legacy from the merging of two businesses.

Apparently, the two mailing lists are deemed to provide for different tastes, so the monthly offers vary and Les Amis members get *en primeur* offers and priority booking for tastings.

Apart from the confusion regarding what you will be offered and how much you will pay, the Wine Portfolio is well worth getting hold of. Many of the wines have come through another associated company – Geoffrey Roberts – who is a major importer and wholesaler to the trade. The emphasis on California is particularly strong, with a terrific range from Acacia, Calera, Edna Valley, Heitz, Phelps, Sanford and

Schramsberg, to mention just a few. Each area and winery is introduced and described in the list.

The Australian section has the excellent wines of Rothbury, Pewsey Vale and Petaluma and a complete range from Yalumba. Chile and South Africa are strangely absent but the European stars are from Italy and France – the Italians from admired reliable producers such as Tedeschi, Borgogno and Pagliarese; the French wines revealing a satisfying selection of clarets and burgundies. Once again, top-notch producers abound.

The two London shops are well worth a visit. Small, cramped and stacked to the ceiling with goodies, how they manage to hold tastings there we just can't imagine!

Best buys

Spanna del Piemonte 1988, Agostino Brugo, Italy, £
Bel Arbors Chardonnay 1989, California, £
Pinot Noir, Jensen Vineyard 1988, Calera, California, ££
Savigny, Champ-Chevrey 1986, Tollot-Beaut, ££

John Armit Wines 

190 Kensington Park Road, London W11 2ES *Tel* 071-727 6846

Case sales only **Open** Mon–Fri 8.30–7 **Closed** Sat, Sun, public holidays **Credit cards** Access, Visa; personal and business accounts **Discounts** Not available **Delivery** Free for 3+ cases; otherwise £10 for 1 case, £15 for 2 cases; mail order available **Glass hire** Not available **Tastings and talks** Tastings held 3 times annually; regular special dinners **Cellarage** Approx £6.90 per case (inc insurance)

The style of this list tells you that you are dealing with a quality merchant: the pages of wine are interspersed with prints of specially commissioned modern paintings. For the 1991/2 list the featured artist is Paul Benney; the originals are for sale.

France is the mainstay of this list, with clarets introduced vintage by vintage and accompanied by good notes for each region and wine. Classed growths are available not only in bottles but in magnums, double-magnums and imperiales. It is always a good idea to compare prices when buying top clarets and at John Armit this rule still applies. On Ausone 1983 you can save £140 a case by buying from Adnams; however, the same vintage of Ducru-Beaucaillou is considerably cheaper here than from the rest of the competition.

Not all the wines on the list have prices in three or four figures; there are pockets of good bottles, particularly from Fronsac, at quite tolerable prices. Burgundies are arranged by grower or domaine. There are plenty of reasonable wines, but Armit hits the heights with a grand collection from Domaine de la Romanée-Conti. The rest of France is fairly limited: four wines from the Loire, three from Alsace; however, the Rhône section has a little more choice with astute selections from Guigal and Jaboulet. Nothing from Italy, Portugal or Germany but the New World gets some acknowledgement – Groth, Hess, Ravenswood and the Dominus wines from California. Australia is limited to Cape Mentelle and the small but lovely Nicholson River winery.

Sales are strictly by the unmixed case and delivery free only on three or more cases, which limits custom to serious punters. You will have to be very serious to fork out £175 for an Armit dinner featuring mature wines from Domaine de la Romanée-Conti but the Argentine dinner at £40 is more digestible.

Best buys

Ch. Pitray 1988, Côtes de Castillon, £
Côtes-du-Rhône Domaine Bel Air 1990, Ryckwaert, £
Ch. Canon de Brem 1988, Fronsac, ££
Nicholson River Winery Pinot Noir 1989, Victoria, Australia, ££

Arriba Kettle

Mail order
Buckle Street, Honeybourne, Evesham, Hereford & Worcester WR11 5QB

Tel (0386) 833024 (24-hour telephone answering service)

Case sales only **Open** 24-hour telephone answering service **Credit cards** None accepted; business accounts **Discounts** From £1.75 on 3 cases to £3.25 on 11+ cases; £2 per case collected (by prior arrangement) **Delivery** Free on UK mainland (min 2 cases) **Glass hire** Free with order in West Midlands and north Cotswolds **Tastings and talks** For mail-order customers in November **Cellarage** Not available

'In the past few years,' says Barry Kettle, 'Spain's competitive edge has declined and so we look more and more to France.' Even so, this is still very much a Spanish list and deliciously so. Riojas are here in force from Bodegas Marqués de Cáceres, Marqués de Riscal, Martínez Bujanda, Berberana, Rioja Alta and others. Despite Barry's quote about value, the price of these Riojas is very competitive compared with those of other less-specialised mail-order merchants. Still in Spain, but outside Rioja, Torres represents the Penedès region, and the wines of Chivite provide the Navarras.

Sherries have pride of place at the start of the list. Five almacenistas from Lustau are not outrageous in the price stakes for such exclusive drinking.

The French wines are mainly from the Loire and Bordeaux: Pouilly Fumé comes from Domaine Caibourdin and Vouvray from Le Clos Baudoin. Clarets are limited but well chosen. Ch. Cissac is here, as is Les Gravières, a wine made by Cissac from grapes grown nearby. Other clarets include La Tour du Mirail from the Haut-Médoc and Ch. Victoria from Graves. Languedoc-Roussillon is an area new to this list.

The range is limited and, as Barry Kettle admits, is more influenced by personal choice than by commercial good sense. His taste is good, although the list is slightly disconcerting as he constantly refers to someone called Arriba whom we understand to mean A. Barry Kettle himself. (It is almost an anagram of the first bit of his name.) Still, if you can cope with this split personality, give Barry a ring.

Best buys

Chivite Gran Feudo Tinto 1987, £
Señorio de Los Llanos Gran Reserva 1983, £
Vouvray Le Clos Baudoin 1985, Prince Poniatowski, ££
Ch. La Tour du Mirail 1985, Haut-Médoc, ££

ASDA

Head office
ASDA House, South Bank, Great Wilson Street, Leeds, West Yorkshire LS11 5AD — *Tel* (0532) 435435
Approximately 205 branches nationwide

Open Mon–Fri 9–8 (Sat 8.30–8); Sun (selected stores) 10–5; selected stores also open on public holidays **Credit cards** Access, Visa **Discounts, delivery, glass hire** Not available **Tastings and talks** Approximately every four weeks (in specified stores) a selection of wines can be sampled **Cellarage** Not available

With wide aisles and artistic labels, ASDA is one supermarket where browsing becomes a pleasure. The range in bigger stores is huge and includes a sizeable fine wine section. As with most multiples, not all the stores have all the range, but even if your nearest store is a small one, there is still enough choice to make life interesting.

ASDA's main strength is its own-label wines. In some supermarkets this would mean downmarket packaging but not here. The artistic design reflects each wine and each country; they are distinctive without shouting ASDA in large letters. But you can't drink the label, so what of the wines? Value is the key word among the own-labels and, in general, each wine is good quality and individually reflects its grape and its region. Most of these own-labels sell for less than £3.50 which makes their quality and style even more amazing. Particularly good are León from Spain, and the Semillon/Chardonnay blend from South-Eastern Australia.

At the other end of the scale, ASDA is always worth checking out for finer wines which are displayed horizontally in racks. Not all are hugely expensive. The Australian Oxford Landing wines are available, both priced under £5. The racks are also where you will find Lustau's Almacenista sherries, Pavillon Rouge de Ch. Margaux, and the English-sounding Shiraz from Goulburn called Longleat.

In between the two extremes of fine wine and own-label is a reasonable selection of wines which are well worth a try. Organic claret from Ch. Vieux Georget; Maître d'Estournel, made by Bruno Prats; Bianco di Custoza from Zenato and the Argentinian Trapiche wines.

ASDA tells us that it is endeavouring to give staff more wine training, but, as in many supermarkets, there is often no one around to give help. Informative back labels are a distinct bonus in this case.

Best buys

ASDA Merlot, Vin de Pays d'Oc, £
Ch. Mayne de Grissac 1989, Côtes de Bourg, £
Wachenheimer Rechbachel, Riesling Kabinett, 1989, Nahe, Bürklin-Wolf, ££
Barolo Riserva 1986, Borgogno, ££

Askham Wines

Askham, Newark, Nottinghamshire
NG22 0RP

Tel (077 783) 659

Case sales only **Open** Mon–Fri 9–6; Sat 9–12 **Closed** Sun, public holidays **Credit cards** None accepted; personal and business accounts **Discounts** Available **Delivery** Free within 5-mile radius of Askham (min order 1 case) **Glass hire** Free with order **Tastings and talks** Two tastings per year (entrance charge discounted against orders) **Cellarage** Not available

Any wine merchant who attempts to run a business in this isolated area deserves a medal. Askham is a tiny (really tiny) village which you may come across as you drive from Lincoln to the A1. The area is known as the salesman's graveyard – there is no passing trade, no big towns, just lots of fields, pheasants and farms. In fact, it is rather pleasant. People who enjoy good wine are thin on the ground, and to survive a wine merchant must know his stuff and provide a good service. That is just what Andrew Brownridge does. He doubles as a prep-school headmaster during the day while his wife Elspeth keeps the business going. Between them their customers get pretty good service.

The range is small but well chosen. The emphasis is on individual growers and producers rather than the big names. Bordeaux is mainly affordable petits châteaux, burgundies are sparse but good, and Alsace wines come from the co-operative at Turckheim. Portugal is a particular enthusiasm and provides quality drinking at a reasonable price. South Africa is a fairly new addition to the range with four wines from Groot Constantia and the Fairview Pinot Noir.

When time permits, Andrew can be persuaded to give talks about his wines. His style is good (years of practice at the chalk-face) but you have to listen properly or you could find yourself staying in at play-time!

Best buys

Pinot Blanc Cave Tradition 1991, Cave Vinicole de Turckheim, £
Château Val Joanis Rouge 1990, Côtes du Lubéron, £
Gigondas Domaine de Montmirail 1986, ££
Chardonnay Hawk Crest 1990, California, ££

The Australian Wine Centre

AUSTRALIAN SPECIALIST AWARD

'Down Under', South Australia House, 50 Strand, London WC2N 5LW

Tel 071-925 0751
Tel 071-839 9021

Open Mon–Fri 10–7; Sat 10–4 **Closed** Sun, public holidays **Credit cards** Access, American Express, Visa; business accounts **Discounts** 5% on 1 case (to be collected) **Delivery** Free to mainland UK (min order £75); smaller orders £5; mail order available **Glass hire** Free **Tastings and talks** Winemakers' dinners and tastings to coincide with visiting Australian winemakers; Great Australian Wine Tastings held annually for members of The Australian Wine Club **Cellarage** Not available

If the thought of row upon row of Aussie wines just waiting to be bought excites you, experience a real thrill by taking a dive off the Strand into the Australian Wine Centre. There you will find the biggest range of Australian wines in the UK in a big, high-ceilinged cellar under South Australia House. Craig Smith and his team (Aussies naturally) are chatty and helpful, and will happily steer you through the assembled 300 wines, from good-value Jacobs Creek right up to the various vintages of Grange Hermitage which slumber in racks in the centre of the floor space.

With such a wide range, it is hard to pick out strengths, but Coldstream Hills, Mountadam, Tarrawarra, Yalumba and St Hallett are just some of the delights. A new range of wines from

Charles Melton includes the sensational Nine Popes and there are plenty of winter-warming Liqueur Muscats and Tawnies.

Conveniently for central London, there is a loading bay at the back of the building, and for those who don't want to battle through the traffic, the Australian Wine Centre has a mail-order service. Delivery is free anywhere in mainland UK for orders over £75. Once on the mail-order list, customers receive regular newsletters with details of new lines and special offers. The annual tasting is a splendid bash with hundreds of wines open for tasting and many visiting winemakers available for a chat.

Operating from the same address and from the same list is the New Zealand Wine Club. This is a mail-order operation with wines from 26 estates and companies. Villa Maria, Mills Reef and the Dashwood wines from Vavasour are here among many others. The list is well written and gives details about the wineries which might help you to make your selection: with a range as wide as this you need all the help you can get.

Best buys

Oxford Landing Chardonnay 1990, South Australia, £
Jacobs Creek Riesling 1991, £
St Hallett Old Block Shiraz 1990, Barossa Valley, ££
Cyril Henschke Cabernet Sauvignon 1989, Adelaide Hills, ££

Averys of Bristol

7 Park Street, Bristol, Avon BS1 5NG *Tel* (0272) 214141

Open Mon–Fri 9–6; Sat 9–5.30 **Closed** Sun, public holidays
Credit cards Access, Visa; personal and business accounts **Discounts** Available
Delivery Free within a 5-mile radius of Bristol; otherwise £5.50 if less than 2 cases ordered; mail order available **Glass hire** Free with orders **Tastings and talks** To groups on request **Cellarage** £4.50 per case per year

'Life is too short to drink cheap wine' announces the Averys' list, and to prove just what bad value a cheap bottle is, it provides a graphic comparison. In a £3 bottle the value of the wine is a mere 5 per cent, or 15p, whereas if you spend £6 then since duty, transport and bottling costs all stay the same the wine inside should be worth over £2. Every time this kind of cost breakdown is done, different people get different answers. Even so, the message is clear. The Government takes a large chunk of what you spend on a bottle and the only way to drink better wine is to spend more money. With Averys' list to hand, you will have no problems finding suitable wines. Clarets are here in depth – a good range of affordable generics and petits châteaux are followed by three pages of classier châteaux. Against each wine is an indication of whether it is ready to drink or whether it should be kept. This theme continues into the burgundies of which there are many, mainly from Remoissenet and Lupé-Cholet. The Rhône is fairly restrained while the Loire boasts no fewer than five Muscadets and also has some good Bourgueils and Chinons from Jacques Morin. French country wines and vins de table provide reasonably priced drinking while you wade through the rest of this heavyweight list.

The New World is splendid. Tyrrells, Rouge Homme and Penfolds are the main players from Australia with Piper's Brook Chardonnay from Tasmania making an appearance. New Zealand is represented (mainly) by Nobilo; California is a delight with wines from Belvedere, Swanson, Far Niente and many more; and South African wines include the excellent Rustenberg, Hamilton-Russell and Klein Constantia. (Old and rare wines such as vintage madeiras, aged ports and pre-Seventies clarets are not on the main list and have to be asked for separately.)

Averys operates a Bin Club, members of which pay in a regular amount each month and the credit is used to build up a cellar at discounted prices. There are also *en primeur* and special mixed-case offers, details of which are in the regular informative newsletters.

Averys is a traditional merchant which does not try to compete at the £3 level with high-street supermarkets – instead, it offers a quality range, traditional service and helpful advice, as befits a merchant established over 200 years ago.

Best buys

Merlot Domaine de Thelin 1990, Vin de Pays d'Oc, £
Cuvée Lupé-Cholet Blanc Vin de Table, £
Rustenberg Chardonnay 1990, South Africa, ££
Averys Fine Red Burgundy 1988, ££

All love at first, like generous wine,
Ferments and frets until 'tis fine;
But when 'tis settled on the lee,
And from th'impurer matter free,
Becomes the richer still the older,
And proves the pleasanter the colder.

Samuel Butler, *Miscellaneous Thoughts*

Barnes Wine Shop

51 Barnes High Street, London SW13 9LN *Tel* 081-878 8643

Open Mon–Sat 9.30–8.30; Sun 12–2 **Closed** Public holidays and Chr period **Credit cards** Access, Visa; personal and business accounts **Discounts** 5% on 1 mixed case (payment by credit card); 7% on payment by cash/cheque **Delivery** Free locally (min 2 cases); elsewhere negotiable; mail order available for 5 cases **Glass hire** Free with order **Tastings and talks** Regular in-store tastings (Sats); occasional private tastings **Cellarage** £6 per case per year

Francis Murray of the Barnes Wine Shop sees a trend away from the New World and back to traditional European wines. Even so, his New World list makes good reading, with Penley Estate, Coldstream Hills and Tim Adams among the Australians, Martinborough and Cloudy Bay weighing in for New Zealand, and a delightful choice from North America including Matanzas Creek from Sonoma and the hybrid Maréchal Foch from Canada. The resulting effect is variety, quality and style.

Back amongst the Europeans, Italy looks particularly impressive with a full countrywide range reflecting the terrific variety available. Umani Ronchi, Capezzana and Altesino are just some of the highlights; all are worth exploring.

The French list is equally enjoyable. Quality wines within a realistic price range is the key, with a good selection of rhônes, clarets and burgundies slipping well under the £10 price band. This company seems particularly well stocked for pudding wines from France, Germany and Australia.

Barnes Wine Shop does not issue a full list, but twice a year it points out certain interesting wines. Tastings are held every Saturday; it is by far the best way to find out what is in stock. There are expansionist plans in the pipeline, but no details yet. If this means another shop, it can only be good news for local residents.

Best buys

Caliterra Sauvignon Blanc 1991, Chile, £
Côtes du Ventoux 1990, Paul Boutinot, £
Vernaccia di San Gimignano 1990, Teruzzi & Puthod, ££
Shaw and Smith Chardonnay 1991, Adelaide Hills, ££

A man cannot make him laugh; but that's no marvel; he drinks no wine.

Shakespeare, *Henry IV (Part II)*

Augustus Barnett

Head office
3 The Maltings, Wetmore Road, Burton-on-Trent, Staffordshire DE14 1SE *Tel* (0283) 512550
Approximately 567 branches nationwide

Open Varies from store to store; most outlets open Mon–Sat 10–10; Sun, public holidays 12–2, 7–9.30 **Closed** Chr Day **Credit cards** Access, American Express, Visa; personal and business accounts **Discounts** 5% on 1 case **Delivery** Free locally from outlets (min 1 case) **Glass hire** Free **Tastings and talks** At selected branches **Cellarage** Not available

Like many chains in this *Guide*, Augustus Barnett has assessed and regraded all its branches this year. The aim of this exercise is to look more closely at customer needs to try to match demand with supply. The down side of any grading exercise is that if you live near a shop which is expected to sell beer, fags and Liebfraumilch then that is probably all you will get. The up side is that any good wines that are in your local Augustus Barnett store will not have been gathering dust under fluorescent lights for years. The stock is tailored to demand, and if you require something on the list which is not normally stocked you can order it by the single bottle. The manager we spoke to said he could get most items within a day or two.

The range is quite surprising: despite the 1.5-litre bottles of Lambrusco crowding the bottom shelves, there are some reasonable labels lurking above. France is well represented with a good supply of petit-château wines from £3.99 upwards. Parent company Bass owns Ch. Lascombes in Margaux and so there is a choice of vintages from this property. Burgundy, Alsace and the Loire provide further choice of reasonable drinking, and the French regional range has good names such as Duboeuf, Listel, Plaimont and Caves St-Pierre.

The New World range is fairly strong with Coldridge Estate, Hardy, Lindemans, Orlando and Penfolds supplying variety for between £3 and £6 a bottle. Wolf Blass President's selection and Black Label wines add a few top-notes. Santa Rita from Chile and several Bulgarians also have big flavours and small price-tags.

With local delivery, glass loan and occasional tastings in some branches, Augustus Barnett is beginning to look like a serious act in the wine business.

Best buys

Domaine St-Paul, Vin de Pays de l'Hérault 1990, £
Pinot Blanc Nagyrede 1990, Hungary, £
Ch. Lascombes 1985, Margaux, ££
President's Selection 1985, Wolf Blass, Australia, ££

Barwell & Jones

Head office
24 Fore Street, Ipswich, Suffolk IP4 1JU *Tel* (0473) 232322
Off-licences
118 Sprowston Road, Norwich, Norfolk NR3 4QH *Tel* (0603) 484966
70 Trumpington Street, Cambridge, Cambridgeshire CB2 1RJ *Tel* (0223) 354431
94 Rushmere Road, Ipswich, Suffolk IP4 4JL *Tel* (0473) 727426
The Cross Inn, 2 Church Street, Woodbridge, Suffolk IP12 1DH *Tel* (03943) 3288
Bacchante Wine Club, Freepost, Colchester, Essex CO4 5BR *Tel* (0206) 272868

Open Hours vary from branch to branch **Credit cards** Access, Visa; business accounts **Discounts** Quantity discounts available **Delivery** By arrangement; mail order available **Glass hire** Free with breakages charged for **Tastings and talks** To groups on request by arrangement with individual managers **Cellarage** Not available

Barwell & Jones has recently launched the Bacchante Wine Club for customers who are not within easy reach of its five East Anglia shops. Membership costs £16 (a once-only payment) and gives access to the full B & J list. Delivery isn't cheap for this mail-order service: single cases cost £6, and up to six cases are charged at £3 each. There is also another £1.20 surcharge for mixed cases.

However, the list is good. It is strong in the classic areas of France – Bordeaux, Burgundy and Loire wines – with agency Labouré-Roi featuring heavily in the Burgundy section. Alsace wines are from Pierre Sparr. Italy has an almost overwhelming number of Veneto wines from Guerrieri-Rizzardi; Piemonte wines are from Grimaldi, with the expensive but good 1985 Barolo from Bruno Giacosa making an appearance.

The South African selection is well worth spending some time on, featuring wines from Stellenryck, Meerlust and Uitkyk Carlonet. Hungarian wines include a massive selection of old vintages of Tokaji. All wines are available by mail order or through the retail shops.

Best buys

Uitkyk Carlsheim Sauvignon Blanc 1990, South Africa, £
Ch. Belingard Rouge 1989, Bergerac, £
Columbia Pinot Noir 1988, Washington State, ££
Côtes de Beaune La Régente 1989, Labouré-Roi, ££

The Battersea Wine Company

4 Battersea Rise, London SW11 1ED *Tel* 071-924 3631

Open Mon 5–9; Tue–Fri 12–9; Sat 10.30–9; Sun 12–3 **Closed** Public holidays **Credit cards** Access, Visa; personal and business accounts **Discounts** Available **Delivery** Free in south-west London (min order 1 case); free elsewhere (min order 3 cases) **Glass hire** Free with 1-case order **Tastings and talks** Weekly tastings (Sats); to groups on request **Cellarage** £5 per case per year

Rory MacNally, formerly of the Belfast Wine Company, is now manager in Battersea. He welcomes browsers and, apparently, has an ever-changing range of fine, mature wines. The list is well worth taking home for a study: there are no particularly strong areas; each region has a few well-chosen wines picked out from some of the most notable growers and producers.

From Spain, there are collections from CVNE and Berberana in Rioja, and Ochoa in Navarra. Italy is represented by the reliable wines of Umani Ronchi and Antinori; Miguel Torres appears not in the Spanish section but in Chile. From California come the wines of Villa Mount Eden and Shafer, as well as the collectors' pieces, Opus One and Dominus.

France is covered well – white burgundies are from Leflaive and Alsace wines from Gisselbrecht.

Best buys

Montepulciano d'Abruzzo 1990, Umani Ronchi, £
Tollana Shiraz/Cabernet 1990, Australia, £
Côtes-du-Rhône 1988, Guigal, ££
Givry Blanc 1989, Olivier Leflaive, ££

Bedford Fine Wines

Faulkners Farm, The Marsh, Carlton, Bedford, Bedfordshire MK43 7JU *Tel* (0234) 721153

Case sales only **Open** During office hours or by appointment only **Credit cards** None accepted; personal and business accounts **Discounts** Negotiable **Delivery** Free within 15-mile radius of Bedford (min value £80); elsewhere £5 per case on 1–2 cases, £3 per case on 3–4 cases **Glass hire** Free **Tastings and talks** Regular tastings **Cellarage** Not available

A fairly limited but well-chosen range is on offer from Bedford Fine Wines, with France being the main feature. A few respected properties form the core of the claret list: Palmer Angludet, Chasse-Spleen and Ch. de la Rivière, with a sprinkling of others here and there depending on the vintage. Burgundies are selective rather than being present in force but the names are good: Mongeard-Mugneret, Faiveley, William

Fèvre and Moillard. The Rhône's representative is essentially Guigal and the Alsace range comes from Caves de Turckheim and Dopff 'Au Moulin'.

Outside France, the complete works from Torres lead the Spanish entry, with wines from Australia, New Zealand, Chile and California also making an appearance.

Tastings are held frequently in the modern barns at this farm-based business. Pre-shipment and *en primeur* offers from Bordeaux and Burgundy add to the attractions. At the same address (and run by the same people) is another outfit called the Real Burgundy Company. This range is a real treat of domaine wines from classy growers; William Fèvre, Armand Rousseau and Jean Grivot are just some of the names available in unmixed cases. Unfortunately, this stock is not kept on site and has to be ordered.

Best buys

Domaine de Révérend 1989, Corbières, £
Dry Muscat Resplandy 1991, Vin de Pays d'Oc, £
Ch. de la Rivière 1987, Fronsac, ££
Condrieu 1990, Guigal, ££

Belfast Wine Company

130 Stranmillis Road, Belfast BT9 5DT *Tel* (0232) 381760

Open Mon–Sat 9.30–9 **Closed** Sun, public holidays **Credit cards** Access, Visa; personal and business accounts **Discounts** Available **Delivery** Free in Greater Belfast; mail order available **Glass hire** Free with 1-case order
Tastings and talks Free tastings approximately once a month by invitation
Cellarage Not available

The ex-VAT, by-the-case list suggests that the Belfast Wine Co does more wholesale than retail business, but there is a small shop and we have heard good reports of the range available in it. France is the main focus, with all the regions covered. It is difficult to assess some of the wines, as producers' names are not always included in the list; nevertheless there are a few worth pointing out. Premier Cru Chablis from La Chablisienne co-operative is good, as is the range of moderately priced clarets. From Languedoc-Roussillon come reserve wines from Caramany, and from the Loire a St-Nicolas de Bourgueil and a Savennières make good drinking.

Real excitement is reserved for regions outside France: a range from Masia Bach in Spain and the red wine from the aristocratic Marqués de Griñon, for example. Italy sports a few unusual treats such as the Tuscan Morellino di Scansano. From Australia the wines of Plantagenet, Ch. Tahbilk and Leo Buring are worth trying. Free monthly tastings add to the attractions.

Best buys

Masia Bach Tinto 1986, Spain, £
Spanna 1985, Dessilani, Italy, £
Leo Buring Cabernet Sauvignon 1987, South Australia, ££

Benedict's

28 Holyrood Street, Newport, Isle of Wight PO30 5AU *Tel* (0983) 529596

Open Mon–Sat 9–5.30 **Closed** Sun, public holidays and the Chr–New Year period **Credit cards** Access, Visa; personal and business accounts **Discounts** 5% on mixed case of table wines (payment by cash/cheque only) **Delivery** Free on Isle of Wight (min 1 case); otherwise £1 per delivery; mail order available **Glass hire** Free; 80p per breakage **Tastings and talks** Two tastings per month from Sept to Apr **Cellarage** £3 per case per year

A welcome first entry for this independent wine merchant on the Isle of Wight run by former Royal Naval officer Malcolm Rouse. Our interest was prompted by a reader's report so glowing that we could not ignore it.

The range takes in most of the world, but there is a distinct Iberian flavour with 20 Spanish wines and another dozen from Portugal, not counting a fair selection of ports. Riojas come from CVNE, Muga and Berberana; other wines come from Torres and sherries from Garvey and Hidalgo. Portuguese wines feature Fonseca's Quinta de Camerate and the wines of João Pires made by Australian winemaker Peter Bright.

Clarets range from the basics to classed growths; burgundies include wines from Bouchard and Chanson on the *négociant* side and Jayer-Gilles and Etienne Sauzet for the growers. Stars from the Rhône include Ch. Fortia in Châteauneuf-du-Pape, Chapoutier in Hermitage and Crozes, with Ch. du Grand Moulas making a very satisfactory Côtes-du-Rhône. Italy includes Chianti from Rocca delle Macie and Castello di Volpaia, Barolo from Fontanafredda and Oddero and some up-market vini da tavola from Aldo Conterno.

The New World rates a reasonable selection with Lindeman's, Brown Brothers and a few specialities from Geoff Merrill representing Australia, Te Mata doing the same job for New Zealand, and a full range of Caliterra wines from Chile.

Benedict's is also a delicatessen, so you can buy tempting foods to go with your wines. Regular wine tastings are a feature, and once a year a happy band of travellers escapes from the Isle to tour the vineyards of France.

Best buys

Sauvage de la Bri Blanc Fumé 1991, Franschhoek, South Africa, £
Plaimont Colombard 1990, Vin de Pays des Côtes de Gascogne, £
CVNE Blanco Reserva 1985, Rioja, ££
Bollinger Special Cuvée, ££

Bennetts Wines and Spirits 

High Street, Chipping Campden, Gloucestershire GL55 6AG   *Tel* (0386) 840392

Open Mon–Fri 9–1, 2–5.30; Sat 9–5.30 **Closed** Sun, public holidays **Credit cards** Access, Visa; business accounts **Discounts** 5% on 1 case, 7.5% on 5–9 cases, 10% on 10+ cases **Delivery** Free locally (min 1 case); free within 50-mile radius for 5+ cases; elsewhere at cost; mail order available **Glass hire** Free with order **Tastings and talks** Large free public tastings twice a year in town hall **Cellarage** Not available

Charles Bennett decided not to follow up a career in music despite training as a pianist; instead he seems to have found his *forte* in wine. He runs a tiny shop in Chipping Campden, with a wonderful range from classic French regions and small New World properties.

The clarets are good. A couple of AC Bordeaux wines start off the bidding before the list climbs rapidly to the classed growths. White burgundies come from a collection of top-name growers: Chablis from Fèvre; Chassagne-Montrachet from Leflaive; and Puligny-Montrachet from Sauzet; among the reds, the names Tollot-Beaut, Rousseau and Domaine Dujac stand out from a pretty impressive crowd. Alsace wines are mainly Schlumberger and Hugel, with Jaboulet featuring from the Rhône.

The New World selection is huge. From Australia there are Petaluma, Taltarni and Moss Wood in depth, with Moorooduc Estate, Main Ridge and Yarra Yering providing sufficient choice to last for months. Representing California are Simi, Joseph Phelps, Calera and Mondavi wines (including Opus One). Quality sherries are provided by Lustau and Don Zoilo.

Bennetts is full of excellent quality and famous names but all this comes at a price. Only a handful of wines is less than £6; most are over £10 – it would be encouraging to see Charles Bennett re-tune his palate to provide a few more wines for weekday drinkers as well as supplying the Saturday dinner-party high notes.

Best buys

Domaine de Maubet 1991, Vin de Pays des Côtes de Gascogne, £
Barbera d'Asti 1990, Viticoltori dell'Acquese, £
Mâcon Viré 'Domaine Emilian Gillet' 1989, Jean Thévenet, ££
Bannockburn Pinot Noir 1988, Geelong, Victoria, ££

Benson Fine Wines

96 Ramsden Road, London SW12 8QZ *Tel* 081-673 4439

Open Mon–Fri 9–5.30 **Closed** Sat, Sun, public holidays **Credit cards** None accepted; personal and business accounts **Discounts** Not available **Delivery** Free in London **Glass hire** Not available **Tastings and talks** To groups on request **Cellarage** Not available

This specialised company run by Clare Benson has a specialised list. There is an 1874 Ch. Lafite (pre-phylloxera) and a 1976 Ch. La Tour Carnet and in between these vintages there are enough wines to launch a hundred anniversary or birthday parties. The selection is essentially classic – claret and sweet white Bordeaux, red burgundy plus port and a few spirits, some from the nineteenth century. The stock is cellared at Ramsden Road but can also be purchased in the city by prior arrangement.

Best buys

Your best buy depends on which anniversary you want to celebrate

Bergerac Wine Cellar

37 Hill Street, St Helier, Jersey JE2 4UB *Tel* (0534) 70756

Open Tue–Sat 10–1, 2–6 **Closed** Sun, public holidays **Credit cards** All accepted; personal and business accounts **Discounts** 10% on 1 case **Delivery** On Jersey only (min 1 bottle) **Glass hire** Free; breakages charged for **Tastings and talks** Available **Cellarage** Not available

VAT-free prices make any Jersey wine-list look attractive, but the Bergerac list is worth a second look for its range as well as for its prices. It is a small but reliable range and, despite Jersey's proximity to France, is chosen from around the world. Clarets are fairly classic – lots of classed growths with prices at the top end of the range seeming to benefit most from the VAT-free status. Burgundies are mainly from Faiveley and Mommessin. The Rhône is not exciting, but Alsace and the Loire provide a wide choice of whites to chill and enjoy in the Jersey sunshine. Spanish wines also seem popular: a full range from La Rioja Alta is topped off with six vintages of Vega Sicilia. The Australian selection is mainly from big producers Hardy and

Rosemount, with a handful from Yarra Yering at the top end of the price range. The collection could change during the year after Mary Lloyd's trip to the Australian vineyards.

Port is a popular choice, with vintages stretching back to 1927. Delivery is free for just one bottle around Jersey but with a 10 per cent case discount you might think it worthwhile selecting a mixed dozen.

Best buys

Touraine Gamay 1990, Langlois-Château, Loire, £
Domaine du Grand Mayne 1990, Côtes de Duras, £
Ch. Beychevelle 1983, St-Julien, ££
Mazis Chambertin 1983, Grand Cru, Faiveley, ££

Berkeley Wines

See Cellar 5

Berkmann Wine Cellars

See Le Nez Rouge

Berry Bros & Rudd

3 St James's Street, London SW1A 1EG — *Tel* 071-839 9033; *Tel* (answering machine 071-930 1888)

The Wine Shop, Houndmills, Basingstoke, Hampshire RG21 2YB — *Tel* (0256) 23566

Open Mon–Fri 9–5.30; Sat 9–1 (Dec only) (London), Mon–Fri 9–5; Sat 9–1 (Basingstoke) **Closed** Sat (London, exc Dec), Sun, public holidays **Credit cards** Access, Diners Club, Visa; personal and business accounts **Discounts** 3% on 3 cases, 5% on 5 cases, 7.5% on 10+ cases **Delivery** Free on UK mainland (min 1 case); mail order available **Glass hire** £3.25 per 30 glasses (inc cleaning) **Tastings and talks** Tastings in June and November at Basingstoke at £7.50 per person refundable aganst purchase; tastings to groups on request; tastings by invitation **Cellarage** £4.56 per case per year

What is happening? Is nothing sacred? Who would believe that Berry Bros, one of the last bastions of the traditional wine trade, has late-night opening? Admittedly, it is just in December and only one night a week – Thursday.

Perhaps it indicates that despite the museum air of its St James's Street premises, Berry Bros & Rudd is well in tune with the twentieth century. The London shop is an experience not to be missed. Do not try to have your suitcase weighed on the famous scales, or even yourself: such a privilege is reserved for eminent personages. One of the latest to be noted in the famous book was a Sumo wrestler who had to be weighed in cases of Cutty Sark because they ran out of weights. Even without the scales, this wine shop is unlike any other you may encounter. No serried ranks of wine and a check-out counter, the service here is pure Dickensian drama.

But the London shop is only half the story; much of the business has relocated to Basingstoke. This is hardly the centre of the wine trade, but with a purpose-built temperature-controlled warehouse and easy distribution it seems very sensible. To get there you have to negotiate Basingstoke's many roundabouts to one of the industrial sites on the outskirts of the town. Parking is right outside and there is a discreet sign directing you to the shop (not really a shop, more of an office with a few wines on show). Not all the range is displayed but, as in St James's Street, courtesy is everything. Take a seat and a charming chap will advise you on the right wines for the right occasion and then take your order. It may take a little time for the wines to be brought to you but at least you know that they have been stored properly in that modern warehouse. Pleasant members of staff even carry the cases out to your car; in circumstances like these, spending serious money becomes a real pleasure.

The range at both venues is comprehensive with a tendency to excel in the traditional areas – Bordeaux, Burgundy and classic German wines. The New World is not neglected, though, with Australian wines from Henschke, Rothbury, Petaluma and Peter Lehmann. Italy and Spain are good, and if there is a weak area Portugal could be it. Still, there is plenty of choice from other regions to provide a lifetime's drinking.

Once you have made a purchase you will go on to Berry's mailing list and receive the delightful list (chunky, pocket-sized), the magazine (stiff-backed, pleasant post-prandial reading) and lots of special offers. The normal *en primeur* claret offer this year was replaced by a retrospective selection of past vintages. We have had good reports of the mail-order service and delivery is free anywhere in the UK for 12 assorted bottles or more.

Best buys

Berry's Own Selection wines, £
Ch. Grand Bois 1989, Costières de Nîmes, £
Berry Bros' United Kingdom Cuvée Champagne, nv, ££
The King's Ginger Liqueur, ££

▲ DETACH ALONG PERFORATION ▲

Try Which? Wine Monthly FREE for 3 months, and see for yourself how it gives you the facts.

The publishers of Which? Wine Guide present a highly informative companion newsletter, designed to give you the most up-to-date advice on buying wine – including news of special bargains, prices and availability – the results of blind tastings and the latest news and views from the wine world.

Accept this remarkable offer and you'll receive the next 3 issues ABSOLUTELY FREE and WITHOUT COMMITMENT.

See overleaf for further details.

HOW TO CLAIM YOUR **FREE** ISSUES

To receive Which? Wine Monthly FREE for 3 months, just complete and return the direct debiting mandate on the coupon below. We will send you the next three issues of Which? Wine Monthly as they appear. If you do not wish to continue receiving Which? Wine Monthly, you can cancel your subscription by writing to us – and your direct debiting mandate by writing to your bank – before payment is due on the first of the month three months after the date on the mandate. You can keep everything you have received, and you won't owe us a penny.

If you want to go on receiving Which? Wine Monthly, you need do nothing more. Your subscription will bring you Which? Wine Monthly each month for £5.75 a quarter, until you cancel your mandate or we advise you of a change in the price of your subscription. If there should be any change in the price of your subscription at any time we would advise you at least six weeks in advance. This gives you time to tell us if you do not wish to continue your subscription, and to cancel your direct debiting mandate. You are, of course, free to do this at anytime. To accept this offer, just complete the coupon and post it – you don't even need a stamp. So why not post it off now?

Consumers' Association
Castlemead, Gascoyne Way,
Hertford X, SG14 1LH.

WHICH? WINE MONTHLY

I would like to accept this free offer. Please send me the next 3 months issues of Which? Wine Monthly as they appear. I understand that I am under no obligation – if I do not wish to continue with Which? Wine Monthly after the free trial, I can cancel my order before payment is due on the first of the month three months after the date below. But if I decide to continue, I need do nothing – my subscription will bring me Which? Wine Monthly each month for the current price of £5.75 a quarter, payable by Direct Debit.

FREE TRIAL ACCEPTANCE

Direct Debiting Mandate.

I/We authorise you until further notice in writing to charge to my/our account quarterly unspecified amounts which may be debited thereto at the instance of Consumers' Association by Direct Debit.

Date of first payment: 1st of the month three months after the date below.

Signed ______________________ Date ______________

Bank/Building Society Account in the name of ______________________

Bank/Building Society Account Number ☐☐☐☐☐☐☐☐

Name and address of your Bank/Building Society in BLOCK LETTERS PLEASE

TO ______________________

____

____

______________ Postcode ______________

Your name and address in BLOCK LETTERS PLEASE

Mr/Mrs/Miss/Ms ______________________

____

____

______________ Postcode ______________

W__KJ9__

Banks may decline to accept instructions to charge direct debits to certain types of account other than current accounts.
We occasionally make our customer list available to companies whose products or services may be of interest to you.
Please tick here if you do not wish your name to be passed on to other companies. ☐

B H Wines

Boustead Hill House, Boustead Hill, Burgh-by-Sands, Carlisle, Cumbria CA5 6AA

Tel (0228) 576711

Case sales only **Open** 'All reasonable hours', but advisable to phone before calling **Credit cards** None accepted **Discounts** Occasionally **Delivery** Free within Carlisle/North Cumbria, Newcastle upon Tyne, Durham areas and the Scottish Borders (depending upon quantity ordered) **Glass hire** Free; breakages charged at 75p **Tastings and talks** Free pre-Christmas tasting; monthly meetings to wine society members (from £5 per person); talks to groups on request **Cellarage** Not available

'Visitors beware!' says B H Wines – not an unfriendly lot, just warning customers that the road to Boustead Hill sometimes floods at high tide. Once you do make it to the lovely Georgian house on the edge of the Solway Firth you can while away the hours until the waters retreat by playing croquet on the back lawn with proprietor Linda Neville and her husband Richard.

B H Wines' list has grown considerably since the last *Guide* was published. Laid out differently from most lists, it tackles reds, then dry whites, medium and sweet whites followed by sparklers and fortifieds; within each section the choice is alphabetically by country from Argentina to USA. This layout is just the start of B H's sensible approach. Each wine is accompanied by detailed tasting notes and mentions of the various medals it has recently acquired.

The range is wide with no real gaps anywhere. There are good French wines from the south as well as from the classic regions; no endless columns of classed-growth clarets here. Just a few well-chosen top-notes to a good collection of crus bourgeois and petits châteaux.

Further afield, Italy deserves special mention with a trio of wines from Umani Ronchi, including two vintages of Cumaro. Chiantis are from Frescobaldi and Farneta. California is a delight with wines from Simi, Firestone, Trefethen and others, including the glorious Saintsbury Pinot Noir. Among the Australians the names Dromana, Mountadam and Vasse Felix are outstanding.

This is a dedicated company – it not only trades in wine sales but in advice, knowledge and appreciation and customers seem to be well served.

Best buys

Eden Ridge Dry White 1991, South Australia, £
Undurraga Cabernet Sauvignon 1988, Chile, £
Viña Hergabia Reserva 1982, Navarra, Spain, ££
Renaissance Cabernet Sauvignon 1984, California, ££

Bibendum

113 Regent's Park Road, London NW1 8UR *Tel* 071-722 5577

Case sales only **Open** Mon–Sat 10–8 **Closed** Sun, public holidays **Credit cards** Access, American Express, Visa; personal and business accounts **Discounts** Negotiable **Delivery** Free within M25 (min 1 mixed case); mail order available **Glass hire** Free with order **Tastings and talks** Regular tutored tastings held in tasting room **Cellarage** 42p per month or part thereof

Bibendum celebrated its tenth birthday in the summer of '92 – it comes as a surprise to find that it has only been around for such a relatively short time. From nowhere it has become one of the best-known names in wine, not just in London but throughout the UK.

Operations are centred on the splendid warehouse in Primrose Hill. Case sales only but, with a superb range on show, you will have no trouble choosing an assorted dozen to take home. Like all the best lists, this one is focused on growers: small, independent, often family concerns that are mostly exclusive to Bibendum. Buying Director Simon Farr introduces each one in a way that makes you feel that you have just arrived at the vineyard gate on a bicycle. From the Rhône, Marc Sorrel provides the Hermitage, Paul Avril the Châteauneuf-du-Pape and the Côtes-du-Rhône-Villages is the splendid one by Gerard Meffre from Ch. la Courançonne.

In general, burgundy and value are terms which don't go together, but this range has been well chosen to provide interesting, quality wines that are worth forking out the money for. Bibendum is not just a French specialist. The Italian range is a delight, worth several weekends' research; California has wines from Saintsbury, Chalk Hill and Konocti. From Australia, the super Basedow wines have just been taken on board.

You don't have to go to Regent's Park Road to take advantage of all these goodies. Bibendum has extended its same-day delivery to include the inner M25 area. Outside that area you pay for delivery by the consignment, not by the case.

Regular tastings cover such topics as champagne and sparkling wines (£15) and 'Classics from the pre-1960s' (£100). Other features of this busy company are *en primeur* offers of Burgundy, Bordeaux and Rhône wines, and a Fine Wine list, published five times a year. It gives details on claret, burgundy, port, and a few up-market Italians which Bibendum has access to, either in its own stock or from customers' cellars.

A recent development is the purchase of Yorkshire Fine Wines, based outside York. The name will stay and so will many of the wines but Bibendum's range is to be added. Simon

Farr is planning to develop Yorkshire Fine Wines as a northern base and hold tastings in much the same way as in London.

Best buys

La Serre Cabernet Sauvignon 1990, Vin de Pays d'Oc, £
Basedow Semillon 1990, Barossa Valley, Australia, £
Beaujolais Villages, Domaine Dalicieux 1991, ££
Vernaccia di San Gimignano, Elisabetta Fagiuoli 1991, Tuscany, ££

Bin 89 Wine Warehouse

89 Trippet Lane, Sheffield, South Yorkshire S1 4EL — *Tel* (0742) 755889

Case sales only **Open** Sat 10.30–2 **Closed** Mon–Fri, Sun, public holidays **Credit cards** None accepted **Discounts** Available **Delivery** Free in Sheffield and North Derbyshire (min 3 cases); elsewhere at cost **Glass hire** Free with order **Tastings and talks** Two in-store tastings per year **Cellarage** Not available

You have to be quick: this business is open on Saturdays between 10.30am and 2pm only, but regulars know that they can leave mesages at Jonathan Park's other enterprise, Trippet's Wine Bar.

The emphasis in this list is on value for money. Most of the wines are under £10, but those that go over can justify it on the grounds of quality. Italy is a good example: plenty of choice here – Teroldego, Rosso Cònero and Barbera d'Alba all under £5 – but also included is a super Barolo from Bruno Giacosa at nearer the £25 mark.

Jonathan has worked hard to get Australia accepted in conservative (with a small 'c') Sheffield. The wines of Woodstock, Pirramimma and Mount Helen all deserve their places in this range. There is an element of fun, too: not only are wines from California and Washington State included but there are three wines from Texas, one called Ivanhoe which surely no one could resist. The South African range is set to increase later in 1992.

France is divided into reds and whites, and then listed region by region. Among the reds is a good selection of petits châteaux at under £10 and some classed growths at remarkably good prices. Rhônes and southern French wines should make up an interesting mixed case.

See the back flap for an explanation of the symbols used in the *Guide*.

Best buys

Vin de Pays des Bouches-du-Rhône 1989, Saporta, £
Montepulciano d'Abruzzo 1988, Cornacchia, £
Masia Barril Classico 1987, Priorato, Spain, ££
Meerlust Rubicon 1985, South Africa, ££

Bin Ends

Toone House & Cellars, 83–85 Badsley Moor Lane, Rotherham, South Yorkshire S65 2PH — *Tel* (0709) 367771

Associated outlet

(By the case only), Patrick Toone Personal Wine Merchant, Pavilion House, Oswaldkirk, York, North Yorkshire YO6 5XZ — *Tel* (04393) 504

Open Mon–Fri 10–5.30; Sat 9.30–12.30 **Closed** Sun, public holidays **Credit cards** Access, Visa; personal and business accounts **Discounts** 5% on 1 unmixed case (still wines) (2.5% on all other wines); 7.5% on 3+ mixed cases (still wines) (5% on all other wines) **Delivery** Free within 25-mile radius of Rotherham (min 1 case) **Glass hire** Free with order **Tastings and talks** Monthly tastings for general public; tutored tastings to groups on request **Cellarage** Not available

The name Bin Ends doesn't really do this company justice. It implies a hotch-potch of assorted wines or the dregs of someone's cellar. In reality, this is a well-structured list with wines from a variety of good producers.

Refreshingly, the list is arranged alphabetically: Australia comes first, quickly followed by California, Chile and China – China? The two good Tsingtao wines, Riesling and Chardonnay, are included – bound to get the conversation going at any dinner party! Chilean wines are from Montes, the Australians are mainly Brown Brothers, and the Gallo monopoly on American wines will soon be broken by the arrival of a range from Washington State.

From France, representing the burgundies, is the splendid range from Faiveley; Chablis is from William Fèvre. A full range of Vidal-Fleury wines from the Rhône is listed in addition to four Châteauneufs-du-Pape and three white Rhônes from other producers. Garvey's sherries are here in depth and it is good to see finos and manzanillas in half-bottles. More halves and a few magnums are grouped together at the end of the list.

Retail sales are available from the Rotherham shop. Patrick Toone 'Personal Wine Merchant' operates from Oswaldkirk, York on a mixed-cased basis only.

> Once in the bottle a cork can last for decades but eventually it becomes brittle and crumbly with age.

Best buys

Montes Merlot 1990, Chile, £
Domaine de la Hitaire 1991, Vin de Pays des Côtes de Gascogne, £
Sancerre Croix d'Ursin 1990, Sylvain Bailly, ££
Kopke Colheita Port 1977, ££

Blayneys

See Cellar 5

Booths

Head office

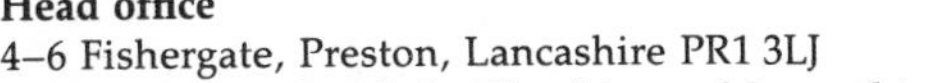

4–6 Fishergate, Preston, Lancashire PR1 3LJ *Tel* (0772) 51701
20 branches in Cumbria, Cheshire and Lancashire

Open Varies from store to store **Closed** Sun, public holidays
Credit cards Access, Visa **Discounts** Available **Delivery** Not available
Glass hire Free **Tastings and talks** Customer tastings limited – on application; occasionally bottles available in-store **Cellarage** Not available

1992 has seen some major changes at Booths, the northern supermarket chain. In the face of the recession the mail-order operation has been closed down and the range of fine wines pruned in anticipation of sunnier days ahead. Yet, considering this is a supermarket, the range is surprisingly good. Fine clarets are thick on the shelves. Mouton and Latour are pretty impressive but Booths sells Pétrus 1981 as well (at a saving of £94 bottle compared with Corney & Barrow). For weekday evenings you could content yourself with a stroll though the cheaper clarets: Potensac, Lynch-Bages and Prieuré-Lichine. Burgundy obviously has fewer fans in this part of the world, but selections from Drouhin, Leflaive and Moillard make appearances on the shelves. Alsace wines are from Hugel, with Guigal and Chapoutier providing some of the Rhônes. Italy is someone's favourite area – Tignanello, Tunina from Jermann, and Conterno's Barolo; the three Chiantis are almost a disappointment in such company. Australia has a fine spread from Jacobs Creek to Grange Hermitage (now renamed Grange), with interesting excursions to Mountadam, Yarra Yering, Vasse Felix and Cape Mentelle.

As with all multiples, not all the range is carried in every store, but we are told that the Knutsford store offers the best choice.

Best buys

Pinot Blanc 1990, Cave Vinicole de Turckheim, Alsace, £
Dão Terras Altas 1987, Portugal, £
Ch. Chasse-Spleen 1983, Moulis, ££
Côte Rotie 1983, Chapoutier, ££

Bordeaux Direct

Mail order

New Aquitaine House, Paddock Road, Reading, Berkshire RG4 0JY
Tel (0734) 481711 (enquiries)
Tel (0734) 471144 (orders)

5 Bordeaux Direct shops in Reading, Windsor, Beaconsfield, Bushey and Woking

Open Mon–Fri 9–8; Sat, Sun, public holidays 10–5 **Closed** Chr Day, Boxing Day **Credit cards** All accepted; business accounts **Discounts** Available **Delivery** Free nationally for orders over £50; mail order available **Glass hire** Free **Tastings and talks** Weekly tastings through retail outlets on request **Cellarage** Not available

This is one of the faces of Direct Wines of Windsor, the other being the Sunday Times Wine Club. It operates as a mail-order club but also has five retail shops within easy reach of Reading. The shops are staffed by enthusiasts who will talk you through the range, which is probably a good thing as the names on the labels are not the familiar ones you might see in other wine shops.

Bordeaux Direct is innovative. It is spearheaded by Tony Laithwaite who tends not to buy what is available but makes available what he wants to buy. Long before it was the fashionable thing to do he had a group of 'flying winemakers', usually Australians, who took their techniques to the more remote parts of France to make wine the way they wanted it – fruity, full-flavoured and with character. Bordeaux Direct discovered many of the southern French wines which are now to be found on other merchants' shelves. This flying-winemakers approach has now been extended to take in Chile, Czechoslovakia and Spain.

The monthly mailshots are full of enjoyable hype, describing the endless quest to find the best flavours and value in the vineyards of the world. Only Bordeaux Direct could sell a wine called Vin de Pays des Côtes du Brian although no doubt the supermarkets will soon be off in search of this new Holy Grail. The latest region to come in for the hype treatment is South Africa, with wines from Rooiberg Co-operative and Backsberg Estate. California is soon to feature in the selection as well. If you prefer, you can always stick with the 'house wine' which is a Côtes de Castillon from Ch. Clarière Laithwaite. The name says it all.

Bordeaux Direct shops always have bottles open for tasting and if you get on the shop mailing-list you will be invited to more specialised tastings as well. Much of the range is shared with the Sunday Times Wine Club, although Ch. Laithwaite is exclusive to Bordeaux Direct! Some of the mailshots are identical, including prices, which is nice to note – some organisations charge different prices to people on different lists.

Wine-buying here is fun. Prices are around the middle range, cheap enough not to worry about comparing values and expensive enough to let you know this is something worth having. A new move for this year is the plan to hold tastings around the country.

Best buys

Cave de Montouliers 1991, Vin de Pays des Côtes du Brian, £
Domaine des Hortensias 1989, Minervois, £
Chardonnay 1991, Cuvée de l'Alliance, Vin de Pays d'Oc, ££
La Fontaine, Chenin Blanc 1991, Vin de Pays d'Oc, ££

Bottoms Up

See Thresher

The Broad Street Wine Company

Emscote Mill, Wharf Street, Warwick, Warwickshire CV34 5LB — *Tel* (0926) 493951

Case sales only **Open** Mon–Fri 9–6; Sat 9–1 **Closed** Sun, public holidays **Credit cards** Access, Visa; personal and business accounts **Discounts** By negotiation **Delivery** Free in UK (min 6 cases); otherwise £6 surcharge; mail order available **Glass hire** Free **Tastings and talks** To groups on request **Cellarage** 4p per case per week

Spirits are a speciality at this company, but not just any spirit will do. Vintage cognacs roll back through the years as far as 1820, a year when Napoleon, who has lent his name to many a good cognac, was still alive and kicking. The armagnacs come from small domaines – such as Domaine Laberdolive where the grapes, distilling and even the oak for the casks are controlled by one family. English brandy, from Lamberhurst in Kent, is another unusual spirit.

Returning to wine, the regions of France are well covered but there is a fondness for old vintages here too. Among a quality selection of Rhône wines lurks a 1923 Châteauneuf-du-Pape, and a 1904 Romanée-St-Vivant rounds off a respectable choice of burgundy from Drouhin, Faiveley and others. The German selection starts at 1983 and works back to 1963, including on the way a few gems from the glorious 1976 vintage. The New World has plenty of drinking wines: the superb wines of Rongopai and Cloudy Bay represent New Zealand; and Australia shows a western bias with three Margaret River wines and only two, Rouge Homme and Taltarni, from the south-eastern corner. There are nods in the directions of Washington State, Chile and Spain, while the vintage port section spans 50 years from 1935 to 1985.

Mixed cases are available, but you have to be fairly thirsty to qualify for free delivery which is available on orders of six cases or more.

Best buys

Pinot Blanc 1990, Cave Co-operative de Turckheim, Alsace, £
Le Texas Syrah 1989, Domaine Guy Chevalier, Vin de Pays de l'Aude, £
Ch. Clement Pichon 1986, Haut-Médoc, ££
Rongopai Te Kauwhata Reserve Chardonnay 1990, New Zealand, ££

Bromley-Stephens

271a Leicester Road, Wigston, Leicestershire LE18 1JA — *Tel* (0533) 881458

Open Mon–Sat 10–1, 5–10; Sun 12–1.30 **Closed** Chr Day, New Year's Day **Credit cards** Access, Visa; personal and business accounts **Discounts** 5% on 1 case, 7.5% on 5 cases, 10% on 12+ cases **Delivery** Free in eastern Lincolnshire, Leicestershire and Northants (min 3 cases); otherwise £3.45 for one case, £2.30 per case on 2+ cases; elsewhere at cost; mail order available **Glass hire** Free with 1-case order; otherwise £1.20 per dozen **Tastings and talks** Major autumn tasting; to groups on request; monthly in-store tastings **Cellarage** £5 per case per year (or part of year)

Two years ago there was a change of ownership for G E Bromley and its associated shop, J H Measures in Spalding, but buying remains firmly within the control of the Bromley family.

Sales of German wines seem to be holding up well in this part of the world: Bromley-Stephens has a comprehensive range of traditional-style German wines from quality producers such as Langwerth von Simmern, Bürklin-Wolf and von Schubert. So far, halbtrocken and trocken wines do not seem to have found favour. The Italian section of the list contains such gems as Rubesco di Torgiano from Lungarotti at the top end of the scale as well as good Chiantis from Villa di Vetrice, Villa Cerna and Antinori.

The Spanish contribution plays safe with Torres, but the Ochoa Navarra wines are good value. Australian, New Zealand and South African wines are mainly from big name, reliable producers; California seems to have offended someone – only a solitary contribution from there. France appears to be the main area of interest, with a good collection of 1988 petits châteaux among the clarets. White burgundies include Aubert de Villaine's Aligoté, while the reds are select but worth buying.

Rhônes provide good drinking at both ends of the price scale: Côtes-du-Rhône, Ch. du Grand Moulas for value and a choice of four red and two white Hermitages at the expensive end.

Best buys

Cépage Colombard 1990, Vin de Pays des Côtes de Gascogne, Plaimont, £
Ch. La Combe Des Dames 1988, Bordeaux, £
Mâcon Chardonnay 1990, Cuvée J Talmard, ££
Woodstock Cabernet Sauvignon 1986, McLaren Vale, South Australia, ££

Bute Wines

Mount Stuart, Rothesay, Isle of Bute PA20 9LR — *Tel* (0700) 502730

Associated outlet
2 Cottesmore Gardens, London W8 5PR — *Tel* 071-937 1629

Case sales only **Open** Mon–Fri 9–5 **Closed** Sat, Sun, public holidays **Credit cards** None accepted; personal and business accounts **Discounts** Occasionally **Delivery** Outside Glasgow, Edinburgh and London there is a minimum order value of £250; £7 for 1 case, £9 on 2 cases **Glass hire** Not available **Tastings and talks** Tastings by invitation only **Cellarage** Not available

This most aristocratic of wine companies is run by Jennifer, Marchioness of Bute. It has a huge range of clarets, burgundies and other wines, and you don't have to live in the Scottish Highlands and Islands to take advantage of it. Delivery is expensive but nationwide.

France is the main focus of the range. Claret vintages from the 1970s and 1980s are available, with a choice of 68 wines from the 1985 vintage alone. *En primeur* and ex-cellar offers increase the choice even further. All the good burgundy names are on the list: Rousseau, Grivot, Leflaive, Domaine de la Romanée-Conti and lots more.

Rhônes are also here in depth. Guigal's top vineyard wines are available in choice of vintages. There is a huge range of Hermitage and Châteauneuf-du-Pape from Jaboulet, Perrin, Chapoutier and Paul Avril. White Rhônes include three vintages of Condrieu. From Alsace the pattern is the same – Lady Bute has concentrated on buying the good names and good wines of Trimbach, Zind Humbrecht and Faller.

The classic wines of Antinori, Torres and Hochar represent Italy, Spain and Lebanon. Australia includes Dromana Estate, Cape Mentelle and the Show Reserve wines from Rosemount.

This is not a cheap list. There is very little under £6, quite a lot over £20, and pricing is somewhat erratic: there are fabulous bargains such as the 1990 clarets, yet other wines look rather expensive. If you live outside London, Edinburgh, Glasgow or the Isle of Bute the minimum order is £250. Free delivery starts at fives cases or more.

Best buys

Côtes-du-Rhône, Domaine du Terme 1988, Rolland Gaudin, £
Sauvignon Blanc 1989, Lievland, South Africa, £
Ch. Lynch-Bages 1989, ££
Vouvray, Domaine La Saboterie 1989, demi-sec, ££

The Butlers Wine Cellar

247 Queen's Park Road, Brighton, East Sussex BN2 2XJ — *Tel* (0273) 698724

Open Tue–Wed 9–5.30; Thur–Sat 9–7 **Closed** Mon, Sun, public holidays
Credit cards Access, Visa; business accounts **Discounts** Not available
Delivery Free within 10-mile radius (min 1 case); elsewhere at cost (3+ cases free); mail order available **Glass hire** Free with case order
Tastings and talks Available; bottles occasionally open on premises
Cellarage Not available

If you are looking for a special vintage to celebrate a particular anniversary then this is the place to start your search. Burgundies and Bordeaux wines go back through the years, often with only one or two bottles of each vintage available. Ch. Calon-Ségur 1945 or Echézeaux 1934 could recall a magic moment in someone's life.

However, Butlers is not just a museum – there are plenty of wines which can be drunk without the accompanying strains of the Anniversary Waltz. The range is wide, if slightly unusual. Russian wines feature heavily with a choice of vintages of Moldavian Cabernet Sauvignon. There is also a 1986 Director's Reserve. (Did the Soviets have directors in 1986 or should this really be Communist Party Worker's Reserve?)

French regional wines are here in depth and are well priced with good tasting notes to help you make your choice. The Rhône is well represented with a few oldies providing a touch of interest. There are some well-chosen wines from the rest of the world, including the good-value Peteroa range from Chile and a full-flavoured Argentinian from Bodegas Weinert.

Butlers runs regular tasting evenings, each with a different theme – they sound like fun.

Best buys

Ch. Grinou Blanc 1990, Bergerac, £
Ch. Fabas Rouge 1990, Minervois, £
Krasny Reserve 1983, Krikova, Russia, ££
Ch. Haut-Brisson 1983, Grand Cru St-Emilion, ££

Anthony Byrne Fine Wines

88 High Street, Ramsey, Cambridgeshire PE17 1BS *Tel* (0487) 814555

Open Mon–Sat 9–6 (Sat till 5) **Closed** Sun, public holidays **Credit cards** Access, Visa; personal and business accounts **Discounts** 5% on 1 case **Delivery** Free on 5+ cases; otherwise £6 per delivery **Glass hire** Not available **Tastings and talks** Tastings on request **Cellarage** Not available

This company is a major wholesaler to the trade but it does have a retail shop and offers mail order to private customers. The range is huge – not everything is on show in the shop, but the warehouse is only 600 yards down the road, and we are assured that anything a customer wants can be obtained quickly.

The list is not for light bedtime reading: there is no chatty introduction, no descriptions. The only pointers to quality are a few stars dotted against those wines which are particularly recommended. Prices are given in four columns, the price charged depending on whether you are a private customer buying a mixed case or a retailer buying a pallet-load. VAT has to be added to all prices.

The French section is by far the biggest, with good names, many of them exclusive agencies, crowding the pages. Burgundies are a major interest with wines from Gagnard-Delagrange, Michelot-Buisson, Etienne Sauzet, Tollot-Beaut, Armand Rousseau and more – the spending potential is limitless. Alsace features with what must be the most comprehensive choice of Zind-Humbrecht wines anywhere. The Loire, Rhône and Bordeaux regions are well represented; the only area which might be thought a little sparse is the south of France.

Penfolds, Delatite and Brown Brothers are the main players from Australia, exhibiting comprehensive selections from each. Wolf Blass and Plantagenet feature in addition. With a fair range from California and a few from South Africa and Chile, it is unlikely that anyone could ever manage to work though the entire list.

We have had one reader's report that the shop is not the easiest place in which to browse, and the vast list is certainly not very user-friendly. Do the advantages of dealing with such a major wholesaler outweigh the disadvantages? Please let us know.

Best buys

Côtes de St-Mont 1990, André Daguin, £
Beaujolais-Villages 1991, Cellier des Samsons, £
Cuvaison Chardonnay 1988, Napa Valley, California, ££
Drappier Carte d'Or nv, Brut Champagne, ££

D Byrne & Co

12 King Street, Clitheroe, Lancashire BB7 2EP *Tel* (0200) 23152

Open Mon–Sat 9–6 (Thur, Fri till 8) **Closed** Sun, Easter holidays
Credit cards None accepted; personal and business accounts **Discounts** £1 on mixed case, £1.20 on unmixed case, 5% on orders over £250 **Delivery** Free within 50-mile radius of Clitheroe (min 1 case) **Glass hire** Free with orders
Tastings and talks Free annual tasting; to groups on request **Cellarage** Free

What a gem! Do the good people of Clitheroe realise how lucky they are? This shop aims to have the most comprehensive stock in Lancashire and in most counties it would succeed with ease but this is Lancashire where determination and competition are strong. As it is, this merchant still provides one of the most varied ranges of any independent in the business.

Although there is a list, a visit to the shop in King Street should be compulsory. The large shop leads into a rabbit warren of cellars and with a bit of luck more will be opened up soon. The plan is to tidy up the clutter of boxes and bottles by transferring some stock over the road to the old postal sorting office. Our guess is that this business only has to clear a small space before it finds yet another range of wines to fill it.

Bordeaux starts off the list with classed growths supported by a good crop of petits châteaux. Unfashionable vintages of the great and good are here at reasonable prices, one of the few ways most of us can afford to drink these top wines. Burgundy wines are available in depth: Armand Rousseau, Bruno Clair and Mongeard-Mugneret feature among the reds while William Fèvre, Sauzet and Leflaive crowd the white burgundy section – the choice goes on and on. The list continues into the Rhône with 15 red Châteauneuf-du-Papes and five whites. Hermitage, Côte Rôtie and Condrieu add to the distractions. The Loire follows in the same way – famous names, vintages and wines are all here. Ninety well-chosen wines from the south and south-west of France complete the Gallic picture, but then it's time to hold your breath and plunge into the rest of Europe and the world beyond – Germany, Spain, Italy, California, Chile, Australia and New Zealand are all represented with a relentless enthusiasm for providing the best selection of well-made wines from everywhere.

One problem with this list is that it is purely a list: no regions are described, no tasting notes given. If you are confident of finding your way around such a document, it is glorious but it could equally confuse and intimidate. There is a tremendous amount of knowledge here and it would be good to see it being spread around but, if you call in or ring, advice is freely given.

If you tire of the selection of wine, D Byrne can offer you 150 beers, 35 coffees and 50 teas, and it is probably the only place within 50 miles where you can have your own blend of 'baccy' mixed. Michael Byrne has plans to retire soon, leaving the company in the capable hands of his children. It will be interesting to see if he can relinquish totally the reins of this exciting and well-stocked business.

Best buys

Ch. Tour Martines 1983, Bordeaux Supérieur, £
Montana Chardonnay 1990, New Zealand, £
Rully Premier Cru 1990, Olivier Leflaive, ££
Wachenheimer Rechbachel Riesling Spätlese 1989, Bürklin-Wolf, ££

Bywater & Broderick

Lime Trees, 7 Main Street, Nether Poppleton, York, North Yorkshire YO2 6HS — *Tel* (0904) 793540

Open Mon–Fri 8–6 **Closed** Sat, Sun, public holidays **Credit cards** None accepted; personal and business accounts **Discounts** 1.5% on 5+ cases, 2.5% on 10+ cases **Delivery** Free in Yorkshire and orders of 5+ cases; elsewhere £4.50 per case; mail order available **Glass hire** Free **Tastings and talks** Regular tastings **Cellarage** Not available

The name Bywater & Broderick has a wonderful long-established feel about it. That's what David Bywater thought when he set up the company in November 1991 and dreamt up a Mr Broderick to lend his name to the new company.

There are two lists depending on whether you are trade or public, but since the minimum purchase on both lists is one mixed case it seems an odd distinction to make. The public list is arranged, like the first part of this *Guide*, in a 'style by style' approach, but you have less choice than in the trade list which has a more conventional country and regional format.

The range is limited but very good. From France there is no attempt to compete in the classed-growth claret market, just a few petits châteaux with a 1987 Vieux-Château-Certan hitting the highest note. Burgundy is much more adventurous with Domaine Leflaive's Puligny-Montrachet, Bernard Dugat's Gevry-Chambertin and good-value St-Aubin from Henri Prudhon. You will not go far wrong with other French wines: Vouvray from Gaston Huet and Sancerre from Henri Natter, for example. The choice from the rest of the world is characterised by a few quality wines from two or three good producers in each region.

This new business deserves encouragement. Not only are the wines well chosen, but free delivery for one case within the that big county of Yorkshire is quite an undertaking. Perhaps Mr Broderick helps out there?

Best buys

Vin de Pays des Landes Blanc 1990, Domaine de Paguy, £
Côtes-du-Rhône 1989, Domaine les Goubert, £
Sancerre 1990, Henri Natter, ££
Crianza 1987, Viña Amezola Rioja, ££

Cachet Wines

Lysander Close, Clifton Moor, York, North Yorkshire YO3 4XB *Tel* (0904) 690090

Case sales only **Open** Mon–Fri 9–5.30; Sat 9–12.30 **Closed** Sun, public holidays **Credit cards** Access, Visa; business accounts **Discounts** Not available **Delivery** Free in Yorkshire and Derbyshire (min 1 mixed case); elsewhere at cost **Glass hire** Free **Tastings and talks** Three/four tastings per year (£7–£15 per person including food) **Cellarage** Not available

It is case sales only from this York-based merchant. Nevertheless, there is a good choice within the middle price range (from most parts of the globe) to fill your mixed case.

The New World pages have seen considerable expansion since the last *Guide*. From Australia there is the complete works from Taltarni as well as some from Rosemount, Haughton and Yalumba's Oxford Landing. California is represented by Fetzer and the Sanford Winery, and Chilean wines come from Viña Carmen, a second label of Santa Rita. Another new addition is a small range of South Africans from Simonsig Estate. Italy has seen some new faces with Barolo from Giacomo Ascheri and Villa di Capezzano in Tuscany. Spanish wines are almost all from CVNE.

France is still the major part of the list, focusing on small reliable producers. Clarets are grouped by vintage and nearly all are petits châteaux or crus bourgeois under £10, including the delicious Ch. Côtes Daugay from St-Emilion. The burgundies are mainly property wines from Domaine Parent, Vallet Frères and Domaine Jean Germain – an unusual wine is the Chardonnay de Jura from the latter. Willy Gisselbrecht features in the Alsace section, there is an interesting collection of wines from the South-West, three good-value wines from Producteurs Plaimont and three from English winemaker Hugh Ryman.

We have had encouraging reports on the service at Cachet. Regular tastings and special offers keep customers informed about the range.

Best buys

Chardonnay de Jura 1990, Domaine de Jean Germain, £
Côtes-du-Rhône Domaine de la Soumade 1990, £
Ch. Carteau Côtes Daugay 1987, St-Emilion, ££
Taltarni Shiraz 1988, Victoria, Australia, ££

Cairns & Hickey

17 Blenheim Terrace, Woodhouse Lane, Leeds, West Yorkshire LS2 9HN *Tel* (0532) 459501

Outlet

856 Leeds Road, Bramhope, Leeds, West Yorkshire LS16 9ED

Open (Woodhouse Lane branch) Mon–Fri 9–6; Sat 9–1; Sun 9–1 in Dec (Leeds Road branch) Mon–Sat 10–9; Sun 12–2, 7–9 **Closed** Sun, public holidays **Credit cards** Access, Visa; personal and business accounts **Discounts** 5% on 1 case **Delivery** Free within 40-mile radius of Leeds (min 1 case); mail order available **Glass hire** Free if collected and washed by customer **Tastings and talks** Annual customer tasting **Cellarage** £3 per case per year

Are the residents of Leeds really so staid? Cairns & Hickey tells us that it tries to encourage customers to sample wines from outside France but with limited success. Perhaps it is not trying hard enough? The Italian section of the list is rather bland, no real excitement there. The California wines are all a bargain price from Sutter Home Winery, eminently drinkable but not top-drawer material. Australia has a similar feel – reasonable wines from Orlando, Mitchelton and Coldridge but nothing from the Adelaide Hills or Coonawarra. If your customers are used to drinking Léoville, Lascombes and Lagune they are not likely to switch to Jacobs Creek.

There are a few rays of sunshine: Viña Linderos from Chile, Fonseca from Portugal and Stoneleigh from New Zealand. The

Spanish range is worth a second look with some Torres and a few good Riojas. Chateau Musar from Lebanon puts in an appearance.

For the traditional drinker, Cairns & Hickey provides good reliable clarets, burgundies and champagnes.

Best buys

Ch. La Gaborie 1985, Bordeaux Rouge, £
St Emiliana Cabernet Sauvignon 1988, Chile, £
Bourgogne Aligoté Domaine Carnot 1989, Bouchard Père et Fils, ££
Stoneleigh Sauvignon Blanc 1990, New Zealand, ££

Cantina Augusto

91–95 Clerkenwell Road, London EC1R 5BX *Tel* 071-242 3246

Open Mon–Thur 9–6; Fri 9–6.30; Sat mornings in Dec **Closed** Sat (exc Dec am), Sun, public holidays **Credit cards** Access, Visa; personal and business accounts **Discounts** Approximately 10% on 1 case **Delivery** £5 in London on orders under £100; mail order available **Glass hire** Free with order **Tastings and talks** In-store tastings on Fri lunchtimes (during most of year) **Cellarage** Not available

Cantina Augusto sounds like an Italian specialist but in fact the range is much broader than that. Good clarets and burgundies, a few Spanish wines – all well chosen – and a selection of Australians from Penfolds, Cape Mentelle and Wolf Blass give this list a well-managed, enthusiastic feel. The miscellaneous section covers Romania, South Africa and Lebanon.

Nevertheless, Italy is the main focus on a list that is a little tricky to decipher. No clear order (apart from pricing) means that six Barolos are jumbled between seven Chiantis and five super Vini da Tavola, and lots more. It is worth making the effort to read through the confusion: Antinori and Borgogno feature among the reds, and look out for Arneis from Ceretto in the whites.

Regular tastings and special offers keep the interest going in this competitive part of London.

Best buys

Chianti 1990, Le Chiantigiane, Tuscany, £
Chardonnay 1990, Berri Estates, Australia, £
Gattinara 1985, Travaglini, Piemonte, ££
Terricci Vino da Tavola 1987, Guarnieri, Tuscany, ££

Most wine merchants will supply wine for parties on a sale or return basis.

Cape Province Wines

1 The Broadway, Kingston Road, Staines, Middlesex TW18 1AT *Tel* (0784) 451860/455244

Open Mon–Fri 9–9 **Closed** Sun, public holidays **Credit cards** Access, Visa **Discounts** On South African wines collected from stores **Delivery** £5.25 per consignment in London; otherwise £5.40 for 1 case, £4.90 per case on 2–5 cases, £4.40 per case on 6+ cases **Glass hire** Free with order **Tastings and talks** In-store tastings **Cellarage** Not available

Through all the threatened sanctions and general public opposition to South Africa, Cape Province Wines' managing director Peter Loose has battled on, stocking the good wines of the region. Now, as that country slowly emerges from its political isolation, so interest in its wines is growing.

The shop claims to have one of the biggest ranges of Cape wines outside South Africa. This is difficult to check out but the list extends to 150 and there are a few more available in quantities too small to include. The real gems are the estate wines with names such as Meerlust, Fairview, Neethlingshof and Twee Jongegezellen. It will take some time before the drinking public becomes familiar with these strange names and spellings but in wine quality terms the potential is there for South Africa once again to become a leading light in the world of wine.

The Nederburg annual auction is a major event and Peter Loose was there earlier in 1992 to buy some unusual and rare wines for his shop – wines such as the Nederburg Private Bins and the sweet wine Edelkeur. If you are interested in these specialities ask for the separate list. Generally, prices for South African wines are still very reasonable. This could be the right time to try a few.

Wines are available by the single bottle at the shop and by the mixed case by mail order.

Best buys

Nederburg Edelrood 1988, £
Cape Country Colombar, £
Zonnebloem Cabernet Sauvignon 1987, ££
Allesverloren Tinta Barocca 1987, ££

A 125ml glass of wine, a 170ml glass of sherry and half a pint of beer all contain approximately the same amount of alcohol called a 'unit'. The Health Education Authority's recommendations for sensible drinking limits are 21 units per week for men and 14 units per week for women.

A Case of Wine ('Pigs 'n' Piglets')

Harford, Pumpsaint, Llanwrda, Dyfed SA19 8DT — *Tel* (05585) 671

Open Mon–Sat 9–9 **Credit cards** Access, Visa **Discounts** 2.5% on 1 unmixed case (payment by cash/collected from shop) **Delivery** Free in Dyfed (min 1 case) **Glass hire** Free with order; breakages charged for **Tastings and talks** Tastings on Mons in next-door restaurant; to groups on request **Cellarage** Charges by arrangement

We are delighted to welcome this new addition to the *Guide*. Good wine merchants are few and far between in Wales, particularly amongst the independents. This business is run by Jennifer Taylor and Aldo Steccanella.

France is a strong area: clarets are the affordable petits châteaux variety rather than the expensive classed growths. Burgundies include the organic wines of Jean Musso (organic wines are quite a feature with this merchant) and there is a wide choice of French regional wines, most of them well below £6. Italy runs to two pages of the list (and is set to increase), with a fine Tuscan selection and no fewer than four Barolos. Spain, Chile, Germany and California are also represented. It is interesting to see the Welsh wine Croffta, from neighbouring Glamorgan, joining Three Choirs in the England and Wales section. Australia runs to 11 wines, including the terrific St Hallett's wines and Shaw and Smith's Chardonnay.

It is amazing just how far some independents are prepared to drive to deliver your order – a case is delivered free to the whole of Dyfed. If Welsh readers can point us in the direction of other merchants we may have missed, please let us know.

Best buys

Gran Feudo Crianza Red 1989, Julián Chivite, Navarra, £
Chianti Rufina 1988, 'Banda Blu', Grati, £
St Hallett's Old Block Shiraz 1988, Barossa, Australia, ££
Cabernet Sauvignon, Domaine la Soumade 1989, Vin de Pays de la Principauté d'Orange, ££

The Wine Standards Board is the trade's disciplinary department and wine watchdog. Its inspectors are responsible for rooting out any malpractices – but it is concerned largely with labelling irregularities. If you have genuine reason to suspect that the wine in a bottle is not what the label claims it is, contact the Board at 68½ Upper Thames Street, London EC4V 3JB; tel 071-236 9512; or contact your local Trading Standards Officer.

Cellar 5

Head office
China Lane, Warrington, Cheshire WA4 6RT *Tel* (0925) 444555
497 branches

Open Mon–Sat 10–10; Sun and public holidays 12–2, 7–10 (with some local variations) **Closed** Chr Day **Credit cards** Access, Visa; personal and business accounts **Discounts** 5% on 1 case; negotiable on larger orders **Delivery** Free from selected branches (generally within a 5-mile radius) **Glass hire** Free with order **Tastings and talks** Weekends at selected stores **Cellarage** Not available

The 185-strong chain of Blayney's off-licences was sold earlier in 1992 to the Cellar 5 group, a subsidiary of Greenall Whitley. By the end of 1992 they will have been totally swallowed up by this North of England chain. Out of the 500 Cellar 5 shops that this acquisition now gives them, the top 25 stores, named Berkeley Wine, are good news for wine drinkers.

The range includes some clarets – Ch. Monbousquet from St-Emilion and the reliable Ch. Cissac among them. There are quite a few burgundies, although the all-important producers' names were missing from our list. Other highlights include Campo Viejo Riojas and Chianti from Ricasoli. Australia is represented by Mitchelton, Lindemans and Coldridge; other producers are Christian Brothers from California, Errazuriz Panquehue from Chile and Bodegas Weinert from Argentina.

It is a shame that these few good wines are presently stocked by only a handful of shops within the Cellar 5 group. With the backing of vodka giants Greenall Whitley it could easily improve the range in all its shops.

Best buys

Coldridge Estate Semillon/Chardonnay 1991, Australia, £
Cabernet Sauvignon 1988, Errazuriz Panquehue, Chile, £
Mitchelton Reserve Chardonnay 1989, Victoria, Australia, ££
Ch. Haut-Marbuzet 1985, St-Estèphe, ££

The Celtic Vintner

73 Derwen Fawr Road, Sketty, Swansea, West Glamorgan SA2 8DR   *Tel* (0792) 206661

Case sales only **Open** Mon–Fri 8.30–6; Sat by arrangement **Closed** Sun, public holidays **Credit cards** Access; personal and business accounts
Discounts Negotiable for quantity discounts **Delivery** Free in south and south-west Wales (min 5 cases unless on regular delivery run); elsewhere at cost
Glass hire Available with charge **Tastings and talks** Large annual tasting in Swansea; to groups on request **Cellarage** Possible

Brian Johnson's Celtic Vintner continues to flourish in Swansea. He foresees 1992 as being the year to move the office out of his breakfast room at home in order to cope with his rapidly increasing business.

The range has all the hallmarks of being a personal selection of wines, with quality and individuality the main consideration. From Australia there are wines from Hardy and Yalumba, but in addition there is a liberal sprinkling of small producers such as Coldstream Hills, Moss Wood and Fermoy Estate. New Zealand follows suit with Palliser and Vavasour adding to the Selak's selection. South Africa has seen a rapid expansion with wines from Klein Constantia and the splendid Hamilton-Russell range. Argentina provides the full-flavoured wines of Bodegas Weinert.

From France there is a fine selection of wines from traditional areas, but the Loire and southern France are particular specialities. Chais Baumière from the south produces French wine in the Australian style; Château Baudare and the Hugh Ryman range both provide good flavours at reasonable prices.

It is case sales only *chez* Brian Johnson, but mixed dozens are available; delivery can be arranged and is free around South Wales. If you cannot make up your mind, give Brian a ring and let his mellifluous tones guide you through the range.

Best buys

Vin de Pays d'Oc 1991, Hugh Ryman, £
Ch. de Breuil 1991, Sauvignon Blanc, Loire, £
Ch. de Tracy 1990, Pouilly Fumé, ££
Cabernet Sauvignon 1983, Bodegas Weinert, Argentina, ££

A man may surely be allowed to take a glass of wine by his own fireside.

Sheridan (on being encountered drinking a glass of wine in the street, watching his theatre, the Drury Lane, burn down)

The Champagne House

Office ONLY
15 Dawson Place, London W2 4TH *Tel* 071-221 5538

Case sales only **Open** Mon–Thur 9–6 **Closed** Fri–Sun, public holidays, Sept and early Jan **Credit cards** None accepted **Discounts** Available **Delivery** Free in Kensington & Chelsea, Westminster and City of London and for orders of 4+ cases; otherwise at cost **Glass hire** Not available **Tastings and talks** On an occasional basis for established customers **Cellarage** Not available

The Champagne House did not issue a new list this spring. Prices and vintages remained unchanged and it was hoped that by the summer the overall downturn in UK sales would somehow bring sense back into the minds of the Champenois.

Meanwhile, with the recession still biting and good sparklers coming from all corners of the globe, it is surprising that there is sufficient demand for a company to deal exclusively in champagne. But for some people only champagne will do and this business, run by former merchant banker Richard Freeman and his wife Jenny, specialises in matching the right wine to the right occasion.

The list is a commendable summary of the champagne process and producers' profiles. The vintage champagnes and specialities are largely from the major houses such as Bollinger, Pol Roger, Krug and Roederer. It is in the non-vintage range that small family producers appear, names such as Albert le Brun, Adam-Garnotel and Roger Driant. Here is the chance to taste wines not found on many shelves. Prices for this range seem reasonable as far as champagne prices go. For the better-known names, they are roughly the same as those found elsewhere. Service seems a little limited and delivery is free only within the cities of London and Westminster, and in Kensington and Chelsea. Sales are by the case only and mixed cases are strongly discouraged. This is a bare bones service – are customers happy with it? Please write and tell us.

Best buys

Richard Freeman declined to indicate that any of his wines were of better value than others. 'The whole purpose of the Champagne House is to list wines which we are totally happy with.'

Chaplin & Son

35 Rowlands Road, Worthing, West Sussex BN11 3JJ *Tel* (0903) 235888

Open Mon–Sat 8.45–5.30 **Closed** Sun, public holidays **Credit cards** Access, Visa; personal and business accounts **Discounts** 5% on 1 case; larger orders by negotiation **Delivery** Free within 7-mile radius; otherwise at cost; mail order available **Glass hire** Free with appropriate case order
Tastings and talks Occasional in-store tastings; to groups on request; mini wine fairs (tastings of 40–50 wines) **Cellarage** £5 per case per year

Ill-health has forced Anthony Chaplin MW to relinquish control of this business and it is now owned by Nigel Baring and Co. This, theoretically, gives the group stronger buying power and reduced administration costs which should be good news all round. Rationalisation within the group means that the range has changed slightly and there will be greater opportunities for customers to buy *en primeur* wines. Chaplin will continue as a retail shop although special offers such as the 'Great Merger Sale' and Domaine Burgundy offers are arranged under the Nigel Baring umbrella and are for case sales only.

The range in Worthing includes a good collection of clarets – notable is the delightful Ch. Monbousquet made by one of St-Emilion's more colourful characters, Alain Querre. Red burgundies are from Chanson, with additions such as Louis Trapet's Gevrey-Chambertin and Nuits-St-Georges from Henri Gouges. Loron appears in the Beaujolais, Burgundy and Rhône columns and, while these wines are sound, they give the feeling that France has not been scoured for diversity and individuality. Italy might be good, but producers' names are not included in the list apart from Antinori's Galestro and Rampolla's Chianti Classico. The range from Spain includes some good Torres and CVNE wines.

Australia is surprisingly sparse: Rosemount, a few Penfolds wines and three contributions from Brown Brothers. California holds some treats with wines from La Crema and Mondavi. Ports are listed but no prices given, an irritation for serious customers.

This list appears slimmer than in past years and we hope that this is just a temporary condition until the immediate effects of the merger have worn off.

Best buys

Vin de Pays des Côtes de Thau 'Terret' 1991, £
Pinot Blanc 1990, Cave Vinicole de Turckheim, £
Ch. Cissac 1986, ££
La Crema Pinot Noir 1988, California, ££

Chennell & Armstrong Ltd

Manor Lane, Shipton Road, York, North Yorkshire YO3 6TX *Tel* (0904) 64799114

Case sales only **Open** Mon–Fri 8–5 **Closed** Sat, Sun, public holidays **Credit cards** None accepted; personal and business accounts **Discounts** Available **Delivery** Free within Yorkshire (min 1-case order); elsewhere by arrangement; mail order available **Glass hire** Free; breakages charged for **Tastings and talks** Two annual tastings in May and Sept **Cellarage** Not available

There is a strong trade-only feel about the Chennell & Armstrong list – with ex-VAT prices and hefty discounts if you buy 100 cases or more. Even so, we are assured that the private customer is welcomed and gets a good deal here. Good service is the key, we are told, and this includes decanting your vintage port for you.

Claret is a speciality: there is a long list of vintages and bottle sizes. The rest of France is fairly classic although Alsace looks a little sparse. Traditional German wines still seem popular, and a 1976 Riesling Beerenauslese appears on the list at a very reasonable price. Australian wines hinge on a selection from Best's, with a few from Penfolds and Brown Brothers to add variety. Champagne includes the delicious Barancourt range.

Mixed cases are available, presumably at no extra cost, but there is also a small range of tasting cases arranged around different themes. Delivery is free for one case within Yorkshire; outside that area costs begin to climb.

Best buys

Best's Victoria Colombard 1992, £
Domaine Lasserre 1991, Vin de Pays des Côtes de Gascogne Blanc, £
Best's Great Western Shiraz 1988, Australia, ££
Barancourt Rosé Brut Champagne, ££

Chippendale Fine Wines

15 Manor Square, Otley, West Yorkshire LS21 3AP   *Tel* (0943) 850633

Open Mon–Tue, Thur–Fri 10–5.45 (Fri from 9.30); Sat 9.30–5 **Closed** Wed, Sun and public holidays **Credit cards** Access, Visa; personal and business accounts **Discounts** 5% on mixed and unmixed cases **Delivery** Free within 3-mile radius of Otley, and within 15-mile radius of Otley for orders of 6+ bottles; elsewhere at cost **Glass hire** Free (min order 6 bottles); 60p charge per breakage **Tastings and talks** Free in-store tastings (Sat); 1 major tasting in May by invitation only **Cellarage** Not available

Just in case you were wondering, this company is named after the master furniture maker, Thomas Chippendale, who was born in Otley; it does not refer to the group of American beefcakes who take their clothes off for a living! Not that proprietor Michael Pollard isn't entertaining in his own way. Send for a list, settle down with a glass of wine and prepare to be amused. There are tirades against supermarkets, the BBC and the government, all best read in a wicked Yorkshire dry-sense-of-humour tone.

And what of the wines? For a fairly new company (just two years old), surprisingly good. Australia is a speciality but there is no attempt to cover all the ground. The range is focused on a few really good growers including Adam Wynn with his Mountadam range, the David Wynn label and the organic Eden Ridge wines. Garry Crittenden's splendid Dromana Estate and Schinus Molle wines are also here in depth. The New Zealand range includes Martinborough and Babich; Californians are from Newton.

French treats include a clutch of organic burgundies from Jean Musso, a compact selection of petits châteaux from Bordeaux and a terrific selection of regional French wines which could keep Otley drinkers busy for a few weekends. More expensive clarets, burgundies and Rhônes are available from a separate section at the end of the list. Most other regions are represented by a few wines; each producer, wine and even the state of the market are commented on in Mike Pollard's inimitable style.

With reasonable prices and free in-store tastings every Saturday, Chippendale seems to be a welcome addition to the Otley landscape.

The Which? Wine Guide does not accept payments for inclusion, there is no sponsorship, and no promotion or advertising may be based on its content.

Best buys

Domaine de Raissac Syrah 1990, Vin de Pays d'Oc, £
Eden Ridge Dry White 1991, Adelaide Hills, Australia, £
Bourgogne Pinot Noir 1988, Jean Musso, ££
Dromana Estate Chardonnay 1990, Mornington Peninsula, Victoria, Australia, ££

Christchurch Fine Wine

1–3 Vine Lane, High Street, Christchurch, Dorset BH23 1AB — *Tel* (0202) 473255

Open Mon 10–1; Fri–Sat 10–7 **Closed** Sun, Tue, Wed, Thur, public holidays **Credit cards** Access, Visa; personal and business accounts **Discounts** 5% on 1+ case to Club members **Delivery** Free within 10-mile radius of Christchurch (min order 1 case); mail order available **Glass hire** Free with order **Tastings and talks** 9 tastings per year for club members **Cellarage** Free for 2 years to customers

There is no better place for a wine business than Vine Lane. No vines there now, just lots of super wines in a former stable and coach-house in the centre of Christchurch. The business is run by former restaurateur John Carter and this list has a definite 'good restaurant' feel about it.

France is the main area of interest. Clarets tend to be biased towards the £20-plus bracket, with Latour, Mouton, Lafite and Margaux heading the classed growths. Older vintages are scattered throughout the list: a clutch of 1966 wines, some 1970s and a few from the 1950s. The Sauternes are a delight, with older vintages including a 1966 Yquem for a mere £126.

Red burgundies are mainly from Prosper Maufoux and his *sous-marque* Marcel Amance, and there are some splendid whites from Louis Latour. Particularly interesting is a collection of wines from the Hospices de Beaune. The Rhône and Loire wines are good – with Chapoutier's Côte Rôtie and Clos les Perrières Sancerre from Vatan. These sections also provide plenty of 'drinking' wines as well as special occasion bottles. Four wines from the Savoie are a pleasant distraction from the classic areas and a big collection of German wines, many from Wegeler-Deinhard, rounds off the list.

Tastings are a feature at Christchurch. Membership of the Wine Club costs £5 and entitles you to a 5 per cent discount on purchases of five or more cases a year. The shop is well-laid out but the list takes some getting used to. It is close-typed and has no clear groupings within a region. A few tasting notes might help too.

Best buys

Vacqueyras Domaine de la Brunely 1988, Carichon, £
Roussette de Savoie Domaine de l'Idylle 1991, Tiollier, £
Wines of the Hospices de Beaune, ££

City Wines

221 Queens Road, Bracondale, Norwich, Norfolk NR1 3AE — *Tel* (0603) 660741
305 Aylsham Road, Norwich, Norfolk NR3 2RY — *Tel* (0603) 405705

Open Mon–Sat 9–9; Sun and public holidays 12–2, 7–9 **Closed** Chr Day, Boxing Day **Credit cards** Access, American Express, Visa; personal and business accounts **Discounts** 5% on 1 case **Delivery** Free in Norwich (min 1 case); elsewhere at cost; mail order available **Glass hire** Free **Tastings and talks** Available on request **Cellarage** Not available

Another change of style at City Wines, and this time for the better. The jokes have gone (thank goodness) and the presentation of the list has improved out of sight. The range of wines has taken a turn for the better, too. The list is not huge but some care and thought have gone into assembling a collection which rarely strays over the £10 mark.

Australia merits a fairly large section with good-value, well-made wines from Hardy, Brown Brothers and Taltarni. Lindemans and Leasingham make an appearance, too. The New Zealand list is limited to Montana and we are told that there is increasing interest in South Africa. So far only three KWV wines are listed; perhaps more are on their way.

France provides a reasonable selection of drinkable clarets but burgundy does not really go much beyond generics. French regional wines are a strong point, with good Bergerac, Cahors and Madiran. Sweet wines are collected together and include Australians, Californians and a choice of Tokajis, as well as an interesting pair of Jurançon wines from Domaine Cauhapé.

City claims to give excellent service to its customers. Can readers confirm this?

Best buys

Trapiche Merlot Reserve 1990, Argentina, £
Cuvée Particulière Vin de Pays des Pyrenées, £
Domaine Tariquet Cuvée Bois 1989, Vin de Pays des Côtes de Gascogne, ££
Ochoa Tempranillo 1987, Navarra, ££

Classic Wine Warehouses

Unit A2, Stadium Industrial Estate, Sealand Road, Chester, Cheshire CH1 4LU *Tel* (0244) 390444

Open Mon–Fri 7.45–6; Sat 9–5 **Closed** Sun, public holidays **Credit cards** All accepted; personal and business accounts **Discounts** Negotiable **Delivery** Free in Cheshire, Lancashire, Merseyside, Clwyd, Manchester, Shropshire and Stafford (min 1 case); mail order available **Glass hire** Free **Tastings and talks** Bottles open on premises; occasional regional tastings **Cellarage** Free

With John Lennon and James Dean as directors of this company all they really need is Elvis to show up and sing a song or two to make it truly an 'all-time classic'.

The majority of Classic's business is selling into the trade, hence the VAT-exclusive list, but the company does have a retail licence which means that you can pick up a single bottle from the Unit A2 address. Champagne is a speciality, with endless vintages and labels. France is fairly classic with burgundies from Drouhin, Bouchard Père and Faiveley. The New World has Cooks and Stoneleigh from New Zealand, Rosemount, Wolf Blass and Penfolds from Australia, and lots of Mondavi from California.

There is a reasonable selection of half-bottles, particularly among the champagnes. Remember, though, to check out prices before you buy – warehouse doesn't always mean cheap.

Best buys

Dalwood Dry White 1991, South-East Australia, £
Claret 'Louis XIV' Nathaniel Johnson, £
Bourgogne 1990, 'Les Caves de la Tour Blondeau', Bouchard Père et Fils, ££
Champagne Massé Brut nv 'Baron Edouard', ££

The Clifton Cellars

22 The Mall, Clifton, Bristol, Avon BS8 4DS *Tel* (0272) 730287

Open Mon–Fri 9.30–6.30; Sat 9–6 **Closed** Sun, some public holidays **Credit cards** Access, Visa; personal and business accounts **Discounts** 5% on 1 unmixed case **Delivery** Free within 20-mile radius of Bristol **Glass hire** Free **Tastings and talks** To groups on request **Cellarage** £2.05 per case per year

Bristol is already home to two of the big names in wine – John Harvey and Averys – but there is still room for this independent merchant, Clifton Cellars. Founded just as long ago as the big shots, this one has remained small and has just been taken over by Alan Wright. The result is a rush of new enthusiasm, better stock and better service.

Clarets are good: Ch. Tertre Rôteboeuf features among the St-Emilions, and other wines rolling back to 1947, although the best choice seems to be among the 1985s. Burgundies are fewer in number but still good – Faiveley, Bouchard and Louis Latour are among the names here. Champagne appears to be a speciality with 25 non-vintage and 20 vintage wines to choose from. Outside France, Spain looks impressive: Riojas from Muga, Murrieta and Berberana; Torres wines are a feature as well as the superb Cabernet Sauvignon from Marqués de Griñon. Portugal has a small but interesting collection; Italy is also worth taking some time over.

Germany might be worthy, but the pages of the list do not seem long enough to cope with the names of the producers. This is the only blot on an otherwise well-produced list. South Africa contains some interest from Twee Jongegezellen, Stellenbosch and the Overgaauw Estate. Australia is limited to just a few wines from Wyndham and Hunter Estate.

With Don Zoilo sherries and a wide range of malt whiskies, the new management seems to be on the right tracks.

Best buys

Hill-Smith Chardonnay 1991, Australia, £
Bergerac Domaine de Beauregarde 1988, £
Ch. Tertre Rôteboeuf 1987, St-Emilion, ££
Champagne Jean Moutardier 1986, ££

Colombier Vins Fins

Ryder Close, Cadley Hill Industrial Estate, Swadlincote, Burton on Trent, Derbyshire DE11 9EU — *Tel* (0283) 552552

Case sales only **Open** Mon–Fri 8.30–5; Sat on request **Closed** Sun, public holidays **Credit cards** None accepted; personal and business accounts **Discounts** 5% on 10 cases **Delivery** Free in Leicestershire, Birmingham, Nottingham, Northamptonshire, Peterborough, Lincolnshire and Derby; free elsewhere (min 5 cases); otherwise £9 per case **Glass hire** Free with orders **Tastings and talks** Organised tastings on premises every month **Cellarage** £3.80 per case per year (£7.60 if wine bought elsewhere)

Colombier has the feel of a trade-only wholesaler. The range is listed in a wine catalogue with lots of descriptions and photos but to find the price you must cross-reference to a separate ex-VAT list – not complicated but a bit tedious. There are additional lists which focus on different areas. The New World and Italy rate one each which come complete with prices, ex-VAT of course.

From France, the speciality is small growers most of whom are exclusive to Colombier. Burgundy has a comprehensive range: a number of wines come through the French arm of Colombier – *négociant éléveur* in Charney-lès-Mâcon. The range from Chablis includes the delicious lightweight Bourgogne Epineuil from the co-operative La Chablisienne. The Bordeaux section has a fine collection of classed growths with some petit château wines. The choice of Rhônes is fairly limited but the Loire expands and boasts six Bourgueils. It would be encouraging to see a few more wines from the south of France to add to this fairly traditional range.

The Italian collection rates a separate catalogue and is impressive – plenty to work through there. Piedmont wines come from Poderi Anselmi and Tuscan wines are from Avignonesi. The New World list has a wide selection from South Africa and a very limited Australian range but it does include Garry Crittenden's Schinus Molle. A sprinkling from New Zealand, California, Chile and Israel rounds off the rest.

With such a heavy emphasis on ex-VAT prices and complicated lists we would be interested to find out from customers of Colombier just how easy it is to buy wine there.

Best buys

Bardolino Classico 1990, Tommasi, Italy, £
Chenin Blanc 1989, Backsberg, South Africa, £
Mercurey 1988, Domaine du Val d'Or, Michel Juillot, ££
Roero Arneis 1989, Poderi Anselma, Piemonte, ££

Connolly's

Arch 13, 220 Livery Street, Birmingham, West Midlands B3 1EU — *Tel* 021-236 9269

Open Mon–Fri 9–6.30; Sat 9–2 **Closed** Sun, public holidays
Credit cards Access, American Express, Visa; personal and business accounts
Discounts 10% on 1 case if collected **Delivery** Free within 15-mile radius of Birmingham (min 1 case); mail order available **Glass hire** Free with order
Tastings and talks Two free major tastings per year; monthly tutored tastings
Cellarage Not available

With a poetic and cautionary tale in the introduction to his list, Chris Connolly urges us to 'Buy from a merchant of greater repute'. We presume he means himself. Significantly, he has put together a small but worthy collection to tempt his customers.

The list is fairly conventional. Good clarets from well-known properties – Palmer, Angludet, Haut-Bages-Libéral and so on – with a fair range of vintages dating back to 1978. Burgundies are mainly from the splendid Domaine Faiveley, with a sprinkling from Robert Arnoux. French regionals are from small estates and apparently there are always a few extra lines available in the shop.

The Italian range is new but small, Ascheri Barolo and the up-market Palazzo Altese provide some excitement. Spain has the complete works from Torres, as well as a white Marqués de Murrieta and Faustino Riojas. Australian wines include Coldstream Hills and Cape Mentelle as well as Hill-Smith, Basedow and Brown Brothers.

A fine range of champagnes (jeroboams of Bollinger, for instance) should go down well and are priced in the list; not, however the vintage ports, which must be an irritation for potential customers. If Connolly's can fix a price for vintage champagne in this volatile market, why not port?

A wide and interesting collection of malt whiskies (with prices!) rounds off the list. Monthly tutored tastings sound like good value and fun.

Best buys

Señorio de los Llanos 1984, Valdepeñas, £
Tour St-Martin 1990, Minervois, £
Cloudy Bay Sauvignon Blanc 1991, New Zealand, ££
Hamilton-Russell Pinot Noir 1990, South Africa, ££

Corney & Barrow

12 Helmet Row, London EC1V 3QJ — *Tel* 071-251 4051
118 Moorgate, London EC2M 6UR — *Tel* 071-628 2898
44–45 Cannon Street, London EC4N 6JJ — *Tel* 071-248 1700
194 Kensington Park Road, London W11 2ES — *Tel* 071-221 5122
Belvoir House, High Street, Newmarket, Suffolk CB8 8OH — *Tel* (0638) 662068

Open Mon–Fri 9–6; Sat 10.30–8 (Kensington) **Closed** Sat (City), Sun, public holidays **Credit cards** Access, Visa; personal and business accounts **Discounts** Negotiable **Delivery** Free within London (min 2+ cases) and outside London (min 3+ cases); elsewhere £6 per delivery; mail order available **Glass hire** Free (charged then credited on return) **Tastings and talks** Regular tastings; regular wine course; to groups on request **Cellarage** £4.50 per case per year

Any merchant who has been established since 1780 and is the proud holder of three royal warrants is bound to be a classy organisation. That much is obvious as soon as you get the list: off-white with discreet gold-block lettering, this chunky publication left on a coffee-table would enhance anyone's social standing.

It opens with Pétrus – expensive, exclusive and here in a variety of vintages dating back to 1947. Corney & Barrow holds the UK agencies for all the wines of Ets. J P Moueix and so Pétrus is joined by other right-bank properties including La Fleur-Pétrus, Latour à Pomerol, Magdelaine and Trotanoy. Other agencies include Lafite, Rieussec, Domaine de la Romanée-Conti and Leflaive – which could keep millionaires in drinking wine for quite some time. Ordinary mortals should not feel too intimidated as there are plenty of other wines to work through without taking out a second mortgage.

The petit château wines of J P Moueix are here in depth, most under the £6 mark. The rest of the clarets have a distinct right-bank bias – it is encouraging to see the super Tertre Rôteboeuf St-Emilion listed. Burgundies are delightful quality names, and there are wines to enjoy below £10 as well as above. Compared with Pétrus, the wines of Domaine de la Romanée-Conti look like positive bargains. The rest of France has been selected with care, with Rhônes from Jaboulet and Alsace wines from Cattin and Heydt. Corney & Barrow's customers are clearly Francophiles, but Spain, Italy, Australia and New Zealand are all acknowledged and have good quality, reliable wines.

In the City, Corney & Barrow has a string of wine bars including the champagne bar at Lloyds. The Moorgate wine bar also has a shop. None of the shops carries the complete range but anything not immediately available can be ordered. The West London shop is also allowed a few little luxuries which don't feature on the main list, such as a few more Italians and a wider choice of New World wines, as well as excellent olive oils.

The mail-order operation works from the Helmet Row offices. A separate company, Corney & Barrow Broker Services, can arrange to sell any surplus wines you bought from it and still have in store at its warehouse.

Best buys

Corney & Barrow's House Claret, £
Ch. Bel Air 1988, Bordeaux Supérieur, £
The Wines of J P Moueix, ££
Parker Estate Coonawarra Cabernet Sauvignon 1988, Australia, ££

'Have some wine,' the March Hare said in an encouraging tone. Alice looked all round the table, but there was nothing on it but tea. 'I don't see any wine,' she remarked. 'There isn't any,' said the March Hare.

Lewis Carroll, *Alice's Adventures in Wonderland*

Cornwall Wine Merchants

Chapel Road, Tuckingmill, Camborne, Cornwall TR14 8QY — *Tel* (0209) 715765

Case sales only **Open** Mon–Fri 9–1, 2–5; Sat 10–1 **Closed** Sun **Credit cards** Access, Visa; personal and business accounts **Discounts** Quantity discounts **Delivery** Free locally; elsewhere at cost; mail order available **Glass hire** Free to customers **Tastings and talks** Regular tutored tastings; bottles open on premises **Cellarage** Available

Ex-VAT prices on this list give it a trade-only feel but mixed cases can be ordered and, with delivery free within Cornwall and Devon, it rates a mention in the *Guide*.

The range from Bordeaux is fairly limited, but burgundy shows enthusiasm with some wines from Louis Latour and Chablis from William Fèvre. There is a full range from Antinori in the Italian section, and from Chile the wines of Concha y Toro take the spotlight. Australian wines are represented by an interesting range from Jarrah Ridge, Basedows and Houghton. California is exclusively Christian Brothers.

The range here is not large but prices seem fair. A few reports needed, please.

Best buys

Jarrah Ridge Chardonnay/Semillon 1990, South-East Australia, £
Casillero del Diablo 1987, Concha y Toro, Chile, £
Ch. Peyrabon 1989, Haut-Médoc, ££
Champagne Claude Dubois Brut nv, ££

Côte d'Or Wines

88 Pitshanger Lane, London W5 1QX — *Tel* 081-998 0144

Open Mon–Tue and Thur–Sat 9.30–6 (Thu, Fri till 8) **Closed** Wed, Sun, public holidays **Credit cards** Access, Visa; personal and business accounts **Discounts** 5% on 1 unmixed case; negotiable on larger orders **Delivery** Free to south-east England (min order 1 case); elsewhere at cost; mail order available **Glass hire** Free with order **Tastings and talks** To groups on request **Cellarage** £3 per case per year

There is a pleasant round-the-world selection from Gavin Whitmee of Ealing-based Côte d'Or Wines. Despite the name, there is no particular focus on Burgundy; if anything, Bordeaux is more of a speciality with a good range of petit château wines and some top-notch 1983 clarets. From the rest of the world there is a sprinkling of everything, although it wouldn't take more than a few weekends in Ealing to run through most of the range. Spain is interesting, with Riojas from Navajas and the reserva Navarra wine from Chivite.

Service is good. Gavin will try to get wines not already stocked, and delivery is free to the South-East of England. Bottles are stored horizontally in racks, which keeps the corks in good condition and makes a nice change from row upon row of shelves.

Best buys

Chivite Reserve 1986, Navarra, £
Domaine de Perras 1990, Vin de Pays des Côtes de Gascogne, £
Corbans Fumé Blanc 1989, New Zealand, ££
Ch. de Belcier 1986, Côtes de Castillon, ££

County Wines of Hagley

2 The Mews, Hagley Hall, Stourbridge, West Midlands DY9 9LG *Tel* (0562) 882346

Open Mon–Fri 9–5.30; Sat 10–4 **Closed** Sun, public holidays **Credit cards** Access, Visa; personal and business accounts **Discounts** Between 5% and 10% depending on volume **Delivery** Free in Midlands area (min order 1 case); elsewhere £6.95 **Glass hire** Free **Tastings and talks** Monthly themed programme of tastings (Sats) **Cellarage** Not available

There is a short, select range from this company operating from the mews at Hagley Hall. Clarets remain in the affordable petits châteaux category apart from a solitary Lafite 1978 which looks almost out of place. Burgundies are reasonably priced *négociants'* wines. Beaujolais fares well, but the Rhône and Alsace are sadly neglected. The Spanish selection from Torres and Señorio de Sarria is worth spending some time on. With a nod in the direction of New Zealand and a handful of Australian wines, this clearly is not a list to hold the attention too long. It would be nice to see a few more producers' names, particularly for Italian and German wines.

Apparently, there is an ever-changing selection of around 80 bin-ends at any one time, which is good news for the adventurous. A wine club operates with regular tastings based around a particular theme.

Best buys

Villa Montes Sauvignon Blanc 1992, Chile, £
Southern Cross Chenin/Chardonnay 1991, New Zealand, £
Chénas Domaine de Chantegrille 1991, ££
Chablis Domaine Brocard 1991, ££

Croque-en-Bouche

221 Wells Road, Malvern Wells, Hereford & Worcester WR14 4HF *Tel* (0684) 565612

Case sales only **Open** Any reasonable time, by arrangement
Credit cards Access, Visa **Discounts** 4% on 4+ cases (cash/cheque and collect)
Delivery Free locally (min 2 cases); elsewhere £5 on orders of £350+; mail order available **Glass hire, tastings and talks** Not available **Cellarage** Short term only

Like a good deed in a naughty world the Croque-en-Bouche wine-list shines out with beacon brightness for sheer mouthwatering variety. If you plan to eat at this restaurant, since that is what it is, then you will need to allow an hour or two to read through all 550 wines. The list comes complete with hand-drawn maps and sensible tasting notes and you can even buy a take-home version so you can plan ahead for your next visit.

But this is not a restaurant guide, so why is this establishment included? The simple reason is that if you like the wine you had with dinner, you can buy a case to take home. Prices are discounted by a set amount, £4 off for bottles up to £10, £5 for bottles up to £20, and so on. There is also a retail list with a heavily pruned selection and these sport retail prices. Sales are by the case only which can be mixed.

However, you do not have to eat at the restaurant to take advantage of the wine business. Ring or call in at any reasonable time, Sundays and Mondays are best, and proprietor Robin Jones will be happy to see you. The choice is amazing. The Rhône is a particular speciality and rates its own additional list. Where else can you get Côte Rôtie from a choice of growers such as Jasmin, Gentaz-Dervieux and Guigal across 12 vintages? Hermitages spill down the page – Chave, Jaboulet, Guigal and Chapoutier – again in vintage after vintage. Each section introduces the growers and their styles.

Wine styles are also the basis for the retail list which does not go country by country but, like the first part of this *Guide*, taste by taste. Full-bodied dry whites include Hamilton-Russell Chardonnay from South Africa, Boyer-Martinot's Meursault and Sonoma-Cutrer Chardonnay. Full-bodied reds range from Ch. Musar to Reserva 904 Rioja and Coudoulet de Beaucastel.

Even if you have the three Croque-en-Bouche lists to hand there is yet another rich seam of wine maturing gently. Around an additional 250 wines are not listed and these, generally, are bottles which are not yet ready for drinking but may be offered if you show an interest in that particular area. The choice across all the lists is worldwide, from the local vineyard in Coddington to Zimbabwe, with a healthy emphasis on good winemaking and exciting flavours. Thank goodness you can get a meal there while you make up your mind!

Best buys

Vin de Pays des Côtes de Gasgogne nv, Plaimont, £
Berri Estates Cabernet Sauvignon 1989, Australia, £
Stoneleigh Sauvignon 1990, New Zealand, ££
Côte Rôtie 1986, Guigal, ££

Cumbrian Cellar

1 St Andrew's Square, Penrith, Cumbria CA11 7AN *Tel* (0768) 63664

Open Mon–Sat 9–5.30 **Closed** Sun, Chr Day, Boxing Day, Good Friday **Credit cards** Access, Visa; personal and business accounts **Discounts** 5% on 1 mixed case **Delivery** Free in Cumbria (min 1 case); mail order available **Glass hire** Free with order **Tastings and talks** Bottles available on premises from time-to-time; to groups on request **Cellarage** Not available

A wide range is available for Penrith drinkers at the Cumbrian Cellars. Ex-RAF navigator Kenneth Gear has steered his way around the wine world, collecting examples from Peru, Brazil, China and Russia, as well as from the more classic regions. Australia is a special interest with a complete range from Rosemount and wines from Orlando, Hardy and Houghton as well. Bosanquet Estate wines from the Southern Vales provide even more variety. Italy includes the standard names, with interest added by Venegazzù, and Teroldego and Chiantis from Rocca delle Macie and Ricasoli. France is handled competently, but it seems that the residents of Penrith do not go in for classy clarets or expensive burgundies. There are a few organic wines including Bossard's Blanc de Blancs. Sales of sherry in this area, bucking national trends, are booming. The range includes Valdespino, Williams & Humbert and Burdon, whose Heavenly Cream probably goes down a treat when the westerlies are blowing a gale.

The emphasis in this little shop is on drinkable wines at reasonable prices, which is as good a reason as any to navigate your way here.

Best buys

Vin de Pays de l'Hérault 1990, Cuvée de la Caumette, £
Kodru Cabernet Sauvigon/Merlot 1984, Moldavia, £
Cerasuolo 1988, Montepulciano d'Abruzzo Rosato, ££
Ackerman '1811' Sparkling Saumur, ££

Davisons Wine Merchants

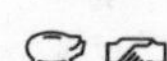

Head office
5 Aberdeen Road, Croydon, Surrey CR0 1EQ *Tel* 081-686 9989
79 branches in London and South-East

Open Tue–Fri 10–8; Sat 10–6; Sun 10–2 **Closed** Mon, public holidays **Credit cards** Access, Visa **Discounts** 2.5% on 10 cases **Delivery** Free locally (min 1 case) and elsewhere (min 10 cases); otherwise charges by arrangement; mail order available **Glass hire** Free with order **Tastings and talks** Tutored tastings in-store and to wine clubs on request **Cellarage** Not available

Davisons is a familiar sight on local shopping parades in the Home Counties, but to think of this chain as just another 'offie' would be a mistake. On the shelves is a good round-the-world range with particular strengths in Bordeaux, burgundy and port. Most of these classic wines were bought *en primeur* and prices are generally fair or, indeed, very fair. If you are thinking of investing in a few bottles of claret it would be wise to check out the price on the Davisons list before you buy. Mixed cases qualify for an additional 8.5 per cent discount which makes some of the fine wine prices unbeatable. From Bordeaux there are over 120 châteaux wines, dating from 1988 back to 1966, including some interesting second and third wines from Ducru-Beaucaillou and Beychevelle. Davisons is also one of the few high-street shops where you can get a good bottle of Sauternes (often Rieussec) at a moment's notice. Friendly staff will even chill bottles ready for collection later.

Burgundies are from individual growers such as Machard de Gramont, Pavelot and Jean Grivot. Still on the classic wines, the range of vintage ports is terrific: all the major names and lots of vintages going back to 1958. Not every shop has every wine from this range but you will certainly find a few gems on the racks and others can be ordered.

Outside these areas the Davisons range is less exciting. Rhônes are lumped together with French country wines; there is only one Châteauneuf-du-Pape and no Hermitage. Loires, too, are fairly predictable. If Davisons stores can sell classed growths, couldn't they also try a Bourgueil or Chinon? The Chilean range is short but includes the lovely Montes wines; Australia is also worth a second look, with some Penfolds, Rothbury, Cape Mentelle and Krondorf.

Under the same parent company as Davisons is the Master Cellar Wine Warehouse in Croydon. It operates from the same list but, being a warehouse, has considerably more stock available. In addition, the manager Keith Nanson buys a few extras. Particularly interesting are the Masia Barril Priorato wines from Spain and a handful of good Chiantis. A recent change has been the granting of a retail licence to this warehouse, so you can buy single bottles as well as by the case.

Best buys

Ch. Mendoce 1988, Côtes de Bourg, £
Villa Montes Sauvignon Blanc 1991, Chile, £
Chassagne-Montrachet Premier Cru Chaumées 1988, Domaine Morey, ££
Ch. Rieussec 1983, ££

Prices were current in summer 1992 to the best of our knowledge but can only be a rough indication of prices throughout 1993.

Del Monico's

23 South Street, St Austell, Cornwall PL25 5BH *Tel* (0726) 73593

Open Mon–Sat 10–6 **Closed** Sun, public holidays **Credit cards** Access, Visa; personal and business accounts **Discounts** 5% on 1 case **Delivery** Free within 30-mile radius of St Austell (min 1 case); elsewhere £2.50 (min 2 cases) **Glass hire** Free with order **Tastings and talks** Monthly tastings via the Wine Club; occasional tasting evenings **Cellarage** Limited; charges negotiable

When you consider how pleasant it is to sit, glass in hand, overlooking the sea, it is surprising that Cornwall, with its extensive coastline, is not littered with wine merchants. As it is, Del Monico's in St Austell flies the flag in this part of the world for variety and quality in roughly equal amounts.

From France there is a selection of clarets which would keep all but the most adventurous occupied, while the burgundies stretch all the way up to Echézeaux, with a scattering of Faiveley and Bouchard Père along the way. The Rhône and Loire sections are adequate and a reasonable collection of country wines provides inexpensive drinking. From outside France, Spain holds most attraction, with a range of Riojas including the blockbuster Reserva 904 from La Rioja Alta and Navarra wines from Ochoa. Australian wines now include the good-value Tollana range, and New Zealand representatives are wines from Nobilo and Montana. Del Monico's has a tasting club where the wines are free and the only charge is £1 to cover the cost of hiring furniture! Perhaps so that you can sit and enjoy the view over the sea?

Best buys

Santa Carolina Cabernet Sauvignon 1986, Chile, £
Cuvée Georges Duboeuf Red and White, £
Reserva 904 1976, La Rioja Alta, ££
Fairview Estate Pinot Noir Reserve 1986, South Africa, ££

Dennhöfer Wines

47 Bath Lane, Newcastle upon Tyne, Tyne & Wear NE4 5SP *Tel* 091-232 7342

Open Mon–Fri 8.30–5.30; Sat 9.30–1.30 **Closed** Sun, public holidays **Credit cards** Access, Visa; personal and business accounts **Discounts** Not available **Delivery** Free locally (min 1 case); elsewhere at cost **Glass hire** Free with order **Tastings and talks** Available **Cellarage** Free

Dennhöfer has had such a busy year that it was unable to find the time to tell us much about itself. The list remains pretty much as before with slightly less emphasis on Germany and a general pruning of the range from the rest of the world.

France takes in a reasonable collection of burgundies and clarets, although the Loire and Rhône seem rather neglected. Spanish wines are nearly all from Bodegas Montecillo and Portugal remains unexplored apart from a Vinho Verde and Mateus Rosé. From the New World, Nobilo represents New Zealand while Wyndhams does a valiant job representing the whole of Australia. Three new Chinese wines add a little variety.

Best buys

Ch. Crillon 1989, Côtes du Ventoux, £
Puligny-Montrachet 1989, Patrick Javiller, ££
Bornheimer Hahnchen 1985, QmP Eiswein Johann Flick, ££

Rodney Densem Wines

Office
Stapeley Bank, London Road, Stapeley, Nantwich, Cheshire CW5 7JW

Tel (for both addresses) (0270) 623665

Retail
4 Pillory Street, Nantwich, Cheshire CW5 5BD

Open Mon–Tue 10–6; Wed–Fri 9–6; Sat 9–5.30 **Closed** Sun, public holidays **Credit cards** Access, Visa; personal and business accounts **Discounts** 5% on 1 mixed case **Delivery** Free within 25-mile radius (min 1 case); elsewhere approximately £8 per case; mail order available **Glass hire** Free with order **Tastings and talks** Available **Cellarage** Not available

Rodney Densem is the name over the door but in fact this retail shop is run by wife Margie, while Rodney takes care of the wholesale business of the same name. The shop does not produce a list but offers pretty much the same as the wholesale range plus a few extras.

The southern hemisphere features strongly, with a good set of Australians (Brown Brothers, Rosemount, Lindemans and Hardy) and de Redcliffe Estates, Cooks and Cloudy Bay batting for New Zealand. Chile is fairly sparse: just a few wines from Torres.

In Europe, France holds most interest – clarets (mainly in the affordable class) and a few special-occasion top-notes. Burgundies are from a number of reliable *négociants*, Faiveley and Drouhin among them. With Pascal in the Rhône and a handful of worthwhile vins de pays there is enough to keep the interest going. One special feature is a separate section of wines priced at £3.50 and under.

It is encouraging to see that at this regional independent even the delivery staff have achieved the Wine and Spirit Education Trust Higher Certificate.

Best buys

Ch. Lamothe 1990, Premières Côtes de Bordeaux, £
Vin de Pays des Côtes de Gascogne Blanc 'Lou Magrat' 1991, £
De Redcliffe Estates Hawkes Bay Chardonnay 1990, New Zealand, ££
Pouilly Fumé 'Les Bascoins' 1990, Domaine Masson-Blondelet, ££

Direct Wine Shipments

5/7 Corporation Square, Belfast, Co Antrim BT1 3AJ — *Tel* (0232) 238700/243906

Associated outlet

Duncairn Wines, 555 Antrim Road, Belfast, Co Antrim BT15 3BU — *Tel* (0232) 370694

Open Mon–Sat 9.30–6 (5pm on Sat, 8pm on Thur) **Closed** Sun, Chr for 3 days, Easter for 2 days, 12–13 July **Credit cards** Access, Visa; personal and business accounts **Discounts** Available on request **Delivery** Free in Northern Ireland (min 1 case) **Glass hire** Not available **Tastings and talks** 6-week courses; to groups on request **Cellarage** Free with purchase

Direct Wine Shipments recently extended its cellars in the dock area of Belfast and even more refurbishment is planned as part of the dock area re-development programme. The business is well named. Shipping direct to Northern Ireland from major producers around the world has given DWS an edge on range and value. Most areas and countries are represented by two or three quality names whose ranges are held in full.

France starts off with a fine collection of clarets. If you want to spend £120 on a 1982 Ch. Latour you can, but there is plenty of drinking available at less than £10 a bottle, too. Burgundy is from good names such as Faiveley, Olivier Leflaive and Domaine Laroche. The Rhônes are almost all from Chapoutier. The German range is enjoying a revival of interest: at present, wines are from Bürklin-Wolf, Prüm and a Nahe co-operative, but we're told that more wines will swell these ranks soon. From Spain, the wines of Torres, Marqués de Cáceres and Chivite are stocked and there are five vintages of Vega Sicilia. Italians are mainly from Pio Cesare and Antinori. Outside Europe there is a representative sample from most countries although Australia is rather limited with only Brown Brothers, plus a few others.

Education ranks high on DWS's list of priorities. Customers can take a six-week in-house course with an examination at the end, and the company hosts 'Winemaker's Dinners' with distinguished guests.

Best buys

Domaine de Barret 1990, Vin de Pays des Côtes de Gascogne, £
Santa Rita 120 Cabernet Sauvignon 1988, Chile, £
Moulin-à-Vent 1988, Domaine Dichon, ££
Ch. Lamothe-Cissac Vieilles Vignes 1988, ££

Domaine Direct 

29 Wilmington Square, London WC1X 0EG *Tel* 071-837 1142

Case sales only **Open** Mon–Fri 8–6 **Closed** Sat, Sun, public holidays **Credit cards** None accepted; personal and business accounts **Discounts** Not available **Delivery** Free in central London and Home Counties (min 1 case) and on UK mainland (min 3 cases); otherwise 1 case £8, 2 cases £11; mail order available **Glass hire** Free **Tastings and talks** 2–3 free tastings a year **Cellarage** £5.75 per case per year (inc insurance and VAT)

Domaine Direct has branched out in a modest way and now its range includes wines from Australia, New Zealand and California, as well as Burgundy. The principle is the same for all its wines: take a quality wine region and find the good or even the best growers. This comes over clearly in Burgundy where wines from Michel Juillot, Tollot-Beaut, Simon Bize and Comte Lafon are just the start of the story. From the whole of the Côte d'Or there is tremendous choice of vineyards, growers and vintages and informative notes to help you decide. As befits a true specialist, many of the wines are available in magnums and if you like your burgundy in smaller packages, this is the place to come. Nearly 80 wines are available in half-bottles, from Beaujolais to Chassagne-Montrachet.

The New World selection is from a variety of sources: Australia features Leeuwin Estate, Cape Mentelle and Penfolds; New Zealand wines are from Cloudy Bay, Redwood Valley and Brookfields; while California supplies wines from Stag's Leap, Hawk Crest and Sonoma-Cutrer. Particularly interesting is the Spottswoode Cabernet Sauvignon from a tiny vineyard in the Napa Valley and the same winemaker's Pinot Noir, called Etude.

All prices are quoted ex-VAT, which could indicate that most of Domaine Direct's customers are restaurants and businesses. The minimum quantity is one mixed case which is delivered free in central London and the Home Counties.

Best buys

Mercurey Premier Cru Clos des Barraults 1988, Michel Juillot, ££
Leeuwin Estate Chardonnay 1986, Margaret River, Australia, ££
There are no wines available from Domaine Direct for under £5.

Peter Dominic

See Thresher

Eaton Elliot Winebrokers

15 London Road, Alderley Edge, Cheshire SK9 7JT *Tel* (0625) 582354

Open Mon–Fri 9.30–6.30 (Fri till 8); Sat 9.30–5 **Closed** Sun, public holidays **Credit cards** All accepted; personal and business accounts **Discounts** 5% on 1 case **Delivery** Free within 25-mile radius of Alderley Edge (min 1 case); elsewhere at cost; mail order available **Glass hire** Free with order **Tastings and talks** Four formal tastings per year; regular informal in-store tastings **Cellarage** Not available

A well-sourced, individual range of wines is on offer from this Cheshire merchant. Within France the emphasis is on domaines, particularly in the 'regional' section which includes Madiran from Ch. Peyros, four Jurançon wines from Domaine Cauhapé and a couple of table wines from La Chablisienne co-operative. Bordeaux wines are good but Burgundy holds more interest with domaine wines again taking centre-stage. In the Loire, Bourgueil from Caslot-Galbrun and Reuilly from Henri Beurdin look interesting.

Outside France there is no more than a nod in the direction of Germany, but Italy is worth spending some time on: Chiantis from Castello di Volpaia, Veneto wines from Villa Girardi and a couple of up-market vini da tavola are among the attractions. Spain is limited to a few Riojas (CVNE and Marqués de Cáceres) and Navarras from Ochoa. Three wines from New York State are an unusual feature in the American section – Long Island Merlot would probably get the conversation going at most Alderley Edge dinner parties. Australia has large and small wineries, with Rosemount weighing in for the big guys and Heathcote and Yarra Yering representing smaller producers. Champagnes from Nicolas Feuillatte and sherries from Lustau round off the wines, but a range of 26 malt whiskies provides further attraction.

Best buys

Ch. Theulet 1989, Bergerac, £
English Vineyard, High Weald Winery, Kent, £
Domaine Cauhapé Vendange Tardive 1989, Jurançon, ££
Reuilly Pinot Noir Rosé 1990, Henri Beurdin, ££

Eldridge Pope

Head office
Weymouth Avenue, Dorchester, Dorset DT1 1QT *Tel* (0305) 251251
13 wine shops/Wine Libraries

Open Generally Mon–Sat 9–1, 2–5.30 (varying half-days); (Reynier) Mon–Fri 11–6.30 (Sat also Exeter branch); (Bristol) 9.30–6.30 **Closed** Sat (Reynier, London and Bristol), Sun, public holidays **Credit cards** Access, Visa; personal and business accounts **Discounts** 5% on mixed or full cases **Delivery** Free within 20-mile radius of Dorchester (min £35 order) and UK mainland (min 2+ cases); smaller orders £5 delivery charge **Glass hire** Free **Tastings and talks** Regular tutored tastings at Wine Libraries; tutored tastings for Dorset Wine Society (£10–£14 per person) **Cellarage** £3 per case per year

A delicate shade of violet makes this an easy list to find on the bookshelf. The colour changes annually – bright pink, pale blue...

Eldridge Pope is a major wholesaler of wine to the trade but also has nine retail shops and four additional outlets – the Reynier Wine Libraries. It would be nice if these libraries operated like book libraries where you could borrow a bottle and return it later, having sampled the contents. Surprisingly enough they don't work like that. They are really off-licences, with eating areas attached, where you can buy your wine at normal prices, pay a £1 corkage and enjoy a simple fixed-price meal. It is a splendid idea. In the evenings the Libraries are used for pre-arranged tutored tastings. There are Wine Libraries in London (SW1 and EC3), and in Bristol and Exeter.

The nine Eldridge Pope shops are spread mainly around Dorset, with the Dorchester one being the biggest. The same range is available in all shops although space may sometimes limit the stock. Anything not immediately available can be ordered. The list is a magnificent production. A thumb index takes you straight to the page you need and each region is introduced with a well-written essay. Joe Naughalty, a Master of Wine for 24 years, is the buyer and his experience shows in the quality of the wines listed. The range has a heavy bias towards France. Good traditional clarets are listed (page after page) and not all of them are hugely expensive. The younger vintages include quite a few reasonably priced petits châteaux. The Chairman's Claret (one of an extensive range of Chairman's wines) is from young vines at Ch. Cissac. Burgundies are equally comprehensive; single line descriptions point punters in the right direction.

The Rhône selection is not huge but the basic Côtes-du-Rhône, Ch. la Renjardière, is soft, peppery and excellent value. Watch out for the arrival of Châteauneuf-du-Pape, Domaine de Monpertuis from Paul Jeune. The 'Tradition' wines are made from 100-year-old vines and reek of pepper, plums and spice – delicious.

Germany and Italy are well represented but the rest of the world is banished to a small section at the back of the list. Even Australia is limited to a mere five wines. Perhaps Joe Naughalty's recent trip to Oz will spark more activity in this area? Delivery is free within 20 miles of Dorchester on orders over £35. Two cases will get you free delivery anywhere in mainland UK.

Best buys

Côtes-du-Rhône 1990, Ch. la Renjardière, £
Abbaye de Valmagne 1989, Coteaux du Languedoc, £
The Chairman's White Burgundy 1990, ££
Savennières 1989, Clos du Papillon, Jean Baumard, ££

Ben Ellis and Associates

The Harvesters, Lawrence Lane, Buckland, Betchworth, Surrey RH3 7BE *Tel* (0737) 842160

Case sales only **Open** Mon–Fri 9–6.30; Sat 9–1 (telephone beforehand); evenings by telephone; other times by arrangement **Credit cards** Access, Visa; personal and business accounts **Discounts** Not available **Delivery** Free in Surrey and central London (min 1 case) and nationally (min 5+ cases); otherwise £9.40 per consignment; mail order available **Glass hire** Free with order
Tastings and talks To groups on request; major customer tastings in May and November **Cellarage** £3.60 per case per year

Ben Ellis's associates in this venture are Mark Pardoe, Master of Wine, and Martin Sheen. In 1990 Mark won the Madame Bollinger medal for excellence in wine tasting – no mean feat and a talent subsequently put to good use in selecting this range.

There is no shop, so the list is the main point of contact; it has a knowledgeable, friendly feel about it. Comments such as 'We never buy on price alone and always seek the best ratio between quality and value' are reassuring, as is the statement about delivery: 'Outside the free delivery area [Surrey and central London] we will always try to arrange a mutually convenient point to avoid carriage charges'. The range takes in both ends of the market: inexpensive everyday wines and top-quality fine wines. From France, generic Bordeaux and petits châteaux are topped off by a classy selection of clarets, some ready and others (a particularly good choice of 1985 and 1988 vintages) needing time to mature. Burgundies are from a variety of growers and *négociants*, the range of prices and vintages ensuring there is something for everyone in this naturally expensive area. Good wines from the Rhône, Loire and Alsace are introduced page by page with a chatty commentary about each region. The selection of French regional wines has been put together with care. Almost all are under £5 with Mas de Daumas Gassac the obvious exception.

The size of the German section reflects a declining interest in this area, but there are two splendid new-style dry wines from Lingenfelder which may reverse this trend. It should come as no surprise in this professional outfit that the producers' names are faithfully included alongside the wines. Italy explores the good regions and estates; Spain and Portugal are more restricted although still well chosen. Australia branches out into a full-scale assault on the wonderful wines of St Hallett in the Barossa, a couple from Shaw and Smith and a round-up from elsewhere.

Especially useful is a summary of the half-bottles available and a pink centrefold listing wines under £5. Twice-yearly tastings keep customers in touch with new additions to the range.

Best buys

Domaine de San Guilhem 1991, Vin de Pays des Côtes de Gascogne, £
Domaine de la Soumade 1989, Côtes-du-Rhône, £
St Hallett Old Block Shiraz 1989, Australia, ££
Freinsheimer Goldberg Riesling Spätlese 1989, Lingenfelder, ££

English Wine Centre

Alfriston Roundabout, Alfriston, East Sussex BN26 5QS — *Tel* (0323) 870164

Open Mon–Sat 10–5; Sun 12–4 **Closed** 25 Dec-2 Jan; Sun Nov-Mar **Credit cards** Access, Visa; personal and business accounts **Discounts** Available **Delivery** Free within 20-mile radius (min order 2+ cases); elsewhere at cost; mail order available **Glass hire** Free with order **Tastings and talks** Series of free Chr tastings; regular tutored tastings **Cellarage** Not available

Unless you happen to live near a vineyard, your choice of English wine will probably be limited to the two or three examples available nationally. At the English Wine Centre, Christopher Ann has brought together a wide range of wines from across the south of England, including a *méthode traditionelle* sparkling wine and a choice of English reds. These are available on a retail or wholesale basis and there are always a few bottles open for tasting if you call in. The Centre operates not only as a shop but has vineyards and cellars of its own. There is a museum of English winemaking, and tours, tastings and dinners can be arranged. It is also the venue for the English Wine Festival held in September each year.

Best buys

Sussex County 1990, Medium Dry, £
Cuckmere Müller-Thurgau 1990, Sussex, ££
Kingsley Pinot Noir 1989, Surrey, ££

Philip Eyres Wine Merchant

The Cellars, Coleshill, Amersham, Buckinghamshire HP7 0LS

Tel (0494) 433823 (enquiries)
Tel (0494) 432402 (The Cellars)

Case sales only **Open** Personal callers by appointment; telephone enquiries during office hours Mon–Fri 8–10, Sat, Sun 9–10 **Closed** Public holidays and during annual holiday **Credit cards** None accepted; personal and business accounts **Discounts** 2.5% on unmixed cases **Delivery** Free within surrounding areas together with central London and other parts of London by mutual agreement (min 1 case); otherwise 1–3 cases charged flat fee of £5; mail order available **Glass hire** Free **Tastings and talks** Tastings given at various locations **Cellarage** Customers introduced to Octavian, Corsham, Wilts

Philip Eyres and his four associates run this business which operates in the south Buckinghamshire and north Berkshire areas as well as in Aylesbury and Bicester. There is no shop; instead there is an extensive list and wines can be bought by the mixed case supplemented by *en primeur* and special offers. Recent offers include the 1990 German vintage and 1991 Beaujolais, both regions sadly neglected by many merchants and consumers. Perhaps this approach is the best way to sell wines, focusing on quality producers such as Dr Loosen and Friedrich-Wilhelm-Gymnasium from the Mosel and Eventail des Vignerons Producteurs in Beaujolais. Prices seem reasonable for this quality and include delivery. This year, Philip Eyres has decided not to offer the 1991 clarets but is concentrating on wines from other parts of the world, including South Africa.

As well as these offers there is a well-presented list with comprehensive descriptions against each wine. France provides plenty of choice although the Loire is a little restricted. German estate wines feature heavily, but these are quality wines going right up to Trockenbeerenauslese and Eiswein, with not a

Liebfraumilch in sight. Spain and Italy provide even more variety. The New World selection is extensive: Moss Wood, Leasingham and Coldstream Hills are some of the Australians; Chile, Argentina and California are listed as well.

Prices seem reasonable and we have had good reports of the service. Annual tastings keep customers in touch with the range.

Best buys

Domaine Pech-Redon Chardonnay 1990, Vin de Pays des Coteaux de Narbonne, £
Manzanilla La Gitana, £
Maximin Grünhäuser Herrenberg Riesling Kabinett 1989, Mosel-Saar-Ruwer, ££
Moss Wood Pinot Noir 1989, Australia, ££

Farr Vintners

Mainly mail order
19 Sussex Street, London SW1V 4RR *Tel* 071-828 1960

Case sales only **Open** Mon–Fri 10–6 **Closed** Sat, Sun, public holidays **Credit cards** Access, Visa; personal and business accounts **Discounts** Variable (min 10 cases) **Delivery** £8 per consignment within London; elsewhere at cost; mail order available **Glass hire** Free with suitable case order **Tastings and talks** Regular tastings **Cellarage** £5 per case per year

'Thank you for introducing me to Farr: it has saved me a lot of money,' wrote one of our readers; we have heard similar sentiments from others. This specialised merchant offers *en primeur* claret at prices that look like printing errors. You end up double-checking the small print just to make sure that there are no colossal extras (there aren't, apart from normal shipping and duty). The only stipulation is a minimum order of £200 excluding VAT, with delivery charges extra. There are doubts about offering the 1991 vintage but Farr has plenty of other wines available in two other areas of the market.

The first of these is in fine and rare wines. If you are looking for 30 vintages of Ch. Lafite, some going back to the pre-phylloxera days of the 1800s, then this is the place to come to. Pétrus, Mouton, Latour, Margaux and Yquem are available in endless vintages and bottle sizes. Many have been bought from private cellars, and Farr does a surprisingly brisk trade in selling older vintages back to Bordeaux where they are difficult to find. A retail licence has recently been obtained, so now you can buy a magnum of 1947 Pétrus (only £2200!) without upsetting the licensing magistrates.

Away from First Growths, there is a wonderful range of cru classé wines dating from recent vintages back to 1921, mostly in unbroken cases. The 1982 collection (22 châteaux), in particular, looks impressive enough for immediate drinking, and all at very reasonable prices. Farr's interest is not confined to Bordeaux. Burgundy merits the same attention, with wines from Domaine de la Romanée-Conti being a particular speciality. From the Rhône there is Ch. de Beaucastel, Guigal and Jaboulet, from Alsace the wines of Humbrecht and Trimbach are listed. A clutch of wines from New Zealand (Wairau and Redwood Valley) add a New World touch to this essentially Old World selection.

Farr is run by Stephen Browett and Lindsay Hamilton who, together with Jonathan Stephens in sales, have tasted most wines from most vintages this century. With quality tasting practice of that kind, their advice can only be good.

Best buys

Côtes-du-Rhône 1989, Guigal, £
Ch. de Beaucastel 1989, Châteauneuf-du-Pape, £
Ch. La Mission-Haut-Brion 1964, Graves, ££

Farthinghoe Fine Wine and Food 

The Old Rectory, Farthinghoe, Brackley, Northamptonshire NN13 5NZ — *Tel* (0295) 710018

Open Mon–Fri 9–5; Sat, Sun, public holidays by arrangement only
Credit cards None accepted; personal and business accounts **Discounts** 6–10 cases £1 per case, 11+ cases £2 per case **Delivery** Free on UK mainland (min 3 cases); otherwise 1 case £6, 2 cases £3 per case; mail order available
Glass hire Available with charge (£2.50 for 48 glasses cleaning charge)
Tastings and talks Occasional customer tastings **Cellarage** By arrangement

Simon Cox MBE and MW runs this successful food and wine double-act with his wife Nicola at their big old rectory near Banbury. The wine merchant part of the enterprise has a retail licence but this is possibly just to enable the cookery guests to take home whatever bottle they enjoyed over lunch. The list remains resolutely wholesale, with prices given for unmixed cases. However, mixed cases are allowed and we presume there is no extra charge for this service.

The range has shrunk this year in order to concentrate on France – with just a handful of wines from elsewhere. It is a good personal selection with tasting notes alongside each wine. There are Alsace wines from Gisselbrecht and a few specialities from Trimbach. Clarets include a reasonable selection of petits châteaux with a few classier 1982 wines recommended for laying down, although some should be drinkable now. Burgundies are from Domaines Thénard and Corsin, with a few representatives from Armand Rousseau and Tollot-Beaut.

Rhônes include wines from Jaboulet and the good-value Vieille Ferme wines from Perrin of Ch. de Beaucastel fame. The two non-French wines, Brown Brothers Shiraz from Australia and Villa Montes Cabernet Sauvignon from Chile, seem rather lonely but are terrific wines and perhaps more southern hemisphere wines will eventually join them.

Best buys

Johnston Reserve Claret nv, £
La Vieille Ferme Blanc 1991, Côtes du Lubéron, £
Ch. de Sours 1991, Bordeaux Rosé, ££
Domaine Petit Château, Chardonnay 1991, Vin de Pays du Jardin de la France, ££

Ferrers le Mesurier

Turnsloe, North Street, Titchmarsh, Kettering, Northamptonshire NN14 3DH — *Tel* (08012) 2660

Case sales only **Open** (Best to telephone before calling) Mon–Fri 8–8; Sat, Sun, public holidays by arrangement **Credit cards** None accepted; personal and business accounts **Discounts** By arrangement (min 1 case) **Delivery** Within a 50-mile radius of Kettering and London (min 1 case); elsewhere at cost **Glass hire** Not available **Tastings and talks** Annual Cambridge college tasting **Cellarage** Free for up to two years if wine purchased from premises

Ferrers Le Mesurier (that's the name of the company and the man who runs it) offers a personal selection of wines from small French growers. We leave it to him to explain on the front of his list that these growers are generally under 5ft 2ins!

The choice is restricted to around 50 wines, all French and each one the only representative of its area or quality grade. It is good to see that even in such a small selection M. Le Mesurier finds space for Condrieu, two Alsace wines and a Chardonnay from the Charentes. Among the reds, Beaujolais and burgundy hold most interest but the four clarets provide well-priced drinking. Highlight of the year is the annual tasting in a Cambridge college.

Best buys

Domaine la Taste 1991, Vin de Pays de Gascogne, £
Domaine de l'Armarine Rouge 1989 Costières de Nîmes, £
Lirac 1990, Cuvée Reine des Bois, ££
Meursault Rouge 1990, Bouzereau Esmonin, ££

Alex Findlater

Vauxhall Cellars, 72 Goding Street, London SE11 5AW — *Tel* 071-587 1644

Office

Heveningham High House, Halesworth, Suffolk IP19 0EA — *Tel* (0986)798274

Case sales only **Open** Mon–Fri 10–6 **Closed** Sat, Sun, public holidays **Credit cards** Access, Visa; personal and business accounts **Discounts** Available **Delivery** Free locally (min 1 case); mail order available **Glass hire** Free with order **Tastings and talks** To groups on request **Cellarage** £5.28 per case per year

Alex Findlater was one of the first merchants to specialise in Australian wine. While the rest of the world was dipping a toe in 'Kangarouge', Alex was busy sorting out the Wirra Wirra from the Tarrawarra and helping his customers to do the same. His Australasian list is well worth a browse. He informs, sometimes at great length, about the regions, vineyards and winemakers. The wines are listed by region and then, for total clarity, cross-referenced by grape variety in another section. This man is nothing if not thorough. Now that every merchant in the country has at least a handful of Australians, the novelty has gone out of this list but it still wins points for being the most comprehensive. When the new list comes out in the autumn it will be a little slimmer but will still take some beating. New Zealand and Tasmania come in for the same detailed approach as Oz.

As an alternative to the Antipodes, you can buy other wines from Alex Findlater. He has a range from France, mainly from small producers in Burgundy, the Rhône and Loire, a few clarets and an interesting selection from Italy. You could always try the 'House Wine' made in the dining-room at Heveningham from locally grown grapes. Alex Findlater deals mainly with the trade – hence the tendency to produce ex-VAT, straight-cases-only lists. However, we are assured that customers wanting a mixed case are equally valued.

Best buys

Vin de Fin de la Terre Rouge, £
Skilly Gap White 1990, South Australia, £
Pommard 1989, Denis Carré, ££
Vasse Felix Cabernet Sauvignon 1988, Western Australia, ££

Findlater Mackie Todd

Deer Park Road, Merton Abbey, London SW19 3TU *Tel* 081-543 7528

Open Mon–Fri 9–6; Sat also, during December **Closed** Sun, public holidays **Credit cards** All accepted; personal and business accounts **Discounts** Available **Delivery** Free on UK mainland (min 1 case); Northern Ireland and offshore islands £3.50 per case; mail order available **Glass hire** Available **Tastings and talks** Tastings vary in size, frequency and venue **Cellarage** £5.01 per case per year

Findlater Mackie Todd is one of the oldest names in the wine industry. Established in 1823, it continues to supply its own brand of sherry, Dry Fly, to the trade. It also operates as a mail-order company although there is a retail licence so that single bottles can be mailed out as well as cases. We are told that being a customer of Findlaters is like being a member of an exclusive wine club, except that there are no membership fees and no commitment to buy. Perhaps some of its customers could let us know if the service lives up to that description.

The annual list has regular updates, bin-end sales and opening offers. The 1990 Burgundy offer included a splendid range from good growers and *négociants*. Otherwise, the list is a fairly classic romp through the regions with clarets, burgundies and German wines being the specialities. It is always wise to check prices before you buy and this company is no exception. For example, you could save £13 a bottle by buying your 1983 Léoville-Las-Cases from Harveys of Bristol instead of Findlaters; the same vintage of Ch. Ducru-Beaucaillou is around £10 a bottle cheaper at Lay & Wheeler than here. On the other hand, some of the Rhônes are very realistically priced. Spain and Italy provide good distinctive drinking while Australia produces a pleasant collection from Basedow, Hill-Smith and Tyrrells.

Towards the middle of the list is a section entitled 'The Inner Cellar'. The criteria used to select wines for these pages are unclear. Why La Mission-Haut-Brion 1983 is on the main list while the 1982 is locked away in a glass case – or swept into the corner, depending on your viewpoint – is a mystery. However, do not overlook these inner pages when you are making your selection; not all are rich and rare – Guigal's 1982 Hermitage looks a positive bargain. Fortified wines are a particular delight, with Findlater's sherries, tawny and vintage ports and a collection of madeiras making an interesting selection.

Best buys

Dão Terras Altas 1989, Fonseca, Portugal, £
Hermitage, M. de la Sizeranne 1985, Chapoutier, ££
Ch. Musar 1983, Lebanon, ££

Le Fleming Wines

9 Longcroft Avenue, Harpenden, Hertfordshire AL5 2RB — *Tel* (0582) 760125

Case sales only **Open** 24-hour answerphone **Credit cards** None accepted; business accounts **Discounts** Occasionally **Delivery** Within a 25-mile radius **Glass hire** Free **Tastings and talks** Regular tastings every 4 months; to groups on request **Cellarage** Not available

There is a new entry to the *Guide* this year for this one-woman band operating from Harpenden. So far it is case sales (mixed) and local deliveries only, but the range is fine and well worth a try if you live in this part of the world.

The Australian section has expanded considerably since Cherry Jenkins' trip to Oz and now includes the good-value Orlando range, the Eden Ridge organics, Oxford Landing, Schinus Molle and Mountadam. St Hallett's Old Block Shiraz and Charlie Melton's Nine Popes reveal what glorious flavours the old Barossa vines can produce. Other New World wines include Rongopai from New Zealand and Newton from California.

Back in Europe, the Spanish selection is limited but worthy, Italy includes the vino da tavola Sangioveto from Badia a Coltibuono and Portugal provides three good-value reds with individual characters. The French range is well chosen and most wines are well under £10, with just a few burgundies straying over the £15 mark. Beaujolais wines are from the reliable Cellier des Samsons; clarets are represented by a collection of crus bourgeois, including Loudenne, Malescasse and de Pez. The French country section features a Bourgogne Passetoutgrains from Jean Musso and the peppery, spicy Mas de Gourgonnier Tradition, Coteaux d'Aix-en-Provence – both wines are organically grown.

Best buys

Côtes-du-Rhône, Domaine Belair 1988, £
Ch. Tizac 1988, Bordeaux Supérieur, £
Rongopai Sauvignon Blanc 1991, New Zealand, ££
Lugana Cà dei Frati 1989, ££

John Ford Wines

8 Richardson Road, Hove, East Sussex BN3 5RB *Tel* (0273) 735891

Associated outlet

The High Street, East Hoathly, East Sussex BN8 6EB *Tel* (0825) 840321

Open Mon–Fri 10–1, 3–7, Sat 9–7, Sun 12–2, public holidays 9–1 **Closed** Chr Day, Boxing Day, New Year's Day **Credit cards** Access, Visa; personal and business accounts **Discounts** 5% on 1 case **Delivery** Free locally (min £25 order); otherwise £2.50 charge; mail order available **Glass hire** Free with case order **Tastings and talks** Regular Friday evening tutored tastings; to groups on request **Cellarage** £5 per case per year

There are now two outlets for this small family business. Ex-university administrator John Ford has moved out to East Hoathly where he runs the local post office and general store. Not surprisingly, this shop also happens to have a good range of wine. Meanwhile, son Robert runs the original Hove branch, with the shop, cellar and tasting room. Tastings are an important feature in Hove. Friday night is tasting night, Mondays too, for some more exclusive wines. A vertical run of Ch. d'Yquem should get a good response from Brighton residents.

The selection of wines is wide, with a particular focus on Ch. Musar in Lebanon; nine vintages of this lovely wine are available, some in magnums. A couple of wines from the Tsar's Massandra collection add highlights but mostly the list is well chosen and reasonably priced. Italy's enthusiasm is for the wines of Antinori. Newsletters, gourmet evenings, books and accessories are just a few of the other delights from this family business.

Best buys

Cabernet Sauvignon 1989, Undurraga, £
Zinfandel 1988, Fetzer, California, £
Pinot Noir 1988, Hamilton-Russell, South Africa, ££
Ch. Musar 1977, Lebanon, ££

Fortnum & Mason 

181 Piccadilly, London W1A 1ER *Tel* 071-734 8040

Open Mon–Sat 9.30–6 **Closed** Sun, public holidays **Credit cards** Access, American Express, Visa; personal and business accounts **Discounts** 5–10% (min 1 case) **Delivery** Free in Greater London (min £30 order exc account holders); otherwise at cost; mail order available **Glass hire** Not available **Tastings and talks** Promotional tastings of champagne and port; regular tastings of sherry, Italian and Spanish wines; tastings and talks given only by private arrangement **Cellarage** £3.45 per case per year

No one who strolls by chance into Fortnum's Piccadilly emporium could mistake it for a bargain basement warehouse. The stiff collars and splendid tailcoats of the staff clearly let you know that this is a Quality Establishment.

The wine department is not vast, just the right size to spend ten minutes or so browsing around before going on to partake of one of Fortnum's famous afternoon teas. Pick up a list as you do so and you will have some interesting reading. As you might expect, the range is well chosen and provides everything that the well-heeled clientele of London and the Home Counties could require in the way of wine.

There is a wide range of quality champagnes (many of them available in half-bottles and magnums), clarets through the vintages and the price bands and, of course, a good selection of port. Half-bottles are a speciality with vintage champagne, classed-growth clarets and an enticing choice of quality Sauternes, including six vintages of Yquem, joining a well-established range of own-label wines. Most of the classic areas have an own-label wine at the bottom of the price range – but in no way are these poor relations. The crusted port comes from Dow, the hock from Guntrum, and the clarets from well-known châteaux hiding behind anonymous labels.

Fortnum's choice does not end with the classics. There are interesting pockets of wine from the rest of the world: Shaw and Smith Chardonnay and Yarra Yering Cabernet Sauvignon from Australia, for example. It is pleasing to see the Hamilton-Russell wines from South Africa but you would need friends at Fort Knox to pull the cork on Tokaji Essencia 1947 at over £600 a bottle. Fortnum has expanded beyond the level of just a wine section in a department store. The range qualifies it as a wine merchant in its own right and it obviously adds a certain something to have liveried vans plying to and from the suburbs laden with their excellent comestibles. Fortnum will never be a cheap place to buy wine, but it is so very solid, reliable and reassuring to deal with.

Best buys

Fortnum & Mason Claret, Bordeaux Supérieur 1988 (produced by Ch. Segonzac), £
Fortnum & Mason Mosel (produced by Dr Loosen of Bernkastel), £
Fortnum & Mason Graves 1988, Ch. Le Bonnet, ££
Fortnum & Mason Champagne (produced by Théophile Roederer, sister company of Louis Roederer), ££

John Frazier

Warehouse
Stirling Road, Cranmore Industrial Estate, Shirley, Solihull, West Midlands B90 4XD — *Tel* 021-704 3415
Associated outlets
252 Longmore Road, Shirley, Solihull, West Midlands B90 3ER
4 Trinity Court, Stoke Road, Aston Fields, Bromsgrove, Hereford & Worcester B60 3EJ
New Inn Stores, Stratford Road, Wootton Wawen, Solihull, West Midlands B95 6AS
618 Yardley Wood Road, Billesley, Birmingham, West Midlands B13 0HW
56 Thornhill Road, Streetly, Sutton Coldfield, West Midlands B74 3EN

Open Mon–Sat 10–10; Sun 12–2, 7–10 **Credit cards** Access, American Express, Visa; personal and business accounts **Discounts** Negotiable **Delivery** Free within a 50-mile radius (min 4 cases); mail order available **Glass hire** 45p per dozen **Tastings and talks** Available **Cellarage** Free

There are five retail shops and a wholesale warehouse in this Midlands-based family business. The range takes a general look at the wines of the world, picking out a few well-known names from each region.

From France comes a good choice of Bordeaux wines, mainly crus bourgeois with a few second wines of grander châteaux. In Burgundy, the wines are mainly from reliable *négociants* such as Louis Latour, Prosper Maufoux and Drouhin. The Rhône section is strong, with wines from Jaboulet, Guigal and the well-made Ch. du Grand Moulas. Among an already good selection from south and south-west France, Ch. de Fonscolombe in Provence and Ch. Laroze in Gaillac add a touch more quality and flavour.

Outside France, Spain has a wide choice of Riojas while Portugal includes the delicious Quinta de Santo Amaro. The New World is well represented with Yalumba, Penfolds and Lindeman in Australia, Mondavi and the classy Cuvaison from California and Concha y Toro from Chile.

Prices at the warehouse in Solihull tend to be a bit cheaper than at the retail shops so it might be worth taking a drive there or ordering four cases to qualify for free delivery. Definitely worthwhile is the bin-end sale with substantial reductions.

Best buys

Domaine de Rieux 1990, Vin de Pays des Côtes de Gascogne, £
Sunnycliff Chardonnay 1990, Australia, £
Ch. Caronne-Ste-Gemme 1985, Haut-Médoc, ££
Cornas 1986, Guy de Barjac, ££

Friarwood

26 New Kings Road, London SW6 4ST *Tel* 071-736 2628

Open Mon–Fri 9–7; Sat 10–5 **Closed** Sun, public holidays **Credit cards** All accepted; personal and business accounts **Discounts** 5% per case **Delivery** Free inside M25; mail order available **Glass hire** Free **Tastings and talks** Free twice monthly tastings to customers and general public **Cellarage** 12p per case per week

Although very willing and with bags already packed, we were unable to check out the two off-shore retail outlets of Friarwood, one in Barbados and the other in Antigua. Perhaps our well-travelled readers could let us know more about them.
Meanwhile back in Fulham, Friarwood has opened a retail shop and is actively seeking a second site as retailing becomes a more attractive proposition. The range is classic French, although there is slight acknowledgment of New Zealand, Australia and South Africa. Bordeaux is very strong, with classed-growth clarets going back to 1970 and a splendid collection of Sauternes and Barsacs. Surprisingly, only one of these, Ch. Broustet, is available in a half-bottle.

Burgundies are from some fairly classy growers but outside these areas the list begins to look a little sparse: one Alsace wine, a few from the Loire and the Rhône. Cognac and armagnac are available under bond or duty-paid and include venerable spirits under the Lafite-Rothschild label.

Prices in the list are given ex-VAT by the case. Single bottles are available at the shop at approximately a 10 per cent premium (plus VAT); mixed cases are available by mail order.

Best buys

Ch. Cana 1986, Côtes de Bourg, £
Gevry-Chambertin 1987, Domaine Claude Marchand, £
Ch. La Cardonne Rothschild 1987, Cru Bourgeois Médoc, ££

The Fulham Road Wine Centre

899/901 Fulham Road, London SW6 5HU *Tel* 071-736 7009

Open Mon–Sat 10–9 **Closed** Sun, public holidays **Credit cards** Access, Visa; personal and business accounts **Discounts** 5% on 1 case **Delivery** Free in central London (by arrangement); mail order available **Glass hire** Free **Tastings and talks** Wine school in purpose-built tasting room; regular in-store tastings on Sat **Cellarage** Available

Angela Muir, Master of Wine and proprietor of the Fulham Road Wine Centre, has had a busy year. She is one of the driving forces behind the new wave of quality wines now emerging from Czechoslovakia. These fresh lively whites and soft generous reds are appearing on the shelves of the major multiples and, not surprisingly, at the Fulham Road Wine Centre.

Good winemaking is the key to the range at Fulham Road. You are just as likely to be bowled over by an Australian, Italian or Argentinian wine as by a French one. There are top-notch burgundies, delicious Gevry-Chambertin from Trapet and Chambolle-Musigny from Domaine Dujac. But for those who need to eat as well as drink there are terrific wines, particularly in the £5 to £10 range, which all have the stamp of quality. The New World is well represented with Rothbury, Rouge Homme and Wynns weighing in for Australia. Three wines from Argentina, Santa Rita and Undurraga from Chile and Clos du Bois and Cuvaison from California add to the variety. The Italian range brings together classic names and some of the lesser-known but decent vini da tavola – all well made and packing splendid flavours.

But this is not just a shop. If you want to learn about wine in a more structured way than just pulling the cork, enrol for one of the courses at the Wine School (underneath the shop). You can start as an absolute beginner and work though 'What's My Wine', 'The Great Wines of France' and other such delights – tutored by Angela Muir, James Rogers and visiting speakers. With regular tastings in the shop on Saturdays and a variety of wine books, maps, prints and antique decanters available, there is every reason to call into this part of the Fulham Road.

Best buys

Pinot Blanc 1990, Czechoslovakia, £
Cabernet Sauvignon 1989, Cafayate, Argentina, £
Laurel Glen Cabernet Sauvignon 1986, California, ££
Ch. Lynch-Bages 1989, ££

Fullers (Fuller, Smith & Turner) 

Head office
Griffin Brewery, Chiswick Lane South, London W4 2QB *Tel* 081-994 3691
60 shops in Home Counties

Case sales only **Open** Mon–Sat 9.30–9.30; Sun and public holidays 12–3, 7–9 **Credit cards** Access, Visa; personal and business accounts **Discounts** Available; 1 free bottle with every unmixed case; larger orders attract further discounts **Delivery** Free locally **Glass hire** Free; 50p deposit per glass **Tastings and talks** Free, fortnightly on Saturdays from March to November; also at managers' discretion **Cellarage** Not available

Fullers' managers are a talented lot. The list we were sent was adorned with delightful cartoons, drawn by Shepperton shop manager James Burton. This list does not appear to be in general circulation but is deserving of a wider audience.

Fullers is more than just an 'offie' that stays open late; it is part of the Fuller, Smith & Turner brewing operation of which you might get a delicious malty whiff if you are ever stuck at the Hogarth roundabout in Chiswick, west London. Fullers has a chain of 60 shops in London and the Home Counties and is becoming increasingly serious about the wine business. You may know the company better as a place to pick up the excellent London Pride bitter, but while you are there take a look at the wine shelves as well. The range covers most parts of the world but is particularly strong in Bordeaux and Burgundy, with a good selection of Home-Counties-dinner-party wines at the £5 to £15 mark. Carillon de L'Angélus 1987 and Moreau's Premier Cru Chablis should go down well. The Rhône is represented by plenty of fine names – Chapoutier, Jaboulet and Chave – while at the cheaper end, Ch. du Grand Moulas provides decent Côtes-du-Rhônes-Villages. French country wines rate a big section – all under £5 – and the rest of Europe provides plenty of choice. The Australian range is set for bigger things following buyer Mark Dally's trip around the vineyards. Nevertheless, it presently looks fine, with wines from Cape Mentelle, Penfolds, Petaluma and Rouge Homme being available. Fullers also manages to have stocks of Cloudy Bay Sauvignon Blanc when all other merchants around have sold out.

With a good emphasis on reasonable ports and a few Rutherford and Miles madeiras, a Fullers store makes a welcome addition to any High Street. The managers we have come across are pleasant, never pushy and know their stock well. Certainly well worth checking out.

Best buys

Ch. de Paraza Cuvée Spéciale, Minervois, £
Ch. de Sours 1990, Bordeaux Blanc, £
La Petite Ruche, Crozes-Hermitage 1989, Chapoutier, ££
Ch. de Boursault Champagne nv, ££

Garrards Wine Merchants

Mayo House, 49 Main Street, Cockermouth, Cumbria CA13 9JS — *Tel* (0900) 823592

Open Mon–Wed 9–5.30; Thur–Sat 9–8; some public holidays **Closed** Sun, some public holidays **Credit cards** Access, Visa; personal and business accounts **Discounts** 5% on 1 case (not with credit-card payment) **Delivery** Free within 10-mile radius (min 1 case); mail order available **Glass hire** Free **Tastings and talks** Tastings through the Cockermouth Wine Club; to groups on request **Cellarage** Not available

This small family business manages to squeeze quite a lot into its long thin shop in Cockermouth. New World wines are gaining popularity and Garrards has responded with a good Australian selection from Orlando, Rosemount, Brown Brothers and Tyrrells. New Zealand sees a few new faces with Timara and Montana joining Cooks, Babich and Cloudy Bay. South African wines have always been available here but the range now includes Fairview Estate as well as a selection from KWV; Chilean wines come from Undurraga and Santa Carolina. Spain provides reliable wines from Torres, Ochoa and a selection of Riojas. German wines are extensive, mainly from Sichel and Deinhard. From France, clarets include a fair range for under £13 and then shoot up-market to the heights of Palmer 1978 and Pichon-Lalande 1970. Alsace wines are from Hugel and Beaujolais from Duboeuf, but the rest of France looks a little tired.

If the price list we were provided with is still correct, there are some bargains to be had in Cockermouth such as Ch. Cissac 1985 at £8.45. Perhaps this is what they mean by the motto 'Your astonishing good fortune'.

Best buys

Sauvignon Blanc, Undurraga 1990, Chile, £
Rosemount Shiraz/Cabernet Sauvignon 1990, Australia, £
Faustino I Grand Reserva Rioja 1982, ££
Rosemount Pinot Noir 1990, Australia, ££

Please write to tell us about any ideas for features you would like to see in the next edition of *The Which? Wine Guide* or in *Which? Wine Monthly*.

Gateway

Gateway House, Hawkefield Business Park, Whitchurch Lane, Bristol, Avon BS14 0TJ *Tel* (0272) 359359

(Approx 700 branches nationwide)

Open Mon–Sat 8.30–6; selected stores open Sun **Closed** Public holidays **Credit cards** Access, Visa **Discounts** Not available **Delivery** Within 10-mile radius of Somerfield stores at Christmas only **Glass hire** Not available **Tastings and talks** Monthly in-store tastings of approx 6 wines **Cellarage** Not available

With nearly 700 branches from Aberdeen in Scotland to Ystrad Mynach in Wales it is quite likely that there is a Gateway store near you. The range of wine in these neighbourhood shops has been undergoing a transformation in the last two years under the direction of wine buyer Angela Mount. Now with basic lines radically improved and a huge selection of new lines, Gateway gains an inclusion in this *Guide*. Its particular strength is in wines under £5. Among the French reds there is a well-made Côtes-du-Rhône-Villages, Domaine des Coteaux des Travers, a peppery Vacqueyras – Vieux Clocher – and a soft, fruity Merlot from Collines de la Moure. Inexpensive French whites include a fresh and lively Corbières, a vin de pays de l'Hérault and the Australian-style Chais Baumière.

Value comes from other parts of the world too. Hugh Ryman's Gyöngyös Estate wines from Hungary, Seaview Cabernet/Shiraz, a terrific own-label dry white from Australia and a full-flavoured Terre di Ginestra from Sicily. There are more up-market wines in all sections. A rich smooth Santenay 1988, Penfolds Bin 389 from Australia and a really good Chianti Classico, Riserva di Fizzano from Rocca delle Macie. Small Gateway stores have a fraction of the full range but there should be some representatives from each region. Larger Gateways are being transformed into Somerfield stores with a bigger, more up-market range and image. All Somerfield stores, currently numbering 60, have the full range of wines. One particular piece of good news is that Somerfield stores deliver wines within a ten-mile radius at Christmas time. What a good idea for a supermarket!

Best buys

Chardonnay Vin de Pays de l'Hérault 1991, £
Seaview Cabernet/Shiraz 1989, Australia, £
Ch. Citran 1987, Cru Bourgeois, Haut-Médoc, ££
Châteauneuf-du-Pape, La Jacquinotte (changing to La Solitude) 1990, ££

Gauntleys of Nottingham 

4 High Street, Exchange Arcade,
Nottingham, Nottinghamshire NG1 2ET
Tel (0602) 417973

Open Mon–Sat 9–5.30 **Closed** Sun, public holidays **Credit cards** Access, Visa; personal and business accounts **Discounts** 5% on 1–5 cases; 10% on 5–10 cases **Delivery** Free in Nottingham, Derby, Southwell, Newark and Leicester (min 1-case order); mail order available **Glass hire** Free with order
Tastings and talks Monthly tutored tastings; specific tastings by growers
Cellarage Not available

'Hints of tobacco' would be a reasonable tasting note for the list produced by Gauntleys of Nottingham. We are not talking about an up-market Médoc wine but the booklet itself, infused with the aroma of Gauntleys other merchandise – high-class cigars. The wine business started only a few years ago and grew out of John Gauntley's hobby and the need to react to a shrinking cigar market. Now the shop has a fine selection of both products.

Education is the theme of the list. It starts with a quick run through of what customers should be looking to buy in the next year or so, followed by basic tips on storing, decanting and serving wine. Then region by region there is a summary of the last few vintages and the styles of wine. It is a good touch and we hope Gauntleys' customers take the time to read it all. The range covers France in depth with the Rhône coming in for special treatment. There are no fewer than 23 Côte Rôtie wines from seven growers in a variety of vintages. The pattern is repeated in Hermitage with vintages of La Chapelle going back to 1979. The Loire is also put under the spotlight but is focused on the sweet wines such as Vouvray, Quarts de Chaumes and Coteaux du Layon. Alsace wines from Trimbach, Domaine Weinbach, Dopff 'Au Moulin', Ostertag and Humbrecht provide a splendid selection, particularly at the top end of the price and quality range.

Spanish and Italian wines are well chosen, with a fine collection from good growers, while Germany is almost neglected apart from four wines from Prüm. Perhaps the bottom really has gone out of the German wine market in Nottingham. The New World presents a collection of quality wines from Petaluma, Wynns and Lindemans in Australia, Mondavi and Beringer in California and a wide and varied choice from South Africa.

This is a high-class list of quality wines with very little scraping in under £10. Even Provence and Languedoc, traditional homes of good value, manage to sail by at prices well above a tenner. It is to be hoped that there are lower priced wines in the shop that perhaps have not been included in the list.

Best buys

Côtes du Ventoux 1990, Chapoutier, £
Nederburg 'Private Bin 103' 1982, South Africa, ££
Gigondas 'Les Gouberts' 1988, Cartier, ££

General Wine Company

25 Station Road, Liphook, Hampshire GU30 7PW — *Tel* (0428) 722201

Open Mon–Sat 9–9; Sun and public holidays 12–2, 7–9 **Closed** Chr Day, New Year's Day **Credit cards** Access, Visa; personal and business accounts **Discounts** 5% on 1 mixed case, 10% on 4+ cases **Delivery** Free within 20-mile radius; mail order available **Glass hire** Free with order; breakages charged for **Tastings and talks** Three tutored tastings a year **Cellarage** Not available

There are many reasons for recommending wines but Alan Snudden of the General Wine Company has possibly the most unusual. Ch. Fourcas Hosten is favoured because his wife went into labour whilst drinking it, and then went on to produce their son. It certainly makes a tasty change from castor oil. There are other wines on the shelves of this shop in Liphook which should have a less drastic effect on the drinker. Clarets range from petits châteaux to classed growths, with a pretty decent collection of 1985 wines. Burgundies are from Chanson with some new additions from Louis Latour. The Rhône and Loire representatives are good as far as they go.

Spain plays safe with Torres and CVNE, Italy follows close behind with Fontanafredda Barolo and Chianti from Villa Carfaggio. South Africa is the region of the moment with 40 wines including Meerlust, Groot Constantia and Hamilton-Russell. From Australia the familiar names of Hardy, Mitchelton and Tyrrells give reliable flavours at reasonable prices. Undurraga and Villa Montes represent Chile, with L A Cetto from Mexico adding variety.

Only around half the wines on the shelves are included in the list so you have to browse around the shop to see the full range. Bottles are open for tasting every Saturday, although probably not the Fourcas Hosten.

Best buys

General Wine Company Claret, £
Undurraga Cabernet Sauvignon 1988, Chile, £
Beaujolais Villages, Quincié 1990, Georges Lenoir, ££
Ch. Le Sartre 1986, Graves, ££

Matthew Gloag & Son 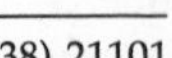

Bordeaux House, 33 Kinnoull Street, Perth, Perthshire PH1 5EU *Tel* (0738) 21101

Open Mon–Fri 9–5 **Closed** Sat, Sun, public holidays **Credit cards** Access, Visa; personal and business accounts **Discounts** Not available **Delivery** Free on mainland Scotland (min 1 case); free in England & Wales (min order 2+ cases); single-case orders £7.05; mail order available **Glass hire** Free **Tastings and talks** Two large tastings per year; tutored tastings throughout the year **Cellarage** Not available

Matthew Gloag & Son has been supplying the Scots with their whisky and claret for nearly 200 years. The list is a rather modest pocket-notebook size which contrasts dramatically with the expensive and hefty publications that some merchants issue. But good things come in little packages and this one has a rounded if rather limited choice.

Gloag's Reserve house claret is from Ch. Cissac and the main wine from that château features through the vintages in the list. Other clarets include a good round-up of cru bourgeois wines with a few classed growths. Burgundies and Rhônes are from reliable names; Chablis from Albert Pic looks good. Wines from Italy and Spain are all present and correct but the limited selection hardly does justice to the huge variety of styles available from these two countries. New Zealand wines have been rationalised, and the Australian selection is reduced to Mitchelton with a few from Rosemount and Hill-Smith. All these are good wines but anyone with a taste to experiment would soon run out of steam. South Africa provides a little more variety.

Sherries are from the splendid Barbadillo range and there are fine examples of vintage port.

Best buys

Domaine de Camberaud 1990, Minervois, £
Gloag's Reserve Claret, Haut-Médoc, £
St Véran, Ch. De Leynes 1990, ££
Mitchelton Cabernet Sauvignon 1988, Victoria, Australia, ££

A 125ml glass of wine, a 170ml glass of sherry and half a pint of beer all contain approximately the same amount of alcohol called a 'unit'. The Health Education Authority's recommendations for sensible drinking limits are 21 units per week for men and 14 units per week for women.

Gordon & MacPhail 

58–60 South Street, Elgin, Moray IV30 1JY *Tel* (0343) 545111

Open Mon–Fri 9–5.15; Sat 9–5 **Closed** Wed pm (Jan, Feb, May, June, Oct, Nov), Sun, public holidays **Credit cards** Access, Visa; personal and business accounts **Discounts** 5% on 6 bottles; 10% on 12 bottles **Delivery** Free within 30-mile radius (min 1 bottle) **Glass hire** Free with 1-case order **Tastings and talks, cellarage** Not available

Any merchant who is prepared to deliver a single bottle within a radius of 30 miles deserves a round of applause. The business at Gordon & MacPhail is aimed mainly towards the wholesale trade but there is a retail shop and nationwide mail order is available. The real attraction of this company is the totally unrivalled range of whiskies. These come in a list twice as fat as the wine-list and include dated whiskies, specially bottled whiskies and several pages of miniatures.

The wine-list takes in the world with a surprising emphasis on the southern hemisphere. KWV provides many of the South African wines but there is a good selection of estate wines from Neethlingshof, Groot Constantia and Fairview. Chilean wines are from the old-style Santa Carolina bodega and Cooks provides most of the New Zealand range, including the up-market Stoneleigh label. German wines are obviously still selling well in Elgin – producers names tend to disappear in this section but von Simmern, Bischöflichen and Prüm feature occasionally.

A good range of clarets, burgundies and Rhônes cater for more traditional tastes, and a fine selection of vintage ports, dating back to 1948, should keep out the worst of the winter weather.

Best buys

Ch. du Grand Moulas 1990, Côtes-du-Rhône, £
Valentin Bianchi Malbec, Argentina, £
Hidalgo La Gitana Manzanilla Sherry, ££
Ch. Cissac 1983, Haut-Médoc, ££

But that which most doth take my Muse and me,
Is a pure cup of rich Canary wine,
Which is the Mermaid's now, but shall be mine:
Of which, had Horace or Anacreon tasted,
Their lives, as do their lines, till now had lasted.

Ben Jonson, *Epigrams: Inviting a Friend to Supper*

Grape Ideas

3/5 Hythe Bridge, Oxford, Oxfordshire OX1 2EW — *Tel* (0865) 791313/724866

Associated outlet

Grape Ideas, 2a Canfield Gardens, London NW6 3BS — *Tel* 071-328 7317

Open Mon–Sat 10–7 **Closed** Sundays and public holidays **Credit cards** Access, Visa; personal and business accounts **Discounts** 5% on 1 unmixed case, 2.5% on 1 mixed case; larger orders by negotiation **Delivery** Free locally approx 10-mile radius of Oxford (min order £50); elsewhere free on 3+ cases; mail-order available **Glass hire** Charge for breakages and unclean glasses only **Tastings and talks** Tutored tastings on request; large annual tasting **Cellarage** Not available

Grape Ideas in Oxford may look like a warehouse but you can buy single bottles as well as by the case (mixed cases qualify for a smaller discount). Part of the warehouse is in fact a different company (Fine Vintage Wines), although this is not apparent to the casual customer. That means there are two ranges available but since all bottles go through the same till-point we are considering them together. Just in case you are not totally confused, there is a shop in London, also called Grape Ideas, which is, in a complicated way, part of the same operation. That shop has access to pretty much everything that is available in Oxford, although it may take a day or two to be delivered.

The range is fairly comprehensive with a good spread of New World wines. Australians are from Leasingham and Coldstream Hills as well as the widely available Rosemount and Wyndhams. New Zealand wines are a mixture of familiar names like Cooks, Cloudy Bay and Delegat's, with some less well-known wines from Vidal and Redwood Valley. Chile sports a full range from Viña Carmen, part of the Santa Rita operation, plus a few from Viña Linderos. The Californian and South African sections are rather limited.

Italy is quite good: Chiantis are from Isole e Olena, Villa di Vetrice and Frescobaldi. Spanish wines are less exciting although Torres and Marqués de Riscal provide a reasonable choice. In France, Bordeaux and burgundy are the major sections, with a surprising choice of white Mâcons under £8. The Fine Vintage Wines list provides the top-notes to this range, with clarets, burgundies and ports from recent and not so recent vintages. Some of these wines are available by the straight case only, so check before setting your heart on a particular bottle.

Best buys

Viña Carmen Cabernet Sauvignon 1988, Gran Seleccion, Chile, £
Sauvignon Blanc Vin de Pays d'Oc 1990, Domaine de la Baume, £
Mâcon-Viré Domaine André Bonhomme 1989, ££
Redwood Valley Sauvignon Blanc 1990, New Zealand, ££

Great English Wines

Freepost RG 786, Reading, Berkshire RG3 1BR — *Tel* (0734) 451958

Open Please telephone before visiting **Credit cards** Access, Visa; business accounts **Discounts** Between 5% and 10% depending on quantity purchased **Delivery** Free to Reading postcodes RG1–8, other Reading postcodes at £5 per order; otherwise 1 case at £7.50, 2–5 cases at £5.50 per case, 6–10 cases at £3.50 per case **Glass hire** Not available **Tastings and talks** Two annual tastings (May and Oct); to groups on request **Cellarage** Available for short-term storage

It isn't easy to track down English wines but at this mail-order company you can choose wines from vineyards across the south of England. The list is divided into wine styles, so you can compare 45 different dry white wines from vineyards as far apart as Mumford's in Avon and Tenterden in Kent. For those who thought all English wine was white, there is a range of rosés and reds, with Westbury Pinot Noir commanding a price to equal some burgundies. Pudding wines are another feature: Late Harvest Ortega and Siegerrebe from Three Choirs would make an unusual finale to any dinner party. There are sparkling wines too – the Carr Taylor 1984, Méthode Traditionnelle competing firmly in the champagne market.

If you have never encountered English wine before or are still confused by that product known as British wine (neither wine nor British, according to proprietor Maurice Moore), then why not try before you buy? Up to four people are welcome to visit the Great English Wines' offices in Reading and taste six wines free of charge or obligation. You can even be visited at your own home, for a small fee. Mixed cases are available and, if you find you do not like the wine you have just bought, Great English Wines guarantees to replace it with another.

Best buys

Boze Down Medium Dry 1990, Oxfordshire, £
Valley Vineyards Stanlake 1989, Berkshire, £
Valley Vineyards Ascot Brut Sparkling, ££
Pilton Manor Special Reserve 1989, ££

Great Northern Wine Company

Dark Arches, Leeds Canal Basin, Leeds, West Yorkshire LS1 4BR *Tel* (0532) 461200

Open Mon–Fri 9–6; Sat 9.30–5; Sun 12–3; public holidays 9–5 **Closed** Chr Day, Boxing Day, New Year's Day **Credit cards** Access, Visa; personal and business accounts **Discounts** 8% on 1 case **Delivery** Free within 30-mile radius of Leeds (min 1 case); otherwise at cost; mail order available **Glass hire** Free with order **Tastings and talks** Speciality tastings; monthly tutored tastings **Cellarage** £2.50 per case per year

Another branch is planned soon for this Leeds-based merchant. Whether that new outlet can manage to have quite such an atmospheric address remains to be seen – the Dark Arches, Leeds Canal Basin is a hard act to follow. Railway arches seem to breed good wine merchants and this one is no exception. With shelves well stocked from around the world, but with a particular enthusiasm for New World wines, Great Northern provides good drinking throughout the price range.

Australia is particularly strong, with big names such as Brown Brothers, Rosemount and Penfolds leading the team. A worthy selection from smaller wineries, such as Tarra Warra (great Pinot Noir) and Yarra Yering (excellent Cabernet Sauvignon), adds individuality and style. Some of the prices seem a little out of line with the competition, for example Wirra Wirra Church Block 1989 is £8.60 here but only £6.60 from the Wine Society, but others are pretty much the same as elsewhere. As usual it is always worth checking around before you buy. New Zealand offers a fine selection, with wines from Nobilo, Delegat's and Kumeu River amongst others. Chile sports the splendid Montes and Undurraga wines. The USA range has been expanded to show the various styles and grape varieties available: Mondavi, Oak Knoll, Silverado and Sonoma-Cutrer are some of the prestigious names.

Portugal is worth exploring (eight whites and nine reds); Spain includes a range from Berberana, CVNE and two new additions from Somontano which must be worth a try. France takes in a good round-up of the classic areas: Alsace has wines from Schlumberger and the Turckheim co-operative, clarets stay well within the affordable range and burgundies are largely through Drouhin and Louis Latour. Particularly good is the wide range of French regional wines, and a handful of Jura wines including three Vins Jaunes.

See the back flap for an explanation of the symbols used in the *Guide*.

Best buys

Domaine de Perras 1991, Vin de Pays des Côtes de Gascogne, £
Cuvée Jean Paul House Wine, £
Sancerre 'Les Roches' 1990, Vacheron, ££
Baileys Shiraz 1989, Glenrowan, Victoria, ££

Great Western Wine Company

2–3 Mile End, London Road, Bath, Avon BA1 6PT *Tel* (0225) 448428

Case sales only **Open** Mon–Sat 9–7 **Closed** Sun, public holidays **Credit cards** Access, Visa; business accounts **Discounts** Available; up to 10% on selected wines **Delivery** Free within 20-mile radius of Bath (min order 1 mixed case); elsewhere at cost **Glass hire** Free **Tastings and talks** Regular tastings **Cellarage** £2.50 per case per year

This is yet another wine company named after a railway (see Great Northern). Perhaps the trend will continue and soon we will be able to buy wine from the Trans-Siberian Wine Cellar or small bottles from the Hornby Double 'OO' Wine Company.

Great Western does not operate out of railway sidings but out of offices in Bath which have seen a transformation in recent months. There is now a shop which looks as if it should have a retail licence but doesn't, so purchases have to be made by the mixed case. This is no real problem since the range is wide enough to hold the interest for quite some time.

France takes in all the classic areas. Good basic clarets are mainly under £10 and are supplemented by a grand cru section which will explore the inner recesses of your wallet more thoroughly. Burgundies include a range of affordable wines called Les Villages de Jaffelin as well as a mixed range from *négociants* and growers. From the South, a clutch of good vins de pays and a few domaine wines from Provence (Domaine La Mascaronne) and Corbières (Ch. Lastours) provide plenty of choice, mostly for under a fiver. Spain has a fine collection from Rioja, Navarra and Penedès; however, the full potential of Italy has not yet been brought to Bath. In the New World, Australia has most to offer but a new range from South Africa is eagerly awaited.

Best buys

Domaine Labarthe 1989, Gaillac, £
Cépage Terret Vin de Pays des Côtes de Thau 1991, £
Hermitage 'Marquise de la Tourette' 1988, Delas, ££
Pouilly-Fuissé 1988, Thierry Guerin, ££

Peter Green

37a/b Warrender Park Road, Edinburgh EH9 1HJ *Tel* 031-229 5925

Open Mon–Fri 9.30–6.30; Sat 9.30–7 **Closed** Sun, public holidays
Credit cards None accepted; personal and business accounts **Discounts** 5% on unmixed cases **Delivery** 50p per trip in Edinburgh; mail order available
Glass hire Free **Tastings and talks** Regular tastings; to groups on request
Cellarage Not available

Does you local wine merchant give you a choice of 11 Alsace Rieslings and 13 Gewürztraminers? Is there a terrific selection of clarets and four vintages of Quarts de Chaume among a tongue-tingling array of Loire Chenin Blancs? And is delivery within city limits supposedly charged at 50p but isn't really (that's only a threat in case someone wants a bottle of lemonade delivered)? If all this has a familiar ring then you must live in Edinburgh, within sight and sound of Peter Green.

This independent merchant is run by Michael and Douglas Romer who appear to be extremely modest of their buying skills. 'We are lucky to have such interested customers, they teach us a lot,' the brothers tell us. Well, luck cuts both ways here and if you needed a reason to live in this lovely city, Peter Green would rate pretty high on anyone's list. The collection is not just good, it is very good. Germany seems to be taken seriously: a letter 'e' or 'g' alongside each wine tells you whether it is from a single vineyard (*Einzellage*) or a collection of vineyards (*Grosslage*). Since even the Germans get muddled over their vineyards this devastatingly simple idea seems a good way to dispense information. Italian wines are worth several weekends' research. Not only are the super-expensive Super Tuscans here but an enticing range of Italian grapes from excellent producers, too. Spain, Portugal and the New World have been explored with great enthusiasm. Twenty-two Chilean wines, six Argentinians and a couple from Mexico provide a vinous tour guide of South and Middle America. An extensive range of Californians and two Inniskillin wines from Canada continue the journey northwards. With a couple of Swiss wines, five Greek, two each from Luxembourg and China and a fistful of vintages from the Lebanon's Musar, an explorer's pith helmet may be needed to fully map out the range.

A variety of half-bottles is available – particularly good in the sweet-pudding direction. If you fancy a drop of the hard stuff, over 100 whiskies could prolong decision-making indefinitely.

Best buys

La Vieille Ferme 1990, Côtes du Ventoux, £
Houghton's Chenin Blanc 1990, Australia, £
Marqués de Murrieta Blanco 1985, Rioja, ££
Quarts de Chaume 1990, Baumard, ££

Greenwood & Co

See Nickolls & Perks

Guildford Wine Market

216 London Road, Burpham, Guildford, Surrey GU4 7JS *Tel* (0483) 575933

Open Mon–Sat 10–9; Sun, public holidays 12–2, 7–9 **Closed** Chr Day, Boxing Day, Jan 1, 2, Easter Sun and Mon **Credit cards** All accepted **Discounts** 10% on 1 case **Delivery** Free locally **Glass hire** Free with suitable case order **Tastings and talks** In-store tastings on occasional basis; tastings for groups on request **Cellarage** Not available

Nicholas Brougham of the Guildford Wine Market was planning a major re-shuffle of his range when we visited him at his shop on the outskirts of Guildford. After a trip to Australia early in 1992, most of the present range was due for a facelift. Out will go the Wyndham selection to be replaced by more individual wines, including the super Wignalls wines from Western Australia. The organic Botobolars with their beeswax capsules are staying, their big fruity flavours justifying a place on the shelves. Also expanding is the 'sundry French' section where good-quality wines from lesser-known regions compete at a reasonable price level. One of the mainstays of this section is Domaine du Grand Mayne, Côtes de Duras from Nick Brougham's own row of vines in France.

The recession has not been kind to his wonderful Italian selection nor to classic burgundy sales, which will probably continue to contract until people start spending money again. He would also like to sell more serious German wines but explained: 'We find it difficult because of the bad image that the muck end of German wines gives to the serious end'. South African wines have consistently sold well, with the competitively priced Laborie sparkler adding to the already impressive selection of non-champagne sparkling wines. Hamilton-Russell wines are also part of the South African range. Most merchants manage one or two Torres wines, but this shop has them all, from the Black Label Coronas downwards. The Guildford Wine Market makes sure it looks after its customers: six Greek wines might be five too many for most merchants but they have some customers who want them and consequently they are in stock.

If you're interested in beer as well as wine, then check out the weird and wonderful selection: various trappist monk brews, with high alcohol and high prices, are available at Burpham – perhaps the most appropriate place to buy them.

Best buys

Anjou Blanc 1991, Les Producteurs Réunis Union Agricole du Pays de Loire, £
Undurraga Pinot Noir 1989, £
Omar Khayyam Brut 1987, ££
Scharzhofberger Riesling Kabinett 1989, Reichgraf von Kesselstatt, ££

Hadleigh Wine Cellars

See Wines of Interest

Half Yard Wines

Regatta View, River Road, Taplow, Buckinghamshire SL6 0BE — *Tel* (0628) 24155

Case sales only **Open** Mon–Fri 9–6; always available for telephone orders **Credit cards** None accepted; personal and business accounts **Discounts** 5% on 10+ cases **Delivery** Free within 25-mile radius (min order 10+ cases) **Glass hire** Free with order **Tastings and talks** Four tastings a year; two tutored tastings per year **Cellarage** Not available

Maggie Richardson continues the fine tradition of many sole traders in the wine business – she has a day job, too. As a change from all the doctors, dentists and teachers who juggle two jobs until the wine side gets big enough to rely on, Maggie is a purser with British Airways. She recently cut her hours to part-time, so trade must be looking up, despite a recent relocation from Sussex to Bucks.

The list is limited but good, and whatever deficiencies there are in the range, Maggie makes up for in the boundless enthusiasm she shows for the subject. Prices are keen, reflecting her low overheads. Most wines fit comfortably under the £10 mark, only the champagnes and a handful of wines creep above this level. There is a fine collection from Spain and Italy, Bordeaux stays firmly in the petits châteaux range apart from a grand cru St-Emilion – Ch. Haut-Sarpe – while burgundies are of the white variety, no reds! The Loire shows no such prejudice, including two impressive reds among a small collection of whites. The range from the New World demonstrates a talent for picking out value and variety.

Best buys

Caliterra Chardonnay 1991, Chile, £
Cape Selection Reserve Sauvignon 1991, South Africa, £
CVNE Reserva 1985, Rioja, ££
Ch. de Berbec Blanc 1989, Premières Côtes de Bordeaux, ££

Hall Batson Wine Importers

168d Wroxham Road, Sprowston, Norwich, Norfolk NR7 8DE — *Tel* (0603) 415115

Case sales only **Open** Mon–Fri 8.30–6; Sat 9–1 **Closed** Sun, public holidays **Credit cards** None accepted; personal and business accounts **Discounts** Available **Delivery** Free within 50-mile radius of Norwich; elsewhere at cost **Glass hire** Free; breakages charged for **Tastings and talks** Regular tastings; in-store tastings **Cellarage** Not available

Hall Batson, based in Norwich, is a welcome new addition to the *Guide*. It is a relatively new company (only eight years old) but has grown rapidly via a series of acquisitions of small importing companies. This has given it expertise in a number of areas, particularly Burgundy, Germany and the New World.

Buying wine at Hall Batson seems to be a fairly civilised process. Customers go along to the warehouse and instead of pushing a trolley around they can sit in the tasting room and discuss their requirements with a member of staff. Bottles are always open for tasting to help make the decision easier. If you cannot get to the warehouse, free delivery of a case or more within a radius of 50 miles brings your wine to you hassle-free. The range is big and takes in all the major wine areas. From France, clarets are the affordable type, mainly cru bourgeois and young vintages of classier wines. Burgundies are represented by a wide variety of villages, vintages and producers. The Rhônes are mainly from Père Anselme, while the Loire and Alsace provide a reasonable choice of white wines. Château Chalon from the Jura is one of the more unusual offerings from this firm. Italy features the wines of Antinori including the up-market Peppoli Chianti; Spanish activity is centred on Berberana and Marqués de Murrieta. With Mondavi among the Californians and Petaluma adding top-notes to a good Australian collection, this range could provide interesting drinking for quite some time.

Best buys

Ch. de Corneilla Rouge 1988, Côtes du Roussillon, £
Concha y Toro Sauvignon/Semillon 1991, Chile, £
Bourgogne Haute Côtes de Nuits 'Tête de Cuvée Les Caves des Hautes Côtes, ££
Petaluma Chardonnay 1986, Australia, ££

Halves

Wood Yard, off Corve Street, Ludlow, Shropshire SY8 2PG — *Tel* (0584) 877866

Case sales only **Open** Mon–Fri 9–6; Sat 10–1 **Closed** Sun, public holidays **Credit cards** None accepted **Discounts** 4% on 1 unmixed case; £2.35 per order on 2+ cases **Delivery** To UK mainland (charge inc in price quoted) **Glass hire** Not available **Tastings and talks** Periodic tastings on a nationwide basis **Cellarage** Not available

Halves was a good idea just waiting to happen, but it took Tim Jackson to get it all started. The principle is simple: there are thousands of people who would like to drink decent wine but who don't want to open a full bottle. Restaurants are an obvious market but, for home drinkers too, there are many occasions when it is more fun to open two different half-bottles than to plough through 75cl.

Some producers are more amenable than others to the idea of half-bottles. In Jerez everyone drinks sherry from half-bottles and, accordingly, Halves has a good range of Hidalgo sherries. Champagne producers are already used to the idea of halves; the house champagne here is the delicious Bruno Paillard. Burgundy in half-bottles is less usual but Tim Jackson has managed to get some splendid Gevry-Chambertin from Alain Burguet as well as wines from Louis Latour, Prosper Maufoux and Chablis from Louis Michel. Clarets are limited in number but include Ch. Sénéjac, Ch. de Francs and a 1985 Léoville-Poyferré. There are interesting wines among the Rhônes, with Château de Beaucastel and a clutch of wines from Guigal. The New World has obviously taken this company to heart and bottled a surprising range of Australian and California wines in the smaller version.

To avoid all your half-bottles slipping through the holes in your normal-sized wine rack, Tim Jackson can arrange for special half-size racks to be made. This sounds like a clever idea, as is free delivery of one case (24 halves) within mainland UK.

Best buys

Hidalgo sherries, six styles available, £
Crozes-Hermitage 1988, Jaboulet, £
Warre 1982, Quinta da Cavadinha, Single Quinta Port, ££
Condrieu 1990, Georges Vernay, ££

Hampden Wine Company

Jordan's Courtyard, 8 Upper High Street, Thame, Oxfordshire OX9 3ER

Tel (0844) 213251

Open Mon, Tue, Sat 9.30–5; Wed 9.30–1; Thur, Fri 9.30–5.30 **Closed** Sun, public holidays **Credit cards** Access, Visa; personal and business accounts **Discounts** 5% on 1 case; quantity discounts negotiable **Delivery** Free within 20-mile radius of Thame (min 1 case); free elsewhere for larger orders; mail order available **Glass hire** Free with order **Tastings and talks** Eight tastings per year with dinner at £30 per person **Cellarage** Free for customers

The Hampden Wine Company is run by Lance Foyster and Ian Hope-Morley, and it is one of Ian's ancestors whose face stares at you from the cover of the wine-list. He was Puritan John Hampden who apparently refused to pay ship-tax to Charles I. What he would think of his descendant making a living from something as enjoyable as wine doesn't bear thinking about. Hampden shares a shop with a delicatessen called Jordans – you have to walk through the deli to get at the wine. In 1991 radical expansion increased the wine area by two and a half times, so now it looks more like a proper wine shop instead of a bit bolted on. Supermarkets provide the main competition in this area but Ian and Lance counter them by providing a personal, friendly and informed service. Lance recently passed the Master of Wine exams so you can be sure of getting some pretty competent advice.

In all areas of the list there are quality wines at reasonable prices. A selection of vins de pays starts off the range, and among the clarets there are some decent petits châteaux. Portugal is well worth exploring, exhibiting some traditional wines from small quintas. New World areas have a fair cross-section of well-priced drinking including Cousiño Macul and Concha y Toro from Chile. But this is not just a cheap list; there is plenty available to encourage customers to climb the quality ladder. Among the Rhônes, a single vineyard wine from Marius Gentaz allows you to try just the Côte Brune part of the normally blended Côte Rôtie. Ch. Fuissé from J Jacques Vincent and Montrachets from Leflaive are superb wines when the occasion demands such quality. A separate list of fine and very fine wines is also available.

Tutored tastings with dinner are a regular feature and there are always a few bottles open in the shop, especially on Saturdays. The motto of this establishment is 'Life is too short to drink bad wine', a sentiment with which we agree wholeheartedly.

Best buys

Domaine St-Pierre Rouge 1990, Vin de Pays de l'Hérault, £
Corbières Blanc 1991, Jean Berail, £
Moss Wood Cabernet Sauvignon 1989, Western Australia, ££
Côte Rôtie 1987, Côte Brune Marius Gentaz, ££

Harcourt Fine Wine

3 Harcourt Street, London W1H 1DS *Tel* 071-723 7202

Open Mon–Fri 9–6; Sat 10.30–5 **Closed** Sun, public holidays **Credit cards** All accepted; personal and business accounts **Discounts** From 5% per case **Delivery** In central London and the City (charges depend upon value); mail order available **Glass hire** Free **Tastings and talks** Two free annual tastings **Cellarage** 10p per case per week

Harcourt Fine Wine tackles the tricky end of the market – German wines (including a fine collection of reds), English wines and fine vintage brandies. These three areas are handled with great skill, although it is encouraging to see a few other wines on the list – a relief to regular customers who might fancy a change now and then.

English wine is still a difficult concept to put over. There are still a few people who have not yet grasped the difference between imported grape juice diluted with tap water and fermented into something fairly second-rate (British wine) and the product of an English vineyard, carefully nurtured through fermentation and bottling (English wine). This list explores vineyards from Breaky Bottom in Sussex to Sharpham in Devon, a total of 27 properties, most of them sporting two or three wines in various styles. There are a few English red wines and the Rock Lodge Méthode Traditionnelle sparkler – interesting conversation pieces as well as being good wines. The German range is estate-based and from quality producers, including Bürklin-Wolf and Schloss Reinhartshausen. The German wines of Karl Heinz Johner make an appearance, and he must feel particularly at home in this list as he used to make wine at a major English vineyard and still acts as consultant to some. The range of brandies includes cognac, armagnac, calvados, eaux-de-vie and marc, all from a variety of vintages and companies.

Best buys

Hambledon 1990, £
Breaky Bottom 1989, Müller-Thurgau, £
Staple St James 1989, Huxelrebe, ££
Zanna Illuminati 1987, Montepulciano d'Abruzzo, ££

Harpenden Wines

68 High Street, Harpenden, Hertfordshire AL5 2SP — *Tel* (0582) 765605
Watford Wine Company, 185 The Parade, Watford, Hertfordshire WD1 1NJ — *Tel* (0923) 211254

Open Mon–Fri 10–10; Sat 9–10; Sun 12–3, 7–9; public holidays 12–8.30 **Closed** Good Friday **Credit cards** All accepted; personal and business accounts **Discounts** 5% on 1 case for credit card or 7.5% for cheque/cash; negotiable on 5+ cases **Delivery** Free within 10-mile radius of Harpenden **Glass hire** Free **Tastings and talks** To groups on request **Cellarage** By arrangement

Now with two shops, one in Harpenden and the other in Watford, Paul Beaton is planning a period of consolidation. Good choice, honest advice and reliable service are his keywords. Australia seems to be a favoured region: Coldridge, Mitchelton and Brown Brothers are the main players but there are wines from Mountadam and Heggies Vineyard as well as three organics from Buchanan in Tasmania. New Zealand provides a basic range from Montana but there are some additional treats from Te Mata, Millton and Cloudy Bay. Other New World areas include the Christian Brothers from California and the well-made wines of Columbia Crest from Washington State. Santa Rita and Montes wines provide choice and value from Chile.

Italy is worth spending some time browsing through. Pagliarese Chianti, Barco Reale from Capezzana and Barolo from Borgogno are featured. Cannonau di Alghero from Sardinia is unusual and worth a try. France includes a fair selection of clarets, burgundies and Loire wines, but the Rhône hasn't yet been explored fully. Ports, ancient and modern, are available; Quady's Californian Rich Ruby 'Starboard' Batch 88 is in the same section and is certainly different. Paul Beaton also has a wide range of malt whiskies always in stock.

Best buys

McWilliams 'Inheritance' Cabernet/Shiraz 1987, Australia, £
Ch. Lamothe Blanc Sec 1990, Bordeaux, £
Ch. Haut-Piquat 1988, Lussac St-Emilion, ££
Mountadam Chardonnay 1990, Eden Valley, Australia, ££

Gerard Harris Fine Wines

2 Green End Street, Aston Clinton, Buckinghamshire HP22 5HP — *Tel* (0296) 631041

Open Tue–Sat 9.30–8 **Closed** Sun, Mon, public holidays **Credit cards** Access, American Express, Visa; personal and business accounts **Discounts** 10% for 1 mixed case **Delivery** Free within an area bordered by the M1/M25 in the East and Buckingham in the West, and from the M40 in the South to Milton Keynes in the North (min order 1 case); mail order available **Glass hire** Free **Tastings and talks** Two major wine fairs each year; the Bell Fine Wine Society organises 6 tutored tastings per year **Cellarage** Not available

The Bell at Aston Clinton is renowned for its good food and wine so it comes as no surprise that its sister company, Gerard Harris Fine Wines, is just as good. It operates from a retail shop near the Bell and has a particularly wide-ranging stock of fine wines, many of them with the bottle age not easily found elsewhere. The best wines are not kept sitting in the shop waiting for a customer but are in the temperature-controlled cellars which close at 4pm. So if you want a bottle of 1961 Ch. Calon-Ségur there is no point bowling along at 7.55pm expecting to pick it off the shelves. Phone ahead for anything fairly special.

The range takes in the good and the great from most of the world. There are not many merchants who start off their lists with German wines but this is the exception. First there is a slight nod in the direction of Nierstein and Piesport followed by a quick sprint up the quality grades to a 1976 Beerenauslese. These are mainly good estates, such as Dr Loosen, Schloss Reinhartshausen and Bürklin-Wolf. Bottle age here means that the collection of 1983 wines has had time to develop those wonderful aged-Riesling flavours.

Bordeaux too has the look of a well-loved cellar. 1983 features again, with Châteaux Pavie and Talbot looking particularly good buys. The roll of vintages goes back to 1961 with a clutch of 1978s providing much temptation. Burgundy, Alsace and the Rhône have the same feel: good wines from excellent growers and always a selection of older vintages. Four wines from the Arbois, including Ch. Chalon, an oak-aged Muscadet and a 1959 Vouvray, make this shop a good place to start expanding your tasting horizons. A broad range of French regional wines will keep you supplied while you decide where to start. Wines from Italy and Spain, and two Swiss representatives, make appearances. The New World merits a big section, Coldstream Hills from Australia, Heitz Zinfandel from California and Te Mata from New Zealand are some of the highlights. Barbadillo sherries and splendid vintage ports are also among the attractions but older port vintages are available only to regular customers, which seems fair enough.

The Bell Fine Wine Society costs £15 for life membership and gives access to tastings, dinners and special offers.

Best buys

Chardonnay del Piemonte 1991, Dell'Acquese, £
Ch. Malvies 1989, Côtes de la Malpère, £
Riesling Prince Abbés 1989, Schlumberger, Alsace, ££
Crozes-Hermitage 1989, Alain Graillot, ££

Roger Harris

Loke Farm, West Longville, Norfolk NR9 5LG *Tel* (0603) 880171

Case sales only **Open** Mon–Fri 9–5 **Closed** Sat, Sun, public holidays **Credit cards** All accepted; personal and business accounts **Discounts** 2 cases at £2 per case, 3 cases at £2.50 per case, 5 cases at £3 per case **Delivery** Free on UK mainland (min 1 case); mail order available **Glass hire** Not available **Tastings and talks** To groups on request **Cellarage** Not available

If your only contact with Beaujolais tends to be of the Nouveau variety, send for a copy of Roger Harris's list and prepare to have your eyes opened and your tastebuds awakened.

Roger Harris is a Beaujolais specialist. He admits that what started out as a simple enjoyment of the wine has now developed into a passion, and this enthusiasm comes across in his list. For a start, it is not just a list. First, you study the booklet. This is a detailed story about the area, the soil, people, vintages and villages and is full of the kind of information you can get only if you spend years researching just one area. There are even recommendations for hotels and restaurants should you decide to visit the source of this interest. Next comes the list, again no half-hearted effort. The growers and their wines are introduced: nine Beaujolais-Villages, four Juliénas, the same number from Chénas, then comes Chiroubles, Morgon, St-Amour and so on. Some of the wines are available in a variety of vintages – undoubtedly the most comprehensive collection of Beaujolais you will come across.

In addition to these major documents come regular mailshots with special offers, new vintages and mixed-case offers. If, perish the thought, you might want to drink something other than Beaujolais, Roger Harris takes care of that, too. There is a small range from the Mâconnais, a couple of vins de pays, a grower's champagne, and a marc made from the Beaujolais grape skins. Prices of Beaujolais are falling, so this may be a good time to start your education of the area.

Best buys

Vin de Pays des Côtes de Gascogne 1991, £
Vin de Pays du Vaucluse 1991, £
Moulin-à-Vent 1989, Château Moulin-à-Vent, ££
Morgon, oak-aged 1989, Domaine Noël Aucoeur, ££

For merchants who sell a minimum of twelve bottles, we say 'Case sales only' in the details at the head of an entry.

Harrods

Knightsbridge, London SW1X 7XL *Tel* 071-730 1234

Open Mon–Sat 9–6 (till 8 on Wed); public holidays 10–6 **Closed** Sun **Credit cards** All accepted; personal and business accounts **Discounts** 1 free bottle per case **Delivery** Free in central London (min order £25) and within 25-mile radius of M25 (min £50 order); £5 charge for orders under £50; mail order available **Glass hire** Not available **Tastings and talks** Weekly tastings to customers **Cellarage** Not available

There is a wind of change blowing through the hallowed halls of Harrods. The wine range is being revamped to such an extent that the company was reluctant to tell us exactly what is staying and how much will just fade away. Essentially, buyer Alun Griffiths MW is looking at all the wines, re-sourcing a lot of the Harrods own-label wines and going for more individual growers' wines rather than *négociants'*. Value-for-money considerations are creeping into even this up-market emporium; French country wines and innovative winemakers are also beginning to appear.

Harrods will never be the cheapest place to buy wine but it might just be more interesting in the future. Watch this space.

Best buys

Ch. Fonscolombe 1991, Coteaux d'Aix-en-Provence, £
La Vieille Ferme 1991, Côtes du Ventoux, £
Ch. Léoville-Barton 1982, St-Julien, ££
Bourgogne Rouge 1990, Chopin-Groffier, ££

John Harvey & Sons

Order office and shop
31 Denmark Street, Bristol, Avon BS1 5DQ *Tel* (0272) 268882
16 The Hard, Portsmouth, Hampshire PO1 3DT *Tel* (0705) 825567

Open Mon–Fri 9–6; Sat 9–1 **Closed** Sun, public holidays **Credit cards** All accepted; personal and business accounts **Discounts** £2 on 2–5 cases, £3 on 6–10 cases, £3.50 on 11+ cases **Delivery** Free within 30-mile radius (min 1 case/£5 order) **Glass hire** Free with order **Tastings and talks** Free autumn tasting for customers; gourmet wine tastings and dinner from £50 per person; special tastings with supper/lunch £7.50 per person **Cellarage** £3.80 per case per year

Harvey's says that it has been trying hard to expand its list but, despite the best of endeavours, claret is what the customers want and that is what they get, in abundance. A friendly map points you in the right direction before plunging into the Médoc, with essays and tasting notes signposting the way. Each commune in the Haut-Médoc is well represented. Classy names exist but so too do good-value cru bourgeois wines, such as Cissac and Hanteillan. Ch. Latour (owned by the same parent company – Allied Lyons) is available in all the vintages and most of the bottle sizes. Forts de Latour goes back through the years, too. It is in one of the many notes and comments that we learn that Forts de Latour is only (in part) the second wine of Latour: much of the wine comes from separate vineyards nearby. An anonymous Pauillac is the label for what is probably the classiest 'third' wine in Bordeaux. Pomerols and St-Emilions complete the claret range and whites, both dry and sweet, are here in depth. Even the rare Pavillon Blanc de Margaux is available at a price. Yquem, Rieussec, Climens, Coutet and others crowd the Sauternes page.

Just about half-way through the list the attention turns to other regions. The Burgundy section covers all the areas you might expect, but the Loire, Rhône and Alsace have a slightly 'rationalised' feel to them. Just one red Loire wine, one Vouvray, one Côte Rôtie, and so on. Perhaps Harvey's customers are truly claret people. French regional wines have more appeal: a Marsanne from the Hérault and a vin de pays Pinot Noir are almost out of character in this traditional list. Germany is well represented, but Italy and Spain seem to have fallen off the Harvey's map. The New World is here but only just – one token New Zealand wine, three Australians and three Staton Hills wines from north-west USA make up the whole range. Given the success of New World wines elsewhere, couldn't Harvey's encourage its customers to look beyond Bordeaux?

Many fortified wines, a good range of sherries, ports and madeiras (including some rare old wines) provide the backbone to this fairly lop-sided list. Harvey's issues six additional mail-order selections through the year, with some new faces and a few special reductions. For Bristol residents the shop in Denmark Street carries a few extra lines and some bin-ends, while well-heeled gourmets can enjoy tastings in the famous cellars followed by dinner in Harvey's restaurant. *En primeur* offers, mainly of Bordeaux wines, as well as cellar planning are among Harvey's other services.

Best buys

Ch. Le Raz 1990, Sauvignon de Bergerac, £
Ch. Valcombe 1989, Costières de Nîmes, £
Pauillac 1987, Societé Civile de Château Latour, ££
Sancerre Rosé 1990, Paul Prieur, ££

Richard Harvey Wines

Not a shop

Bucknowle House, Bucknowle, Wareham, Dorset BH20 5PQ *Tel* (0929) 480352

Mainly telephone and mail order

Case sales only **Open** Mon–Fri 9–6 **Closed** Sat, Sun, public holidays **Credit cards** None accepted; personal and business accounts **Discounts** 5% on 7+ cases **Delivery** Free within 30-mile radius (min 3 cases); free delivery on 7+ cases elsewhere; otherwise £6 per consignment **Glass hire** Free with order **Tastings and talks** Major annual tasting by invitation; tutored tastings, dinners, etc. by arrangement **Cellarage** £4 per case per year (plus insurance)

Master of Wine Richard Harvey has moved to the other side of Wareham but his business continues much as before. He buys direct from the producers and caters for private customers who like his expert advice and personal selection of wines. The focus is on France, particularly the good-value areas of the South and South-West. From Languedoc there is a choice of eight reds and four whites, all estate wines and only one sneaking in over £6. Clarets are very affordable, with petits châteaux and a sprinkling of second wines adding to the more well-known names of La Lagune, d'Issan and Gloria. A separate Fine Wine list contains a wider and ever-changing choice. Burgundies look attractive, again from small growers, and the Rhône includes an interesting vin de table from Paul Avril, who also makes a rather good Châteauneuf-du-Pape. The rest of the world is very selective: one wine each from Spain, New Zealand and Chile, but even these are pretty good. Barbadillo sherries and champagne from Alexandre Bonnet round off this small but worthwhile collection.

Best buys

Cabardès 1987, Domaine des Caunettes Hautes, £
Ch. Bauduc Blanc 1990, Bordeaux Supérieur, £
Ch. Hanteillan 1986, Haut-Médoc, ££
Wairau River, Sauvignon Blanc 1991, New Zealand, ££

Haughton Fine Wines

Rowe's Ground, Chorley Green Lane,
Chorley, Nantwich, Cheshire CW5 8JR
Tel (0270) 74537

Case sales only **Open** Mon–Fri 9–5.30; Sat 10–12.30 **Closed** Sun, public holidays **Credit cards** Access, Visa; personal and business accounts **Discounts** Available **Delivery** Free nationwide (min order 2+ cases); otherwise £3 per delivery; £3 discount if customer collects; mail order available **Glass hire** Free with order **Tastings and talks** Two open weekends per year; to groups on request **Cellarage** Not available

There are some wine lists you can leaf through in a few minutes and others that need a little more thought. Haughton's list fits into the latter category and really needs a good train journey or transatlantic flight to do it proper justice. It is the size of a chubby paperback, ring-bound and packed with information – serious stuff but in a digestible form.

Bruce and Judy Kendrick founded Haughton Fine Wines only six years ago and discovered organic wines fairly quickly. They were not blinkered in their approach and if a wine was not good enough they didn't list it, organic or not. The list is in no way totally organic, these wines are more like the cherry on top of a well-made cake. What Haughton has done is to sweep away a lot of the flannel and waffle. Long before others jumped on the bandwagon Haughton explained what organic means – and identified the organisations that some growers belong to and their standards. More importantly, it identified the growers whose belief in good winemaking encompasses all that is good in organic, but who do not want to get involved in the bureaucracy of an organisation. Growers such as François Perrin at Ch. de Beaucastel in the Rhône, Aimé Guibert at Mas de Daumas Gassac in the Hérault and Serge Hochar in Lebanon. The quality of these wines and their winemakers says more than an official sticker ever could. Now, new legislation means that wines described as organic must come with the blessing of an organisation, but this is no real guarantee of quality, merely of method. Haughton lists 80 or so organic wines, it also has another 40 from 'freelance' organic growers who are identified at the front of the list.

But back to the paperback... the mission to debunk and inform continues. Tannin is the title of an essay tucked between Beaujolais and Bordeaux. It describes the different sources of tannin, hard tannins, soft tannins, and their effect in the wine. This is the stuff of winemakers, not normally entrusted to the likes of mere consumers. It makes fascinating reading if you want to tackle it; if not, skip it and go on to the wines.

The list is alphabetical going from Australia through to the USA. The focus is very much on the regions, the vineyards, and the winemaker who has shaped each wine. So we are introduced to Adam Wynn and told how he came to make Eden Ridge and develop the Organic Vignerons Association of Australia. We learn how Larry McKenna of Martinborough in New Zealand vinifies his wines and in France we follow the soil structure changes between St-Emilion and Pomerol.

But enough education – what of the wines? Generally good to very good. Classic French wines are here in number and quality (Bordeaux has seen a lot of work recently). The Rhône is a delight of well-made, full-flavoured wines. The South and South-West are rewarding, with a wide and interesting selection. The ranges from Italy and Spain are not huge but they are certainly impressive. Australia is represented by five excellent growers.

The only slight gripe is that there is very little for under a fiver, especially since mail order means that a bottle costs 25p more than collecting from Chorley. That apart, quality is good, service reliable, delivery free for two cases or more and the Kendricks are friendly people to deal with – what more could you ask for?

Best buys

Eden Ridge Dry White 1991, Adam Wynn, South Australia, £
Domaine de Raissac, Chardonnay 1991, Vin de Pays d'Oc, £
Mas de Daumas Gassac Rouge 1990, Vin de Pays de l'Hérault, ££
Martinborough Pinot Noir 1991, New Zealand, ££

Haynes Hanson & Clark

Head office and wholesale warehouse
17 Lettice Street, London SW6 4EH — *Tel* 071-736 7878
Retail
36 Kensington Church Street, London W8 4BX — *Tel* 071-937 4650

Open Mon–Sat 9–7 **Closed** Sun, public holidays **Credit cards** None accepted; personal and business accounts **Discounts** 10% on 1 unmixed case
Delivery Free in central London, Gloucestershire, M4 valley, Newmarket area (min order 5+ cases); otherwise 1 case £5.80, 2 cases £3.80 per case, 3–4 cases £2.50 per case; mail order available **Glass hire** Free **Tastings and talks** 6–10 free tastings per year by invitation only **Cellarage** Not available

1992 has seen a few changes at the top end of this company. The Haynes part of Haynes Hanson and Clark (Denis Haynes) has retired to be succeeded by Robert J McAlpine and a new board member, Philip Rogers-Coltman, has been appointed. The part of the company most of us come across, the list, is just as consistent as ever.

If you are looking for quality, particularly from Burgundy, then this is the place to start. Anthony Hanson MW is a burgundy specialist who has written (and updated) the definitive book on the subject. He is responsible for the selection of the range and his choice of wines cannot be faulted – he knows the growers and their wines well. The list is a collection of the good and the great: Simon Bize, Gagnard-Delagrange, Meo-Camuzet and more. But there are sound choices lower down the price scale which will not demand a second mortgage. Juliénas from André Pelletier and Joseph Drouhin's Bourgogne both provide stylish drinking at prices considerably less than those guaranteed to give customers a heart-attack.

Outside Burgundy the same search for quality has continued. The Bordeaux section is not an endless list of well-known châteaux but a selected group of wines from good winemakers. There is a high proportion of second wines here: Lady Langoa, Ch. l'Hospitalet, Réserve du Général and Fiefs de Lagrange among them. Most clarets are of recent vintages – 1988s and 1989s with a few from 1985. An indication of when these wines will be ready to drink would be an improvement to the list, although advice is only a phone call away. There are interesting wines to try from the Rhône and Loire sections and the New World beckons with Murphy-Goode and Saintsbury from California and the delicious Merlot from Matanzas Creek. Petaluma, Dromana and Plantagenet are the highlights from Australia.

HH&C operates a national mail-order business but you can buy by the case from the warehouse in Lettice Street. The retail shop in Kensington is small and not everything is immediately available. *En primeur* offers of clarets are normally made but the company has decided not to offer the 1991 vintage in the belief that prices will not rise. Meanwhile, a delicious offer of wines from the Hospices de Beaune could take care of any embarrassing spare cash.

Best buys

Cépage Merlot, Domaine Castéras Miele, Vin de Pays d'Oc, £
Ch. La Chapelle 1989, Bordeaux Supérieur, £
St-Véran 1990, Domaine des Deux Roches, ££
Champagne Pierre Vaudon Premier Cru, Brut, nv, ££

The Heath Street Wine Co

See La Réserve

Hedley Wright

10–11 The Twyford Centre, London Road, Bishop's Stortford, Hertfordshire CM23 3YT   *Tel* (0279) 506512

Case sales only **Open** Mon–Wed, Sat 10–6; Thur and Fri 10–7 **Closed** Sun, public holidays **Credit cards** Access, Visa; personal and business accounts **Discounts** By arrangement **Delivery** Free within 15-mile radius of Bishop's Stortford; mail order available **Glass hire** Free with 1-case order **Tastings and talks** Selection of wines always available in-store; to groups on request; approx 4 tutored tastings per year **Cellarage** £3.95 per case per year

With new supermarkets mushrooming in the Bishop's Stortford area, Hedley Wright has to work hard to hold on to its customers. It rises to this challenge by offering interesting wines, personal service as well as the usual (but vital) sale-or-return and glass-hire facilities that supermarkets cannot cope with. In addition, the list is chatty, informative and well laid out and the regular mailshots will keep you informed about special offers.

Hedley Wright is a case-only merchant, but this means a dozen assorted bottles and there is plenty to choose from. The list includes a good selection of wines under £5 which are grouped together at the front of the list under the heading 'Top quality wines for everyday'. Most interesting amongst these are the Troisgros Blanc – house wine at the 3-star restaurant of the same name – and a 1988 Spanna, a neglected wine which needs and deserves all the encouragement it can get. Beyond the bargain buys, Chile is the speciality region possessing the splendid Villa Montes wines in strength. Hedley Wright is also the agent for Cellier le Brun (based in Marlborough, New Zealand) who make quality sparkling wines. The clarets on the list are affordable and Martin Wright's buying notes direct you to the best bargains in the different price bands. Alsace wines are provided by the co-operative in Kientzheim, and the Australians include Heggies Vineyard from Hill-Smith and James Halliday's Coldstream Hills.

Hedley Wright may be surrounded by supermarkets but it looks as if it can rise to the challenge and win.

Best buys

Villa Montes Cabernet Sauvignon 1989, Chile, £
Southern Cross Chenin/Chardonnay 1990, New Zealand, £
Montes Alpha Cabernet Sauvignon 1987, Chile, ££
Daniel le Brun Brut nv, New Zealand, ££

Douglas Henn-Macrae

Not a shop
81 Mackenders Lane, Eccles, Aylesford, Kent ME20 7JA
Tel (0622) 710952

Case sales only **Open** Telephone enquiries welcome Mon–Sat up to 10pm **Closed** Sun, Chr & Easter **Credit cards** Access, Visa; personal and business accounts **Discounts** Negotiable **Delivery** Free on UK mainland (min 5 cases); otherwise £7 per order; mail order available **Glass hire** Not available **Tastings and talks** Tutored tastings to societies on request **Cellarage** Not available

'We like to deal with countries where we speak the language,' says German teacher Douglas Henn-Macrae, and so it is easy to understand why half his range is from Germany. How he also came to stock Texan wines is a little more difficult to comprehend unless DHM goes around in a stylish stetson.

Here in Aylesford, for 'German wines' read 'fairly unusual German wines'. No Liebfraumilch and Piesporter, DHM likes to tackle the regions other merchants cannot reach with trockens, halbtrockens, red wines and higher quality wines such as auslese. Occasionally, some of these styles coincide and he has some red auslese trocken wines – unusual to say the least.

For anyone planning an Oil Baron's Ball, Texan wine is what you will need and DHM has the perfect example. J R (aka Larry Hagman) helped pick the grapes for the 1986 vintage Sanchez Creek but, looking at the bargain price, it seems he didn't demand his usual fee for this work. Four Texan vineyards are represented, including Llano Estacado as served to the Queen on her recent visit there.

Prices at this company are not high although VAT has to be added.

Best buys

Mülheimer Grafenstück Riesling Spätlese 1979, Winzerkeller Leiningerland, Rheinpfalz, £
Ivanhoe Blush 1986, Texas, £
Grünstadter Höllenpfad Portugieser Auslese Trocken 1983, Rheinpfalz, ££
Llano Estacado Cabernet Sauvignon 1987, Texas, ££

Drink no longer water, but use a little wine for thy stomach's sake and thine often infirmities.

New Testament Timothy 5:23

Charles Hennings

London House, Lower Street, Pulborough, West Sussex RH20 2BW — *Tel* (0798) 872485/873909

10 Jenger's Mead, Billingshurst, West Sussex RH14 9TB — *Tel* (0403) 783187

Golden Square, Petworth, West Sussex GU28 0AP — *Tel* (0798) 43021

Open Mon–Thur 8.30–6; Fri 9–7.30; Sat 8.30–6 **Closed** Sun, public holidays **Credit cards** Access, Visa; personal and business accounts **Discounts** 5% on 1 case; negotiable on larger orders **Delivery** Depends on distance and size of order **Glass hire** Free with suitable order **Tastings and talks** Free in-store tastings on Saturdays **Cellarage** Not available

There are some good wines lurking among the Liebfraumilch in this small independent Sussex wine merchant. From the New World a line of Penfolds wines ranging from the basics right up to Grange provides reliable, flavourful drinking; New Zealand has the wines of Cloudy Bay as well as Montana. Two California wines from Wente provide refuge from Gallo, while Villa Montes from Chile, Musar from Lebanon and Ch. Carras from Greece give different interpretations of Cabernet.

Spain has a splendid collection of Torres; Chivite and Ochoa provide good flavour from Navarra. With such variety it is surprising that the German section is still heavily into Liebfraumilch and Piesporter Michelsberg – although a token trocken and halbtrocken indicate a ray of hope here. France provides a balanced range of clarets and *négociant* burgundies, although the Rhône is rather thin. Three wines from the Sussex vineyard Nutbourne Manor add local interest. Free weekend tastings at the shop are worth calling in for.

Best buys

Montes Cabernet Sauvignon 1989, Chile, £
Faugères Domaine Cauvy 1990, £
Elston Hawkes Bay Chardonnay 1990, New Zealand, ££
Rully 1988, Charles Vienot, Tastevin, ££

The Hermitage

124 Fortis Green Road, Muswell Hill, London N10 3DU — *Tel* 081-365 2122

Open Mon–Sat 10.30–8; Sun 12–2.30 **Closed** Public holidays **Credit cards** Access, Visa **Discounts** 5% on mixed cases; further discounts negotiable **Delivery** Free locally; elsewhere at cost **Glass hire** Free with orders **Tastings and talks** Free monthly in-store tastings **Cellarage** Not available

We have heard good reports of this shop in Muswell Hill. Proprietor Gill Reynolds has been in business since July 1989 and has built up a remarkable range based on the quality of wine rather than on convenient sourcing. From France there is a splendid selection of Alsace wines – Humbrecht, Faller and Hugel. Burgundies are a good mixture from Tollot-Beaut, Faiveley, Jayer Gilles, Mongeard-Mugneret and others. The Rhônes are equally well chosen. Italy shows a particular enthusiasm with a few of the more unusual upper-class vini da tavola, including Coltassala, Barbarossa and the wonderfully named Alto Mango. The New World selection should keep Muswell Hill residents busy. Australia, New Zealand, Chile, California and Washington State all have the same quality theme running through the range.

For a small one-woman business with no major buying muscle, prices are quite reasonable. One reader described this as an 'uncompromisingly serious wine shop'. We agree, and hope it attracts plenty of serious wine customers.

Best buys

Marius Riserva 1985, Almansa, Bodegas Piqueras, Spain, £
Dolcetto d'Acqui 1990, Viticoltori dell'Acquese, Italy, £
Vouvray le Mont 1983, Gaston Huet, Loire, ££
Oloroso Viejo de Jerez, Lustau Almacenista, ££

Hicks & Don

Order office — *Tel* (0258) 456040
Blandford St Mary, Dorset DT11 9LS
4 The Market Place, Westbury, Wiltshire BA13 3EA — *Tel* (0373) 864723
Park House, North Elmham, Dereham, Norfolk NR20 5JY — *Tel* (0362) 668573
Mainly mail order

Open Mon–Fri 9–5 **Closed** Sat, Sun, public holidays **Credit cards** Access, Visa; personal and business accounts **Discounts** By negotiation **Delivery** Free to Dorset, Wiltshire, Hampshire (parts of) and Somerset (min order 3 cases); otherwise £3 per case for 1–2 cases; mail order available **Glass hire** Free **Tastings and talks** To groups on request; several tastings a year **Cellarage** Available

Hicks & Don has been taken over by the brewers Hall and Woodhouse based in Blandford St Mary; Messrs Hicks and Don (both Masters of Wine) continue to be involved and are responsible for buying, along with Angus Avery.

There is no shop and the business revolves around the list and special offers – *en primeurs* are particularly strong. The main disadvantage of this company is that wines are available only by the full case, and mixed dozens allowed only for fortified wines. This is a shame because there is a tremendous variety and it would cost a fortune to sample your way through it. The keynote throughout the list is quality – good producers and growers prevail in every section and each wine is described in loving detail.

Burgundy, Bordeaux, Alsace and the Loire have well-chosen selections. German wines seem to be a particular enthusiasm although a complete case of Beerenauslese might tax even the most ardent admirer of these wines. The choices from Italy and Spain are good, although much of the Spanish collection is widely available in shops where you can buy by the single bottle at much the same price or even less. The main attraction of this company is its ex-cellar offers which, at the time of writing, include burgundy, champagne, Beaujolais and the Loire.

Best buys

Costières de Nîmes, Reserve St-Hubert 1990, £
Domaine de Rieux 1991, Vin de Pays des Côtes de Gascogne, £
Mountadam Chardonnay 1991, South Australia, ££
Ch. Peyraud Premières Côtes de Blaye 1986, ££

High Breck Vintners

Cellars
Bentworth House, Bentworth, nr Alton, Hampshire GU34 5RB
Tel (0420) 62218
Tel (office) 081-946 6372

Case sales only **Open** Mon–Fri 9.30–5.30; Sat, Sun by appointment **Credit cards** Access, Visa; personal and business accounts **Discounts** Not available **Delivery** Free locally to London, Hampshire, Surrey and Berkshire (min 3+ cases); nationwide 4 cases (min value £250); otherwise £6 **Glass hire** Free with case order **Tastings and talks** 5 to 6 tastings per year **Cellarage** Not available

Mixed cases are allowed only if you chose a maximum of three different wines or spirits (not so very mixed, really). That is the disadvantage of buying from High Breck Vintners, but once you get over that problem it is good news all the way. The company is owned by Howard Baverstock and run by manager Wilf Nelson. Mr Baveystock claims his wine qualifications to be '40 years dedicated consumption', which suggests that his wines are there to be enjoyed and are not just names to bolster the ego. The range is a personal selection from France, Italy, Rioja and South Africa. All are selected for 'backbone and character, with that all-important rapport between quality and price', to quote the proprietor. Small growers are the keynote here: single-estate Beaujolais, bottled by the Eventail producers, a collection of vineyard Sancerre and Pouilly Fumé wines, three domaine red burgundies for under £11 and four good-value Rhône wines from Wilf Nelson's cousin, who happens to be an oenologist, are among the attractions. This is an individual list and the result of much hard work.

Clarets include four vintages of Domaine la Grave from Peter Vinding-Diers, with the white available as well. A full range from Henry Ryman at Ch. La Jaubertie makes up the Bergerac section. Antinori from Italy, Berberana from Rioja and Lustau's wonderful sherries add variety. Mr Baveystock claims that visitors seldom leave thirsty, which makes High Breck Vintners sound like an enjoyable place to buy wine.

Best buys

Domaine de Chamberts Cuvée Bacchus 1989, Coteaux Varois, £
Ch. de Campuget Blanc 1990, Costières de Nîmes, £
Gigondas Domaine des Tourelles 1988, ££
Domaine la Grave 1989, Graves, Vinding-Diers, ££

George Hill of Loughborough

59 Wards End, Loughborough, Leicestershire LE11 3HB — *Tel* (0509) 212717

Open Mon–Sat 9–5.30 **Closed** Sun, public holidays **Credit cards** Access, Visa; personal and business accounts **Discounts** Approximately 10% on 1 case **Delivery** Free within 50-mile radius (min 2 cases) **Glass hire** Free **Tastings and talks** Customer tastings available; tutored tastings for groups **Cellarage** £5 per case per year

'There is still immense potential for wine sales in this country,' says Gillian Collins, sales director at George Hill. It is good to hear this optimistic note despite the recession having hit the Midlands just as hard as the South. By providing a well-balanced list with wines from most parts of the globe, this company is doing its best to capture some of that potential.

France is strong but does not dominate the list. Bordeaux provides a good selection at all prices; particularly interesting is a Margaux Private Reserve which is the second wine of Ch. Kirwan. There are decent red burgundies, with a number from the 1986 vintage (Domaine Parent features here). Chablis is mainly from the small producer, Domaine Rottiers Clothilde. The Rhône section is small, evenly divided between Michel Mourier and Jaboulet. German wines feature large in this list but apparently their popularity in Loughborough has fallen – a shame because most of these are quality estate wines from Guntrum and Prüm. The Italian section provides some excitement, with Bolla's Recioto Amarone and an impressive Rubesco di Torgiano from Lungarotti. Australia includes the

Peter Lehmann range and some from Pirramimma. New Zealand's contribution is mainly from Cooks and Nobilo. Sherries are worth a look, with a fine range from Emilio Lustau. Tastings are used to introduce customers to the new additions to the list.

Best buys

Syrah Rouge 1989, Vin de Pays des Collines Rhodaniennes, Michel Mourier, £
Domaine de la Hitaire 1991, Vin de Pays des Côtes de Gascogne, £
Bourgogne Rouge Pinot Noir 1988, Domaine Parent, ££
Pouilly Fumé L'Arrête Buffatte 1990, Tinel-Blondelet, ££

J E Hogg

61 Cumberland Street, Edinburgh EH3 6RA *Tel* 031-556 4025

Open Mon, Tue, Thur, Fri 9–1, 2.30–6; Wed, Sat 9–1 **Closed** Sun, public holidays **Credit cards** None accepted **Discounts** Not available **Delivery** Free in Edinburgh (min 6 bottles); £1 per consignment for less than 6 bottles **Glass hire** Free; breakages charged for **Tastings and talks** To groups on request **Cellarage** Not available

No one could accuse James Hogg of wasting money when he comes to produce a list. It is basic, utilitarian, close-typed on A4 paper and you almost need a magnifying glass to read the list of whiskies. However, we suspect that the customers of J E Hogg (nicely old-fashioned, and the shop closes for lunch) would rather enjoy prices at these levels than have a glossy brochure on their coffee tables.

The prices are excellent – not only a match for most independents but undercutting a lot of the multiples by pence and sometimes by pounds. And since customers know they are getting a good deal, we hope it encourages them to be adventurous. Specialities include Alsace – a terrific range from basics up to grands crus and vendanges tardives from no fewer than six producers. Sweet Loire wines merit a separate section, three vintages of Quarts de Chaumes from Jean Baumard look enticing. White burgundies are not just for the seriously wealthy, there are good Mâconnais wines – with change from £6. Outside France, Germany is taken fairly seriously with trockens as well as traditional styles from respected producers such as Prüm, Deinhard and Bürklin-Wolf. Clarets are represented by affordable châteaux below £10 before the list goes on to explore further up the price scale. Italian reds are worth investigating, as is the wonderful range of sherries. With over 100 wines available in half-bottles, presumably at keen prices too (they do not fit on to the crowded list), Edinburgh drinkers could confine themselves to little bottles and still not run out of choice.

The greatest disappointment about J E Hogg is that deliveries are made within the city of Edinburgh only, so you may have to travel some distance to take advantage of this wonderful little shop.

Best buys

Pinot Blanc 1989, Dopff & Irion, Alsace, £
Côtes-du-Rhône 'Parallèle 45' Jaboulet, £
Ch. Terrey-Gros-Caillou 1986, St-Julien, ££
Barbaresco 1982, Bruno Giacosa, ££

Holland Park Wine Company

12 Portland Road, London W11 4LA *Tel* 071-221 9614

Open Mon–Fri 10–8.30; Sat 9–8.30 **Closed** Sun, public holidays **Credit cards** Access, American Express, Visa; personal and business accounts **Discounts** 5% on 1 case **Delivery** Free locally (min 1 case); otherwise at cost; mail order available **Glass hire** Free with case order **Tastings and talks** Regular in-store tastings; to groups on request **Cellarage** £5 per case per year

Any company that is prepared to deliver your wine order within three hours (locally) deserves all the customers it can get. It is that level of service which puts the Holland Park Wine Company ahead in a very competitive market. MD James Handford also makes the promise that if you do not like the style of any recommended wine, he will replace it with the minimum of fuss. Sounds like a good shop to have down any High Street.

The list has a friendly 'handwritten' feel about it. Personal selections help guide you through the pages but it starts off with a few mixed cases. Names like 'Wander Down Under' and 'The Dirty Dozen' give the impression that this might not be the stuffiest place in London to buy wine. A good selection of wines under a fiver include La Vieille Ferme from the Côtes du Ventoux, Gran Feudo from Navarra and Butterfly Ridge from Australia. Elsewhere, higher up the price range, New Zealand comes in for special attention with Redwood Valley, Hunters and Te Mata. Australian wines are quality driven with Pirramimma, Moss Wood and Heggies Vineyard. The collection from Europe is focused on flavour, quality and value.

With tastings, fun days (whatever they are!) and excellent service, this part of Holland Park is well worth a visit.

Best buys

Domaine du Parazols Magee 1990, Vin de Pays d'Oc, £
Butterfly Ridge Colombard/Chardonnay 1991, Angoves, South Australia, £
Saumur Champigny 1990, Dubois, ££
Ch. de Chenonceau nv, Méthode Traditionnelle de Touraine, ££

House of Townend

Head office
Red Duster House, 101 York Street, Hull, Humberside HU2 0QX — *Tel* (0482) 26891
14 branches in Humberside and Yorkshire

Open Mon–Sat 10–10.30; Sun 12–2.30, 7–10.30 **Closed** Chr Day and Good Friday **Credit cards** Access, Visa; business accounts **Discounts** On request **Delivery** Free within 60-mile radius of Hull **Glass hire** Free
Tastings and talks Monthly wine club tasting (£6 per head); wine tasting for clubs on request **Cellarage** £2.60 per case per year

The head office and main outlet of House of Townend is in Hull with 13 additional shops around Humberside including one at the Willerby Manor Hotel which also happens to be Townend-owned. This merchant claims to have the largest range of wines in the county, but holding on to that title if and when this part of Humberside reverts back to Yorkshire could provide it with an exciting challenge.

The classic areas are handled very well at House of Townend. The range of burgundies is extensive, with good growers and producers well represented. Clarets tend to be the well-known names that go down well in board rooms: there is a lot more emphasis on wines at above £10 a bottle than below. The Rhône provides more affordable drinking, including splendid Vacqueyras and Gigondas from Roger Combe. Alsace appears to find little favour in this part of Humberside which is a shame since this limited range includes wines from Blanck and Schlumberger. German wines are here in variety but sadly not in the newer drier styles, Italy and Spain are both trying hard, but Portugal is still languishing among the Mateus Rosé. Australian and New Zealand wines seem a good bet, though, with reliable names at reasonable prices.

£5 a year entitles you to membership of the Townend Wine Club which meets monthly at Willerby Manor; this is also the venue for the new venture, a School of Wine.

Best buys

Tollana Shiraz/Cabernet 1990, Australia, £
Pinot Blanc 1988, Blanck Frères, Alsace, £
Ch. Caronne Ste-Gemme 1989, Haut-Médoc, ££
Vacqueyras, Domaine de la Fourmone 1989, R Combe, ££

Ian G Howe

35 Appleton Gate, Newark, Nottinghamshire NG24 1JR — *Tel* (0636) 704366

Open Mon–Sat 9–7; Good Friday 12–3, 7–9 **Closed** Sun, public holidays exc Good Friday **Credit cards** Access, Visa; personal and business accounts **Discounts** 2.5% for 1–2 cases (may be mixed), 3.5% for 3+ cases **Delivery** Free locally (min 1 case) and within 20-mile radius (min 2 cases); elsewhere by arrangement; mail order available **Glass hire** Free with orders **Tastings and talks** Four themed tastings a year **Cellarage** Not available

This is very much a family business: Ian Howe and his wife Sylvia are always to be found in the shop except when they head off to France to find a few more interesting goodies for the shelves. They have built up this business from scratch and in the small market town of Newark have survived only by offering quality wines and quality service. Delivering the right wine to the right venue at the right time may sound trite but it is a reputation like this which brings repeat custom.

The shop is interesting to browse around and there is always some new discovery or special offer on the racks just inside the door. If you have time, Ian will talk about his wines and he may sprint up the stairs to the stockroom to search out an interesting bottle. The list is not huge – it covers France only – but it has grown over the years to the point where it really needs an index. Chablis is a new enthusiasm with a fine collection of premier and grand cru wines from vignerons Droin, Grossot and Boudin as well as *négociant* wines from Moreau, Laroche and Drouhin. The Loire is another area of keen interest, with wines from Tinel-Blondelet, Joseph Renou and others. The Rhônes include a super selection of Châteauneuf-du-Pape.

Ian Howe is gearing up towards offering a national mail-order service; meanwhile this shop remains a welcome oasis for East Midlands wine drinkers.

Best buys

Côtes du Jura Chardonnay 1989, Jean Germain, £
Domaine de St-Père, Costières de Nîmes, Terroir d'Occitanie, £
Pouilly Fumé L'Arrête Buffatte1990, Tinel-Blondelet, ££
Collioure, 'Cosprons Levants' Domaine Mas Blanc 1985, Parcé, ££

Victor Hugo Wines 

Head office
Tregear House, Longueville Road, *Tel* (0534) 32225
St Saviour, Jersey JE2 7SA *Tel* (order office)
3 retail outlets around Jersey and a cash & carry at Longueville Road

Open Mon–Sat 9–6 **Closed** Sun, public holidays **Credit cards** Access, American Express, Visa; personal and business accounts **Discounts** Available **Delivery** Free in Jersey **Glass hire** Free **Tastings and talks** Regular tastings **Cellarage** Free

Yet more expansion for Victor Hugo on Jersey. 1991 saw the opening of a cash-and-carry warehouse to add to the three existing retail shops. The warehouse has a retail licence so you can buy by the single bottle at all outlets. As you might expect, the range has a French bias with good clarets (a particularly wide selection from the 1985 vintage), burgundies are mainly from Louis Latour and Domaine Laroche and Alsace wines from Schlumberger. The German range seems to have expanded in variety and moved upwards in quality. Guntrum is the main supplier but two wines from Robert Weil give a taste of the drier German style.

The choices from Italy and Spain are reliable, while Portugal boasts a surprisingly wide selection. Australian wines are growing in popularity despite the close proximity to the French coast. Penfolds, Brown Brothers and Hardys are the big names here. Villa Maria and Cloudy Bay represent New Zealand and the South African section has expanded considerably to take in estate wines from Oude Nektar, Kanonkop and Blaauwklippen. Two local wines are included in the list: Clos de la Mare and Ch. la Catillon provide the true taste of Jersey.

Delivery is free across the island and the untaxed prices look attractive to those of us on the mainland.

Best buys

Chardonnay, Vin de Pays des Coteaux de l'Ardèche 1990, Louis Latour, £
Chénas Ch. de Jean, Loron 1990, £
Hermitage Rouge 1987, Guigal, ££
Kitterlé Riesling, Grand Cru 1986, Domaine Schlumberger, ££

Best buys
£ denotes a bottle costing under £5
££ denotes a bottle costing over £5

Hungerford Wine Company

Head office
Unit 3, Station Yard, Hungerford, Berkshire RG17 0DY — *Tel* (0488) 683238
Shop
24 High Street, Hungerford, Berkshire RG17 0NF — *Tel* (0488) 681201

Open Mon–Fri 9–1, 2–5.30; Sat 9.30–1, 2–5 **Closed** Sun, public holidays
Credit cards Access, American Express, Visa; personal and business accounts
Discounts By negotiation **Delivery** Free within 15-mile radius of Hungerford; international mail order available **Glass hire** Free to customers
Tastings and talks Tutored tastings available on request **Cellarage** £7.99 per case per year (inc insurance)

Hungerford Wines is run by Nick Davies, a music graduate who started as a van driver in 1978 and to borrow a phrase, liked the business so much he bought the company. Rather than issue one main list per year which could go out of date as lines sell out, Hungerford concentrates on particular areas or types of wine in specialised offers. Champagne, Bordeaux and Burgundy have all come in for this treatment and at the time of going to press there was a Down-Under selection being assembled too. The advantage of majoring on one area at a time is that a much larger range can be offered than many merchants would attempt. 'Monster Sales' and 'Recession Specials' tempt you to part with cash in between the specialised offers. Most wines are accompanied by Nick Davies' tasting notes which range from the serious mini-essay to succinct 'bons mots' such as 'stunna', 'mind-blowing' and 'sensational'.

En primeur offers are another speciality, with Bordeaux a particular strength. The company also has a strange 'Prior Commitment Scheme' which means that you agree to buy a wine at a price not exceeding its estimate. There is also a 'Price Guarantee Scheme' which ought to ensure the lowest prices available. Some readers have been lulled into a false sense of security by this boast of 'You cannot buy cheaper', sometimes to their considerable cost. Nick Davies is intending to shave his profit margins this year on the 1991 Bordeaux offer so perhaps *Guide* readers will have fewer complaints.

Storage is expensive at Hungerford at almost £8 per case, although it does include insurance at full replacement value, but watch out for the £10 whacked on for each consignment removed from storage. Hungerford Wines has a shop on the High Street but admits that most of its customers make contact by phone. The shop has plenty of affordable, interesting wines: house claret from Sichel, Côtes du Ventoux from Jaboulet, and a full-bodied Periquita from Fonseca in Portugal will all give quality drinking and plenty of change from a fiver.

Hungerford is certainly not the boring traditional wine merchant. Once on the mailing list, you will be kept well informed in a gloriously unstuffy way but it could be worth checking around before parting with your money.

Best buys

Côtes du Ventoux 1989, Jaboulet, £
Côtes de Duras Blanc 1990, Domaine de Laulan, £
Ch. La Prade 1988, Côtes de Francs, ££
Ch. Filhot, Sauternes, ££

Ingletons Wines

Head office and warehouse
Maldon No 1 Bond, *Tel* (0621) 869474
Beckingham Business Park,
Tolleshunt Major, Maldon, Essex CM9 7NF
Cash & carry outlet
Station Road, Maldon, Essex CM9 7LF *Tel* (0621) 852433

Open (Cash & carry) Mon–Fri 9–5; Sat 9–12.30 **Closed** Sun, public holidays **Credit cards** None accepted **Discounts** Not available **Delivery** Free within East Anglia (min order 5 cases) **Glass hire** Available **Tastings and talks** To groups on request **Cellarage** Not available

Ingletons is a major supplier to the trade but it also has a cash and carry warehouse with a retail licence, so in theory you can buy by the single bottle if you wish. The lists are definitely for the trade (ex-VAT and listed in columns according to your quantity discount) but they are still worth getting hold of. Apparently all the wines are available in the cash & carry, although we would welcome reader confirmation of this.

The Fine Wine list is a gem: page after page of wonderful burgundies from the good growers and domaines of the region, with Etienne Sauzet, Mongeard-Mugneret and Comte Senard featuring most prominently. From Bordeaux the range runs from the basics to Mouton with a fine collection from the 1985 vintage. Quality German wines also qualify for the Fine list but are less exciting than the Fine French selection. The rest of the world is covered in the regular list and tends to be focused on one or two suppliers from each country. Thus Spanish wines are mainly from Bodegas Olarra, Portuguese from Fonseca and the Australians are limited to Seppelt. Only Italy manages a wider choice with wines from no fewer than five suppliers.

Some bottles are open for tasting at the cash & carry, but to qualify for free delivery you have to buy five cases.

Best buys

Ch. Jean Dugay 1988, Bordeaux, £
Mâcon Blanc Villages 1990, Comte de la Chevalière, £
Chassagne-Montrachet Premier Cru 'Les Chenevottes' 1987, Marc Morey, ££
Corton Clos des Meix Grand Cru 1989, Daniel Senard, ££

Christopher James & Co

White Hart Vaults, 64 South Street, Exeter, Devon EX1 1EF *Tel* (0392) 73894

Open Mon–Fri 10–7.30; Sat 9.30–6.30 **Closed** Sun, public holidays **Credit cards** All accepted; personal and business accounts **Discounts** 7% on a mixed case **Delivery** Free within 5-mile radius of Exeter (min 1 case) **Glass hire** Free with order **Tastings and talks** Three tastings a year (£15 per person inc buffet) **Cellarage** Not available

A welcome new entry to the *Guide* for this Exeter shop run by Christopher Ward. For Devon drinkers the range may not have the depth of Christoper Piper in Ottery St Mary nor the delicious variety of the Nobody Inn at Doddiscombsleigh but nevertheless it is conveniently sited in the middle of Exeter and has a well-chosen quality selection.

Everyday drinking wines start the list and the names of Yarra Ridge and Gamay de Touraine jump off the page for style and value. Within the small selection of only 13 clarets, Mr Ward manages to encompass both ends of the price scale with a range of petits châteaux and cru bourgeois wines, and then effortlessly hits the high notes with Châteaux Latour, Beychevelle and Léoville-Las Cases. Red burgundies seem to be a slight speciality here; the names of Louis Latour, Faiveley and Domaine Dujac indicate sound buying. Elsewhere in Europe the selection is reliable but there is more excitement in the New World: the wines from Australia, New Zealand, South Africa and Argentina have variety and style and most are priced well under £10. A good collection of ports, Lustau sherries and madeiras from Henriques & Henriques are worth browsing through.

Best buys

Rioja Tinto 1989, Navajas, £
Yarra Ridge Chardonnay/Semillon 1990, Australia, £
Ch. Corton-Grancey 1982, Louis Latour, ££
Nobilo's Dixon Valley Chardonnay 1988, New Zealand, ££

Tony Jeffries Wines 

69 Edith Street, Northampton, Northamptonshire NN1 5EP — *Tel* (0604) 22375

Open Tue–Fri 10–3; Sat 9–5; public holidays 12–3 **Closed** Mon, Sun **Credit cards** Access, Visa; personal and business accounts **Discounts** 10% on 1 case if payment by cash/cheque; 5% on 1 case if payment by credit card **Delivery** Free within 15-mile radius of Northampton town centre (min 2+ cases); less than two cases by arrangement **Glass hire** Free with order **Tastings and talks** In-store tastings (alternate Sun mornings between June and September) at £1.50 per person **Cellarage** Not available

A recent trip to Australia has given Tony Jeffries' shop a distinctly Antipodean slant. The range has increased to over a hundred and even more will be added before Christmas 1992. This must give Northampton's residents one of the best selections of Australian wines for many miles around. Penfolds, Peter Lehmann, Hill-Smith, Dromana and Seppelt are just some of the delights. There are a dozen Aussie sparklers too, from the good-value Killawarra to the delicious and difficult-to-find Mountadam. Other New World areas look sparse in comparison: New Zealand has some Palliser Estate and Savidge wines and there are three Chileans and three South Africans.

The other major area of this list is Spain but a little pruning has been going on. Tony Jeffries berates the general quality of Riojas, especially since prices have gone up. Even so, he has a range of 30 and among these there are some excellent examples from CVNE, La Rioja Alta and Muga. A clutch of wines from Navarra, Penedès and Lerida provides interesting drinking, mainly for under £6. Italy comes in for another of Mr Jeffries' brickbats and is rewarded with a very select range of seven wines only. France has its share of clarets although it is difficult to assess the burgundies and Rhônes in this list without producers' names.

Shop tastings on alternate Sundays provide an opportunity to sample the range and seem like a friendly way to learn about wine.

Best buys

Chenin Blanc 1990, Normans, South Australia, £
Tollana Shiraz/Cabernet 1989, South Australia, £
Blanquette de Limoux 1991, Baron Pierre, ££
Lar de Barros 1986, Extremadura, Spain, ££

S H Jones

Shop
27 High Street, Banbury, Oxfordshire *Tel* (0295) 251177
OX16 8EW

Open Mon–Fri 9–5.30; Sat 9–5 **Closed** Sun, public holidays
Credit cards Access, Visa; personal and business accounts **Discounts** Available
Delivery Free in Banbury and district; mail order available **Glass hire** £1 per dozen or free with large wine orders **Tastings and talks** 5 to 6 tastings per year, 4 of which are tutored **Cellarage** £3.50 per case per year

Despite a diploma in malting and brewing, M S Jones has decided to eschew the grain and take to the grape as wine buyer for this family business. S H Jones operates from a wonderful old building in Banbury, dating from 1537. The shop is well laid-out, as is the list which is printed on recycled paper (it is easy to start liking this company). The first few pages of the list are taken over by a round-up of the vintages in various regions and an assessment of when they will be ready to drink. This is a splendid idea and acts as a reference to the rest of the list.

The range is fairly classic: good clarets with a fine selection from the 1982 vintage; Sauternes seems to be a bit of a speciality with five vintages of Ch. Rieussec going back to 1975; the Rhône is a delight showing examples from Guigal, Chave and Chapoutier and four vintages of Ch. de Beaucastel from Jean-Pierre Perrin; also worth trying are the Vacqueyras wines from Roger Combe. Still in France, a string of burgundies stretches back to 1973 with a fair sprinkling of wines under £10 before prices start climbing towards Grands-Echézeaux.

The German section is also clearly laid out with producers' names diligently included. Ochoa Tempranillo is a welcome new addition to the Spanish range, while Italy and Portugal are sound if rather unexciting. With Mondavi from California and a handful of wines from the larger Australian producers, this list should keep Banbury residents busy for quite some time. Half-bottles are a particular speciality: 28 clarets, 5 Chablis and a very good selection of pudding wines.

Best buys

Côtes-du-Rhône, Troubadour 1989, Caves des Vignerons Vacqueyras, £
Domaine de Rieux 1990, Vin de Pays des Côtes de Gascogne, £
Dolcetta d'Alba 1989, Prunotto, Italy, ££
Châteauneuf-du-Pape 1988, Domaine du Vieux Télégraphe, ££

Justerini & Brooks

61 St James's Street, London SW1A 1LZ — *Tel* 071-493 8721
45 George Street, Edinburgh EH2 2HT — *Tel* 031-226 4202
Rokehay Farm, Furleymembury, Axminster, Devon EX13 7TS — *Tel* (040488) 766

Open Mon–Fri 9–5.30; Sat 9.30–1 (Dec only in London) **Closed** Sun and public holidays **Credit cards** Access, American Express, Visa; personal and business accounts **Discounts** 2–4 cases £1 per case; 5–7 cases £2 per case; 8+ cases £3 per case **Delivery** Free in London (min 2 cases), otherwise £8; UK mainland free (min 3 cases), otherwise £9; mail order available **Glass hire** Free **Tastings and talks** Regular tastings to existing customers by invitation **Cellarage** £5.20 per case per year (including insurance)

Just when other companies are closing shops and tightening their belts, Justerini & Brooks decides to set up a West Country office. There is no shop in Devon as yet, but there is a small warehouse and some stock can be supplied immediately while the rest of the range takes around three days. The London face of Justerini & Brooks is in up-market St James's. The company has a string of royal warrants going back to the reign of George III and so you might be forgiven for thinking that this is an exclusive, expensive company. That impression is only part of the story: the list, classy as it is, starts off with a substantial collection of wines under £6.50. This is where to find French country wines, a selection of petits châteaux and basic burgundies, including a Bourgogne Aligoté from Tollot-Beaut which just squeezes under the price barrier. Côtes-du-Rhône, Vacqueyras, two Alsace wines and a reasonable selection from the New World are also included, so drinking at J & B doesn't have to cost a fortune.

If you do feel extravagant turn the pages of the list to find any number of ways to take the weight off your bank account. Clarets are a speciality – this must be one of the finest selections of clarets available on a retail basis: 66 wines from the 1989 vintage alone, ranging from Bordeaux Supérieur to Ch. Lafite. The 1985 range gives a choice of 30 châteaux, each one with an indication of its maturity. Sweet Bordeaux wines are also here in abundance, including the ultimate for a sweet-toothed millionaire, *impériales* (8 bottles' worth) of Ch. d'Yquem. Burgundies follow suit with all the best growers and domaines – the same goes for the Rhône with a choice of 13 Côte Rôtie wines and from the Loire a fine selection from Gaston Huet. The rest of the world is less comprehensive but still very good; only Portugal seems overlooked apart from some splendid ports.

J & B operates a cellar plan whereby it takes care of your short-term and long-term drinking requirements. The regular mailshots are also worth having and mixed cases and special offers make the job of acquiring a stock of good bottles almost painless. This will never be a bargain basement place to buy wine, but prices are roughly comparable with many merchants, the range is excellent and the London tastings seem well worth trying.

Best buys

Cépage Sauvignon 1991, Vin de Pays des Côtes de Thongues, £
Ch. Méaume 1989, Bordeaux Supérieur, £
Bourgogne Pinot Noir 1988, Faiveley, ££
Ch. Lynch-Bages 1985, Pauillac, ££

King and Barnes

The Horsham Brewery, 18 Bishopric, Horsham, West Sussex RH12 1QP *Tel* (0403) 270870

Open Mon–Sat 9–5.30 **Closed** Sun, public holidays **Credit cards** Access, Visa **Discounts** 5% on 1 mixed case **Delivery** Free in Horsham and surrounding villages (min 2 cases) **Glass hire** Free with order **Tastings and talks** Tastings on most Sats; thematic tastings for the 'Case & Cellar Club'; tutored tastings to groups on request **Cellarage** Not available

This shop is the retailing arm of brewers King and Barnes and, unlike many brewery-owned wine shops, this one has a range selected for quality and variety and not just for ease of sourcing.

The list takes a general look at all the classic French regions. Burgundies are mainly from growers rather than the large *négociants* and there is a reasonable collection of petits châteaux from Bordeaux at well under £10. The Rhône includes a splendid St-Joseph from Dr Emile Florentin and from Corbières you can support the work of a hospital for the handicapped with the wine of Ch. Lastours which is said to be very good. With Alsace wines from Gisselbrecht and champagne from Georges Goulet, this French range is looking impressive. Further afield, the main areas of interest are Spain – a reliable range of Riojas and Navarra wines – and Australia, with Seppelt, Taltarni and two wines from Yarra Yering. South America contributes the flavoursome wines of Bodegas Weinert from Argentina and Santa Helena from Chile.

Best buys

Domaine des Pins 1989, Côtes du Roussillon, £
Quinta da Santa Amaro 1985, João Pires, Portugal, £
Weinert Cabernet Sauvignon 1983, Argentina, ££
Saumur Champigny, Vieilles Vignes 1989, Domaine Lavigne, ££

Lay & Wheeler

Head office and wine shop
The Market, Gosbecks Road, Shrub End, Colchester, Essex CO2 9JT — *Tel* (0206) 764446
Culver Street Wine Shop, 6 Culver Street West, Colchester, Essex CO1 1JA — *Tel* as above

Open (Wine Market) Mon–Sat 8–8; (Wine Shop) Mon–Sat 8.30–5.30 **Closed** Sun, public holidays **Credit cards** Access, American Express, Visa; personal and business accounts **Discounts** 1.5% on 4–11 assorted bottles; 3% on 1+ case **Delivery** Free within 60-mile radius (min 1 case); free nationwide on 2+ cases; otherwise £5.05 per 1 case; mail order available **Glass hire** Free **Tastings and talks** Tasting workshops with meals; food and wine workshops with 4/5-course dinners; general tastings and prestige tastings **Cellarage** £4.45 per case per year (under review)

Lay & Wheeler sets the standard by which all wine lists are measured: attractive (colour photographs), interesting (introductions to the regions) and informative (tasting notes for all the wines) – students of wine would do well to get a copy and study it as there is a wealth of up-to-date information to be gleaned from its pages. But that doesn't mean it is boring, far from it – it merely sets the tone. From a lovely picture of Mouton the horse at work in the vineyards of Ch. Magdelaine in St-Emilion to a snap of a solitary Kym Tolley waiting by the tracks for a train at Coonawarra, this list gets the tastebuds a-tingling.

But Lay & Wheeler is more than a list. It has two retail outlets and a trade cash and carry, and also organises probably the best programme of tastings and wine workshops available as well as an efficient mail-order service.

The range runs to over 1000 wines, apparently all in stock and ready to be plucked from the shelves at the Wine Market. The strengths of the range are really too many to list but classic areas such as Bordeaux, Burgundy, Rhône, Alsace and Loire are very good. There is also quality, variety and value. It is possible to buy top-growth clarets from a number of vintages but you also get a good choice of wines from less well-known châteaux. The style of the list and this company makes you feel that as much consideration has gone into selecting these wines as the classier bottles. Outside France, the choice is virtually limitless. Australia, New Zealand, California, Germany and Italy are all here providing typical flavours from excellent producers. If we had to nit-pick we might hesitate to mention that Eastern Europe looks a bit thin, and the South African selection as yet does not reflect the huge variety now available. If this compendium of delight becomes too difficult to choose from then managing director Richard Wheeler and his colleagues have selected their own desert island dozens. These should be as interesting an introduction to the range as any.

Once you are on the mailing list, Lay & Wheeler will send you its monthly newsletter with special offers, *en primeur* offers and details of the wine workshops. Telephone queries about the range and services always meet with an informed and intelligent response.

Best buys

Lay & Wheeler Claret 1988, J P Moueix, £
Southern Alps Dry White 1990, St Helena, New Zealand, £
Henschke Keyneton Estate 1988, Adelaide Hills, South Australia, ££
Chardonnay Pedroncelli 1989, Sonoma, California, ££

Laymont & Shaw

The Old Chapel, Millpool, Truro, Cornwall TR1 1EX   *Tel* (0872) 70545

Case sales only **Open** Mon–Fri 9–5 **Closed** Sat, Sun, public holidays **Credit cards** None accepted; personal and business accounts **Discounts** Available on 2+ cases **Delivery** Free (min 1 case); mail order available **Glass hire** Free with order **Tastings and talks** Rarely **Cellarage** £2.50 per case per year

If you try to imagine a convenient place to set up a company distributing wine around the country then Truro, on the very tip of Cornwall, is probably the last place you would think of. But way back in the Seventies it really wasn't such a bad idea. Boats left Plymouth for Spain laden with Cornish china clay and returned empty. That is, until china clay executive John Hawes had the brilliant idea of putting a container of wine aboard. With the help of a Señor Montelay in Spain and a little shuffling of their combined names the wine merchant Laymont & Shaw was born. The wine no longer travels the same route but the company, based in an old chapel in the shadow of Truro cathedral, continues to stock one of the widest and most interesting ranges of Spanish wines.

Rioja was on the first boat-load and it still continues to be a major part of the range. Wines from eight bodegas are listed but the most prominent is La Rioja Alta with its delicious Viña Ardanza and massive Reserva 904, and prices have stabilised a little after hefty increases a year or so ago. Neighbouring Navarra provides good value for under a fiver, but if money is no object there are seven wines from Vega Sicilia. Penedès is represented by the elegant wines of Jean León and a full range from Torres. From further inland, Raimat proves that irrigation does not mean poor quality with its fine range of varietal wines.

Wines from Toro, Priorato, Rueda and Jumilla add more variety while the range from Majorca, blessed with the new name of Binissalem, keeps the interest going. New this year is a bargain-basement Vino de Mesa named Don John, but modest John Hawes declines to reveal how he thought up the name.

Sherries are from Hidalgo, Lustau, Barbardillo and González Byass while the Málaga selection from Scholtz Hermanos is excellent. Mixed cases are available, prices include UK delivery and once on the mailing-list regular mailshots and special offers will land on your doormat.

Best buys

Señorio de Los Llanos 1987, Valdepeñas, £
Viña Cantosan 1991, Rueda, £
Reserva 904 1982, Rioja 'Gran Reserva', La Rioja Alta, ££
Yllera 1988, Viño de Mesa, ££

Laytons

20 Midland Road, London NW1 2AD *Tel* 071-388 5081
Outlets
14 Davies Street, London W1Y 1LJ
50/52 Elizabeth Street, London SW1W 9PB
21 Motcomb Street, London SW1X 8LB

Open Mon–Fri 8–6; Sat 9.30–4 **Closed** Sun, public holidays **Credit cards** All accepted; personal and business accounts **Discounts** Not available
Delivery Free on UK mainland (min £100 order); mail order available
Glass hire Free with certain orders **Tastings and talks** Regular free tastings
Cellarage £60 per case per year

'Laytons are André Simon' it declares in large letters at the top of the broadsheet of special offers. Graham Chidgey is the man behind Laytons and he has recently acquired the three André Simon shops in the smarter parts of London. The shops sell by the bottle while Laytons continues to operate on a case-sales basis (mixed cases carry a £2 supplement).

If you are addicted to expensive Burgundy then this is the place to get your fix. A page of grands crus of the Côtes de Beaune lists wines at prices that would give most of us a heart attack. A choice of vintages and growers of Le Montrachet is available at prices veering either side of £100, but this is a tiny fraction of the range and the emphasis is on good wines at whatever price you can afford to pay. France is the nub of the list, with clarets and particularly burgundies as the focus. Burgundy has been a passion for Graham Chidgey for many years and here the range expands to take in small growers and some that are even smaller than small. The only names missing are those of the major *négociants* that appear everywhere else. This is a personal list with tasting comments scattered around to add character. Clarets start off with Laytons' own 'Jolly Good Claret' and steadily climb the quality ladder. *En primeur* claret, burgundy and even champagne are all part of the service. Outside the classic areas there are little nuggets of interest from further afield. Spain is limited to one wine, Pesquera; Italy rates a special new supplement after extensive tasting at the Vinitaly wine fair. Moldavia presents four wines for approval and a handful of favoured Australian producers, Taltarni, Len Evans and the tiny Peacock Hill, is included in this unashamedly biased list.

A special mention must go to Angela Chidgey who designs the stunning list covers (the regular one, not the broadsheet specials). Also, if you are under 30 and want to learn about wine, the Circle of Wine Tasters operates from Laytons. Since Graham Chidgey last saw 30 a couple of decades ago, is this some subtle form of ageism or the vinous equivalent of a Club 18–30 holiday?

Best buys

Jolly Good Claret, Bordeaux, £
Domaine de Bellevue, Sauvignon 1990, Vin de Pays des Côtes de Thongues, £
Mâcon Villages Blanc 1990, Verget, ££
Laytons Oak-Aged Claret, ££

Lea & Sandeman

301 Fulham Road, London SW10 9QH *Tel* 071-376 4767

Open Mon–Fri 9–8.30; Sat 10–8.30 **Closed** Sun, public holidays, 2 January, Easter Sat **Credit cards** Access, Visa; personal and business accounts
Discounts Quantity discounts (by the case) **Delivery** Free in central London, and west to Reading and Basingstoke; mainland England, Scotland south of Perth and most of Wales free delivery on any order of £100+; mail order available
Glass hire Free with suitable order **Tastings and talks** Approximately once every two months **Cellarage** Wines bought from premises stored free for 1 year, thereafter £2.50 per case per year (exc VAT)

Lea & Sandeman is the kind of wine shop that most enthusiasts would like to have in their neighbourhood, namely one that specialises in good-value wines. Not cheap wines, nor expensive collector's pieces, but wines between £4 and £50 which genuinely reflect the quality of the grapes and the excellence of winemaking. Burgundy is especially good, with a fine collection of growers' wines from Bourgogne Aligoté to Chambertin. Many of these wines are exclusive to Lea & Sandeman and are shipped direct from the vineyards to the

Fulham Road. These are wines from small, individual growers who are introduced and described in the list. Bordeaux has a worthy collection of classed growths but there is a clear effort to provide less expensive, quality wines such as Ch. la Grenière from Lussac St-Emilion and the second wine of Léoville-Poyferré, Ch. La Mouline Riche. There is a huge choice from Alsace, all from Domaine Marcel Deiss; the Rhônes and Loires are less extensive but still good. Some regional French wines manage to creep in under £4.50.

Italy is another favourite area with Barco Reale from Capezzana, a full Antinori range and more Chiantis and Tuscans from Isole e Olena. The Australian section is limited to a few good wines: Shaw and Smith, Cape Mentelle and Yarra Yering, but California hits the jackpot with a splendid range from producers Mondavi, Phelps, Sanford and Sonoma-Cutrer among others.

Sweet wines merit a section to themselves, many in half-bottles including Vin Santo from Castello di Cacchiano. Ports, sherries and vintage armagnacs round off this impressive selection. Although firmly based in London, Lea & Sandeman has a less blinkered view of delivery than some other merchants.

Best buys

La Vieille Ferme 1989, Côtes du Ventoux, £
Domaine de Joy 1991, Vin de Pays des Côtes de Gascogne, £
Chablis Domaine Adhémar Boudin 1990, ££
Givry 'La Grande Berge' Domaine Gérard Mouton 1988, ££

Leo's

CRS Head Office, National Office, 29 Dantzic Street, Manchester M4 4BA — *Tel* 061-832 8152
Approximately 120 outlets in England and Wales (53 outlets) and Stop & Shop (260 outlets)

Open Generally Mon–Sat 8–8; some public holidays **Closed** Generally Sun, public holidays **Credit cards** Access, Visa **Discounts, Delivery, Glass hire** Not available **Tastings and talks** Occasional in-store tastings **Cellarage** Not available

The organisation of the Co-op is fairly complicated and not suited to these pages; however, Leo's is a national chain of supermarkets, part of the Co-op family but run as a separate group. It is not the same as the Co-op stores you may see on your travels. They in turn are not the same as each other, but that's another story.

Leo's buys some of its wines centrally from the Co-operative Wholesale Society, mainly generic own-label wine, and some are bought independently for Leo's. Like any large chain, the range available at your local store ultimately depends on its size, but we have had encouraging reports from at least one store which ordered wine which wasn't normally stocked.

Leo's is not the place to come for the finest wines you may ever want, but there are a few rays of sunshine between the Rougemont Castle and the Concorde. The Australian section is well worth a try with wines from Peter Lehmann, Orlando and Penfolds. From New Zealand, Cooks and Montana are reliably good, and from California the Beringer Fumé Blanc will go down well. Spain has two wines from Raimat and a contribution from Torres, Italy has Chianti from Rocca delle Macie, whilst among the French wines is a very tolerable 1982 Ch. Cissac.

Leo's has embarked on a programme of staff training: not before time, according to one reader, who was informed by the chap in charge at one store that one bottle of wine is the same as any other, contents immaterial!

Best buys

Leo's St-Chinian 1990, Maurice Chenu, £
Domaine Moulin de Peries Vin de Pays d'Oc, £
Raimat Cabernet Sauvignon 1985, ££
Ch. Cissac 1982, Bordeaux, ££

London Wine Emporium

72 Goding Street, Vauxhall Cross, London SE11 5AW *Tel* 071-587 1302

Case sales only **Open** Mon–Fri 10–7; Sat 10–5 **Closed** Sun (exc week before Chr), public holidays (exc Good Friday 10–4) **Credit cards** All accepted; personal and business accounts **Discounts** Not available **Delivery** Free within M25 (min 1 case) or nationwide (min 3 cases); otherwise 1 case at £5.95, 2 cases at £4.95 each; mail order available **Glass hire** Free; breakages charged for **Tastings and talks** Available **Cellarage** Not available

This Emporium is based at the same address as Alex Findlater's London office (see entry) and, as you might expect, there is a tie up between the two companies. This one operates as a separate entity but as many of the wines are sourced through the sister company, there is a strong Australian influence with wines from all regions, grape varieties and styles. New Zealand is also here in depth and there are plans to extend the range even further.

Outside these areas, the list develops more of its own character with a new selection from South Africa, good estate wines from Hamilton-Russell, Simonsig and Blaauwklippen included. Spain and Italy are worth a browse while Chile has been expanded along Villa Montes lines. New additions from Moldavia, Turkey and Greece are on their way to Vauxhall. From France small producers prevail, particularly in Burgundy, while the country wines section provides a wide choice (mostly for under £4). Free delivery within the M25 is available if you cannot get into Vauxhall Cellars, and a newsletter keeps you in touch with any changes.

Best buys

Chianti 1990, Tenuta Farneta, £
Domaine Jean Cros Gamay 1990, £
Crabtree's Watervale Cellars Shiraz/Cabernet 1988, Clare Valley, Australia, ££
Morgan 1990, Noël Bulliat, ££

Lorne House Vintners

Unit 5, Hewitts Industrial Estate, Elmbridge Road, Cranleigh, Surrey GU6 8LW — *Tel* (0483) 271445

Case sales only **Open** Mon–Fri 9.30–5.30; Sat 9–1 **Closed** Sun, public holidays **Credit cards** None accepted; personal and business accounts **Discounts** Available on large orders **Delivery** Free within 25-mile radius of Cranleigh (min 1 case); mail order available **Glass hire** Free **Tastings and talks** Monthly tastings at warehouse; to groups on request **Cellarage** Not available

A retail outlet may soon be on the cards for Dirk Collingwood of Lorne House Vintners. At present the operation is case-sales only (mixing encouraged) from the warehouse. The range is a personal selection based around small growers, particularly from France. The Loire is a favoured area – there are not many other small wholesalers with a range of six Domaine Muscadets. Also from the Loire are three sweet Vouvrays, a Gros Plant sur Lie and a Menetou-Salon, all from domaines. This certainly is not the list for lovers of bulk Rosé d'Anjou.

Bordeaux and burgundy are both good; affordability seems to be taken just as seriously as quality. French country wines keep costs down as well and include Domaine Richeaume from Provence and Ch. Eugénie from Cahors. Spanish wines are mainly red, with CVNE Riojas, Colegiata from Toro and Señorio de Los Llanos. Italy promotes small growers again, particularly Landini in Chianti, maker of a wonderful Super Tuscan, Prunaio. With a handful of German wines, the Tisdall range from Australia and two Hamilton-Russell wines from South

Africa, this is probably not the biggest list you will come across, but everything here earns its place.

As well as the regular list there are special offers from the Lorne House Vintners 'Shipping Club'. An annual membership fee entitles you to a discount of 10 per cent if you order and pay up before the wine is shipped. With prices already seeming reasonable this gives the customer an even better deal.

Best buys

Ch. de Juge Sec 1991, Bordeaux, £
Ch. Sarrail la Guillaumière 1988, Bordeaux Supérieur, £
Prunaio 1988, Vino da Tavola, Landini, ££
Vouvray Moelleux Clos de Gaimont 1989, Tellier, ££

Wm Low & Co

PO Box 73, Baird Avenue, Dryburgh Industrial Estate, Dundee DD1 9NF *Tel* (0382) 814022
67 branches

Open Mon–Sat 9–8 (till 9 on Thur; some regional variations); Sun 10–5 **Closed** Chr Day, New Year's Day **Credit cards** Access, Visa **Discounts, delivery** Not available **Glass hire** Free **Tastings and talks** Tutored tastings for wine clubs, etc. on request **Cellarage** Not available

Wm Low recently appointed a specialist wine buyer to move its range away from the brand names and towards better wines and better value. Kevin Wilson has been in the job only a short time but already there is sufficient good news to welcome Wm Low to the pages of this *Guide*.

Most exciting is the new Australian range with Eden Ridge, Oxford Landing, Penfolds and Schinus Molle, all at very reasonable prices. Compare this with the German range which still bears the thumbprint of former times (five types of Liebfraumilch in a range of nine wines) and you see how things have changed. Italy shows promise with Rosso Cònero from Umani Ronchi and Chianti from Rocca delle Macie. The Spanish section of the list has acquired some Torres and Raimat wines. France is improving, with good-value wines from Plaimont and those French wines in Aussie style, Vins de Pays d'Oc from Chais Baumière.

There is a long way to go before the range shows balance in all departments but Wm Low customers should feel encouraged by the developments so far. Watch this space.

Best buys

Merlot, Vin de Pays des Coteaux de l'Ardèche 1991, £
Ch. de Rabouchet 1989, Bordeaux, £
Chardonnay, Schinus Molle 1990, Victoria, Australia, ££
Gran Coronas 1986, Miguel Torres, Penedès, Spain, ££

Majestic Wine Warehouses

Head office
Odhams Trading Estate, St Albans Road, Watford, Hertfordshire WD2 5RE *Tel* (0923) 816999
44 branches

Case sales only **Open** Mon–Sat 10–8; Sun and public holidays 10–6 **Closed** 25–27 Dec, 1 Jan **Credit cards** All accepted; business accounts **Discounts** Available on large orders; 15% discount on cases of champagne **Delivery** Free in London and within a 10-mile radius of stores outside London (min order 1 case); mail order available **Glass hire** Refundable deposit of £9 per dozen **Tastings and talks** Themed tastings throughout the year; tutored tastings to groups on request; all stores have free tasting counters during shop hours **Cellarage** Not available

Majestic has gone through some major changes since the last edition of this *Guide*. The story so far: Wizard took over Majestic and the two merchants have pooled resources to come up with 44 branches in all, including the old Wizard warehouses; very shortly all will change to the new Majestic colours of black, white and bright green.

There is a list, but at any one time there will be additional parcels of wines available which come and go too quickly to make it into print. Among the regulars there is a hefty reliance on good-value and well-made wines with big, positive flavours. The Australian section demonstrates this in particular, with 20 wines under £5 and nothing over £9. The wines are all from favoured names: Wyndhams, Rouge Homme, Brown Brothers and Penfolds. All are reliable wines sold at reasonable prices. There are a few wines from New Zealand and some from California, but Eastern Europe expands to take in all those easy-to-drink gluggers. The Spanish range is full of old friends – Riojas from CVNE, Ochoa Navarra and Toro Colegiata. Portugal includes the chunky Tinta da Anfora from Peter Bright and Garrafeira Particular from Caves Aliança. The range from France majors on regional wines, again at the good-value end of the market; among the clarets the prices rise a little with a few châteaux wines between £10 and £20 before reaching the heights of Mouton 1988. Burgundies are mainly from Faiveley, Alsace wines from Kintzheim and Rhônes from Chapoutier, Guigal and Jaboulet.

Prices seem good throughout. All branches have bottles open for you to try, and weekend themed tastings seem like a good idea. Enthusiastic and informed help is usually available from staff. Mail order has resumed for those who cannot get to a branch and delivery is free within ten miles.

Best buys

Montepulciano d'Abruzzo 1989, Santangelo, £
Oak Vale Sauvignon Blanc 1991, Hawkes Bay, New Zealand, £
Crozes-Hermitage, La Petite Ruche 1989, Chapoutier, ££
Preece Chardonnay 1990, Australia, ££

Marks & Spencer

Head office
Michael House, 57 Baker Street, London W1A 1DN *Tel* 071-935 4422
269 licensed branches nationwide

Open Varies from store to store but generally 9–6 **Closed** Sun, public holidays (some stores) **Credit cards** Marks & Spencer Chargecard **Discounts** 12 bottles for the price of 11 **Delivery** Mail order available **Glass hire** Not available **Tastings and talks** Tastings of new ranges **Cellarage** Not available

M&S occupies a unique niche in the shopping trolleys of the nation. Very few people buy all their food here but many will happily load up a basket or two with the specialist items that M&S do so well. Things like ready-made meals, baby vegetables, smoked salmon starters and, of course, wine. Quality and M&S go together like a well-matched set of their silky undies. A team of technologists makes sure that the products, whether wine or food, are made in the best way to give a quality result. Wineries and bottling lines are inspected to make sure they come up to standard. Reliable is a word which springs to mind when thinking about this company. But is reliable also boring? The short answer is, no. In its own way M&S is an innovator, setting the pace for a number of retailers who follow in the 'me-too' brigade.

It was the first with a range of clarets from classy Bordeaux châteaux, masquerading under fairly plain labels such as Margaux, St-Julien and Pauillac. The labels have been brought up to date and the theme extended to include Bordeaux Supérieur and Médoc from a succession of petits châteaux. A range of wines made by some of the best names in the business is also available: nowadays it is no longer good enough to know just where a wine comes from because customers also want to know who made it. Therefore, rather than import the established and expensive wines of well-known winemakers,

M&S asked each of them to make one specially. And so seven winemakers, such as Len Evans of Australia, Serge Hochar of Château Musar in the Lebanon and Christian Moueix of Bordeaux have produced wines at affordable prices with the character of the region and the stamp of their personalities. Particularly good in this range is an Italian Cabernet Sauvignon made by the Lungarotti family; and the Moueix Merlot has the soft velvety fruit of the right bank of the Gironde. The white Rueda from the Marqués de Griñon is fresh, lively and stylish.

New lines continue to appear from other regions, too. Five wines from South Africa, two from Chile and a handful of Bulgarians have been added to the range, while France, Italy, Spain and Germany continue to develop interesting drinking. One quiet and welcome change is the gradual movement of the St Michael logo to the back label, as buyers sense that in the confident Nineties people do not need their wine to go to the table emblazoned with the name of the shop from which they bought it.

In the past, if you could not get to an M&S store with a car park nearby, buying more than a bottle or two could be a problem; now, happily, there is a mail-order service. It offers various mixed cases delivered to your door and two cases delivered free of charge. Marks & Spencer will never have a 600-strong selection of wines, nor will it compromise quality just to fill a gap in the range. Instead, it will continue to think up new ideas and no doubt keep shoppers on their toes by switching the displays around, but the quality will stay the same – reliable.

Best buys

Cape Country Chenin Blanc/Colombard 1991, South Africa, £
Merlot 1989, Christian Moueix, Bordeaux, £
Chablis 1990, ££
Cabernet Sauvignon 1987, Lungarotti, ££

Master Cellar Wine Warehouse

See Davisons

Wine is best stored in a cool, dark place where the temperature is steady at around 11°C. If you intend to keep the wine for more than three months store the bottle on its side so that the cork and the wine remain in contact.

Mayor Sworder & Co

381 Kennington Road, London SE11 4PT *Tel* 071-735 0385

Open Mon–Fri 9–5 **Closed** Sat, Sun, public holidays **Credit cards** None accepted; personal and business accounts **Discounts** Possible by arrangement **Delivery** Free within radius of M25; otherwise £5.50 per consignment; mail order available **Glass hire** Free **Tastings and talks** Annual tasting for customers on mailing list **Cellarage** £4.50 per case per year

Bouquets of praise have come in for Mayor Sworder since the last *Guide*. Comments on the excellent service, interesting wines and not-to-be-missed bin-end sales stand out amongst the plaudits. In 1992 the company moved out of its cellars near London Bridge station because of the impending arrival of the new Jubilee Line extension; the new multi-level storage facility in Kennington, south London is probably more efficient but perhaps has less atmosphere than the old railway arches. A great deal of Mayor Sworder's business is with the City and corporate institutions, but free delivery within the M25 and a nationwide mail-order service extends the customer network. The range is predominantly French, a great many wines selected from individual growers by buyer and Master of Wine Martin Everett. The list is well written, with each area and wine being carefully described. Who could resist Phillipe Brenot's Bourgogne Chardonnay when you have been introduced to the winemaker through Martin Everett's detailed notes?

The traditional areas of claret and burgundy are the main strengths, but Alsace, the Rhône, Loire and French country wines have again been well chosen and specially selected to provide individual character and flavour. The Spanish and Italian ranges are small; one Argentinian wine (from Bodegas Weinert) and two Californians provide a little more choice. The Australian and New Zealand representatives are slightly more encouraging, and we are told that South Africa may soon make an appearance in this list.

The special offers seem good value and prices are gradually converting to VAT-inclusive. The annual tasting is one of the highlights of the year.

Best buys

Chardonnay de Gibalaux 1990, Vin de Pays des Coteaux de Peyriac, £
Domaine de Signac Côtes-du-Rhône 1989, £
Idyll Vineyard Chardonnay 1990, Australia, ££
Ch. du Moulin Rouge 1988, Cru Bourgeois, Haut-Médoc, ££

J H Measures & Sons

See Bromley-Stephens

Mi Casa Wines

77 West Road, Buxton, Derbyshire SK17 6HQ *Tel* (0298) 23952

Open Mon–Fri 3–10; Sat 11–10; Sun 12–2, 7–10; Chr Day 12–1
Credit cards None accepted **Discounts** 5% on 1 case **Delivery** Free within 10-mile radius of Buxton (min 1 case) **Glass hire** Free with 1-case order
Tastings and talks, cellarage Not available

Anthony Moore has stopped printing an annual list because he likes to ring the changes on his limited shelf space. From the name of the shop you might guess he is a Spanish specialist, and wines from Rioja, Navarra, Jumilla, Valdepeñas and Penedès take up most of the space. There is a corner where other wines are allowed, inhabited by Montana and Cooks from New Zealand, a range from Romania and a full set of English fruit wines. Kopke port, Blandy's madeira and Spanish brandy provide fortification after taking the local Buxton waters.

Best buys

Romanian Cellars Fetească (no vintage specified), £
Vega de la Reina Tinto 1982, Valladolid, Spain, ££

Midhurst Wine Shippers

The Wine Shop, Elsted Marsh, Midhurst, West Sussex GU29 0JT *Tel* (0730) 812222 *Tel* (0243) 513109

Case sales only **Open** Mon–Fri 10–6; Sat, Sun, public holidays 10.30–1
Credit cards None accepted; personal and business accounts
Discounts Negotiable **Delivery** Free within 10-mile radius of Midhurst (min 1 case) **Glass hire** Free **Tastings and talks** To invited guests and to groups on request **Cellarage** Not available

This business used to be called Duras Direct but has changed its name, probably because it no longer confines its activities to just Duras. The theme is still wines from small family-run vineyards, imported direct and sold on at very reasonable prices. Overheads are presumably quite low for this partnership of modern languages graduate Sally Chadwick and partner Brian Wooding.

The range is small, but beautifully presented in an illustrated catalogue. One St-Emilion, one Margaux and a Graves make up the Bordeaux section. There is a single red burgundy – Premier Cru Chassagne-Montrachet – and a single Domaine Pouilly-Fuissé. South-west France provides most variety with a Madiran from Ch. de Perron, a Cahors from Domaine de Fages and a handful of other reasonably priced wines. New additions to the range include examples from further afield: two Spanish wines, a South African and two Australians, which are presumably not shipped direct.

Best buys

Vin de Pays Charentais 1991, Cépage Sauvignon, Marquis de Didonne, £
Domaine Las Bruges-Mau Michau 1989, Côtes de Duras Rouge, £
Pouilly Fumé 1990, Gilles Chollet, ££
Sancerre 1990, Les Caves du Gué d'Argent, ££

Millevini

3 Middlewood Road, High Lane, Stockport, Cheshire SK6 8AU *Tel* (0663) 764366

Case sales only **Open** Mon–Fri 9–3 (answering service outside these hours) **Credit cards** None accepted; business accounts **Discounts** 4% on 3+ cases **Delivery** Free within 20-mile radius of shop (min 1 case); mail order available **Glass hire** Free **Tastings and talks** Six tutored tastings per year **Cellarage** Not available

This is a specialist Italian wine business run from the home of Richard Lever who also manages to teach the piano when he is not selling bottles. He aims not to provide a thousand wines as suggested by the name, but to reflect the terrific variety of styles of good-quality wines available from Italy.

Italy vies with Germany for having the most indigestible names for its wines and Richard helps overcome this problem by introducing each region and each wine. The list starts at the top of the boot and steadily works down to the toe. Three Barbarescos, the same number of Barolos and an interesting collection of Gattinara, Ghemme and Spanna start the range which then takes in Teroldego Rotaliano from Trentino, a choice of Recioto from Veneto and Barbarossa from Emilia-Romagna. Small, quality producers heavily outweigh the big names. The Super Tuscans are out in force: there is a Cepparello from Isole e Olena, Flaccianello della Pieve from Fontodi and Fontalloro from Felsina, among others. Apulia, Basilicata and Calabria provide representatives, as do the islands of Sicily and Sardinia.

Best buys

Montepulciano d'Abruzzo 1988, Barone Cornacchia, £
Moscato d'Asti 1990, Viticoltori dell'Acquese, £
Trebbiano d'Abruzzo 1988, Valentini, ££
Barolo 1985, Bussia Sottana, Giacomo Fenocchio, ££

Milton Sandford Wines

Head office
PO Box 3, Twyford, Reading, Berkshire RG10 9UG — *Tel* (0734) 345251
Main outlet
The Old Chalk Mine, Warren Row, Berkshire — *Tel* (0734) 345251

Case sales only **Open** Mon–Fri 9–6; Sun, public holidays (sometimes) **Closed** Sat, Sun, public holidays **Credit cards** None accepted; personal and business accounts **Discounts** Available on 10+ cases **Delivery** Free by arrangement to Oxfordshire, Berkshire, Buckinghamshire and Wiltshire (min order 1 case) **Glass hire** Not available **Tastings and talks** Tutored tastings to groups on request **Cellarage** £3 per case per year

It may be that the name Milton Sandford sounds familiar: it was the name of a top restaurant just outside Reading run by Richard Sandford. He sold the restaurant a few years ago but carried on the wine importing business which had supplied the restaurant. Now this has expanded, selling mainly to restaurants, but also to the public (mixed cases). The range is limited and has a definite New World slant but there are sound choices from France, too. Burgundies are from quality producers such as Comte Lafon in Volnay and Guy Roulot in Meursault. There is a fine collection of red and white Loire wines and a handful of Rhônes, mainly from Guigal. The number of clarets is not extensive but there are a few well-chosen wines at all points of the price scale, and half-bottles are here in force.

Only in Australia does the list really get into its stride, with wines from Basedow, Yeringberg and Rouge Homme. Western Australia has a more than fair representation: Capel Vale, Chateau Xanadu, Leeuwin and Cape Mentelle. Five vintages of Penfolds Grange add to the variety. The Californian range goes for quality with its selection from Sonoma-Cutrer, Stag's Leap and the rather good if relatively unknown Spottswoode.

An old chalk mine in Berkshire is the latest acquistion by Richard Sandford. This will provide ideal storage conditions for wine and the eventual aim is to open a tasting- and dining-room. The ex-VAT list looks very reasonable and, even with the tax added on, prices are competitive.

Best buys

Stuart Point Cabernet Sauvignon 1988, Barossa, Australia, £
St Hallett Semillon/Sauvignon Blanc 1991, Barossa, Australia, £
Pierro Estate Chardonnay 1990, Margaret River, Australia, ££
Stag's Leap Cabernet Sauvignon 1988, Napa Valley, California, ££

Mitchell & Son

21 Kildare Street, Dublin 2 *Tel* (0001) 760766

Open Mon–Fri 10.30–5.30; Sat 10.30–1 **Closed** Sun, public holidays
Credit cards All accepted; personal and business accounts **Discounts** 10% on 1 case **Delivery** Free in Dublin (min 2 cases); otherwise £3.50 per consignment; elsewhere £2 per case; mail order available **Glass hire** 10p per glass
Tastings and talks Customer tastings held in Cellars restaurant on request
Cellarage Not available

If you ever go across the sea to Ireland, take plenty of money. With duty at £1.56 a bottle and VAT at 21 per cent, prices for even the most modest wines sail over the IR£5 mark. This affects all merchants equally but Mitchells in Dublin does a reasonable job of providing variety for your money. This fairly classic list takes most of its wines from France. Prosper Maufoux and Mommessin feature within the burgundy section, and also crop up in the Rhône. Mitchells is the agent for these wines but even so it would be encouraging to see a touch more inspiration in the selection. Clarets stay in the affordable range apart from a quick flurry among the first growths. German wines remain popular and include the Deinhard Heritage selection and two drier styles from the Rheingau.

Spain offers wines from Bodegas AGE (including the full-flavoured Marqués del Romeral) and Portugal is well represented with a range from Fonseca. So far, Mitchells has only dipped a toe in the Australian wine scene but California looks interesting with Sequoia Grove and Concannon Vineyard. Irish whiskey outnumbers Scotch significantly but they are both outweighed by vintage armagnac going back to 1937.

Organised tastings are held downstairs in the cellar restaurant and frequently there are bottles open for tasting in the shop.

Best buys

Sequoia Grove Cabernet Sauvignon 1987, California, ££
Haughtons Wild Flower Chardonnay 1988, Western Australia, ££

Mitchells Wine Merchants

Head office and main outlet
354 Meadowhead, Sheffield, South Yorkshire S8 7UJ — *Tel* (0742) 740311/745587
Branches
148 Derbyshire Lane, Sheffield, South Yorkshire S8 8SE — *Tel* (0742) 583989
25 Townhead Road, Dore, Sheffield, South Yorkshire S17 3GD — *Tel* (0742) 366131

Open Mon–Sat 8.30–10; Sun, public holidays 12–3, 7–9 **Closed** Chr Day **Credit cards** Access, Visa; personal and business accounts **Discounts** 5% on 1 unmixed case; 2.5% on 1 mixed case **Delivery** Free in Sheffield, parts of South Yorkshire and north Derbyshire; elsewhere at cost; mail order available **Glass hire** Free to customers **Tastings and talks** In-store tastings Fri and Sat; various events held for club members; new product launches; tutored tastings to groups on request **Cellarage** £2.40 per case per year (under bond only; 50p per case in/out)

'Look out, Oz Clarke,' says John Mitchell as he embarks on yet another venture – this time writing about wine for a local magazine. He may say this with his tongue set firmly in his cheek but it is an indication that this Sheffield-based merchant never stands still.

Now that the recent extension has given Mitchells more shelf space, the range has increased: 750 wines is the claim, with 250 under £5. Among the cheaper wines there is a good selection from Southern France including Ch. Val Joanis from the Côtes du Lubéron and house wines from Georges Duboeuf. There are Caliterra and Santa Emiliana from Chile and a whole range of Eastern Europeans. Interesting, too, is a Seyval Kerner 1989 from Chiddingstone Vineyard in Kent.

Sheffield is well served with Mitchells' collection of wines at £5 plus. Clarets kick off the list with a good selection and, although the top notes are a magnum of 1986 Pétrus and a bottle of 1961 Ch. Margaux, they include a decent clutch of petits châteaux, too. There is a potted version of the 1855 classification on the clarets page and this pattern of informing customers continues throughout the list. Burgundy's representatives are mainly from Chanson and Moillard with smatterings of Faiveley, Lupé-Cholet and Domaine de la Romanée-Conti.

Spain remains a speciality, with Riojas in depth: ten reservas and 11 gran reservas as well as vinos de crianza and Rioja Blanco completing the picture. Australia is represented by Peter Lehmann, Hunter Estate, Penfolds, Coldridge Estate and others, with Vidal, Stoneleigh and Cloudy Bay from New Zealand. Also in this section is the wine from a tiny island just off Auckland,

Goldwater Estate. California and the rest of the world are handled well.

Mitchells now boasts a tasting room where local wine groups can meet and tutored tastings are held. The Wine Club has taken off in a big way and now has 250 members who receive mailshots and special offers. A Quarterly Club is planned to restock members' cellars automatically. This part of Sheffield is humming with activity and by next year John Mitchell envisages yet another acquisition – he is going to buy a typewriter!

Best buys

Côtes-du-Rhône 1989, 'Parallèle 45', Jaboulet, £
Ch. Val Joanis 1989, Côtes du Lubéron, £
Beaujolais-Villages, Ch. des Vierres 1990, Duboeuf, ££
Ch. St Michelle 1987, Columbia Valley, Washington State, ££

Moffat Wine Shop

8 Well Street, Moffat, Dumfriesshire DG10 9DP *Tel* (0683) 20554

Open Mon–Sat 9–5.30 **Closed** Sun; Wed pm from Oct to Mar
Credit cards Access, Visa **Discounts** 5% on 1 case (may be mixed)
Delivery Free in Dumfriesshire; mail order available **Glass hire** Free with order
Tastings and talks Not available **Cellarage** Free

The recession has had a major effect on the Moffat Wine Shop. Not that business has been unduly affected in Well Street but the demise of several suppliers has caused some major rethinking of the range.

Tony McIlwrick sees a significant move away from the wines of France in this rural part of Scotland, and so he offers a selected range from Australia and New Zealand for those who are prepared to let their tastebuds travel. Moondah Brook, Cape Mentelle and the Peter Lehmann wines are some of the Australian attractions, with the reliable Montana wines pitching in for New Zealand. Highlights from Spain include a heavy Torres presence with four vintages of Gran Coronas Mas La Plana in the upper price bands. Understandably, these are on allocation but to list them at all indicates an enthusiasm for good wines. Navarra sports the full-bodied wines of Chivite and sherries include the top end of the González Byass range. France has not been left to languish. Highlights include a full range of Beaujolais crus collected from Drouhin and Fessy, and two organic Alsace wines. To finish, Ch. Pigoudet from Provence provides flavour and style at a reasonable price.

Best buys

Montepulciano d'Abruzzo 1990, Co-operative Casalbordino, £
Chivite Reserva 1986, Navarra, £
Torres Marimar Chardonnay 1989, Sonoma County, California, ££
Regnié, Henri Fessy 1989, ££

Moreno Wines

2 Norfolk Place, London W2 1QN — *Tel* 071-706 3055
11 Marylands Road, London W9 2DU — *Tel* 071-286 0678

Open Mon–Fri 9–8 (Norfolk Pl), 10–9 (Marylands Rd); Sat 10–8 (Norfolk Pl), 10–9 (Marylands Rd); Sun 12–2 and public holidays – generally (Marylands Pl) **Closed** Sun and public holidays (Norfolk Pl) **Credit cards** Access, Visa; business accounts **Discounts** 5% on 1 case; 10% on 5+ cases **Delivery** Free in central London (and in UK on 5+ cases); otherwise £8 on 1 case, £7 on 2 cases, £5.50 on 3 cases, £4 on 4 cases; mail order available **Glass hire** Free with order **Tastings and talks** Monthly tutored tastings through Moreno Wine Club **Cellarage** Not available

When we asked merchants what trends they saw in the market most managed a few words on the effect of the recession on their sales. Not so Moreno. Instead, we received a detailed forecast of winemaking trends such as an increase in Cabernet-based wines, less ageing in oak and more in bottle, use of French oak instead of American and an increasing use of the Tempranillo grape. It is this level of information, hopefully passed on to customers as well to us, which separates true wine merchants from mere sellers of bottles.

Moreno is a Spanish specialist, with a few extras from Portugal and Chile. There are two retail shops in London and a nationwide mail-order service. The list starts by taking a long and lingering look at Rioja (from 20 bodegas), varying in style from the traditional López de Heredia to French-influenced Marqués de Cácares. Vintages go back as far as 1968 in this section but even older vintages are on a special reserve list. This special list also contains older Vega Sicilia vintages. Penedès comes under close scrutiny, with a full range from Torres and Jean Léon. Seven vintages of the León Cabernet Sauvignon are listed. Navarra wines come from Ochoa, Chivite and Bodegas de Sarria. Other regions are touched on, too: Alella, Jumilla and Somontano, while Toro, Cariñena and Priorato are explored in some depth. From Rueda come the wines of Marqués de Griñon as well as the local outpost of Marqués de Riscal. The dazzling wines of Ribera del Duero come from Vega Sicilia and the co-operative at Peñafiel.

With a wide choice of cavas, including the family firm of Juvé y Camps, and sherries from Barbadillo, Bobadilla, Garvey and González Byass, there is enough here to keep even the most fervent Hispanophile amused. Should the attention wander, a selection from Chile (Santa Rita, Cousiño Macul and Concha y Toro) will keep the tastebuds occupied. A monthly wine club meets for tastings, and by all accounts these are well-organised affairs.

Best buys

Bodegas Navajas Tinto Sin Crianza 1990, Rioja, £
Vega de Toro Tinto 1987, Mateos, Toro, £
Bodegas Navajas Tinto Crianza 1985, Rioja, ££
Reserva 904 Gran Reserva 1981, La Rioja Alta, ££

Morris & Verdin

28 Churton Street, London SW1V 2LP *Tel* 071-630 8888

Case sales only **Open** Mon–Fri 8–6; Sat 9–1 **Closed** Sun, public holidays **Credit cards** None accepted; personal and business accounts **Discounts** By negotiation on large orders **Delivery** Free in central London and Oxford; otherwise £7.05 per consignment elsewhere for orders less than £500 **Glass hire** Free with 1-case order **Tastings and talks** To groups on request; available on premises Sat only **Cellarage** £5 exc VAT per case per year (inc insurance)

There are two ways to buy a decent bottle of burgundy: the first is to start off with a wallet full of money and work through a lot of bottles until you find one that really merits its price; the other way is to go to a specialist such as Morris & Verdin. There you will find a collection of individual domaine wines, each one selected by Master of Wine, Jasper Morris.

In Burgundy it is not enough to know the vineyard and the vintage, you also have to know who the grower is and the style of his wines – you may even have to keep up with family inheritances as vineyards are split up and winemakers change. Jasper Morris does all this for you. He knows the region and the people and is not afraid to change suppliers if quality dips. His range includes ten Meursaults from four different producers, eight Volnays and endless Gevrey-Chambertins, each with individual style and quality. But it is not just the top wines that are good – basic Bourgogne Rouge from Jean Philippe Fichet, Mâcon La Roche Vineuse from Olivier Merlin and Chablis from Vincent Gallois are all first-class wines at affordable prices. Most burgundies in this range are from recent vintages, so cellaring may be needed for the top wines.

Although this company is a burgundy specialist, it does not confine its activities to just this narrow strip of territory. Loire wines include a fine selection from Coteaux du Layon and Vouvray. The Rhône heads straight for quality with six wines from Condrieu and a fascinating array from Côte Rôtie. Alsace wines are from quality producers Domaine Ostertag, and a selection of French country wines provides fine drinking in between financial windfalls. Clarets, particularly the recent vintages, are here in depth.

California is the only other region explored to any real degree in this list and here the focus is on new-wave winemakers such as Jim Clendenen of Au Bon Climat, Bob Lindquist of Qupé and Randall Grahm of Bonny Doon.

Best buys

Domaine de Limbardié Rosé 1991, Coteaux de Murviel, £
Domaine Boyer 1991, Côtes de Thongue, £
Gevrey-Chambertin 1988, Denis Bachelet, ££
Au Bon Climat Pinot Noir Benedict Vineyard 1989, California, ££

Morrisons

Head office
Hilmore House, Thornton Road, Bradford, West Yorkshire BD8 9AX — *Tel* (0924) 821234
Approximately 60 branches

Open Variable Mon–Sat **Closed** Sun, some public holidays **Credit cards** Access, Visa **Discounts** Selected promotional lines **Delivery** Not available **Glass hire** At selected stores **Tastings and talks, cellarage** Not available

This group of supermarkets is growing steadily and by the end of 1992 there will be 60 stores based in the Midlands and the north of England. There is a new wine-buyer, Stuart Purdie (ex-Peter Dominic), and a new philosophy which makes this range rather less exciting but possibly more reliable. The Morrisons Fine Wine range used to be good. There were interesting clarets, a few second wines from the top châteaux and a handful of burgundies – always something new to find on the sloping racks. Now that top end has been sliced off, mainly because sales were not good enough to warrant the stockholding. There were also worries, reasonably enough, that by the time the occasional bottle of Puligny-Montrachet was sold it might not be in the best condition.

Now the emphasis is on quicker turnover stock and good-value wines from around the world. French regional wines are here in depth, with Vieille Ferme from the Côtes du Ventoux being worth a special mention. Bordeaux stays firmly in the shallow end (a few petits châteaux) except for a leap up to Ch. Gruaud-Larose. The red burgundies are barely worth a separate section on the list. Spain has been pared down to the bone while Italy fares only slightly better. From Australia, Coldridge, basic Penfolds and a few Wyndhams wines provide reliable flavours at reasonable prices. New wines from South Africa (Simonsig and Culemborg) and Chile (Villa Montes) give the range a slight lift. One good feature is that glass loan is available in selected stores. It is a brilliant idea that other supermarkets should think of adopting.

Best buys

Coldridge Shiraz/Cabernet Sauvignon, Australia, £
Villa Montes Cabernet Sauvignon, Chile, £
Ch. Caronne-Ste-Gemme 1983, Haut-Médoc, ££
Tokaji Aszú 5 Puttonyos 1983, Hungary, ££

Nadder Wine Company

Manor Farmhouse, Sandhills Road, Dinton, nr Salisbury, Wiltshire SP3 5ER — *Tel* (0722) 716734
The Wine Cellars, 2 Netherhampton Road, Harnham, Salisbury, Wiltshire SP2 5HE — *Tel* (0722) 325418

Case sales only **Open** Mon–Fri 9–6; Sat 10–6 **Closed** Sun, Chr Day, Boxing Day, Good Friday, Easter Day **Credit cards** Access, Visa; personal and business accounts **Discounts** 2.5% for orders of £100+; 5% on orders of £500+ **Delivery** Free within 30-mile radius of Salisbury and Central London (min 1 case with a value of £50) and UK mainland and Isle of Wight (min 10 cases); otherwise at cost; mail order available **Glass hire** Free with order **Tastings and talks** Regularly to groups on request **Cellarage** Not available

A new venture in 1992 for the Nadder Wine Company is the opening of a cash-and-carry warehouse in the old village school in Harnham on the outskirts of Salisbury. Here the whole range is spread out over two floors, less expensive wines downstairs, more expensive upstairs. Sales are still by-the-case only but mixed cases are positively encouraged and there is plenty to choose from. The main business continues to be run from the Manor Farmhouse in Dinton.

Tastings are a feature at the new Wine Cellars. Six bottles are open every day, and if there is something in particular that you want to try, let the staff know and they will endeavour to arrange it. The range is fairly wide but the Australian section is due for expansion after MD Chris Gilbey's trip around the Antipodean vineyards. At the time of writing, the wines of

Peter Lehmann, Petaluma, Mountadam, Rosemount and Rothbury were due to bolster an already impressive selection of Aussie wines.

Other southern hemisphere wines are also available. New Zealand wines are from Montana, Cooks and Martinborough. The South African section is small but contains some good estate wines such as Meerlust and Stellenryk. From Europe the emphasis is on wines from small but quality growers such as Reverdy in Sancerre and Domaine Martin in the Rhône. Burgundies are rather limited to the Misserey range for which Nadder is the agent.

The rest of the list is an interesting mix of wines from Italy and Spain, and once again these focus on small producers rather than the big names. Chris Gilbey likes his customers to have some say in what the company stocks. With frequent local tastings for wine societies, yacht clubs and the like, there are plenty of opportunities to let him know what you think.

Best buys

Ch. Le Fagé 1990, Sauvignon Sec, Bergerac, £
Côtes-du-Rhône 1988, Domaine Martin, £
Ch. Rahoul 1986, Graves, ££
Sauvignon de St-Bris 1990, Jean Goisot, ££

New Zealand Wine Club

See Australian Wine Centre

Le Nez Rouge

12 Brewery Road, London N7 9NH *Tel* 071-609 4711

Open Mon–Fri 9–5.30; Sat 10–2 **Closed** Sun, public holidays
Credit cards Access, Visa; personal and business accounts **Discounts** On large quantity orders only **Delivery** Free in London; England 1–2 cases £3.50 per case, 3+ cases free; Scotland and Wales 1–2 cases £3.50 per case, 3–4 cases £4 per case, 4+ cases by arrangement; mail order available **Glass hire** Free
Tastings and talks Regular in-store tastings; 4 tastings per year to Nez Rouge Club members; occasional tutored tastings **Cellarage** £2.60 per case per year

Le Nez Rouge is the retail arm of Berkmann Wine Cellars and as such has access to the huge range of agency wines that Berkmann supplies to the trade. The two lists used to be identical with nearly 600 wines, but now Le Nez Rouge has undergone radical surgery and has emerged slimmer – and very attractive.

The new list is described by Joseph Berkmann as 'The essential 170 wines a man needs for survival plus five optional ones in case of sudden wealth'. In fact, this is a very good list. There is a tremendous choice on the under-£10 range, even in burgundies. Here a wide selection includes Givry, Fixin and Savigny-lès-Beaune from good growers at prices where you can pull the cork and afford to eat as well, and it is from Burgundy that those five wines have been selected (from the Hospices de Beaune) to celebrate any massive inheritance.

Beaujolais is another Berkmann speciality and the Duboeuf domaine wines are here, most under £6. Some Rhônes are also from the Duboeuf stable. With the idea of value uppermost, it is worth spending some time among Le Nez Rouge Selection of table wines (Duboeuf again) and varietal French wines, such as a Syrah from a hot dry vineyard in the Aude called Le Texas. All but one of these wines will set you back less than £5. New Worlds are grouped together: Rosemount, Morton, Petersons and a couple from Dromana for high days and holidays. Champagne is the super Bruno Paillard version.

Best buys

Crozes-Hermitage 1989, Georges Duboeuf, £
Marsanne Domaine de Montmarin 1990, Vin de Pays des Côtes de Thongue, £
Côtes de Nuits Villages 1984, Domaine Philippe Rossignol, ££
Pinot Blanc 1990, Muré, Alsace, ££

James Nicholson Wine Merchant

27a Killyleagh Street, Crossgar, Co Down BT30 9DG — *Tel* (0396) 830091

Open Mon–Sat 10–7 **Closed** Sun, Chr Day, Boxing Day, Easter Mon, 12 July **Credit cards** Access, Diners Club, Visa; business accounts **Discounts** Available **Delivery** Free in Northern Ireland on 1+ case; mail order available **Glass hire** Free, breakages charged at £1 per glass **Tastings and talks** In-store monthly tastings; supper evenings bi-monthly; themed dinners quarterly with guest speaker **Cellarage** Limited cellarage, prices on application

The retail part of this company is only three years old but has obviously found its niche in the marketplace. We are told that sales have been increasing at a tremendous rate – very good news in these recessionary times. It was while James Nicholson was a restaurateur that he realised how difficult it was to get hold of better-quality wines. Now, as Northern Ireland agent for some of the great names, he has solved that problem.

From France none of the wines of Jaboulet, Guigal, Duboeuf or Drouhin would disappoint. Châteauneuf-du-Pape is from Beaucastel but the delicious Coudoulet de Beaucastel provides drinking at almost half the price while you wait for the main wine to mature. From Bordeaux the emphasis is on wines over £10 rather than under – classed-growth clarets obviously go down well in Crossgar. A selection of French regional wines including Ch. la Jaubertie and Ch. Bellevue-la-Fôret from Côtes du Frontonnais provides quality drinking at lower cost.

The Spanish clutch includes Riojas from Martinez Bujanda and Marqués de Murrieta with Pesquera and six vintages of Vega Sicilia from Ribero del Duero. Italian choices would be the wines of Umani Ronchi and Rocca del Macie, while from Lebanon seven vintages of Château Musar demonstrate that Serge Hochar's wine really does go on maturing and developing for twenty years. James Nicholson has winkled out good wines from all parts of the New World – Australia, New Zealand, South Africa and California – with two or three companies representing each region.

To introduce such a wide range, he keeps bottles open in the shop for customers to try and lays on informal monthly tastings and supper evenings with guest speakers. Mail order for one case is free throughout Northern Ireland.

Best buys

Alsace Pinot Blanc, Caves de Turckheim 1990, £
Domaine de Paillas 1989, Cahors, £
Rosso Conero 1990, San Lorenzo, Italy, ££
Saint-Romain 1990, Joseph Drouhin, ££

Nickolls & Perks

37 High Street, Stourbridge, West Midlands DY8 1TA — *Tel* (0384) 394518
Greenwoods, 178 High Street, Lye, West Midlands DY9 8LH — *Tel* (0384) 422217
Windmill Hill, Cradley, West Midlands DY7 6DI — *Tel* (0384) 394518

Open Mon–Sat 9–10 **Closed** Sun, public holidays **Credit cards** Access, American Express, Visa; personal and business accounts **Discounts** Available **Delivery** Free within 12-mile radius (min 1 case); mail order available **Glass hire** 10p per item **Tastings and talks** Regular tutored tastings **Cellarage** Available (charges vary)

Nickolls & Perks regards itself as 'one of the fastest-growing old wine businesses'. Such optimism in these recessionary times is to be applauded, as is the range which has its feet firmly planted in the classics (but does just look over the wall to the New World).

Bordeaux is the gem of the list. Page after page of the great and the good are here, a dazzling array of first growths from 1961 Latour to seven vintages of Haut-Brion. If you need a choice of vintages of Yquem or Pétrus, they are here in abundance. After this breathtaking whirl, burgundy comes almost as a disappointment. Good as it is, with a fine selection from Domaine de la Romanée-Conti and a sound cross-section from the region, the predominance of *négociant* names such as Mommessin, Bouchard and Ponnelle gives a feeling of safety rather than excitement.

Port is an area to be drooled over. Bottles start at 1904 and climb rapidly through the '20s and '30s towards a real abundance of 1963 wines and beyond. Madeiras, too, have been stored away for decades and present a confusing array of vintage and solera wines from Blandys. The rest of Europe is not neglected: for instance, good Riojas make up most of the Spanish range, while Antinori provides interest from Italy. Australia and California are listed rather than featured. Vintages are apparently thought to be less important in this area, even as far as Opus One, which has a price but no date.

The main list is issued to wholesale customers only but regular newsletters and offers keep retail customers up to date. The Stourbridge Wine Society is run by the company and offers talks, tastings and trips.

Best buys

Ch. La Croix St-Jean 1989, Haut-Médoc, £
Mâcon Rouge 1990, Trenel, £
Champagne Brut nv, Gremillet, ££

Nicolas

98 Holland Park Avenue, London W11 3RB — *Tel* 071-727 5148
157 Great Portland Street, London W1N 5FB — *Tel* 071-436 9636
6 Fulham Road, London SW3 6HG — *Tel* 071-584 1450
282 Old Brompton Road, London SW5 9HR — *Tel* 071-370 4402
71 Abingdon Road, London W8 6AW — *Tel* 071-937 3996

Open Mon–Fri 11–10; Sat 10–10; Sun 12–2, 7–9 **Closed** Public holidays **Credit cards** Access, Visa; personal and business accounts **Discounts** 5% on 1 mixed case **Delivery** Free in London (min 1 case); mail order available **Glass hire** Free with purchase **Tastings and talks** Occasionally **Cellarage** Not available

As you might expect, the five London outposts of the French-based Nicolas empire can come up with a fine range of French wines. The list is divided according to wine type instead of region of origin, which is a splendid idea if it works. So under the 'Soft and Silky' heading comes basic St-Emilion, Bourgogne St-Bris and a 10-litre pack of vin de pays des Côtes du Tarn. Saumur Rouge and Bourgogne Irancy are among the 'Light and Fruity' wines, while Morgon, Morey-St-Denis and Côtes du Roussillon qualify for the 'Spicy and Fleshy' description. Regrettably, no producers' names are included in the list.

There is also a Fine Wine list with remarkable coverage. Clarets are here in depth – 51 wines from the 1982 vintage alone, ten remaining from 1961 and a choice of nine from the 1928 vintage. Burgundies are fewer in number but actually roll back to 1900. Whether these wines are all available immediately or have to be ordered from central stocks in France is unclear.

Other attractions include free gift-wrapping and a delivery service which is described as free within London and inexpensive in Paris and other parts of France.

Best buys

Nicolas Bordeaux Réserve 1989, £
Prieuré d'Amilhac 1990, Vin de Pays des Côtes de Thongue, £
Ch. Rahoul 1987, Graves Blanc, ££
Meursault 1987, Les Vireuils, ££

The Nobody Inn

Doddiscombsleigh, nr Exeter, Devon
EX6 7PS
Tel (0647) 52394

Open Mon–Sat 11–11; Sun and public holidays 12–2 **Credit cards** Access, Visa; personal and business accounts **Discounts** 5% on 1 case **Delivery** Free within 20-mile radius (min 1 case); mail order available **Glass hire** Free with order **Tastings and talks** Monthly tutored tastings (Oct-Apr); other tastings by invitation **Cellarage** Not available

To look at, proprietor Nick Borst-Smith appears perfectly sane, but glance at the wine-list and you might begin to have your doubts. Remember that the Nobody Inn is essentially a pub in a tiny Devon village, not far from Exeter. It is a pretty sixteenth-century place with beams and horse brasses – the sort of venue to have a quiet drink while down in Devon on holiday. Ask for a glass of wine and, shock, horror, unlike 99 per cent of the licensed trade you are not offered a glass of tepid red or a glass of tepid (and oxidised) white. No fewer than 15 wines are open to try by the glass, all kept in perfect condition under nitrogen.

When you have sampled the open bottles, move on to the rest of the range – and this is where the wonderful sense of insanity creeps in. The list is huge and is available either in a drink-in or take-away version. The difference between the two prices is refunded if you decide to buy a mixed case. There is no region unexplored, no style left undescribed in this dedicated journal of wine, though Australia is the region of the moment after Nick's recent trip to the vineyards. The big names are here but so too are the smaller ones: the Red from Mountadam, Cape Clairault from the Margaret River area, even a Zinfandel from Cape Mentelle. We would echo his comment: 'Do the Americans know?'

The Americas, North and South, are explored in a similarly thorough manner. Greece, Israel, Bulgaria, Corsica and China... the list goes on and on. In France, the Loire comes in for special treatment, particularly the sweet wines. We are asked not to reveal that these wines are under-rated and excellent value because that only drives the prices up. And so we won't! We merely point out that the range of 12 Coteaux du Layon, ten Quarts de Chaume and nine Vouvrays is probably the best you will come across. With only two pages devoted to it, red burgundy takes on an almost sparse look compared with other regions; Bordeaux is more of an assault course. Sales are by the bottle or case; delivery is free within 20 miles of the inn, but nationwide mail order is available. Prices seem pretty much in line with elsewhere. Tutored tastings during the winter months make this the best venue for miles around.

And, when you have eventually decided on the wine why not turn your thoughts to the cheese list. There are 52 varieties, all from Devon and lovingly described, with names like Ticklemoor, Colespark, Vulscombe, Meldon and Devon Oke. Now, where's the straitjacket?

Best buys

House Claret, £
Limnos Tsantum, Greece, £
Ch. Montus 1988, Madiran, Alain Brumont, ££
Yalumba Museum Show Reserve Rutherglen Muscat, Australia, ££

Oddbins

Head office
31–33 Weir Road, London SW19 8UG *Tel* 081-944 4400
160 branches

Open (Generally) Mon–Sat 10–10; Sun 12–3, 7–10; public holidays 10–10
Closed Chr Day **Credit cards** Access, American Express, Oddbins Credit Card, Visa; business accounts **Discounts** 5% on mixed cases; 'seven for the price of six' on champagne and sparkling wine at £5.99 or above **Delivery** Free within locality of shop (min 1 case) **Glass hire** Free with order; deposit required
Tastings and talks Regular in-store tastings on Saturdays (2–5) in all branches; to groups on request **Cellarage** Not available

One of the more painful forms of torture is to tell wine drinkers who live in remote parts of the country just how good Oddbins is. Stranded in the sticks they have no way of taking advantage of the terrific range of wines offered by this lively chain. Should a rumour get around that Oddbins might be moving in, the established merchants dive for cover while residents start planning their cellars. Some dedicated drinkers even plan picnics and excursions with an eye to taking in the nearest Oddbins as one of the tourist attractions. So what is it about this operation that inspires such reactions?

You notice an Oddbins shop as soon as you drive up the High Street. Garish front windows are the norm (do shop managers take a course in graffiti painting before starting the job?). The shops manage to look busy even when there are few customers, with piles of cases, special never-to-be-repeated offers, up-to-date pithy tasting notes and big tickets asking low prices. The staff deserve a mention, too. Does Oddbins have a monopoly on engineers taking a year off or out-of-work pilots? These people are keen, work long hours and are invariably studying for the next wine exam on the qualifications ladder. New lines are tasted as they come into the range and shops band together to organise staff tastings so that the people behind the counter actually know the range they are selling. If they don't have the particular bottle you need they can get it from another branch quickly. Oddbins is also one of the few High Street sources for proper recognised tasting glasses for wine clubs and courses.

The range is outstanding – 800 wines is the claim (although few shops have everything in at any one time). It is a dynamic organisation with new lines constantly arriving. Australia is one of the high points: most of the names you have ever heard of crowd the shelves. The good-value wines from Killawarra and Wirra Wirra deserve a special mention but quality is high across the whole range. California has picked up, helped in no small way by the eccentrically named wines of Bonny Doon. The

Catalyst, Vin Gris de Cigare and Grahm Crew all have a story as well as good flavour and value and the labels are just right for the fun but serious atmosphere of an Oddbins shop.

Despite a slump in interest everywhere else Oddbins has held faith with German wines, seeking out the good winemakers and tastiest wines. Lingenfelder, Toni Jost and Breuer are just some of the names. From France, the Rhône selection deserves a round of applause – Guigal's inky 1988 Côtes-du-Rhône at less than a fiver must have been one of the bargains of 1992 and the choice from Bordeaux is appealing. Oddbins' offer of 1989 clarets was outstanding for value, especially since customers' money wasn't held hostage for years before getting the wine. The sparkling range is huge, particularly from outside Champagne, and with seven bottles for the price of six on many lines, Oddbins must rate as one of the best places to stock up on fizz.

If you had to nominate a weak area in the range it would be burgundy but even that is better than many competitors'. One criticism we have had from readers is that a mention in the press about a particular wine clears the shelves for weeks, but this is common to other retailers. In a similar vein, some claret offers have sold out rather fast, leaving disappointed customers.

On balance, the praises heavily outweigh the brickbats, particularly for service and value. Oddbins is planning more shops for 1993 – good news for drinkers and a challenge to merchants everywhere.

Best buys

Eden Ridge Dry White 1991, Australia, £
Santa Rita Cabernet Sauvignon 1989, Chile, £
Vignaserra 1988, Voerzio, Italy, ££
Cuvée Napa Brut nv, California, ££

Pallant Wines

Apuldram Manor Farm, Appledram Lane, Chichester, West Sussex PO20 7PE — *Tel* (0243) 788475

Open Mon–Sat 9.30–5; Sun, public holidays 10.30–1 **Closed** Some public holidays **Credit cards** Access, Visa; business accounts **Discounts** 50p on 5+ cases, £1 on 10+ cases **Delivery** Free within 40-mile radius of Chichester (min 1 case); elsewhere by arrangement; mail order available **Glass hire** Free with order **Tastings and talks** 4 invited wine tastings to clubs per year **Cellarage** Not available

'Many customers come to us after buying from supermarkets for a long time,' says Marian McMillan, buyer for Pallant Wines. So what attracts them to this converted cowshed with a Spitfire parked outside by courtesy of the local D-Day Museum?

The range is not huge but some confident buying has brought together a few highlights from around the world. France looks best among the Bordeaux petits châteaux and a selection of regional wines. Italy includes two wines from Villa di Capezzana and a good example of Vernaccia di San Gimignano from Teruzzi e Puthod. Spain contributes a few reliable wines from Rioja, Navarra and Penedès, and the South Africans extend beyond the ubiquitous KWV wines to the Simonsig Estate. With big names from Australia (Penfolds, Mildara, Rosemount) and the Undurraga range from Chile, choosing a mixed dozen should be no problem. There is also a retail licence so single-bottle purchases are possible but prices will be slightly higher than the printed list. Gift hampers are another attraction down Appledram Lane.

Best buys

Ch Le Relais Fontenelle 1988, Bordeaux Supérieur, £
Chenin Blanc 1991, Simonsig Estate, South Africa, £
Barco Reale, Villa di Capezzana 1988, Italy, ££
Ch. La Tour du Haut Moulin 1985, Haut-Médoc, ££

Pease & Wrightson Wine Merchants

Hill House, Gainford, Darlington, Co Durham DL2 3EY *Tel* (0325) 730320

Case sales only **Open** Mon–Fri 9–6 **Closed** Sat, Sun, public holidays **Credit cards** Access, Visa; personal and business accounts **Discounts** Not available **Delivery** Free within 50-mile radius of Gainford; mail order available **Glass hire** Free; breakages charged for **Tastings and talks** To groups on request; two tastings in Yorkshire and two in London **Cellarage** Between £2.50 and £4.50 per case per year

Welcome to this new entry to the *Guide*! Sales are by the case only – although the list shows prices for straight cases only, mixed dozens are allowed.

The list is alphabetically arranged, with Australia butting in between Alsace and Bordeaux and the Rhône coming right at the end after the ports. Even so, if you add up all the little bits, France comes out as the biggest section by far. Page after page of clarets provide a reasonable collection of petits châteaux and classed growths. Burgundies include some important names – Armand Rousseau, Sauzet and Tollot-Beaut – as well as a clutch of village wines under the Manoir de Setilles banner, which are hinted to be somewhat grander than their appellation declares.

The remainder of the list dots about, with just a few wines from each region. Italy is limited to a 1985 Barolo and a 1988 Sassicaia, certainly serious wines but hardly doing justice to the tremendous variety available from this country. Oregon provides two wines from Oak Knoll, including the splendid Pinot Noir. Ports are big at Hill House, with vintages rolling back to 1912 and a fair clutch from 1960 and 1963 still available.

Best buys

Rioja Ondarre 1988, £
Oak Knoll Pinot Noir 1988, Oregon, ££
Ch. Terre Rouge 1985, Médoc, ££

Thos Peatling

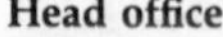

Head office
Westgate House, Bury St Edmunds, Suffolk IP33 1QS — *Tel* (0284) 755948
28 branches throughout East Anglia (including Peatlings Wine Centre in London)

Open Hours vary from branch to branch **Credit cards** Access, American Express, Visa; personal and business accounts **Discounts** 5% on 1 case **Delivery** Free in East Anglia; mail order available **Glass hire** Free with order
Tastings and talks Weekly informal tastings at most branches; monthly tutored tastings at wine centres **Cellarage** £4 per case per year

This 28-strong chain of shops is owned by a brewery – usually the kiss of death when it comes to decent wine. Not so here at Thos Peatling with its owners Greene King, who are committed to maintaining a 'proper wine merchant' image in these retail shops.

Claret is the major area of interest. You could spend weeks just working through the 1985 vintage – 66 wines in all, ranging from the most petit of the petits châteaux to first growths. It is the same story for other vintages, although the big guns are matured before making their debut on the list.

Peatlings is one of the few merchants left which still does some of its own bottling. This gives it a price advantage on those lines and it shows up particularly well among the dazzling array of petits châteaux from Bourg, Blaye and Médoc. Burgundies are almost as impressive as the clarets. Individual estate wines – all the right names – and the prices seem well in tune with the current market.

Elsewhere, German wines are comprehensive and good quality; Spain includes good-value Jumilla and Toro as well as a full set from Torres and two vintages of Pesquera. Australia brings together some of the big names and some of the small. Wolf Blass gets a good airing, with Mountadam, Cape Mentelle and Capel Vale adding to the variety. Most of the shops carry the full range and the Westgate House branch has a Fine Wine

Cellar with a few extra gems which exist in tiny quantities only. Staff training is taken seriously, so advice from behind the counter should be knowledgable. In-store tastings, *en primeur* offers and special reductions add to the attractions.

Best buys

Peatling's Australian Cabernet/Shiraz 1988, Barossa Valley, £
Ch. La Croix de Rousset 1986, Côtes de Blaye, £
Kumeu River Chardonnay 1990, New Zealand, ££
Beaumont de Crayères Cuvée Nostalgie 1983, Champagne, ££

Le Picoleur

See La Réserve

Christopher Piper Wines

1 Silver Street, Ottery St Mary, Devon EX11 1DB — *Tel* (0404) 814139

Open Mon–Fri 9–1, 2–6; Sat 9–1, 2.30–5 **Closed** Sun, public holidays **Credit cards** Access, Visa; personal and business accounts **Discounts** 5% on 1 mixed case, up to 10% on 3+ mixed cases **Delivery** Free in South-West (min 4 cases) and rest of UK (min 6 cases); otherwise £6.90 per consignment; mail order available **Glass hire** Free **Tastings and talks** Three to four large tastings per year; smaller regular tutored tastings; 2 wine weekends at Thurlestone, South Devon **Cellarage** £3.90 per case (inc. insurance)

Don't let the size of Christopher Piper's shop in Ottery St Mary fool you. It may be too small and cramped to swing a corkscrew but the range available is huge. Apart from extensive sales to hotels and restaurants in the area, there are apparently two main groups of customers in this rural part of the world. The tourists come and buy traditional or fashionable wines while the resident agricultural community prefers to register its opposition to the EC by buying anything good as long as it doesn't come from Europe.

For the tourists, France is a treat: good clarets with plenty of crus bourgeois at under £10 a bottle and burgundies from a variety of quality growers and *négociants*. There is a complete range of Beaujolais from Georges Duboeuf or you may prefer the true house wine made by oenologist Christopher Piper at Ch. des Tours in Brouilly. The rest of France cannot be faulted. Every region is well represented, as are Germany and Italy with good wines from respected companies.

If you are in sympathy with the farmers, Australia is not a bad place to start. From here Christopher Piper has selected some super wines from Mountadam, St Hubert and Petaluma. He has also gone for the complete set from Brown Brothers, with New Zealand, California and South Africa available as well. These should provide enough choice to be able to steer clear of EC wines for ever. Half-bottles are a feature, including six from Bordeaux and a whole clutch from California, the Loire, Australia and Alsace.

Christopher Piper acquired the Exeter-based business of David Baillie who has now joined the Piper board but, sadly, the Exeter shop has closed.

Best buys

Pigeoulet Vin de Pays de l'Hérault 1990, Daniel Brunier, £
St-Pourçain Blanc Réserve 1990, Union des Producteurs, £
Sauvignon Blanc 1991, Hunter's Wines, New Zealand, ££
Ch. Lassègue 1982, Grand Cru St-Emilion, ££

Terry Platt Wine Merchant

Ferndale Road, Llandudno Junction, Gwynedd LL31 9NT — *Tel* (0492) 592971

Case sales only **Open** Mon–Fri 8–5.30 **Closed** Sat, Sun, public holidays **Credit cards** Access, Visa; personal and business accounts **Discounts** Available **Delivery** Free to North and Mid-Wales, Cheshire and Shropshire (min order 1 case); mail order available **Glass hire** Free with order **Tastings and talks** Tastings and lunches throughout the year **Cellarage** Not available

Good independent wine merchants in Wales are like gold dust, but when you do find them, they sparkle. This is a family business and while most of its trade is with hotels and restaurants of the area, private customers are welcome; mixed cases are available and the list is user-friendly with VAT-inclusive prices.

The range has a personal feel about it. Most regions offer a choice from small domaines or well-known larger suppliers. In Burgundy there are domaine wines from Emile Chandesais, Alain Geoffroy and Machard de Gramont, with a good range too from Bouchard Père and Antonin Rodet. The 'small grower' theme is continued in Beaujolais, where wines come from the Eventail, a marketing organisation that represents 46 individual winemakers. Bordeaux presents an affordable range of crus bourgeois, with just a sprinkling of classed growths among the older vintages. Domaines feature again in the Loire and in the Arbois and Jura, where the bottles include a Vin de Paille, a Vin Jaune and a Pinot Noir from the Côtes du Jura.

Italy and Spain are both sound but Portugal seems to have been overlooked. German wines are mainly from family firm Michel Schneider in Zell on the Mosel. In California, Platt has followed the trail of nineteenth-century gold-diggers to the Sierra foothills and the Monteviña winery, whilst in Mudgee, New South Wales, its Australian namesake provides a selection of good-value varietals. Other Australians include Brown Brothers, Wyndham and Montrose.

Half-bottles are listed together and regular tastings are arranged throughout the year. Delivery is free for one case over a wide area – good news for those in North and Mid-Wales and in Cheshire.

Best buys

Domaine de Bellevue Sauvignon 1990, Vin de Pays des Côtes de Thongue, £
Ch. La Doméque 1988, Corbières, £
Fumé Blanc Monteviña 1991, California, ££
Chardonnay Carneros, Beckstoffer Vineyard 1988, California, ££

Playford Ros

Middle Park House, Sowerby, Thirsk, North Yorkshire YO7 3AH *Tel* (0845) 526777

Open Mon–Sat 8–6 **Closed** Sun, public holidays **Credit cards** None accepted; personal and business accounts **Discounts** 2.5% on 6+ cases; a further 5% discount on settlement within 10 days **Delivery** Free to Yorkshire, Northumberland and Derbyshire and nationwide on 4+ cases; otherwise £5 for 1 case, £7 for 2 cases, £7.50 for 3 cases; mail order available **Glass hire** Free **Tastings and talks** Approx 8 trade and private tastings per year **Cellarage** £2.75 per case per year

Playford Ros is a new company run by Nigel Munton who was, until recently, with Yorkshire Fine Wines. It operates out of old buildings in Sowerby which seem to have been rescued from the brink of dereliction if the before-and-after photographs are to be believed. A lot of Playford's business is to the hotels and restaurants of the area but they are prepared to mix cases and will deliver one case free within Yorkshire, Northumberland and Derbyshire which sounds like a pretty good deal.

The list has a definite trade feel to it. Prices are ex-VAT and there are two columns depending on how many cases you buy. The range takes a fairly traditional look at France, with a hefty listing of clarets, most under £10. Burgundies are limited but some of the producers look promising. Elsewhere, it really is just a handful from each region: Antinori features from Italy, Villa Montes from Chile; Spain would not take much working through and Portugal is represented solely by that good old restaurant faithful, Mateus Rosé. Only Australia is seen to be getting into its stride with Cape Mentelle, Leeuwin Estate, Yarra Yering and Show Reserves from Rosemount. Half-bottles are a particular speciality with a fair selection from most areas.

Best buys

Domaine de Petit Garderon 1991, Vin de Pays des Côtes de Gascogne, £
Cabernet Sauvignon 1991, Hugh Ryman, Vin de Pays d'Oc, £
Bourgogne Pinot Noir 1990, Domaine Marshall, ££
Cabernet Sauvignon 1983, Bodegas Weinert, Argentina, ££

Portland Wine Company

16 North Parade, Sale Moor, Manchester, Greater Manchester M33 3JS — *Tel* 061-962 8752

Associated outlets

82 Chester Road, Macclesfield, Cheshire FK8 8DL — *Tel* (0625) 616147
79 Scotland Road, Nelson, Lancashire BB9 7YP — *Tel* (0282) 603382
152a Ashley Road, Hale, Manchester WA15 9SA — *Tel* 061-928 0357

Open Mon–Sat 10–10; Sun and public holidays 12–3 **Credit cards** All accepted; personal and business accounts **Discounts** 5% on mixed cases (occasionally 10%) **Delivery** Free to central and south Manchester, and north Cheshire (min 1 case); quantity discounts on large orders **Glass hire** Free
Tastings and talks Monthly tutored tastings (Tue, £3.50 per person); monthly shop tastings (Sun, free); to groups on request **Cellarage** Not available

There is a surprisingly wide range of good-value wines at this small chain of four shops in the North-West. Very few stray over the £10 mark and those that do form a reasonable selection for special occasions – champagnes, a handful of top burgundies and clarets, and the upper reaches of the Penfolds range.

Australia features large in the list and after a trip to the vineyards wine-buyer Geoff Dickinson's enthusiasm for Oz has grown even more. The range explores the basics from Tollana and Jacobs Creek and then climbs the quality ladder via Rosemount, Rothbury and Rouge Homme. There are nearly 40 ways to spend a fiver in this range, all of them eminently drinkable. Ten Aussie sparklers compete for attention among a range from France, California and Spain.

Spain is another favoured region with the reds in particular coming in for special attention. Here the approach is the same as Australia, a carpet-bombing of good-value wines, each one hitting the mark on flavour for money; Altos de Pio from Jumilla, a collection of Riojas and a full set from Torres, rising to Marqués de Griñon and Jean León. Italy is worth spending some time on, as is Eastern Europe where the range includes reserve wines from Moldavia as well as the inexpensive Bulgarians. France is most interesting in the country wines section where a strong presence from Cahors, Corbières and Minervois keep down the cost of drinking.

Long opening hours, discounts on mixed case sales and delivery around Manchester and north Cheshire make this business well worth trying.

Best buys

Seaview Cabernet/Shiraz 1989, Australia, £
Tinto da Anfora 1988, João Pires, Portugal, £
Ch. Musar (six vintages available), Lebanon, ££
Fixin Les Hervelets 1986, Vallet Frères, ££

Arthur Rackhams

Head office and cellars
Winefare House, 5 High Road, West Byfleet, Surrey KT14 7QE — *Tel* (0932) 351585
13 branches in London and Surrey

Open Some outlets Mon–Sat 10–6; Sun, public holidays 12–2; other outlets Mon–Sat 10–10; Sun, public holidays 7–9 **Credit cards** Access, Visa; personal and business accounts **Discounts** Members' Club discount (The Vintner Wine Club) **Delivery** Free on UK mainland (min 5 cases) for wine club; mail order available for wine club **Glass hire** Free **Tastings and talks** Tastings in-store every weekend; monthly tutored tastings **Cellarage** Not available

There are 13 shops in this group, all based around London and the leafy bits of Surrey but that is only part of the operation. Equally important is the Vintner Wine Club, a mail-order business that also holds tastings, events and trips to the vineyards. Membership costs a hefty £16 a year but entitles you to generous discounts on the retail prices, whether by mail order or for single bottles through the shops. At the core of the lists for both the Wine Club and the shops is a collection of wines based on individual winemakers. These are grouped and named according to country and so 'Viticulteur' describes the French collection, the Spanish range is called 'Bodega' and the rest of the world comes under the fairly pompous banner of 'Vintner's Association of International Winemakers'.

Rackhams is one of the few wine retailers where the business is still family controlled. In selecting his growers, MD James Rackham has concentrated on family domaines and winemakers where quality and individual style are taken seriously. Many of these growers are not widely known but they are introduced to customers via 'James Rackham's Notebook', a publication with tasting notes and background information. Worth looking out for are Cheverny wines from Tessier and Alsace wines from Domaine Neumeyer – but there is tremendous variety here, particularly in the £4 to £8 range.

In the Bodega selection, Navarra wines from Bodegas Malumbres provide good-value drinking and from the rest of the world, Concha y Toro from Chile, Beaulieu from California and Hill-Smith from Australia make their contributions. Miguel Torres qualifies as an International Winemaker and so is not included in the Bodega range.

Overall, the range is good and interesting although the 'Viticulteur' name is exhaustingly over-plugged. Advice over the counter should be good as this company takes training seriously.

Best buys

Domaine de Valescure Merlot 1991, Vin du Pays du Gard, £
Domaine de Montcalm Sauvignon Blanc 1991, Vin de Pays des Sables du Golfe du Lion, £
Rasteau 1989, Côtes-du-Rhône-Villages, Didier Charavins, ££
Puligny-Montrachet Premier Cru, La Garenne 1989, Domaine Gérard Thomas, ££

Raeburn Fine Wines and Foods

21/23 Comely Bank Road, Edinburgh EH4 1DS — *Tel* 031-332 5166

Open Mon–Sat 9.30–6; Sun, public holidays 10–5 **Credit cards** Access, Visa; personal and business accounts **Discounts** 5% on unmixed cases, 2.5% on mixed cases **Delivery** Free in Edinburgh (min 1 case); elsewhere negotiable; mail order available **Glass hire** Free with order **Tastings and talks** Two free annual tastings **Cellarage** £4.50 per case per year (under bond)

Shopping list: Mazis Chambertin, Ch. Margaux, can of baked beans and a bunch of gladioli.

No problem, just call by your local grocery shop and pick up the lot – that is if you live within reach of Raeburn Fine Wines and Foods in the delightfully named Comely Bank Road. This shop is the epitome of a corner-shop enterprise. It is not actually on a corner but that is just a geographical nicety. The business is run by the Mohamed family who came to Edinburgh in 1967 from India via Kenya. Zubair Mohamed is the force behind the wine business and he has built up an impressive range, most of which he ships direct to Edinburgh from the growers. This shows particularly in the burgundy section where a fine array of domaine wines competes for attention in the crowded shop. Echézeaux, Le Montrachet, Volnay and

Chambolle-Musigny are all here as well as respectable Passetoutgrains and Bourgogne Rouge.

Classed-growth clarets feature in the list but the main focus is on properties where Raeburn has exclusive or privileged access to the wines, such as those from the Lucien Lurton stable, Brane-Cantenac, Villegeorge, Bouscaut and Climens. The Rhône takes a similar approach, wines from Jaboulet stand among those from Emile Florentin, Noël Verset and Desmeure. Only Alsace has just the one supplier and that is the excellent Rolly Gassmann.

Outside France, Italy has seen some work recently, with wines from Quintarelli and Monsanto providing most of the excitement. Australia contributes the wines of Cape Mentelle, Moss Wood, Seville Estate and Balgownie. The USA is a delight of individuals such as Randall Grahm's Bonny Doon and La Jota from the Howell Mountain area of the Napa. Portugal, as yet, is still unexplored as are Chile and Eastern Europe but the sheer weight of variety and quality from elsewhere more than makes up for these omissions.

Half-bottles will keep Comely Bank residents busy for several weekends and the extensive *en primeur* offers of Bordeaux and burgundy make this much more of a true wine merchant than many others with far grander premises.

Best buys

Ch. Les Ollieux 1989, Corbières, £
Erdener Treppchen Riesling Kabinett 1986, Moenchhof, Mosel, £
Rioja Amezola 1987, ££
St-Joseph Clos de l'Arbalestrier 1987, Emile Florentin, ££

Ravensbourne Wine Company

6.0.2 Bell House, 49 Greenwich High Road, London SE10 8JL — *Tel* 081-692 9655

Case sales only **Open** Mon–Fri 9–5; Sat 10–1 **Closed** Sun, public holidays **Credit cards** None accepted; personal and business accounts **Discounts** Variable **Delivery** Free in Greater London and surrounding boroughs (min 1 case); elsewhere small charge; mail order available **Glass hire** Free with order **Tastings and talks** Tasting tutorials; bottles open on premises **Cellarage** Not available

With a heading of 'Independent Bespoke Vintners' Ravensbourne sounds like a snooty St James' operation run by public school types. It is refreshing to discover instead that the two directors, Steven Williams and Terry Short, hail from Wales and the outfit is run from a business centre in Greenwich.

They started six years ago after a number of years with Oddbins and set out to provide good-value wines and spread the word with a series of tastings. The range includes BBC (as they call Bordeaux, Burgundy and Champagne) but the real emphasis in France is on vins de pays from the Rhône and lesser-known wines from Languedoc and Roussillon. Steven and Terry declare these wines to be woefully neglected which was possibly true on their first list, but now buyers everywhere are scouring these backwaters for flavour and value. Pacherenc du Vic Bilh and Tursan are two of the more unusual finds.

Italy is another tremendous source of individual style at reasonable cost. The full-flavoured wines of Lungarotti feature along with a fair selection of Barolo, Barbaresco and Chianti. Portugal offers a limited range, with Bairrada, Dão and Borba providing most of the action; Bulgaria fares much better with an almost complete set from the basic gluggers to Special Reserves – all excellent value. From the rest of the world there is Concha y Toro from Chile, Firestone from California and Montrose from Australia; nearly all wines are under £10, a great many are under £6.

Ravensbourne takes organic wine seriously and dotted throughout the list are little symbols indicating organic production. The two directors also enjoy speaking and spend many evenings running Wine Workshop Roadshows which are an attempt to educate and inform the drinking public about wine. From the letters of praise we have seen, these evening sessions seem to be well received.

Best buys

Domaine du Jas d'Esclans 1989, Côtes de Provence, £
Domaine de Fenouillet 1991, Côtes du Ventoux, £
Domaine du Mas Amiel Cuvée 15 Ans, Maury, Vin Doux Naturel, ££
Soave Classico 'Costeggiola' 1991, Rizzardi, ££

Reid Wines 1992

The Mill, Marsh Lane, Hallatrow, Nr Bristol, Avon BS18 5EB — *Tel* (0761) 52645

Case sales only **Open** Mon–Fri 10–6 (other times by appointment) **Credit cards** Access, Visa; personal and business accounts **Discounts** Not available **Delivery** Free in central London and within 25-mile radius **Glass hire** Free with order **Tastings and talks** Regular tutored tastings by invitation **Cellarage** Not available

Note that the name of this company is now Reid Wines 1992. The original Reid Wines is no more and the business has been purchased by Simon Wood and his associates, who used to be part of the original Reid team. Reid continues to trade from Bristol, at present by the case but hoping to have a retail licence soon.

The range at the time of writing contains all the wonderful old clarets and burgundies as before but plans are afoot to extend the list even further. The French country wines section will quadruple in size and the New World, already good, will see many new faces. A much larger range of all wines under £5 will also be available. The Mill in Marsh Lane seems worth watching for the future.

Best buys

Minervois Ch. De Gourgazaud 1990, £
Wairau River Sauvignon Blanc 1991, New Zealand, ££
Coteaux d'Aix-en-Provence Cuvée Louis David 1990, ££

La Reserva Wines

Unit 6, Spring Grove Mills, Manchester Road, Linthwaite, Huddersfield, West Yorkshire HD7 5QG

Tel (0484) 846732

Open Mon–Fri 9–5.30; Sat 9–6 **Closed** Sun, Chr **Credit cards** Access, American Express, Visa; personal and business accounts **Discounts** 10% on 1 mixed case **Delivery** Free within 20-mile radius (min 2 cases); mail order available **Glass hire** Free with order **Tastings and talks** Free weekly tastings (Sat); free tastings by invitation; tutored tastings (£10 per person); theme dinner events **Cellarage** Not available

If Expo in Seville, the Olympics in Barcelona and Alan Whicker popping up all over the place have whetted your appetite for things Spanish, then now is the time to head for Huddersfield.

Huddersfield? Hardly the home of flamenco but this is the place where Keith Gomersall, partner of La Reserva Wines, has managed to conjure up the atmosphere and flavour of Spain. With its whitewashed walls, archways and rush mats on the floor, Unit 6 narrowly avoids looking like a set for *Eldorado*. Inside is one of the most comprehensive selections of Spanish wines you could wish to find. Riojas start off the range with crianza, reserva and gran reserva wines from no fewer than 25 bodegas. Exploring these wines could take months but the list marches on to Navarra with a selection of over over 20 wines. Rueda contributes the wines of Marqués de Griñon and the old-style Vega de la Reina, and from there the list leaps to Penedès with a full set from Torres and the splendid offerings of Jean León.

The mission to unearth wines from every region continues into Ribera del Duero, Valladolid, Valdepeñas and La Mancha. Sherry is taken almost as seriously as Rioja, with Lustau, Barbadillo and Diez Hermanos featuring. If, in amongst all this variety, you decide that Spanish wine is not for you, don't leave Huddersfield. La Reserva is gaining on the rest of the world with an increasing number of wines from Australia, New Zealand, Chile and Italy.

There is a tasting room/restaurant which is in regular use for formal tastings and dinners around a theme – and you don't even have to find your sombrero.

Best buys

Señorio de Sarria 1988, Navarra, £
Tinto de Toro 1987, Luis Mateos, Toro, £
Viña Tondonia 1984, López de Heredia, Rioja, ££
Pesquera Reserva 1984, Ribera del Duero, ££

La Réserve

56 Walton Street, London SW3 1RB — *Tel* 071-589 2020
Le Picoleur, 47 Kendal Street, London W2 2BU — *Tel* 071-402 6920
Le Sac à Vin, 203 Munster Road, London SW6 6BX — *Tel* 071-381 6930
The Heath Street Wine Co, 29 Heath Street, London NW3 6TR — *Tel* 071-435 6845
Clapham Cellars (wholesale/by the case only), 7 Grant Road, London SW11 2NU — *Tel* 071-978 5601

Open Times vary from store to store **Credit cards** Access, American Express, Visa; personal and business accounts **Discounts** 5% on 1 case **Delivery** Free in central London (min 1 case); elsewhere free (min 4 cases); mail order available **Glass hire** Free with order **Tastings and talks** Regular programme of tastings; to groups on request **Cellarage** £4 per case per year

There are four retail outlets and a wholesale warehouse in this Mark Reynier organisation. Although they all have a similar core of wines, each outlet is allowed to develop its own personality according to its location and customers. None of the shops issues a full list but there are regular updates showing new wines and vintages. The wines are often from individual growers and there is a tendency to unearth 'declassified' burgundies, dangling the tempting carrot of drinking top-flight Volnay at the price of Bourgogne Rouge.

La Réserve concentrates on up-market wines – burgundies, top Californians and Australians. *En primeur* offers of Rhône, burgundy and Loire wines are made under the La Réserve name, as is an offer of *en primeur* (if that is the right phrase) malt whisky. This is a scheme where you pay now for your cask of Springbank whisky and leave it maturing and evaporating gently for the next 10, 20 or even 40 years. This idea is not for the impoverished, since the cask plus distillate costs £850 and duty will eventually set the purchaser back around £2000.

The Heath Street Wine shop has a broad range of wines, good clarets in the lower and mid-price ranges with access to La Réserve's 'old and rare' stocks for anything a bit special (such as 1948 Pétrus or eight vintages of Yquem). Portugal, Spain and Italy are favourite areas here, with manager Geoff Merrick stocking up the shelves with various Chiantis and interesting little gems such as Salica Salantino from Apulia. Le Picoleur is more biased towards California and white burgundy while Sac à Vin concentrates on foreign beers. Clapham Cellars acts as the central warehouse for the business and sells by the mixed cases.

Best buys

Domaine Meste Duran 1991, Vin de Pays des Côtes de Gascogne, £
Domaine de Triennes 1990, Vin de Pays du Var, £
Bourgogne Rouge 1990, Domaine Marquis d'Angerville, ££
Savennières, Clos St-Yves 1990, Baumard, ££

Reynier Wine Library

See Eldridge Pope

Richmond Wine Warehouse

138 Lower Mortlake Road, Richmond, Surrey TW9 2JZ | *Tel* 081-948 4196

Case sales only **Open** Mon–Sat 10–7 (open Sun in Dec only) **Closed** Sun, public holidays **Credit cards** Access, American Express, Visa; business accounts **Discounts** Negotiable **Delivery** Free within 5-mile radius (min 1 case); mail order available **Glass hire** Free with order **Tastings and talks** Every Saturday from 11–6 **Cellarage** Can be arranged

There are tastings every Saturday at Richmond Wine Warehouse between 11 and 6. With parking right outside and a large airy warehouse to wander around, this seems like a pleasant way to get out of doing the Saturday shopping. It is based in a former Victorian school but the desks have gone and most of the internal walls too, leaving a big floor area stacked high with a tremendous range.

France is strong, with a good collection of clarets in one corner of the schoolroom. Richmond Wine Warehouse makes a feature of larger bottles and so you can buy magnums and double magnums of many wines right up to a monster 18-litre bottle of Ch. Lamothe Bergeron 1986 priced at £290. Apparently, they do a roaring trade in big bottles but if anyone knows the correct name for the 18-litre monster please let Stephen Addy know. He does all the buying, casting an eye to the traditional French regions, backed up by a good range of regional wines under £5.

Italy and Spain provide sufficient interest, with Riojas from Berberana and a wide range of Italians from Antinori, Borgogno and Frescobaldi. The German range is disappointing with very little beyond Liebfraumilch and Piesporter. South Africa is a new venture – the Hamilton-Russell wines provide impressive Pinot Noir and Chardonnay. Australian wines are from a variety of sources but include the good-value Oxford Landing wines from Yalumba as well as the delicious Mountadam Chardonnay at a very reasonable price.

If you ever feel you need to go back to school this seems as good a place as any to start.

Best buys

Château Puyfromage 1988, Bordeaux Supérieur, £
Ch. de Vauclaire Rosé 1991, Coteaux d'Aix-en-Provence, £
Ch. Richard 1990, Saussignac, ££
Moulin-à-Vent des Hospices 1988, ££

Howard Ripley

35 Eversley Crescent, London N21 1EL *Tel* 081-360 8904
Mainly mail order

Case sales only **Open** Mon–Sat 8–10; Sun, public holidays 8–12 **Credit cards** None accepted; personal and business accounts **Discounts** Not available **Delivery** Free in London (min 5 cases); otherwise £9.40 per case **Glass hire** Free **Tastings and talks** To groups on request **Cellarage** Not available

What is it about dentists that attracts them to wine? Not content with tricky bridgework and crowns, Howard Ripley has got to grips with the complicated world of domaines, winemakers and vintages which, to the uninitiated, makes burgundy more of a gamble than the 2.30 at Doncaster. There is no doubting his enthusiasm. Comparing the quality of the 1990 vintage to the overdrive of a long-ago loved sports car, he sweeps you along in a rush of anticipated pleasure.

The list is full of mouthwatering names: Bachelet, Dujac, Bize, Rousseau and Jean-Marc Boillot who is one of the inheritors of the fabulous Sauzet estate. These are but an introduction; there is a dazzling choice of 70 red burgundies from 15 domaines from the 1990 vintage alone. The whites are less extensive but no worse for that. Older vintages compete for attention, going back to magnums of Romanée-Conti 1966. The best way to make your selection is to go along to Howard Ripley, even on a Sunday morning, and enjoy a glass or two as he signposts your way through the range. Given the price of burgundy (no one could ever accuse this region of producing cheap wine), you might be advised to rob a bank on the way there or at least cancel any major dental work you had planned.

Best buys

Oeil de Perdrix 1988, Domaine Dujac, ££
Volnay Santenots 1980, Robert Ampeau, ££
There are no wines in this range under £5.

Robersons

348 Kensington High Street, London W14 8NS — *Tel* 071-371 2121

Open Mon–Sat 10–8; Sun and public holidays 12–3 **Credit cards** Access, American Express, Visa; personal and business accounts **Discounts** 5% on 1+ case (payed for by cash or cheque); negotiable on larger quantities **Delivery** Free in West and Central London (min order 1 case) and locally for smaller quantities; elsewhere at cost **Glass hire** Free with order **Tastings and talks** Monthly tutored tastings to groups (from £9.50 per person) **Cellarage** Not available

No one can accuse Cliff Roberson of setting his sights too low. He aims to become the best wine retailer in London and has got off to a flying start. This shop opened in November 1991 and even as it was being converted from a kitchen showroom, the papered-over windows managed to look more stylish than many wine merchants do when they are open for business.

Stylish is a word which frequently springs to mind when thinking about Robersons. The interior design is like no other wine shop. It is big, with space to walk around, and the wines are not standing on shelves but are displayed on the slant on racks, with spare bottles tucked below. The walls are a muddy putty colour and the curved counter seems to well up from the floor. Stairs leading down to the tasting-room would look more at home on the set of *Dr Who*. A few steps, flanked by elaborate handrails, lead up to another display area – there was no practical reason for this expensive addition but as manager Chris Donaldson admits, it does look good. His presence is another plus point which makes Robersons different from most merchants. He used to be assistant wine buyer for Harrods and passed the Master of Wine exams in 1991. Now he buys for Robersons and since he is based at the shop, is frequently to be found behind the counter. No doubt he dispenses sound wine advice if asked.

The range is huge, around 1000 wines from Bordeaux to Peru, and spans from under £3 to over £600. There are no particular specialist areas, all are pretty good. One eye-catching feature is the old and venerable bottles that are either locked away behind bars or displayed like works of art in glass cases.

Clarets start among the petits châteaux and climb steadily to the first growths. The choice does not fizzle out after a few vintages but keeps on going, 40 from the 1985 vintage, 14 from 1982, 20 wines from 1970 and even a selection of three from as far back as 1953. The white Bordeaux range is startling for its choice of eight vintages of Yquem but there are plenty of wines to enjoy without taking out a second mortgage. Burgundy offers wines from Faiveley, Drouhin and Bouchard, as well as Domaine de la Romanée-Conti and Corton.

The New World merits special mention, with an exciting range from good winemakers. Pipers Brook from Tasmania, Australian Yarra Yering, Coldstream Hills and Bannockburn are just a few of the attractions. With Californians from Sanford, Bonny Doon and the fabulous Au Bon Climat competing for attention, decision-making is difficult. Italy is taken seriously: Barolos from Aldo Conterno and Borgogno, and good-value Chianti from Pagliarese as well as the more expensive Isole e Olena and Castello di Volpaia. Spain and Portugal are well worth serious sampling. Extensive ports, endless malts and a fair selection of cognac round off an impressive range.

Frequent organised tastings provide the opportunity to learn as you taste, and a few bottles are open in the shop at weekends. A new development is nationwide delivery but if you can struggle into Kensington you will enjoy the whole wine-buying experience.

Best buys

San Pedro Merlot 1989, Chile, £
Côtes du Roussillon 1991, Arnaud de Villeneuve, £
Pinot Noir Fleur de Carneros 1989, California, ££
Lagar de Carvara Albariño 1990, Rias Baixas, ££

C A Rookes

Unit 7, Western Road Industrial Estate, Stratford-upon-Avon, Warwickshire CV37 0AH — *Tel* (0789) 297777

Open Mon–Fri 9–6; Sat 9–2 **Closed** Sun, public holidays **Credit cards** Access, Visa; personal and business accounts **Discounts** Negotiable **Delivery** Free within south Warwickshire and surrounding areas **Glass hire** Free with order **Tastings and talks** Tutored and untutored tastings throughout the year on request **Cellarage** Negotiable

When we asked merchants to tell us the wines that they were particularly proud to stock, some managed five, others just two, and a few nameless souls couldn't do even that. For C A Rookes' selection we should have given proprietor John Freeland a bigger piece of paper. He is proud of a lot of his wines and not without reason. He is enthusiastic too: how many other merchants bother to tell you the the percentage of each grape variety in a whole range of champagnes?

This is an independent merchant, currently operating on a retail and wholesale basis from an industrial site, but plans are afoot for retail premises in town and even a wine bar so that customers can taste a wide range of wines more easily. At first glance, the range looks balanced – good clarets with a small but sound collection from Fronsac, the Premières Côtes and St-Emilion – rather than a breathless rush up the classification ladder. Burgundies, Loire and Rhône wines all provide sound drinking, with many wines imported direct from growers. The balance ends there.

Italy is dismissed in three wines, but two of these are classy estate-bottled Chianti; Spain gets equally short shrift with only two wines, but both are good Rioja from Bodegas Bilbainas. Only in Australia do the lists lengthen a little. There is the good-value Seppelt Moysten range and Jamieson's Run, with Lindeman's Pyrus hitting the high notes. South Africa is obviously in favour with Simonsig Estate, De Wetshof and Rooiberg. South Africa also features in the fortifieds, with a bargain-priced 1963 vintage dessert wine which must be worth a try.

With a fine collection of cognacs and malts, the most memorable of which seems to be the Inebriated Newt Scotch De Luxe, C A Rookes seems well equipped to be called 'The Merchant of Stratford'.

Prices were current in summer 1992 to the best of our knowledge but can only be a rough indication of prices throughout 1993.

Best buys

Dão Terras Altas 1987, Fonseca, Portugal, £
Simonsig Adelberg 1990, South Africa, £
Ch. Lamothe de Haut Premier Cuvée 1988, Premières Côtes de Bordeaux, ££
Pouilly Fumé Cuvée d'Eve, Vieilles Vignes 1989, ££

Russell & McIver

Office
The Rectory, St Mary-at-Hill, London EC3R 8EE *Tel* 071-283 3575
Cellars
Arch 73, St Thomas Street, London SE1 *Tel* 071-402 2240

Open Mon–Fri 9–5.30 **Closed** Sat, Sun, public holidays **Credit cards** None accepted; personal and business accounts **Discounts** Not available **Delivery** Free on UK mainland (min 1 case in London, 4 cases elsewhere); otherwise £5.99 per consignment; mail order available **Glass hire** Free with order **Tastings and talks** 5 major annual tastings nationwide; 10 smaller tastings held at the Rectory; to groups on request **Cellarage** £4.70 per case per year

'No reflection on our rivals, of course,' says Director Christopher Davey, 'but we think we offer a good sense of humour and a lack of pomposity here.' In the serious Square Mile that makes up the City of London, a lack of pomposity probably comes as a great relief to all. Perhaps this is why Russell & McIver has survived in such a competitive part of London for over a century.

There is no shop; the business operates out of a rectory in St Mary-at-Hill, but the logo of the company commemorates the now demolished Coal Exchange – an institution which had a prominent role in the foundation of the company. The range is traditional as befits a company supplying City institutions but there is a willingness to experiment, too. The list is just the right size to slip into a briefcase and would make good reading on the train home to the suburbs. It is informative but informal, with photographs of growers and a few labels to help steer you through the range.

In the clarets section, cru bourgeois, Fronsac and Côtes de Bourg are explored before starting to climb the classification ladder. Both here and in the selection of growers' burgundies, there seems to be more emphasis on satisfactory, quality drinking than collecting a top label. The Rhône, Alsace and Loire are all sound but the French country wines deserve a special mention for value. Germany goes for quality producers such as Paul Anheuser and Max Ferd. Richter. Italy and Spain play fairly safe with familiar names, apart from an oak-matured

Almansa wine from Bodegas Piqueras which probably livens up a City lunch tremendously. The New World is welcomed in this list with a few wines from Fetzer and Clos du Bois in California, and Hardys and Yalumba representing Australia. South Africans come from Boschendal, and New Zealand makes a token appearance with Delegat's.

Port, as you might expect, is here in depth and there is a fine range of own-label cognacs, ports and sherries. Madeira must go down well in the Square Mile with Henriques & Henriques 10-Year-Old in force. Purchases can be collected from the offices or the cellars with a little notice, but delivery is free within London for a mixed case.

Best buys

Domaine Comte de Margon 1990, Vin de Pays des Côtes de Thongue, £
Ch. Fondarzac 1991, Entre-Deux-Mers, £
Russell & McIver Red Burgundy 1988, ££
Ch. de la Rivière 1981, Fronsac, ££

Le Sac à Vin

See La Réserve

Safeway

BEST SUPERMARKET AWARD

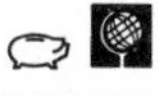

Head office
Safeway House, 6 Millington Road, Hayes, Middlesex UB3 4AY — *Tel* 081-848 8744
322 branches nationwide

Open Mon–Sat 8–8; (Sun 10–4 in half the number of stores) **Closed** Public holidays **Credit cards** All accepted **Discounts** Multibuy facility **Delivery** Not available **Glass hire** Free in some stores **Tastings and talks** Occasional in-store tastings **Cellarage** Not available

While the other big supermarkets have been busy fighting for the biggest market share, Safeway has been quietly catching up on the inside rail. This year Safeway's chief buyer, Liz Robertson, and her team have added around 100 new wines to the range and done a major re-appraisal of the remainder. Safeway does not cover everything in its own name – there are wines in most areas that come under an own-label design, but these are discreet in their markings and most wines shine out bearing their own designs. It gives the shelves a look of interest rather than uniformity.

But it does not matter how the labels look if the quality of the wine is not right, and Safeway scores here again. The wines have been improving steadily to the point where customers new to the range could find them startlingly good. Wine such as a Viognier from the Ardèche. This grape is more normally found in the expensive whites of Condrieu and Ch. Grillet of the northern Rhône but here it is available at a bargain price, singing out its ripe peachy flavours. Basic reds from the South of France show individual style, too. The Domaine Grange du Pin made from the Syrah grape in the Languedoc and Domaine Amérique from the Costières de Nîmes are packed with fruit and flavour. Further up the quality scale there is style again with a good clutch of second wines from grand Bordeaux châteaux and from Madiran there are rich concentrated flavours from Ch. Laroche Viella.

Safeway is not just good at France. It has been working on the German range and manages to pack zippy, zesty style into a basic Rheinpfalz Kabinett and provide more serious flavours in an oak-aged Pinot Blanc from the Rheinhessen. Italy, perhaps, still needs more work to find the same kind of individual flavours that are the hallmark of the French selection, but Spain and Portugal have their high points and Ch. Musar from Lebanon, a bargain Cabernet Sauvignon from Romania and the Tsingtao Riesling from China make up for any disappointment. The Australian range covers some of the familiar names, such as Rosemount and Orlando, but there are some less usual ones such as Moondah Brook Chenin Blanc, Taltarni and the up-market Magill Estate from Penfolds. Wairau River Sauvignon Blanc from New Zealand is also very good.

Safeway has pioneered the movement of organic wines out of health food shops and into the supermarket. It sponsors the Organic Wine Fair and it is not surprising that it has some of the best examples – such as a crisp, dry Ch. Canet from Entre-Deux-Mers and the chunky Domaine Richeaume from Côtes de Provence. Millton vineyard from New Zealand also features in the Safeway range, towards the top of the price band, but at the bottom is a very acceptable glugger under the simple label of Safeway Organic Vin de Table.

Safeway always was environmentally aware. Even in the Seventies its recycled paper bags were an oddity long before anyone else worried about trees. It is also one of the supermarket chains to encourage its staff to attend the courses run by the Wine and Spirit Education Trust although, like the other big supermarkets, it is still unlikely that the person filling up the shelves will be able to give much advice.

Safeway has come a long way in a short time; we hope it keeps on going in the same direction.

Best buys

Gyöngyös Estate Sauvignon Blanc 1991, Hungary, Hugh Ryman, £
Special Reserve Cabernet Sauvignon 1985, Dealul Mare, Romania, £
Domaine Richeaume Cabernet Sauvignon 1989, Côtes de Provence, ££
Safeway Albert Etienne Brut nv Champagne, ££

J Sainsbury  

Head office
Stamford House, Stamford Street, London SE1 9LL — *Tel* 071-921 6000
320 licensed branches; 8 licensed SavaCentres

Open (Generally) Mon–Sat 8.30–6 (Thur/Fri until 9); Sun 12–3; public holidays 8.30–6 (limited opening Good Friday) **Closed** Chr Day, Boxing Day, Easter Day **Credit cards** Access, Visa **Discounts, delivery, glass hire** Not available **Tastings and talks** Tastings and talks on request; in-store tastings resume late 1992 **Cellarage** Not available

Ever since shoppers have been able to pick up a bottle of good-quality, reliable wine with their weekly pile of groceries, sales have rocketed. It is supermarkets like Sainsbury's which have pioneered this attitude and brought wine on to the same shopping list as the meat and two veg it eventually partners. Sainsbury's is still forging ahead in wine and now has a massive selection. Over 450 wines are listed, ranging in price from 95p for a can of vin de pays to rather classy clarets at £18 a bottle – vintage champagnes take the upper price limit even higher.

The top range of wines is called Vintage Selection, displayed with style in the centre of the department. Grand names such as Pavillon Rouge and Petit Cheval consent to have the Sainsbury's seal of approval embellishing their established labels. You will know how good your local Sainsbury's store is judged to be by the number of Vintage Selection wines you are given. Top London stores rate the full 121 wines, lesser stores stop short at the 50 to 70 mark. Gems amongst this range are Quinta da Bacalhoa from Portugal and San Lorenzo Rosso Cònero from Italy. The classiest clarets such as Forts de Latour 1983 and Ch. Palmer 1987 are on limited distribution and may not make it to your neck of the woods, but even so there is enough quality and style in most stores' Vintage Selections to while away a few weekends.

Every retailer of wine needs the top names and qualities to establish a good public image, but it is at the other end of the price spectrum that most of the buying is done. Sainsbury's admits that 65 per cent of its sales are of bottles priced £3 or under; move that price band to £4 and you capture the vast majority of Sainbury's sales. The main challenge in this area is to provide distinctive, interesting drinking at a price which many wine retailers cannot match. Sainsbury's rises to this challenge easily with its own-label range. Earlier this year these labels were looking tired but now they have been given a facelift with a brighter, more individual look. Wines such as vin de pays du Gers, Chianti Classico, Alsace Pinot Blanc and Beaujolais are just some of the highlights. There are no real weaknesses in any of Sainsbury's ranges but favourites outside the Vintage Selection include Hunter Valley Chardonnay from the Denman Estate and Domaine Chancel, vin de pays de Vaucluse. A recent development is the Winemaker's Choice range made in Italy by Australian winemakers who manage to catch two vintages in one year by changing hemispheres.

Sainsbury's never stands still. There is a constant programme to find new wines to slot onto the shelves. Once a wine makes it to a Sainsbury label, the vigilance doesn't stop there. Every batch is checked for quality and regularly tasted against the opposition.

Supermarkets have their irritations and Sainsbury's is not immune. Not all the stores carry the whole range but they will order full cases for you if you spot a particular wine at a bigger store. Another problem is help and advice. Despite always having someone watching your every move as you read the shelf tickets that person may not know the difference between a sercial madeira and a Muscadet. Apart from that, Sainsbury's is a pretty good bet for quality, variety and value.

Best buys

Sainsbury's Vin de Pays du Gers, £
Sainsbury's Chianti Classico 1988, Ricasoli, £
Ch. La Vieille Cure 1988, Fronsac, ££
Sainsbury's Rosé Champagne, nv, ££

Wine comes in at the mouth
And love comes in at the eye;
That's all we shall know for truth
Before we grow old and die.

W B Yeats, *A Drinking Song*

Sandiway Wine Company

Chester Road, Sandiway, nr Northwich, Cheshire CW8 2NH — *Tel* (0606) 882101

Open Mon–Fri 9–1, 2–5.30, 6.30–10; Sat 9–10 **Closed** Wed pm, public holidays
Credit cards Access, Visa; business accounts **Discounts** 5% on 1 case
Delivery Free within 10-mile radius **Glass hire** Free; breakages charged for
Tastings and talks Approximately 1 in-store tasting a month; tutored tastings
Cellarage Not available

This shop is not just the local wine shop but it is the grocery store and post office too. It is run by Graham Wharmsby whose interest in wine started about 10 years ago – to add to the rock-climbing, classic cars and motor-racing which also claim his attention.

Now with around 250 wines, he offers a sound, interesting range, not by way of an annual list but by regular newsletters and offers. Italy and Australia are the areas of strength but there are treats from all around, such as affordable clarets, Hermitage from Chave and fine Almacenista sherries from Lustau.

From Australia the range takes the quality route via Pirramimma, Moss Wood and Shaw and Smith. It also includes a little fun with Seppelt's sparkling Shiraz, a wine almost guaranteed to start a conversation. Italy conjures up Zeni's Teroldego Rotaliano and Barbera d'Alba from Conterno. Even Soave, that standby for any Italian meal, is from quality producer Pieropan.

With in-store tastings and free delivery for 10 miles around, this post office sets the standard for others to follow.

Best buys

Salice Salentino 1986, Taurino, Apulia, Italy, £
Merlot de l'Aude 1990, Boutinot, £
Shaw and Smith Chardonnay 1990, Australia, ££
Riesling Cuvée Frédéric Emile 1985, Trimbach, Alsace, ££

Ashley Scott

P O Box 28, The Highway, Hawarden, Clwyd CH5 3RY — *Tel* (0244) 520655

Case sales only **Open** 24-hour answering service (orders delivered although collection may be arranged from warehouse) **Credit cards** None accepted; personal and business accounts **Discounts** Available **Delivery** Free in North Wales, Cheshire, Merseyside (min 1 case) **Glass hire** Free with order **Tastings and talks** Annual tasting in November by invitation (available on request); talks and tastings provided for local organisations **Cellarage** Not available

No shop, nor even an address for this Welsh merchant who deals solely by mail order. But with free delivery over a wide area it is perhaps worthwhile braving the impersonal treatment to check out the range.

France plays safe most of the time with wines from reliable but not thrilling *négociants*. Beaujolais comes from Thorin, a chunk of Burgundy comes from Chanson with a little help from Thorin, and that name also pops up among the Rhônes. Alsace is single sourced from the splendid co-operative at Turckheim and the name Masson-Blondelet shines out from the Loire collection. Elsewhere, there are pockets of interest: Recioto Amarone from Quintarelli in Italy and the powerful Sassella made from the Nebbiolo grape, Buena Vista in California and Bodegas St Emiliana from Chile. German wines from Guntrum and madeira from Henriques add to this reliable and reasonably priced range.

Best buys

Pinot Blanc 1990, Turckheim, Alsace, £
Ch. Lapeyrère 1989, Bordeaux, £
Buena Vista Cabernet Sauvignon 1987, California, ££
Malmsey 10-Year-Old Henriques Madeira, ££

Sebastopol Wines

Sebastopol Barn, London Road, Blewbury, Oxfordshire OX11 9HB — *Tel* (0235) 850471

Case sales only **Open** Tue–Sat 10.30–5.30 **Closed** Sun, Mon **Credit cards** Access, Visa; business accounts **Discounts** By negotiation on 10+ cases **Delivery** Free within 10-mile radius (min 1 case); mail order available **Glass hire** Free **Tastings and talks** At least once a month on Saturdays; bottles open on premises **Cellarage** Not available

There is a limited but stylish range from this partnership in Blewbury. France is the main focus with a select parcel from

Bordeaux including Bernadette Villars' wines from Chasse-Spleen and Haut-Bages-Libéral. The splendid (in both name and flavour) Ch. Tertre-Rôteboeuf from St-Emilion also makes an appearance. Burgundies speedily head for the high notes with only one wine below £10, but a reasonable collection of regional wines provides value drinking whilst you are saving up. Jean Baumard's Quarts de Chaumes can be seen nestling in the Loire section and the Rhônes are heavily biased towards the excellent Ch. de Beaucastel and Jaboulet. Still no Italian wines in this list – surely there is something in the whole of Enotria that appeals to the Affleck partners? Spain is explored with the help of Torres, Marqués de Murrieta and three vintages of Pesquera.

The Australian range does not yet seem to have benefited from Caroline Affleck's tour of the vineyards. The current range is full of excellent Penfolds and Margaret River wineries, Moss Wood and Cape Mentelle, but so far there are no new additions from the Adelaide Hills or Victoria. California includes two fairly chunky Pinot Noirs from Calera and the very drinkable Eschol from Trefethen.

Best buys

Colombard 1990, Vin de Pays des Côtes de Gascogne, £
Côtes de Buzet 'Tradition' 1988, £
Ch. de Beaucastel, Châteauneuf-du-Pape 1989, ££
Gewurztraminer Clos Windsbuhl 1989, Zind Humbrecht, Alsace, ££

Seckford Wines

2 Betts Avenue, Martlesham Heath, Ipswich, Suffolk IP5 7RH — *Tel* (0473) 626681

Case sales only **Open** Mon–Sat 10–6 **Closed** Sun, public holidays (exc Good Friday 10–6) **Credit cards** Access, Visa; business accounts **Discounts** Not available **Delivery** Free within Suffolk; elsewhere £5; mail order available **Glass hire** Free with order **Tastings and talks** Available **Cellarage** Not available

Between 20 and 40 wines open and ready for tasting sounds like a good excuse to visit this wine warehouse between Ipswich and Woodbridge. It is case sales only but mixing is encouraged and the warehouse itself is not the vast cavernous type, but small and well laid out, with the wines neatly displayed.

The range takes a waltz through the classic areas of France. Burgundies are not extensive but the names are good. Clarets are stacked up in the middle of the floor and provide a selection from Eighties' vintages. Alsace wines are all from Wolfberger and Rhônes include delicious Ch. de Beaucastel from the Perrin family and Côte Rôtie from Guigal.

Spain is notable by its total absence apart from a range of Barbadillo sherries; Italy fares somewhat better with a handful from Piemonte and Tuscany and a smattering from elsewhere. However, Australia is the main feature with quality producers such as Pipers Brook from Tasmania and Cape Mentelle, Moss Wood and Shaw and Smith. New Zealand puts up a good show with Montana, Selaks, Villa Maria and Matua Valley.

Ready assembled tasting cases take the worry out of choosing and fine clarets are offered in unbroken cases at a discount.

Best buys

Tisdall Semillon/Riesling 1990, Australia, £
La Vieille Ferme 1990, Côtes du Ventoux, £
Coudoulet de Beaucastel 1989, Côtes-du-Rhône, ££
Ch. de Sours Rosé 1991, Bordeaux, ££

Selfridges

400 Oxford Street, London W1A 1AB *Tel* 071-629 1234

Open Mon–Fri 9.30–7 (till 8 on Thur); Sat 9–6.30 **Closed** Sun, some public holidays **Credit cards** All accepted; personal and business accounts **Discounts** 12 bottles for the price of 11 **Delivery** From £3.95 in central London; mail order available **Glass hire** Not available **Tastings and talks** Free tastings most Thurs, Fri and Sat **Cellarage** Not available

We asked Selfridges' wine buyer, John McLaren, which of his wines he was particularly proud to stock, but he didn't tell us. Perhaps he is equally proud of them all – but surely everyone has a soft spot for a special discovery or a favourite wine? There is quite a lot to be proud of here. The range is certainly a match for many specialist wine shops and is strong in the classic areas. Bordeaux rolls back to a 1900 Lafite but there is also a fine stock of classed wines from vintages of the Eighties. Burgundies are sound and there is a rich seam of Puligny-Montrachet for the well-heeled of W1. More interesting is the Italian range with difficult names but easier prices. Spain is less adventurous but still worth wading through. Australia and New Zealand spread their wings with a great variety of producers, grapes and regions. Some of the producers are refreshingly different, such as Coonawarra winery in Victoria. California cannot compete with Australia at the £5 level but it has a good try at the £10 to £12 mark with Beringer, Mondavi and Clos du Bois.

Sherry acquires special status at Selfridges – Don Zoilo, Barbadillo, Lustau Almacenistas and the splendid Garvey wines are just part of the range. An in-store sherry tasting has managed to convert more customers to the delights of these excellent wines.

Selfridges manages to woo tourists and Londoners alike with its range of malt whiskies, cognacs and armagnacs. It is even good at beer and liqueurs – with such variety, no wonder John McLaren has difficulty finding a favourite.

Best buys

Domaine le Puts 1991, Vin de Pays des Côtes de Gascogne, £
Classic Pinot Noir 1986, Dealul Mare, Romania, £
Mormoreto Frescobaldi 1985, Tuscany, ££
Manzanilla La Gitana, Hidalgo, ££

Edward Sheldon

New Street, Shipston-on-Stour, Warwickshire CV36 4EN — *Tel* (0608) 661409/661639/662210

Open Mon–Fri 8.30–1, 2–5.30; Sat 9–12 **Closed** Sun, public holidays **Credit cards** Access, Visa; personal and business accounts **Discounts** Available depending upon size of order **Delivery** Free within north Birmingham, Northampton, Oxford and Bath areas (min 1 case); elsewhere at cost; mail order available **Glass hire** Available **Tastings and talks** Various free in-store tastings; tutored tastings **Cellarage** £4 per case per year

Medicated wine was the start of this business way back in 1842, when pharmacist Richard Badger decided that wine was good for his customers. 150 years later, medical opinion is unchanged but the range here is enough to challenge anyone's constitution. Tradition counts for a lot here at Shipston-on-Stour, at least from the look of the list which concentrates on the classics. There is an abundance of clarets, nearly 30 from the 1985 vintage alone, and bottles going back to 1966. Burgundies make the clear distinction between domaine and *négociant* wines, with Dujac, Armand Rousseau and Jayer-Gilles weighing in for the domaines and Chanson and Bouchard among the *négociants*. In comparison, the Rhône and Loire appear almost neglected, as does the French country section although there are plans to increase the selection there.

Spain has plenty to interest customers, with a strong range from La Rioja Alta, Ochoa and Torres. Two vintages of Vega Sicilia provide claret-style drinking from Spain. The Italian range is not extensive but Germany, being a more traditional area, extends over two pages with a fair sprinkling of good names and even a few trocken wines. The New World range is steadily expanding: a reasonable collection from Australia and a clutch of good wines from New Zealand. California is almost a Mondavi monopoly with a little help from Parsons Creek and

Quady. Ports on the list are extensive and there are even more in the cellars which have not made it to the list.

Pricing seems a little complicated, with the list stating that mixed cases will be surcharged, but we are told this is no longer done. Check it out and let us know.

Best buys

Domaine Pioch Ramond, Sauvignon 1991, Vin de Pays des Côtes de Thau, £
Côtes du Ventoux 1990, J Pellerin, £
St-Véran, Domaine de Vignemont 1989, Paul Thévenin, ££
Taltarni Shiraz 1988, Victoria, Australia, ££

Sherborne Vintners

The Old Vicarage, Leigh, Sherborne, Dorset DT9 6HL *Tel* (0935) 872222

Case sales only **Open** Mon–Sat 10–6; Sun and public holidays 10–6 by apppointment; 24-hour answerphone **Credit cards** None accepted; personal and business accounts **Discounts** Variable over 4 cases **Delivery** Free within 20-mile radius of Sherborne (min 2 cases) and UK mainland at cost; mail order available **Glass hire** Free with 2-case order; breakages charged for **Tastings and talks** Four tastings per year; to groups on request **Cellarage** Not available

If medal-winning wines impress you, and let's be honest it is always special to taste wines that have impressed the International Wine Challenge judges, this is the list for you. A wide selection of wines is available from this two-man band in Dorset and all have been awarded medals or commendations in the marathon competitive tastings. From Australia, all the right names are here: Penfolds, Rothbury, Wynns, Hardys, Brown Brothers, and lots more. The California section includes Clos du Bois Chardonnay and Far Niente Cabernet Sauvignon. This list is fairly fat and manages to capture a representative sample of Gold, Silver and Bronze medal winners as well as commended wines in all sections. The disadvantage is that the wines are only available by the unmixed case.

Another list from the same company revolves around Spanish wines. This is a wonderful in-depth study of the region with some big names such as Raimat and Torres but most wines are from smaller companies such as Lar de Barros Reserva from Extremadura and Vega de Toro made by Luis Mateos. Again, these wines are available only by the unmixed case.

Yet another list (can customers cope with all this?) gives some wines from both previous lists which are available by the mixed case. This is quite a complicated arrangement and it would be sensible to see mixed cases extended to all the range. Perhaps the clinical psychologist who is consultant here could find out how customers feel about the situation.

Best buys

Gamay de l'Ardèche 1989, Georges Duboeuf, £
Barbera d'Asti 1988, Viticoltori dell' Acquese, £
Lar de Barros Reserva 1988, Extremadura, Spain, ££
Bonaval Cava Brut, ££

André Simon

See Laytons

Smedley Vintners

Rectory Cottage, Lilley, Luton, Bedfordshire LU2 8LU *Tel* (046 276) 214

Case sales only **Open** Mon–Sat 9–6; Sun and public holidays 10–5 **Credit cards** None accepted; personal and business accounts **Discounts** £1.20 on 1 case **Delivery** Free within 50-mile radius of Lilley (min 1 case); otherwise £5 on first case and 50p on all subsequent cases; mail order available **Glass hire** Free with order; breakages at market price **Tastings and talks** Two main tastings annually; also smaller tutored tastings **Cellarage** Available

Derek Smedley has been a Master of Wine for 24 years and has worked with some of the big companies in the wine trade. He now runs this business from home, offering fast, efficient and friendly service and a good range of wines.

The list tries hard to look comprehensive but it really focuses on quality partnered with value. So Italy gets a good airing with a full set from Antinori, including the delightful Peppoli Chianti and featuring the serious Barolo producer, Alfredo Prunotto. Spain takes in the wines of Marqués de Riscal for both Rioja and Rueda as well as the good-value Altos de Pio from Jumilla. Chile is another well-researched area with the Villa Montes wines and Santa Helena providing bags of flavour at bargain prices. France is not neglected and should provide plenty of choice, particularly among a splendid collection of country wines.

This is a personal list, well chosen and well priced. Lilley does not sound like a big place but Smedley Vintners really puts it on the map.

Best buys

Domaine le Puts Blanc 1991, Hugh Ryman, Vin de Pays des Côtes de Gascogne, £
Villa Montes Cabernet Sauvignon 1989, Chile, £
Daniel le Brun Sparkling Brut nv, New Zealand, ££
Cervaro Della Sala 1989, Vino da Tavola dell' Umbria, Antinori, ££

La Solitude

The Cellar, 4 The Street, Wittersham, Kent TN30 7ED *Tel* (0797) 270696

Open Mon–Sat 9.30–6 (till 6.30 on Fri, Sat) **Closed** Sun, public holidays **Credit cards** Access, Visa; personal and business accounts **Discounts** 8% on unmixed cases; 5% on mixed cases **Delivery** Free within 10-mile radius of Wittersham (min 1 case); mail order available **Glass hire** Free with order **Tastings and talks** Four major tastings per year **Cellarage** Not available

If you can tear yourself away from the list of delicious food that this company sells (gourmet duck pâté, foie gras and cassoulet), then you might notice that it sells a lot of wine as well. The business has recently been taken over by former car company executive, Malcolm Smith, and Alexandra Jarvis, who together have assembled a short but stylish list.

France is the main area of interest, with an extensive range of petits châteaux from Bordeaux claiming much of the action. The burgundy section also remains affordable with careful buying from the Mâconnais and a lot of help from Cellier des Samsons in Beaujolais. French regional wines supply even more good-value drinking with the Rhône, Alsace and Loire adding to the variety. Nine red Riojas and two whites are the mainstay of the Spanish list, Portugal seems to be blessed with four Moscatels and the German range unfortunately loses its producers' names on the list. Australia and California are new areas and are still being developed, but the sherries show tremendous dedication to the splendid Garvey name.

The newsletter is a cross between a special offer list and a village newspaper, and with regular tastings and abundant enthusiasm this company is unlikely to be as lonely as its name suggests.

Best buys

Ch. du Barrail 1989, Bordeaux, £
Mâcon Supérieur 1990, Cave Charnay Les Mâcon, £
Ch. Les Hauts de Palette 1988, Premières Côtes de Bordeaux, ££
Maxim's Prestige Brut nv, Champagne, ££

Somerfield

See Gateway

Sommelier Wine Company

The Grapevine, 23 St George's Esplanade, St Peter Port, Guernsey *Tel* (0481) 721677

Open Tue–Fri 10–5.30 (Fri till 6); Sat 9–5.30; 24-hour answerphone and delivery **Closed** Mon, Sun and public holidays **Credit cards** Access, Visa; personal and business accounts **Discounts** 5% on unmixed cases **Delivery** Free within Guernsey (min 6 bottles) **Glass hire** Free **Tastings and talks** Two general tastings per year; regular tutored tastings to groups on request **Cellarage** Not available

The Sommelier Wine Company serves the wine drinkers of Guernsey with skill. It is run by six wine enthusiasts who each manage to hold down a day-time job as well as open their new shop in St Peter Port five days a week. One of the partners, Richard Allisette, is a full-time journalist and, as you might expect, he has plenty to say about the wines he sells; however, his tasting notes are accurate, informative and to the point.

The range is wide, with favourite producers and suppliers representing far-flung regions. Not surprisingly for an island so far off our own coastline, French wines comprise about half the range. There is a good choice of French country wines from everyday Côtes de St-Mont up to Mas de Daumas Gassac. Bordeaux and Burgundy are handled competently, a Petit Chablis from William Fèvre providing good value in the white burgundy section. Champagnes are from quality producer Georges Goulet.

There is particular enthusiasm for Italy with a clutch of Super Tuscans, including Cepparello from Isole e Olena, and new additions to the range have further increased the interest in this area. The Australians are mainly from Penfolds and Tollana but Shaw and Smith make an appearance, as do Rothbury and Taltarni. A selection from California, including Simi, Sandford and Clos du Val, completes the picture.

Being a wine merchant anywhere brings a certain quality of life, but a wine merchant on Guernsey has the sunshine as well! Delivery on this little island is free for six bottles or more.

Best buys

Ch. St-Jacques, Bordeaux Supérieur 1988 (second wine of Ch-Siran), £
Côtes-du-Rhône-Villages, Domaine de Piaugier 1988, £
Pouilly Fumé, Villa Paulus, Masson-Blondelet 1990, ££
Ch. de Ménota, Sauternes 1988, ££

Spar

Head office
32/40 Headstone Drive, Harrow, Middlesex HA3 5QT *Tel* 081-863 5511
2000 licensed branches

Open Hours vary from store to store **Credit cards** None accepted
Discounts Available **Delivery** Varies from store to store **Glass hire** Available
Tastings and talks In-store tastings and tutored tastings **Cellarage** Not available

The Spar chain of corner shops and small food stores is made up of 2000 independent retailers. The word independent is important since there is nothing to stop each proprietor going to his of her local cash and carry and stocking up with the bargain of the week. But this has been happening less and less since Philippa Carr, Master of Wine, has been in charge of buying for the group. She started by improving the quality of the basic own-label lines (a lot of Liebfraumilch and Lambrusco is sold through these outlets), and then set about introducing better-quality wines under shippers' labels. So from Bordeaux there is a good, keenly priced, basic fruity claret, and the range climbs via Cordier's reliable generic St-Emilion and Médoc to rather classy Baron Villeneuve de Cantemerle from the Haut-Médoc. The rest of the French section is also growing in confidence and style: there is Chablis from La Chablisienne, Alsace wines from the co-operative at Turckheim and Loires from Guy Saget. Regional French wines have expanded by introducing St-Chinian, Corbières and a clutch of vins de pays.

Further afield the picture looks promising. Basic Spanish wines are topped off with a 1981 Viña Albali from Valdepeñas, a new range of Czechoslovakian wines livens up the Eastern Europe section and the New World is home to a few favourite names. Australia provides Lindemans and the Saints Hilary and Hugo from Orlando. There is Errazuriz Merlot representing Chile and Cooks Hawke's Bay wines come from New Zealand.

The best Spar stores are members of the group Wine Club, which allows them to stock a better range and there will be more interest shown behind the counter. Meanwhile, Spar is coming out of the cold and into the cellar. Watch this space.

Best buys

Barbera d'Asti 1991, Viticoltori dell' Acquese, £
Irsay Oliver 1990, Czechoslovakia, £
Orlando St Hilary Chardonnay 1990, Australia, ££
Spar Champagne Marquis de Prevel nv, ££

Frank E Stainton

3 Berry's Yard, Finkle Street, Kendal, Cumbria LA9 4AB *Tel* (0539) 731886

Open Mon–Sat 8.30–6 **Closed** Sun, public holidays **Credit cards** Access, Visa; personal and business accounts **Discounts** 5% on 1 mixed case (for payment by cash/cheque only) **Delivery** Free within 30-mile radius (min 1 mixed case); elsewhere at cost; mail order available **Glass hire** Free with orders over £150; otherwise £1 per dozen **Tastings and talks** Tasting suite available (from £10 per person), includes wines and tutoring **Cellarage** Free for regular customers

This business has recently acquired large underground cellars that must be the envy of merchants everywhere. Frank Stainton puts them to good use with a fine range of wines which concentrate on the classics. Bordeaux wastes very little time on generics and petits châteaux before heading for the big names, although there are a few second wines to help keep costs down. Burgundies are extensive and concentrate on the good *négociants* of Drouhin, Bouchard Père and Louis Latour rather than growers. The Loire and Rhône provide substantial choices, with Jaboulet featuring at all levels from Côtes-du-Rhône up to Hermitage. Alsace is taken seriously with a wide selection from Zind-Humbrecht and Schlumberger, and Germany includes two Franconian wines in its range.

Italy and Spain are sound, and there is plenty of interest among the New World wines, particularly in the New Zealand reds with Stonyridge Pinot Noir and Célèbre from Ata Rangi Vineyards. Only the vins de pays and Southern French selections disappoint at Berry's Yard, with very little in the way of good-value wines to tuck into a picnic box.

Best buys

Riesling 1990, Guntrum, Rheinhessen, £
Ochoa Tinto 1990, Navarra, £
Taltarni Sauvignon Blanc 'Frenchman's Vineyard' 1991, Australia, ££
Châteauneuf-du-Pape, La Bernardine 1985, M Chapoutier, ££

Summerlee Wines

64 High Street, Earls Barton, Northamptonshire NN6 0JG — *Tel* (0604) 810488

LONDON Office

Freddy Price, 48 Castlebar Road, London W5 2DD — *Tel* 081-997 7889

Open Mon–Fri 9–2 **Closed** Sat, Sun, public holidays **Credit cards** None accepted; personal and business accounts **Discounts** Not available **Delivery** Free within area of London, Oxford, Northamptonshire and Cambridge (min 2 cases) **Glass hire** Free with order **Tastings and talks** Occasional in-store tastings; tastings at colleges in Oxford and Cambridge by invitation; monthly meetings; annual tours **Cellarage** £3.70 per case per year

Summerlee Wines has the edge on most other retail shops: it has Freddy Price, with all his 30 years' experience in the trade as consultant and buyer. German wines are his speciality and at Summerlee the range is as far away as anyone could wish from Liebfraumilch and Hock. The delicious, racy flavours of Riesling grapes, ripened in the Mosel, Nahe, Saar or Rheingau, give you as good a tour as any coach trip could. The producers are paramount: there is Paul Anheuser from the Nahe, Max Ferd. Richter from the Mosel and Schloss Saarstein from the Saar. Three Franconian wines from Juliusspital show just how good Sylvaner can be.

However, there is more to this merchant than just Germany. Pockets of wine are explored rather than the more usual broadbrush approach. Petits châteaux from Bordeaux inspire confidence as Freddy's tastebuds have been involved in the selection. Domaine burgundies are from Patrick Javillier and Bernard Morey. From Italy there are just three wines and two of these are Soave – from the top producer Anselmi. Spain has a select look to the range which makes Portugal's solitary contribution of Mateus Rosé even more surprising. Australia, New Zealand and Chile provide a few unusual names to try.

Summerlee holds tastings at Oxford and Cambridge colleges and there is a local wine society which receives support, usually in the form of Freddy himself as a tutor.

Best buys

Domaine du Comte Blanc 1990, Vin de Pays des Landes, £
Erdener Treppchen Riesling Kabinett 1989, Max Ferd. Richter, £
Meursault, Les Narvaux 1989, Javillier, ££
Rüdesheimer Berg Schlossberg Riesling Auslese 1989, Balthasar Ress, ££

Sunday Times Wine Club

Mail order wine club

New Aquitaine House, Paddock Road, Reading, Berkshire RG4 0JY
Tel (0734) 481711 (enquiries)
Tel (0734) 472288 (orders)

Open Mon–Fri 9–8; Sat, Sun 10–5; answerphone outside these hours
Credit cards All accepted; business accounts **Discounts** Available **Delivery** Free nationwide for orders over £50; mail order available **Glass hire** Available
Tastings and talks Approx 6–8 tastings a year **Cellarage** Not available

This is the other face of Direct Wines of Windsor, the first being Bordeaux Direct (*q.v.*). Although it is essentially a mail-order company, it generates more of a club feel by organising regular activities not just in London but around the country. Highlight of the year is the Vintage Festival held in the Horticultural Hall in Westminster, where the people who make the wine meet the people who drink it, and a lot of tasting gets done. This club was also one of the first to organise charabanc trips to the vineyards. By all accounts, these are fairly liquid occasions and, in 1992 there were trips to France, Spain and California.

A quarterly magazine, *Wine Times*, brings entertainment and a little education to members. Special offers and wine-drinking suggestions, such as Summer Party Mix, Alsace Selection or Club Clarets, will land on your doormat with amazing regularity. Many of the wines are the same as supplied by Bordeaux Direct, although both operations have some exclusivities. Hugh Johnson is the Club president and therefore appears to endorse the wines, although his photo doesn't seem to be splashed around quite as liberally as it used to.

Membership costs £5 a year, so if you don't want the Club activities you might just as well deal with Bordeaux Direct, but you get a lot of entertainment for your fiver. Delivery for both organisations is free for orders over £50, a welcome alternative to all those other companies who insist on two or three cases no matter how much you spend.

Best buys

Cabernet Sauvignon Domaine de la Durançole 1991, Vin de Pays des Bouches-du-Rhône, £
Sauvignon 1991, Moravenka Cellars, Czechoslovakia, £
Les Abeilles, Cuvée André Roux 1991, Côtes-du-Rhône, ££
L'Espalier 1991, Bordeaux Blanc, ££

Supergrape

81 Replingham Road, Southfields, London SW18 5LU
Tel 081-874 5963

Open Mon–Fri 10–2, 5–9.30; Sat 10–9.30; Sun, public holidays 12–2, 7–9 **Closed** Chr Day, Boxing Day, Easter Sun **Credit cards** Access, Visa; personal and business accounts **Discounts** 5% on 1 case **Delivery** Free in Greater London (min 1 case) **Glass hire** Free with 1-case order **Tastings and talks** Four annual tastings for club members (£20 per person per year) **Cellarage** Not available

This little wine shop south of the river continues to survive while others fall victim to the recession. The stock may have something to do with it: five Premier Cru Chablis, Corton Charlemagne and a clutch of serious clarets, many from the 1985 vintage. There are good Rhônes, with Ch. de Beaucastel and Jaboulet in attendance and, if you are serious about champagne, there is a fine selection here. Other sparklers include two English wines from Tenterden and Carr Taylor. But weekday drinking is not forgotten, with sensible country wines from France, a reasonable number of petits châteaux from Bordeaux and a lively choice from Spain, Chile and Australia.

The Wine Club costs a hefty £20 to join but you get four tastings a year and around 5 per cent discount on all purchases. With seven-day opening and free delivery around Greater London, this business is trying hard.

Best buys

La Vieille Ferme 1989, Côtes-du-Ventoux, £
Rioja Tinto 1988, CVNE, £
Moss Wood Pinot Noir 1989, Western Australia, ££
Bourgogne Chardonnay 1989, J Pascal, ££

Tanners Wines

26 Wyle Cop, Shrewsbury, Shropshire SY1 1XD — *Tel* (0743) 232400; *Tel* (0743) 232007 (sales order office)

Outlets

72 Mardol, Shrewsbury, Shropshire SY1 1PZ — *Tel* (0743) 366389
39 Mytton Oak Road, Shrewsbury, Shropshire SY3 8UG — *Tel* (0743) 366387
36 High Street, Bridgnorth, Shropshire WV6 4DB — *Tel* (0746) 763148
4 St Peter's Square, Hereford, Hereford & Worcester HR1 2PG — *Tel* (0432) 272044
The Old Brewery, Brook Street, Welshpool, Powys SY21 7LF — *Tel* (0938) 552542

Open Mon–Sat 9–5.30 (9–6 at Wyle Cop branch; 9–1 only on Sat at Welshpool branch) **Closed** Sun, public holidays **Credit cards** Access, Visa; personal and business accounts **Discounts** Available **Delivery** Free on UK mainland (min £75 order); £6 for orders under £75; free in Cheshire, Hereford & Worcester, west Staffordshire, Shropshire, mid and parts of north Wales, and parts of Gloucestershire (min 1 case); mail order available **Glass hire** Free if wine purchased from shop **Tastings and talks** Wine always available in all shops; tutored tastings for customers 5–6 times a year; to groups on request **Cellarage** Not available

Tanners has been celebrating 150 years trading at Wyle Cop in Shrewsbury. To be absolutely honest it was Thomas Southam's wine business that started in these lovely old black and white buildings in 1842 but that organisation merged with Tanners a long time ago and anybody's 150th anniversary is worth popping a few corks for. Tanners is still a family business (established in 1872), now with Richard Tanner at the helm. With its long family tradition and even more ancient premises, this company ought to belong to the stuffy, dusty brigade of wine merchants that sometimes inhabit rural areas – but it doesn't. It is traditional in the quality of its wines and certainly in the efficiency of its service but stuffy and dusty just don't apply here.

The list is a chunky paperback, no glossy photos, but a working document full of information about growers and regions. Quality is a keynote at Tanners but that doesn't mean that the range is full of esoteric wines at outrageous prices. It quietly strikes the middle path with a variety of good-quality wines at reasonable prices. For a change the list starts with a round-up of vins de table and the south of France – sensible drinking at sensible prices. The rest of France has been selected with skill and style. There are Rolly Gassmann and Schlumberger from Alsace and a luscious selection of Barsac and Sauternes, particularly from the 1988 vintage; most of them are available in half-bottles. Clarets are selected 'with painstaking care' the list tells us, and tasting notes are available for each one on request. The same degree of care obviously goes into Burgundy, and the Rhône is surprising for having 14 white wines as well as a wide range of reds. Further afield, the Tanners team has built up an admirable range: Shaw and Smith, Taltarni and Yarra Burn from Australia, Hamilton-Russell and Simonsig Estate from South Africa and Mondavi and Simi from California. The only area where Tanners admits to having little success is in organic wines, where none, except Pierre Perrin's Côtes-du-Rhône, comes up to their quality/price criteria.

On the service front Tanners gets the most applause from our readers, with this merchant regarding most of the West Midlands as its local delivery area.

Best buys

Tanners Claret AC Bordeaux, £
Ch. du Grand Moulas 1991, Côtes-du-Rhône, £
Châteauneuf-du-Pape Domaine du Vieux Télégraphe 1988, H. Brunier et Fils, ££
Menetou-Salon, Le Petit Clos 1990, Jean-Max Roger, ££

Tesco

Head office
New Tesco House, P O Box 18, Delamare Road, Cheshunt, Hertfordshire EN8 9SL — *Tel* (0992) 32222
For wine enquiries write to: Head office, Bentley House, Pegs Lane, Hertford, Hertfordshire SG13 8EG — *Tel* as above
388 licensed branches

Open Varies from branch to branch, but usually Mon–Sat 9–8 (Sat till 7); Sun 10–4; public holidays 9–5 **Closed** Chr Day, Boxing Day **Credit cards** All accepted **Discounts** Multisaver offers **Delivery, glass hire** Not available **Tastings and talks** Regular in-store tastings **Cellarage** Not available

No one can have failed to notice just how good Tesco is at wine – there is always something new to look at. 'New Line' stickers sprout regularly, and there are the Multisaver offers where you can buy two bottles (or sometimes six) and save a little. Occasionally, little yellow stickers indicate a £1 or so off discontinued lines to make way for new stock. In the big, newer stores they have moved away from the long straight shelves which end up looking like soldiers in a row, and instead the display units form bays giving a more relaxed, less 'supermarket' look.

There are over 380 licensed Tesco stores. Not all carry the full range and that is one of the complaints we hear most about. If you want a wine that a bigger branch has but yours doesn't, it can be ordered but only by the full case, which could be fairly expensive if you only want to try it. Tesco is good at keeping its customers informed. A series of leaflets around regional themes – vins de pays or grape varieties – teaches a lot. Tesco has even produced a 'drink wisely' leaflet and indicates on the back-label just how many units of alcohol are in each glassful. That kind of self-help for customers is fine, but like all supermarkets, Tesco is really missing an opportunity by not training the staff on a few basics such as how to pronounce some of the wine names and what a few of them taste like. However, it does seem to keep the same permanent staff within the wine departments so this could be easy to arrange. Admittedly, many supermarket customers want to pick up a bottle without anyone breathing down their necks, but it is disheartening to see a genuine customer query being turned away with a wrong answer.

But enough of the problems, what of the wines? Generally, very good. Tesco tries to seek out unusual wines, but only if they are the right quality: wines such as the creamy, aromatic Van Loveren Pinot Gris from South Africa or the lively Goiya Kgeisje Sauvignon Blanc, also South African. There is also the Tsingtao Riesling from China. Tesco is not afraid to try to sell expensive wines, such as the Kenwood Jack London Cabernet Sauvignon from California or classy clarets such as Ch. Latour 1982 and Pavillon Rouge. It also has one of the best supermarket selections of champagnes – but bargain-basement special offers sit alongside the established house names.

Tesco is good at the basics. There is a fine selection of French country wines: Ch. Toutigeac and Ch. Léon both provide quality Bordeaux flavours. Chablis and Premier Cru Chablis come from the excellent La Chablisienne co-operative. From Spain the basic Riojas, red and white, are surprisingly good and the Tesco Chianti Classico has all the right flavours at a good price. Australian wines include some of the reliable names such as Jacob's Creek and Rosemount, but wines such as the Moondah Brook Verdelho add variety and style. Tesco has held faith with Germany, keeping going with Liebfraumilch and Piesporter until that market dies, but also proceeding up the quality ladder to Auslese and beyond from top-notch producers.

With such a wide range, there are bound to be some mistakes but Tesco is trying hard to lead the way and certainly seems to be going in the right direction most of the time.

Best buys

Domaine de Baumelles 1990, Côtes du Lubéron, £
L A Cetto Cabernet Sauvignon 1985, Mexico, £
Saumur Champigny 1986, Cave des Vignerons de Saumur, ££
Ripa Delle Mandorle 1987, Matta, Tuscany, ££

Thresher Wine Shops/Wine Rack/Bottoms Up

Head office
Sefton House, 42 Church Road, Welwyn Garden City, Hertfordshire AL8 6PJ — *Tel* (0707) 328244
1649 branches nationwide, including 114 Wine Rack and 74 Bottoms Up outlets

Open Mon–Sat 10–10; Sun 12–3, 7–10 **Closed** Chr Day **Credit cards** Access, Visa; personal and business accounts **Discounts** Available **Delivery** Free within 20-mile radius of each branch **Glass hire** Free **Tastings and talks** Occasional tastings **Cellarage** Not available

The people at Thresher have had a busy year. During 1992 they acquired and swallowed up the Dominic chain which had grown so very dreary. Now relaunched, they offer a better quality range in brighter surroundings. Also in the deal were the slightly less dreary Bottoms Up shops which have now been refocused but still retain the name on the High Street.

The result is that Thresher is the biggest force in the UK retail wine scene, outstripping supermarkets Sainsbury and Tesco. It has a mega 1649 shops all around the country, divided between 920 Thresher Wine Shops, 114 more specialised Wine Rack shops and 74 Bottoms Up outlets. There are also a large number of Drinks Stores and Food and Drinks Stores. Each type of shop has its role in the great order of things but for this *Guide* we concentrate on the three brand names: Thresher Wine Shop, Wine Rack and Bottoms Up.

Thresher Wine Shops are the biggest part of the group with a splendid all-round range of wine. They are serious about selling wine, but not quite as serious as the Wine Rack chain which attracts real enthusiasts with an additional specialist range. The Bottoms Up group has been relaunched as a 'Wine warehouse on the High Street' with substantial case discounts and promises of 'You can't buy cheaper'. These shops still have a retail licence so single bottle sales are possible.

Over the last few years the wine buying team at Thresher, headed by Kim Tidy, has gone from strength to strength, looking for quality and style at all price points. It has done particularly well in championing specific areas, such as Alsace and Italy. All three types of shop work from the same core range but Wine Rack and Bottoms Up have their own exclusivities. This also means that they can take on board smaller parcels of wine which would be too small to spread around the whole Thresher estate.

The core range from Thresher is good. It includes sound choices in most areas, with Bordeaux featuring second wines of the great châteaux including Clos du Marquis and Fiefs de Lagrange as well as a reasonable choice of generics and some top-notch names. In comparison, Burgundy is rather lacklustre. From Spain there are the brilliant Bujanda Riojas and Italy provides a superb collection of Chiantis including Peppoli from Antinori and Villa di Vetrice. Hugh Ryman's distinctive wines, from France and from Hungary, are features of the range with good flavours at good prices. Australia is reliable – Penfolds, Rosemount and Wynns are the major players; New Zealand sprouts new names daily, particularly among the whites.

Wine Rack takes on the Thresher range and more, the most significant element being the brilliant Zind-Humbrecht wines from Alsace. These have become the hallmark of Wine Rack, with elegant, racy flavours and distinctive style. Italy is allowed extra treats such as up-market vini da tavola and the wonderful Chianti from Felsina Berardinga. New Zealand white wines have moved in with serious intent. Sauvignon Blanc, Chardonnay and various blends give you the chance to taste gooseberries, nettles and tropical fruits endlessly. The Bottoms Up chain takes on most of the Wine Rack range with a few specialities such as a fine collection of growers' champagnes.

In the wine trade the quality of a company is often inversely proportional to its size. Thresher has set out to prove that rule totally wrong.

Best buys

Villa Maria Sauvignon Blanc 1991, Marlborough, New Zealand, £
Pinot Noir 1990, Bratislava-Raca Slovakia, Czechoslovakia, £
Conde de Valdemar Rioja Reserva 1986, Martinez Bujanda, ££
Vino Nobile di Montepulciano 1989, Le Casalte (Wine Rack only), ££

And Noah he often said to his wife when he sat down to dine, 'I don't care where the water goes if it doesn't get into the wine.'

G K Chesterton, *Water and Wine*

Turville Valley Wines

The Firs, Potter Row, Great Missenden, Buckinghamshire HP16 9LT *Tel* (02406) 8818

Case sales only **Open** Mon–Fri 9–5.30 **Closed** Sat, Sun, public holidays **Credit cards** None accepted; personal and business accounts **Discounts** Not available **Delivery** Locally and in London (min 1 case); elsewhere at cost; mail order available **Glass hire** Not available **Tastings and talks** Three/four times a year **Cellarage** Not available

The front cover of the Turville Valley list says it all. With a copy of a 1947 Pétrus label on show, this company tells us loud and clear that this is not the place to come to for everyday vins de pays. The range is almost exclusively top names from Bordeaux, Burgundy, Rhône, and ports. For those whose tastebuds travel a little further afield there is a miscellaneous assortment at the back of the list but still only exclusive names: Vega Sicilia from Spain, Grange from Australia, Mondavi and Dominus from California and two top Alsace houses. The real business is classy names, from the 1920s to the most recent vintages. So if you have need of a magnum of 1928 Mouton-Rothschild or even a 1985 La Tâche, this is the place to come. Be prepared to spend serious money – since Turville has no retail licence the minimum purchase is an assorted case. VAT is not included in the list but, even so, prices seem comparable with others who also trade in the great and the glorious.

Having bought your piece of history we hope that you pull the cork and enjoy it, and do not send it yet again around the saleroom circuit.

Best buys

Côtes-du-Rhône 1989, Guigal, £
Ch. Latour 1966, ££

T & W Wines

51 King Street, Thetford, Norfolk IP24 2AU *Tel* (0842) 765646

Open Mon–Fri 9.30–5.30; Sat 9.30–1 **Closed** Sun, public holidays **Credit cards** All accepted; business accounts **Discounts** Not available **Delivery** Free within 15-mile radius of Thetford (min 1 case) and elsewhere (min 4 cases); otherwise 1–3 cases £8.95; mail order available **Glass hire** Free with 1-case order **Tastings and talks** Monthly in-store tastings (normally free) **Cellarage** £4.98 per case per year

We are pleased to report that the recession has not yet arrived in Thetford. T & W Wines reports that people are trading up in quality and that sales of vin de table are down. Terrific news. Perhaps we should all go and live there.

Trevor Hughes, once a hotelier, is the force behind this business. He found his interest lay more and more in creating a good list for his restaurant and eventually this interest grew until there was no time for anything else. The range here is amazing. Three thousand wines is the claim but we didn't stop to count them. Not all are included in the chunky A4 list but there is enough within its pages to keep most of East Anglia busy for years.

Quality is the sole criterion for inclusion in this document. 'I never buy on price, only on quality,' Trevor assures us, and the list is his evidence. He starts off with a personal selection of reds and whites: single-vineyard Fleurie, Caprili's Brunello di Montalcino, Mazis-Chambertin from Faiveley and a 1985 Alsace Riesling from Trimbach. These are just a few of his favourite things but there are lots more.

There are growers' champagnes and a hefty contribution from Krug for days when funds are good. Clarets and burgundies go on for pages. Guigal features in the Rhône with Jaboulet standing by to lend assistance, particularly with several vintages of white Hermitage as well as a wonderful selection of reds. The Eastern European section launches straight into Tokay through the ages and also includes a few wines from the Massandra collection. Italy takes in Gaja and Bava from Piemonte, and Spain is only mentioned in connection with several vintages of white Marqués de Murrieta. Australia is allowed to contribute to this glorious selection with the wines of Taltarni.

Half-bottles merit an extensive separate section and apparently run to 300 different wines. Free tastings in the shop every month provide yet another reason for moving to Thetford.

Best buys

Cabernet Sauvignon Silver Oak 1986, Alexander Valley, California, ££
Fleurie, La Madone 1990, Domaine Chaintreuil, ££
Puligny-Montrachet 1988, Olivier Leflaive, ££
Hardly any wines fit into the under £5 category

Ubiquitous Chip Wine Shop

8 Ashton Lane, Hillhead, Glasgow G12 8SJ *Tel* 041-334 5007

Open Mon–Fri 12–10; Sat 11–10 **Closed** Sun, Chr Day, New Year's Day **Credit cards** All accepted; personal and business accounts **Discounts** 5% on 1 case **Delivery** Free within 10-mile radius of Glasgow (min 2 cases); mail order available **Glass hire** Free with 1-case order **Tastings and talks** Occasional tastings (small charge per person) **Cellarage** Available

This shop started out as a way for customers of the restaurant next door to buy wines they had enjoyed with a meal. It is now a wine shop in its own right.

The list is a breeze through some of the most interesting names in wine, with the added attraction of reasonable prices. Clarets include a fair selection of classed growths but a few unfashionable vintages and a clutch of crus bourgeois keep many prices within reach. Burgundy sports names such as Tollot-Beaut, Armand Rousseau and Louis Trapet. There is Jaboulet and Emile Florentin in the Rhône and Gaston Huet providing his brilliant Vouvray in the Loire. Alsace is a favoured area with wines from Rolly Gassmann and Dopff & Irion providing most of the interest.

From Italy there are good wines at both ends of the price scale and a few in between. Montepulciano d'Abruzzo from Umani Ronchi weighs in for weekday nights while Angelo Gaja's Barbaresco probably has to wait for high days and holidays. Spain takes in La Rioja Alta, Torres, Ochoa and León.

Romanian wines are the biggest sellers here – six reds and eight whites, none over £4. Australia builds on the firm foundations of Allridge and Orlando with Cape Mentelle and Tim Adams providing the high notes. Bannockburn from Victoria surely feels quite at home in these Scottish surroundings.

Quality German wines are the most difficult to sell here, which is a shame considering the splendid selection from Schloss Vollrads, Bürklin-Wolf and Schloss Rheinhartshausen. Probably easier to find homes for are the 130 or so malt whiskies, including a 53-year-old Linkwood, that also grace the shelves of this Ubiquitous Chip.

Best buys

Petit Syrah 1986, L A Cetto, Mexico, £
Ch. des Antonins 1989, Bordeaux Supérieur, £
Hunter's Sauvignon Blanc 1991, New Zealand, ££
Scholtz Hermanos Málaga Solera 1885, ££

Unwins Wine Merchants

Head office
Birchwood House, Victoria Road, Dartford, Kent DA1 5AJ — *Tel* (0322) 272711
Approximately 300 branches in south-east England

Open Mon–Sat 10–10; Sun, public holidays 12–3, 7–10 **Credit cards** All accepted; personal and business accounts **Discounts** 10% on case lots **Delivery** Free in south-east England (min 1 case); mail order available **Glass hire** Free with orders; returnable deposit; charge for breakages **Tastings and talks** Occasional branch tastings; to groups on request **Cellarage** Not available

This chain of off-licences in the South-East has a rather dull image – stacks of beer, dump-bins of Lambrusco and lots of British sherry – but if you actually take the time to look at the wines you could be in for a surprise. The list is improving, but as with all chains of shops only the biggest ones carry the full range. The rest is there for managers to call on if they can sell it.

Clarets are there in depth, from a respectable Yvon Mau Bordeaux Supérieur 1988 up to 1982 Mouton-Rothschild. Good clarets are bought *en primeur* by Unwins and matured in their corporate cellars until ready to go on the shelves. Burgundies are less exciting: every wine comes from the huge *négociant* Bichot. Spain is strong with the Castillo Fuentemayor from Bodegas AGE adding to the Riojas from Faustino, Murrieta and Riscal. The fruity Marechal Foch from Canada makes an appearance and apparently Unwins still has a stock of the delicious 1982 Ch. Musar. Prices are reasonable and shop managers are encouraged to take Wine and Spirit Education Trust examinations so there should be some advice available to steer you around the wine section.

Best buys

Roussette de Savoie 1989, Pierre Boniface, £
Alsace Pinot Blanc 1990, Ritzenthaler, £
Sancerre Les Roches (Blanc) 1990, Vacheron, ££
Madiran Ch. de Crouseilles 1987, ££

Valvona & Crolla 

19 Elm Row, Edinburgh EH7 4AA *Tel* 031-556 6066

Open Mon–Sat 8.30–6 **Closed** Sun, 1–7 January **Credit cards** Access, Visa; business accounts **Discounts** 5% on 1 case **Delivery** Free within Edinburgh (min £25 order); natiowide at cost; mail order available **Glass hire** Free with any reasonable order **Tastings and talks** Tutored tastings for customers (from £10 per person) **Cellarage** Not available

Wine drinkers of Edinburgh should move away from this city just so they can return and really appreciate how lucky they are to have so many enthusiastic and well-stocked merchants. Valvona & Crolla is one of these, specialising in Italian wines. The shop has recently been extended to around three times its original size, so now there is more room to display the stock of 550 wines and the Italian delicatessen. Before starting on the wines it is worth mentioning the range of estate olive oils, many bearing names like Lungarotti, Guerrieri-Rizzardi and Villa Banfi which are more usually seen on bottles of wine.

The list of wines is a compact working document, not given to descriptions of the regions or the producers, but the range is certainly here. Barolos in vast array, from a 1947 Borgogno to a choice of 11 different wines from 1985. Angelo Gaja contributes 13 wines from Barbaresco and his Barbera d'Alba, Vignarey. Tuscany is equally comprehensive, with a splendid range of Chiantis and Super Tuscans. But work has gone into finding wines from all parts of this country: there is Torre Ercolana from Lazio, Barbarossa from Emilia Romagna and dessert wines from Pantelleria. There is even a cry for help in sourcing a wine from the Valle d'Aosta, to fit in with Philip Contini's price/quality standards.

Tutored tastings are held in the newly built function room next to the shop, but on any day there are at least four or five bottles open for tasting.

Best buys

Montepulciano Rosso 1991, Bianchi, Abruzzo, £
Terre di Ginestra Bianco 1991, Sicily, £
Barbera d'Alba 'La Monella' 1990, Giacomo Bologna, Piemonte, ££
Pomino Rosso 1988, Frescobaldi, Tuscany, ££

Why not club together with friends to enjoy volume discounts and free delivery?

Helen Verdcourt Wines

Spring Cottage, Kimbers Lane, Maidenhead, Berkshire SL6 2QP

Tel (0628) 25577

Case sales only **Open** All hours (24-hour answering machine)
Credit cards None accepted; personal and business accounts **Discounts** 5% for 1 case order **Delivery** Free in southern England (min order 1 case)
Glass hire Free **Tastings and talks** Regular tastings **Cellarage** Free (though limited space)

Helen Verdcourt went to Australia earlier this year which has lead to an explosion of that part of her list. There are now glorious flavours from Penfolds, Mountadam, Cape Mentelle and Moss Wood to name but a few. New Zealand seems to have climbed aboard the expansionist bandwagon and now features Palliser Estate, Selaks and Esk Valley as well as Cloudy Bay and Montana.

This is a serious one-woman business, launched by Helen 13 years ago after successful careers as both a biologist and a mushroom grower. She works hard: first educating her customers through talks and tastings at every opportunity and then by selling a surprisingly large range of quality wines.

The Rhône is a favoured area. There are the splendid good-value Southern French wines of La Vieille Ferme from JP Perrin and the delicious Côtes-du-Rhône Villages, Ch. La Courançonne. The real gems of the Rhône are six vintages of Ch. de Beaucastel, Guigal's Condrieu and Chapoutier's Hermitage Vin de Paille.

Bordeaux concentrates on quality and affordability and burgundies are select but good. Italy gets straight down to business with Chianti from Villa di Vetrice and Isole e Olena, Barolo from Ascheri, and the delicious Ghiaie della Furba from Tenuta di Capezzana. Spain explores the ranges of Torres, CVNE and Raimat, but also includes a distinguished oak-aged Ribera del Duero from J Arroya. Fortified Spanish wines are for true aficionados – just Scholtz Solera Málaga and a rich dry oloroso from Díez Hermanos.

Helen Verdcourt runs three wine clubs that meet monthly in the Berks/Bucks areas and, as yet another example of her tireless energy, local delivery to her means most of the southern counties. We sit back in exhausted admiration!

Best buys

Cuvée Jean Paul Blanc Vin de Table, £
La Vieille Ferme 1989, Côtes du Ventoux, £
Ridge Paso Robles Zinfandel 1989, California, ££
Côte Rôtie, Brune et Blonde 1988, Guigal, ££

Victoria Wine Company

Head office
Brook House, Chertsey Road, Woking, Surrey GU21 5BE *Tel* (0483) 715066
Nearly 1000 branches nationwide; also approx 140 branches of Haddows in Scotland

Open Hours vary from branch to branch; most are open from 10–10
Credit cards Access, Visa; personal and business accounts **Discounts** 10% on 12 bottles or more **Delivery** Local delivery (charges vary from branch to branch); free delivery per £50 consignment (selected branches); mail order available
Glass hire Free on large orders **Tastings and talks** Promotional tastings in selected branches **Cellarage** Not available

The Victoria Wine estate (as Victoria refers to its massive chain) has grown even bigger in the last year with the acquisition of the northern-based group of Winterschladen shops. The group also includes 139 Scottish stores under the Haddows banner. Victoria Wine has taken a long hard look at its 962 shops and has reclassified them all. Out have gone the 'Family One, Two and Three' groupings to be replaced with new names. Nearly two hundred shops with high wine sales have been redesignated 'Wine Shops'; another 439 shops where wine sales are matched by beer are now referred to as 'Off-licences' and there are another 199 'Locals' where the sales and stock are more akin to the beer and fags variety. These names are for the company's use only since all (apart from Haddows) travel under the same Victoria Wine logo. Eventually the décor will tell you what kind of shop you are in.

The upshot of this reappraisal is that the range available in your local Victoria Wine is determined by the potential of your area. Up-market, car-owning areas have a choice of 275 wines in their Wine Shops while the less fortunates are restricted to a mere 100 wines in their 'Local'; the middle band of 'Off-licences' has a wide but not comprehensive range. No matter where you live everyone has access to the 575 wines on the extensive list which, if not in stock, can be ordered by the single bottle.

All these marketing changes would just be window dressing if Victoria Wine still had the same boring old selection of wine, but that has changed too. The whole range has gone through quite a few favourable transformations over the last year or so. Interesting, individual wines have swept on to the shelves, among them a good-value Czechoslovakian selection. There's a soft, peachy Pinot Blanc, a spicy Irsay Oliver, and a full-flavoured Cabernet Sauvignon, all priced around £3.

The New World and Chile are other specialist areas with big wines from Errazuriz on the shelves, including the damsony soft

Merlot. The excellent Shingle Peak Sauvignon Blanc from New Zealand puts in an appearance too. Good claret has been a strength at Victoria Wine for some time, although you may have to order some of the more expensive ones from the list.

Best buys

Czech Pinot Blanc 1990, £
Errazuriz Merlot 1991, Chile, £
Merlin Estate Chardonnay 1990, Marlborough, New Zealand, ££
Lindauer Brut Rosé, ££

La Vigneronne

105 Old Brompton Road, London SW7 3LE *Tel* 071-589 6113

Open Mon–Fri 10–9; Sat 10–8 **Closed** Sun, public holidays **Credit cards** All accepted **Discounts** 5% on 1 case **Delivery** Free locally (min 1 case); mail order available **Glass hire** Free with order **Tastings and talks** Up to 2 tastings per week **Cellarage** £7.80 per case per year

La Vigneronne is run by Master of Wine Liz Berry and her husband Mike. Liz's enthusiasm is Alsace (she has written a book on the subject) and the variety of wines from that area fills a whole page of the list. The usual variations of grape variety and producer are made infinitely more complex by the endless choice of grands cru. The Alsace section falls just short of 100 wines.

The shop is a haven for those tired of slick corporate images. It is more like a library of wine which just happens to sell a bottle or two. Disconcertingly, some of those bottles, usually the better ones, are empty, which might lead you to think that you have just missed the best bring-a-bottle party in London. Instead, it shows that there is stock of that wine but rather than keep such quality on the shelf it is tucked away in the depths of the cellar to mature gently.

Alsace is not the only gem – the shop is stuffed with mouthwatering temptation. Bourgogne Grand Ordinaire sits easily on the shelves near to Echézeaux from Domaine de la Romanée-Conti, and a splendid range of Spanish wines is given depth by ten vintages of Vega Sicilia. But La Vigneronne is not just for treasure-trove wines. There are well-chosen drinking wines from Australia, South Africa, Italy and France.

Regular tastings add to La Vigneronne's attractions. These may be tutored by Liz or other experts and, considering the wines that are tasted, they represent good value. Some are even free if you decide to order those wines on the day. For £10 a year you can subscribe to La Vigneronne's Wine Journal.

Best buys

Jarrah Ridge Cabernet/Shiraz 1989, Australia, £
Alsace Riesling Grand Cru Kastelberg 1983, Marc Kreydenweiss, ££
Vieux Rivesaltes, Mas de la Garrigue 1959, ££

Villeneuve Wines

27 Northgate, Peebles, Borders EH45 8RX *Tel* (0721) 22500

Open Mon–Fri 10–8 (till 9 on Fri); Sat 9–9 **Closed** Sun, public holidays **Credit cards** Access, Visa; personal and business accounts **Discounts** 5% on 1 case **Delivery** Free within 50-mile radius of Perth; otherwise £5 per case **Glass hire** Free **Tastings and talks** Two major annual tastings (£3.50 per person); tutored tastings to groups on request **Cellarage** Free for personal customers; 4p per case per week for wine bought elsewhere

Good value for money is what Villeneuve's customers seek and they shouldn't be disappointed. Director Alistair Rae and his team have selected a wide range of wines with the emphasis on positive flavours.

Australia shows this with the Penfolds Dalwood range, Rosemount and Wolf Blass. Len Evans' Rothbury Estate and the new Margaret River collection from Sandstone add to the variety. Other New World wines follow suit with Cousino Macul and Concha y Toro from Chile and the Trapiche wines from Argentina all providing good flavour for money. From California, Firestone and Mondavi's Woodbridge rarely disappoint.

In Europe, France takes the biggest share. Guy Saget features in the Loire with Langlois-Château contributing its lovely Chinon. Trimbach and the co-operative at Ribeauvillé provide a good range from Alsace. Burgundies are mainly from reliable *négociants* such as Faiveley and Bouchard Père. Interesting offerings come from Clos Guirouilh in Jurançon and a single-vineyard Minervois owned by the Bishopric of Carcassonne.

Italy does a comprehensive tour of Barolo and Tuscany but also includes Silvio Jermann's up-market vino da tavola; Spain goes back to standard favourites such as Torres, La Rioja Alta and Berberana. If it is possible to get bored with this wide selection of reliable wines, there are around 100 malt whiskies to keep the interest going for quite some time.

Best buys

Eden Ridge Dry White 1991, Adam Wynn, South Australia, £
Jurançon Moelleux 1989, Clos Guirouilh, £
Bairrada 1985, Luis Pato, Portugal, ££
Ser Gioveto 1989, Rocca delle Macie, ££

Vinceremos Wines

65 Raglan Road, Ashley Industrial Estate, Wakefield Road, Leeds, West Yorkshire LS2 9DZ *Tel* (0532) 431691

Case sales only **Open** Mon–Fri 9–5; Sat, Sun by appointment **Closed** Public holidays **Credit cards** Access, Visa; business accounts **Discounts** 5% on 5+ cases; 10% on 10+ cases **Delivery** Free nationwide on 5+ cases; mail order available **Glass hire** Free locally with order **Tastings and talks** Regular tastings (£50 per person); to groups on request **Cellarage** Not available

Vinceremos specialises in organic wine and the company is run by Jerry Lockspeiser, co-author of *Thorsons Organic Wine Guide*. Organic wine is not just for cranks. There are many people who are keen to avoid unnecessary chemicals and pesticides. The term organic has now been defined by the EC and producers claiming organic status must belong to a recognised organisation that controls standards of production.

A primary consideration behind organic wine is that it must taste good first and be organic second. Vinceremos manages this with quite a few wines in its range. The Millton Vineyard wines from New Zealand are a prime example: crisp, lively wines, full of flavour – and the fact they are organic comes as a bonus. The same goes for Domaine de Richeaume from the Côtes de Provence.

In a specialised list such as this the range is bound to be more limited than in a normal list but Jerry has discovered splendid Alsace wines from Pierre Frick, a robust Châteauneuf from Pierre André and a collection of good-value wines from the south of France. Some of the more unusual offerings have disappeared from the new list but there is still Czechoslovakian beer and a comprehensive range of vodkas although these no longer come with organic blessing.

Best buys

Mauzac 1991, Jacques Frelin, Vin de Pays de l'Aude, £
Ch. Balette 1989, Côtes de Castillon, £
Domaine Richeaume, Syrah 1989, Côtes de Provence, ££
Millton Vineyard Chardonnay 1991, New Zealand, ££

Vintage Roots

Sheeplands Farm, Wargrave Road, Wargrave, Berkshire RG10 8DT *Tel* (0734) 401222

Case sales only **Open** Mon–Fri 9–6; Sat, Sun, 24-hour answerphone, public holidays by prior arrangement **Closed** Chr **Credit cards** Access, Visa; personal and business accounts **Discounts** Collection discount £1.50 per case; quantity discount on 5+ cases **Delivery** Free within 30-mile radius of Wargrave and on 6+ cases; otherwise 1 case £3.95, 2 cases £5, 3–5 cases £6; mail order available **Glass hire** Free with order **Tastings and talks** To groups on request **Cellarage** Not available

Vintage Roots became potbound earlier this year and uprooted to a farm in rural Berkshire with more storage space than its cramped Reading premises. The business remains the same, selling a wide range of organic wines, beers and even vinegar by mail order.

The range of wines has expanded and now stands at 135 from around the world. Most are from family domaines where the size of the business is small enough to devote the extra time and care needed for organic culture.

France is a major contributor – it has the greatest number of organic growers. Amongst the selection are some good burgundies from Jean-Claude Rateau and Ch. de Puy from Bordeaux. Italy contributes a fine range of Veronese wines from Guerrieri-Rizzardi and good Chianti from Villa Angiolina. From Australia come the massively flavoured Botobolar wines from New South Wales and the elegant, fruity Eden Ridge wines made by Adam Wynn. Vintage Roots has unearthed organic beers, liqueurs and cognac as well as ciders from the delightfully named Dunkerton Cider Company.

Best buys

Domaine de la Batteuse, Mauzac 1990, Vin de Pays de l'Aude, £
Le Vieux Suchots 1989, Vin de Pays Charentais, £
Côte de Beaune Blanc 1988, La Grande Châtelaine, ££
St Gilbert 1987, Botobolar Vineyard, Australia, ££

The Vintner/Viticulteur

See Arthur Rackhams

The Vintry

Park Farm, Milland, Liphook, Hampshire GU30 7JT *Tel* (0428) 76389

Outlet

Malthouse Farm, Ecchinswell, Newbury, Berkshire RG15 8TT

Case sales only **Open** By appointment only **Credit cards** None accepted; personal and business accounts **Discounts** Available on 10+ cases **Delivery** Not available **Glass hire** Free **Tastings and talks** Six formal tastings a year in Liphook, Newbury and London **Cellarage** Not available

This is a new company formed by Nigel Johnson-Hill. For those who read the small print on bottle labels the name may sound familiar and with good reason: Nigel is the brother of Alan Johnson-Hill, proprietor of Ch. de Méaume in Bordeaux. This wine is well liked and widely stocked but it provided the Vintry with the germ of a good idea.

There are many English/British people busy growing grapes in Bordeaux and elsewhere in France. Nigel J-H concentrates on importing these wines, not because he can't speak French but because he thinks that the Brits have a more searching, less traditional approach to winemaking(!). There is Ch. Bauduc from David Thomas in Bordeaux and Ch. de Sours owned by Esme Johnstone. A new addition is Ch. Léoville-Barton, owned by the Irish Barton family since 1826 who surely have had time since then to acquire a few traditions? Peter Sichel is one of the contributors to this range, unfortunately not with his splendid Ch. d'Angludet but with a clutch of wines from small properties where he advises on winemaking, and with a wine from Corbières, Domaine du Révérend, which is run by Sichel Junior.

Not everything is from France, but elsewhere the Brits theme seems to be abandoned with whites from California and Australia and reds from Chile and Spain. Nigel J-H has plans to grow via new partners, setting up in different parts of southern England.

Best buys

Domaine du Révérend 1988, Corbières, £
Johnson's Blanc de Blancs, Bordeaux, £
Ch. de Méaume 1988, Bordeaux Supérieur, ££
Ch. de Sours Rosé 1991, Bordeaux, ££

Waitrose

Head office
Doncastle Road, Southern Industrial Area, Bracknell, Berkshire RG12 4YA *Tel* (0344) 424680
99 licensed branches in London, Midlands and the Home Counties

Open Mon–Wed 9–6 (Wed till 8); Thur, Fri 8.30–8 (Fri till 9); Sat 8.30–5.30 **Closed** Sun, public holidays **Credit cards** None accepted **Discounts** 5% on 1 unmixed case or purchases of £100+ **Delivery** Not available **Glass hire** Free (deposit required) **Tastings and talks** Occasional evening tastings for invited customers **Cellarage** Not available

Waitrose shops are not like other supermarkets. They generate a degree of loyalty that makes customers drive past Sainsbury and Tesco to get to them. They have a higher ratio of Volvos and BMWs in the car parks and, as one of our readers pointed out, they are the sort of shops where you come across mothers talking about their children's university progress over the meat counter.

The wine section is different too. These departments are part of the main store but they still manage to retain a separate 'wine merchant' image. They usually have a door to the outside world so you can nip in and out for a bottle of wine without queuing at the main checkout. Very few of the Waitrose range are own-labels. There are the basics in each area, such as Good Ordinary Claret which stands out on the shelf like a neon sign, but generally bottles nestle under their own colours, giving a lively individual look. The range is surprisingly wide, around 400 wines, and of good quality – with four Masters of Wine on the buying team it should be. Waitrose has been slotting in new wines all through the price range. A soft, juicy Domaines des Fontaines Merlot, Vin de Pays d'Oc and a concentrated, plummy Ch. de Nages, Costières de Nîmes both fit in at the value end but there is an excellent Chorey-lès-Beaune 1989 from Domaine Maillard, a burgundy that would go well at any dinner party. Among the clarets, apart from the Good Ordinary version which is exactly as it says, there is a rather better oak-aged Médoc, and for just a little more money the St-Emilion is bigger, richer and needs more time to open up. There are a few grander clarets and a second label or two, but the real emphasis of this range is on drinking wines up to £10. Spain and Portugal are not covered extensively but the selection is good. Teroldego Rotaliano and Campo ai Sassi both from Italy and Ribera del Duero from Callejo in Spain stand out for their positive flavours and distinctive styles. At Waitrose Australian wines are not as extensive as other supermarkets but the range is good with Mountarrow Reserve Chardonnay standing out in quality terms in a range that also includes Mitchelton, Rosemount, Penfolds and Houghtons. Sauvignon Blanc from Villa Maria in New Zealand and the new Avontuur Chardonnay from South Africa are also worth looking out for.

Best buys

Waitrose Médoc 1989, £
Tinto da Anfora 1988, João Pires, Portugal, £
Leasingham Domaine Shiraz 1989, Clare Valley, Australia, ££
Waitrose Extra Dry 1986, Champagne, ££

Waterloo Wine Company

61 Lant Street, Borough, London SE1 1QL *Tel* 071-403 7967

Open Mon–Fri 10–6.30; Sat 10–5 **Closed** Sun, public holidays **Credit cards** Access, Visa **Discounts** Not available **Delivery** Free to London (min 5 cases); otherwise a £5 surcharge **Glass hire** Free; breakages charged for **Tastings and talks** Monthly tutored tastings **Cellarage** Not available

New Zealander Paul Tutton runs this business but also has a hand in a vineyard back home, apparently near Waipara Springs. More investment is planned soon in a vineyard in France but it will be a few years before this wine warehouse is totally self-sufficient.

Meanwhile, the range here has a strong Antipodean slant with good Aussie and New Zealand wines. Stonier's Merricks, from the Mornington Peninsula in Victoria, is new to the UK but sounds like it could be good. France is taken seriously, with a selection of good-value country wines from individual domaines and there are the Domaine Cauhapé wines from Jurançon. The Loire is explored and a rich seam of Loire reds featured; Alsace wines are all from *négociant* A Seltz in Mittelbergheim.

Waterloo seems to deal mainly with the trade but it has a retail licence so single bottle purchases are possible. Delivery is only free on orders of five cases or more, even within London.

Best buys

Domaine de la Ferrandière Cabernet Sauvignon 1990, Vin de Pays d'Oc, £
Waipara Springs Sauvignon Blanc 1991, New Zealand, £
Waipara Springs Pinot Noir 1990, New Zealand, ££
Ch. Hélène Corbières Rouge 1989, ££

Weavers of Nottingham 

1 Castle Gate, Nottingham, Nottinghamshire NG1 7AQ *Tel* (0602) 580922
17 Castle Gate (tasting room)

Open Mon–Sat 9–5.45 **Closed** Sun, bank holidays **Credit cards** All accepted; personal and business accounts **Discounts** 10% on 1 case; larger discounts by arrangement **Delivery** Free within 30-mile radius of Nottingham (min 1 case) **Glass hire** 10p per dozen, plus breakages **Tastings and talks** Monthly tastings for groups (some tutored) **Cellarage** £1 per case per year

Weavers shop is tucked away just off Nottingham's High Street. It may be small but it is stuffed to the ceiling with well-chosen wines. Further up the road is a beautiful Georgian house, 17 Castle Gate, which Weavers is gradually restoring to its original splendour. It is here the new School of Wine is taking shape.

Personal, friendly service is the keynote at this company – and this is evident if you contact them by phone or just walk into the shop. Directors Alan Trease and Keith Whitehead are frequently available for advice but training features large so you can get sound recommendations from the staff, too.

The range is comprehensive. Good champagnes and clarets are followed in the list by an interesting group of Alsace wines, mainly from Domaines Schlumberger. Chablis is obviously a favourite with four premier cru wines from William Fèvre and one from La Chablisienne. Other burgundies come from a variety of *négociants* including Latour, Chanson and Bouchard, with Domaine Rousseau providing his excellent Chambertins. The New World selection is wide if rather predictable. Brown Brothers, Penfolds and Rosemount provide most of the Australia range, while from California Robert Mondavi seems to have a monopoly, apart from the super fruity Firestone Merlot. Sherries are a speciality, with 30 types and brands to choose from including the Don Zoilo and Lustau ranges.

Best buys

Domaine de Rieux 1990, Côtes de Gascogne, £
Ch. Berjuquey 1988, Bordeaux, £
Châteauneuf-du-Pape 'Chante Cigale' 1990, ££
Ch. Monlot Capet 1986, St-Emilion Grand Cru, ££

Wessex Wines

197 St Andrews Road, Bridport, Dorset
DT6 3BT

Tel (0308) 23400

Case sales only **Open** Mon–Sat 8.30–9.30 **Closed** Sun, some public holidays **Credit cards** None accepted; personal and business accounts **Discounts** 5% on minimum of 6 bottles (unmixed); 7.5% on 7+ cases (COD) **Delivery** Free within 20-mile radius of Bridport (min 1 case) **Glass hire** Free **Tastings and talks** One large Christmas tasting; other tastings to groups on request **Cellarage** Not available

Michael Farmer is hoping to expand his by-the-case business to a wine warehouse operation. His collection of wines, with the emphasis on impressive flavours at good-value prices, would certainly suit that kind of outlet. Very little in this range strays over the £10 mark and then only with good reason, such as domaine-bottled Chambolle-Musigny and Volnay. From the south of France, Bordeaux and Rhône provide plenty of choice. There are reliable Alsace wines from the co-operative at Turckheim and two red Loire wines among a handful of whites. Italy and Spain provide reliable drinking from familiar names while the German range remains fairly modest. Bulgaria contributes its good-value range but for a little more money the Undurraga wines from Chile come into sight.

Australia is represented by the Bosanquet Estate, for which Wessex are the agents, and the familiar Rosemount. Michael Farmer claims to work 'elastic' hours which expand to fill the needs of his customers.

Best buys

Semillon/Sauvignon St Estelle 1990, Bosanquet Estate, £
Côtes-du-Rhône-Villages 1990, Celliers des Dauphins, £
Ch. Ramage la Batisse 1988, Cru Bourgeois, Haut-Médoc, ££
St-Véran 1988, Domaine Georges Jobert, ££

Whiclar & Gordon Wines

Glebelands, Vincent Lane, Dorking, Surrey
RH4 3YZ

Tel (0306) 885711
(24-hour answering service)
Tel (0306) 885686/888161
(orders/queries)

Open Mon–Fri 9–5.30 **Closed** Sat, Sun, public holidays **Credit cards** None accepted **Discounts** Not available **Delivery** £6 per case for consignments of less than 5 cases; mail order available **Glass hire** Free **Tastings and talks** Available **Cellarage** Not available

Whiclar & Gordon is a major wholesaler but has created a shop in its entrance hall and also operates a fairly energetic mail-order service. Changes could be on the way for this company, since the principal shareholder, Hardy in Australia, has been bought by the giant producers Berri Renmano. Baron Ricasoli in Italy, another Hardy-owned company, is not part of the deal and so those wines may slip off the list in due course.

As it stands, the range concentrates on those companies where the wholesale arm is the agent. So there is Victor Preiss in Alsace, La Chablisienne in Chablis and a collection of co-operatives in Burgundy. Clarets have a similar theme with Ch. La Croix from Pomerol and Ch. Gressier Grand Poujeaux from Moulis featuring, but there are also classed-growth wines which seem to be independent of the agency list. Domaine de la Baume in the south of France, has developed a splendid range of varietal wines made by Australian Hardy winemakers. These are widely listed in the retail trade but are available here, almost at the source, so to speak.

The Australian range is dominated, fairly obviously, by Hardy, with the Early Bird series, Hardy Collection and top-flight Eileen Hardy Reserve wines providing good quality at all price points. Coldstream Hills from James Halliday squeezes in here, as does Ch. Reynella from the McLaren Vale. California wines are mainly from the Franciscan winery in Napa and Caliterra provides wines from Chile.

Best buys

Chais Baumière Merlot 1990, Vin de Pays d'Oc, £
Pinot d'Alsace 1990, Victor Preiss, Alsace, £
Coldstream Hills Pinot Noir 1991, Victoria, Australia, ££
Eileen Hardy Reserve Shiraz 1989, South Australia, ££

Whighams of Ayr

8 Academy Street, Ayr, Ayrshire KA7 1HT *Tel* (0292) 267000

Open Mon–Sat 9.30–5.30 **Closed** Sun, public holidays **Credit cards** Access, American Express, Visa; personal and business accounts **Discounts** Available **Delivery** Free in central Scotland (min 1 case); mail order available **Glass hire** Free with order **Tastings and talks** Major tastings held through wine society; tutored tastings **Cellarage** £4.11 per case per year

Whighams can trace its history back to 1766 when the company, then called Alexander Oliphant & Co, built its cellars on a sandbank, engaged a cooper and ordered a sloop to be built by shipbuilder John Fraser. The *Buck* brought madeira, port, málaga and especially claret direct to the docks at Ayr.

Times have moved on but Whighams still concentrates on the traditional wines which helped establish the business. Claret and yet more claret is the main feature from France: in particular, Ch. Beychevelle and its second wine, l'Amiral de Beychevelle, a Bordeaux Supérieur from Ch. Puyfromage and the wines of Borie-Manoux, Ch. Batailley and Ch. Trottevieille. Burgundies come through *négociants* Chanson and Lamblin. Rhônes are fairly sparse and unidentified on our list, and a handful of Loire wines round off France. German wines are mainly from Dr Wellkomm on the Mosel and Italy contributes the Veneto wines of Pasqua, some Piemonte wines from S Orsola and two fairly unknown Chiantis from Pignatelli.

In this cobwebbed bastion of tradition it is refreshing to see wines from Switzerland and Czechoslovakia making an appearance. We are also told that customers sometimes talk about New World wines but rarely ask for them.

Best buys

Frankova 1989, Czechoslovakia, £
Le Putt, Rouge, Vin de Table, Borie-Manoux, £
Ch. Rochefort Allaman Rouge 1989, Réserve de La Ville de Lausanne, ££
Chablis 1990, Lamblin et Fils, ££

Whitesides Wine Merchants

Shawbridge Street, Clitheroe, Lancashire BB7 1NA — *Tel* (0200) 22281

Associated outlet
39 The Grove, Ilkley, West Yorkshire — *Tel* (0943) 816015

Open Mon–Sat 8.30–5.30 (Sat from 9) **Closed** Sun, public holidays **Credit cards** Access, Visa; personal and business accounts **Discounts** 5% on 1 unmixed case **Delivery** Free within Lancashire, North and West Yorkshire and Cumbria; elsewhere at cost (e.g. £7.50 per case on mainland UK) **Glass hire** Free **Tastings and talks** Weekly in-store tastings; other tastings on request (ave charge £5 per person) **Cellarage** Not available

Whitesides is the other half of the Clitheroe phenomenon alongside D Byrne. Residents here are truly spoilt for choice with an excellent range of wines, estimated at around 900, enough to keep at least half the town busy. The list has an organised feel to it, not just an endless roll-call of stock, but space to include a few tasting notes.

Classic France is taken seriously, with good clarets from the 1980s and burgundies from *négociants* and growers. There are Alsace wines mainly from Sipp, and the Rhône includes a fair showing from Jaboulet. White Loire wines are good but six reds add a touch of zest to the range. Regional French wines include Ch. la Jaubertie from Ryman Snr and Chais Baumière. The splendid organic wines of Henning Hoesch, Domaine

Richeaume in Provence lurk here as well, not cheap but chunky in flavour.

Germany, Italy and Spain look good although this list does not try to match the magpie-approach of D Byrne. Australia is one region where caution is thrown to the wind, with collections of wines from Penfolds, Rosemount and Brown Brothers laying strong foundations for some adventurous buying from Coldstream Hills, Rothbury and Taltarni. New Zealand takes in a tour of ten wineries with several wines from each and South Africa remains well represented by Nederburg, Hamilton-Russell and KWV.

You don't have to live in Clitheroe to take advantage of these wines. On the other side of the Pennines, a white rose outpost of Whitesides supplies Ilkley and surrounding areas.

Best buys

Brouilly 1991, André Jaffre, £
Semillon/Chardonnay Penfolds 1991, Koonunga Hill, Australia, £
Comtes de Jonqueyres 1989, Vieilles Vignes, Bordeaux, ££
Rongopai Sauvignon Blanc 1990, New Zealand, ££

Willoughbys

53 Cross Street, Manchester M2 4JP *Tel* 061-834 6850

Open Mon–Fri 9–6, Sat 9–5 **Closed** Sun **Credit cards** Access, Visa; personal and business accounts **Discounts** 5% on 1 case **Delivery** Free in Greater Manchester; mail order available **Glass hire** £5 per dozen
Tastings and talks Regular weekend tastings held in-store; specific tastings for regular customers; to groups on request **Cellarage** £5 per case per year

Classic French wines are here in depth and variety at Willoughbys. Claret is the first region to grab the attention. Over 50 from the 1988 vintage alone – starting at Willoughbys Daily Claret and travelling up to second and third growths. It is the same picture for older vintages, with petits châteaux providing a fine selection without breaking the bank. Burgundies are almost as many in number: *négociants* Emile Chandesais, Jacques Parent and Labouré-Roi take a lot of the credit but a rich seam from the Hospices de Beaune and Domaine de la Romanée-Conti provide exciting and expensive drinking. After all this glory the Rhône comes as a disappointment and is mainly single sourced though Alexis Boisselet, but Alsace looks bright.

Spain is sound if a little unadventurous with a full set from Torres and Riojas from Berberana, Faustino and the delicious Muga. Portugal is represented by the good wines of Fonseca, and Germany is extensively explored with the help of Deinhard, Guntrum and the family firm Michel Schneider. The New World is brought to Manchester in sturdy blocks from big but reliable names: Fetzer and Firestone from California, Seppelt and Brown Brothers from Australia. Champagnes are worth a special mention for the sheer variety that is missing elsewhere. Endless permutations of bottle size and vintage from Bollinger, Krug, Pol Roger, Roederer and so on.

Best buys

Willoughbys Daily Claret 1988, £
Chardonnay Domaine de Martinolles 1990, Vin de Pays de l'Aude, £
Ch. Roumieu-Lacoste, Premier Cru Classé 1986, Barsac, ££
Rioja Reserva 1985, Muga, ££

Winchcombe Wine Merchants

21 North Street, Winchcombe, Gloucestershire GL54 5LH — *Tel* (0242) 604313

Open Mon–Sat 9–9; Sun 12–2 **Closed** Chr Day, Boxing Day, New Year's Day **Credit cards** Access, Visa; personal and business accounts **Discounts** 5% up to £50, 7.5% on £50+ **Delivery** Free to north Cotswolds area **Glass hire** Free; breakages charged for **Tastings and talks** To local groups on request **Cellarage** Not available

Spain is the main attraction of this list with Riojas from no fewer than eight bodegas, at Crianza, Reserva and Gran Reserva levels. Navarra wines come from Ochoa, and the Marqués de Griñon contributes his red and white wines from vineyards near Toledo. The Adlards have also selected Altos de Pio from Jumilla and the classy table wine Yllera.

Outside Spain the list is less comprehensive but still worth exploring. France sports a reasonable selection of clarets, mainly petits châteaux but taking in the delicious Ch. Monbousquet from St-Emilion on the way to third and fourth growth Médocs. Burgundies are from Boisset and Bouchard, with even more expensive wines available at short notice. The Alsace section is limited to just three wines but these are from quality producers Schlumberger. The New World makes a token appearance with Mitchelton from Australia, Santa Rita from Chile and two wines each from New Zealand and California.

Best buys

Altos de Pio 1988, Jumilla, £
Chardonnay Vin de Pays d'Oc, Seduire, £
Rioja Reserva 1985, Muga, ££
Ochoa Reserva 1982, Navarra, ££

Windrush Wines

Wholesale outlet
The Barracks, Cecily Hill, Cirencester, Gloucestershire GL7 2EF — *Tel* (0285) 650466

Retail outlet
3 Market Place, Cirencester, Gloucestershire GL7 2PE — *Tel* (0285) 657807

Open Mon–Fri 9–6 (shop till 5.30); Sat 9.30–1 (shop 9–5.30) **Closed** Sun, public holidays **Credit cards** Access, Visa; personal and business accounts **Discounts** By arrangement **Delivery** Free within 20-mile radius of Cirencester; and nationwide for 3+ cases; otherwise £5 for up to 2 cases; mail order available **Glass hire** Pay for breakages only **Tastings and talks** 4 free tastings per year for customers; tutored tastings on request **Cellarage** £4.70 per case per year

Windrush Wines is based in what looks like a medieval castle but was in fact the local barracks at Cirencester. There is also a retail shop – a mini food hall of gastronomic delights with cheese, charcuterie and patisserie.

Mark Savage MW, the man behind Windrush, has steered it towards being one of the most interesting merchants in the country. The catalogue introduces producers, their vineyards and their winemaking, a gentle and effective way of explaining why those particular wines have been chosen for the list.

France is a major feature, with a careful collection of clarets; people are more important than classification. Family domaines abound – from the Rhône, Loire and the South of France. Pinot Noir is something of a passion at Windrush, with splendid examples from Burgundy. North America is taken very seriously with Eyrie Vineyards, Snoqualmie and Stags Leap as examples of the quality of producer that Mark Savage tends to deal with. Mainland Australia is limited to Hutt Creek and Cape Mentelle, with the delightful Piper's Brook from Tasmania showing off its terrific Pinot Noir. Italy takes a selective look at the wines of Felsina Berardenga and Angelo Gaja. Hidalgo sherries, fruit brandies (from Alsace and Oregon) and farm calvados are just some of the other attractions that might have you marching down to the barracks.

Best buys

Valdeobispo 1990, León, Spain, £
Mas de Cadenet Rosé 1990, Côtes de Provence, £
Billecarte-Salmon nv Champagne Brut, ££
Terra Rosa Cabernet Sauvignon 1988, Laurel Glen, Sonoma, California, ££

Winecellars

153/155 Wandsworth High Street, London SW18 4JB *Tel* 081-871 2668/3979

Open Mon–Fri 10.30–8.30; Sat 10–8.30 **Closed** Sun, Chr Day, Boxing Day, Easter Mon **Credit cards** Access, Visa; personal and business accounts **Discounts** £1 per case on 5+ cases **Delivery** Free within M25 (min 1 case); elsewhere free (min 2 cases); mail order available **Glass hire** £5, plus 75p deposit per glass **Tastings and talks** Tutored tastings **Cellarage** Not available

If there was ever a wine-producing country that needs a specialist wine merchant, it is Italy. And so, riding to the rescue, come David Gleave and Nick Belfrage, both MWs and Italian specialists and both able to unravel the intricacies of these fascinating wines. Winecellars is big in supplying to the trade but there is also a retail shop and a mail-order business.

The list is a gem and essential reading for anyone preparing to tackle Italian wines seriously. At first sight it might look a little daunting, with descriptions of regions, winemakers and their styles, but it is worthwhile spending the time before spending the money. To start with, there is Barolo – 48 wines from 18 vintages and no fewer than 14 producers – which is when you need to look back at the notes, all written in an easy, understandable style. Piemonte goes on to include six Dolcettos, ten Barbarescos and a collection of other wines made from the Nebbiolo grape. Moving on to the Veneto, Winecellars has brought together really good Soave from Pieropan, Valpolicella from Allegrini and a wonderful Lugana from Cà dei Frati as well as varietal wines from the good producers of the North-East. The Tuscan section is a delight, with Chiantis from 11 producers including the splendid Felsina Berardenga and Isole e Olena. Super Tuscans are cleverly sorted into their component grape varieties, although here the information does fall down a bit. It would be nice to know what separates a Tignanello from a Solaia before spending so much money on it.

The South has been explored for wines worthy to fit into this range and David Gleave has come up with Ramiletto from Di Majo Norante made from native grape varieties in Molise. You can also choose olive oil, for example, Villa di Vetrice, Tenuta di Capezzana or Felsina Berardenga. Be prepared to spend as much as you would on a bottle of wine,the flavours will convert you from the supermarket stuff for ever.

Winecellars are so expert at Italian wines that it is easy to overlook the rest of the range, but France is good, particularly on good-value southern French wines. Australia takes in a personal selection from notable winemakers, with Adam Wynn, Brian Croser, Charlie Melton, Garry Crittenden and Stephen Henschke all contributing.

Best buys

Barbera d'Asti 1991, Viticoltori dell'Acquese, £
Chianti Rufina 1990, Villa di Vetrice, £
Pinot Grigio 1991, Collio, Puiatti, ££
Barolo 'Monprivato' 1986, G Mascarello, ££

The Wine Emporium

7 Devon Place, Edinburgh EH12 5HJ *Tel* 031-346 1113

Case sales only **Open** Mon–Sat 10–6; Sun, public holidays 11–5 **Closed** Chr Day, Boxing Day, 1 & 2 Jan **Credit cards** Access, Visa; personal and business accounts **Discounts** Available on application **Delivery** Free within Edinburgh district; mail order available **Glass hire** Free with order
Tastings and talks Wine course throughout the winter months; regular tutored tastings; in-store tastings on Sat **Cellarage** £2.50 per case per year

Although the good people of Edinburgh are spoilt for choice the Wine Emporium is just too good to leave out. Recently taken over and restructured, it has emerged as a business with a sound range and a knowledgeable team in charge. Sales are by the case only but mixed cases are available at no extra charge and no one could have a problem assembling an assorted dozen.

Spain is one of the strengths of the list, with key regions and producers targeted. Riojas come from CVNE, Navarra wines from Ochoa and there is a range of varietal wines from the new region of Somontano. The 'key producers' approach applies elsewhere: Australia focuses on the wines of Taltarni and Wyndham and the American range comes from quality producers Ch. Ste Michelle in Washington, and from Buena Vista and Robert Mondavi in California. German wines are taken seriously: Prüm, Weil, Bürklin-Wolf, Guntrum and Prinz zu Salm-Dalberg form a tremendous collection to work through. From France, clarets are mainly big names from the 1983 and 1985 vintages, with an everyday selection of more affordable wines from later vintages. Burgundies are still being worked on but so far they look good, Alsace takes in the wines of Gisselbrecht, and Chablis is well represented by La Chablisienne co-operative. Other specialities include vintage cognacs from Hine and Denis Mounié, single domaine armagnacs and a wide range of Warre's ports.

Best buys

Pinot Blanc 1989, Gisselbrecht, Alsace, £
Ch. de l'Orangerie 1990, Bordeaux, £
Contino Reserva 1986, Rioja, ££
Tempranillo 1989, Ochoa, Navarra, ££

Wine Growers Association

See Les Amis du Vin

The Wine House

10 Stafford Road, Wallington, Surrey SM6 9AD *Tel* 081-669 6661

Open Tue–Sat 10–6; Sun 12–2; public holidays variable **Closed** Mon **Credit cards** Access, Visa; personal and business accounts **Discounts** 10% to members of Wine Circle only **Delivery** Free within 5-mile radius (min 1 case); elsewhere at cost; mail order available **Glass hire** Free **Tastings and talks** Two large tastings a year (all ticket) and occasional smaller tastings (also all ticket); tastings and talks to groups on request **Cellarage** Not available

There are some wine shops where the proprietors are very much in control of the stock, where lots of wines come from the same suppliers and where there is no duplication. The other type of shop is where the stock seems to have the upper hand and more and more variety is squeezed on to the shelves and easy buying is cast to the winds. The Wine House belongs firmly in the second category. Page upon page of wines are all neatly introduced and described.

There are no real gaps in the range and even if there were they would be pretty hard to spot in 65 pages of close-typed text. The Rhône manages to pack in eight red Châteauneuf-du-Papes and two whites; Provence and the South-West are a riot of well-priced drinking. Spain is introduced with a few words from Mr Rodker's own school report 'no fireworks but good steady progress'. He seems to have steadily taken on board a huge number of Riojas, 12 Crianzas, 18 Reservas and 10 Gran Reservas. Toro, Navarra, Somontano, Penedès, Priorato... the list goes on for ever. Italy heads off similarly – and there's Germany, Australia and California to follow.

Best buys

Yuntero Tinto 1986, La Mancha, Spain, £
Ch. de Juge 1989, Bordeaux Blanc, £
Dr Loosen Riesling Trocken QbA 1990, ££
Ch. Montus 1990, Madiran, ££

Wine Rack

See Thresher

The Wine Schoppen

1 Abbeydale Road South, Sheffield, South Yorkshire S7 2QL — *Tel* (0742) 365684

Associated outlet

Barrels & Bottles, 1 Walker Street, The Wicker, Sheffield, South Yorkshire S3 8GZ — *Tel* (0742) 769666

Open Mon–Fri 9.30–6; Sat 9.30–5 **Closed** Sun, public holidays **Credit cards** Access, Visa; personal and business accounts **Discounts** 2.5% (min 3 cases) **Delivery** Free to UK (min 3 cases); otherwise £5.80 per consignment **Glass hire** Free with order **Tastings and talks** In-store tastings held every first Saturday of the month; tastings by invitation 4 times per year; wines always available for tasting in-store; monthly tastings through wine tasting club; to groups on request **Cellarage** £2.50 per case per year

Barrels & Bottles is based in the Wicker arches in central Sheffield and is the relatively new off-shoot of the well-established Wine Schoppen to the south of the city. The range at both premises is much the same, with German wines taking centre stage. There is a fine selection from growers in the Mosel, Rheinhessen and Rheinpfalz areas, and a collection of 17 Franken wines including a fairly unusual Trockenbeerenauslese. But no matter how good German wines are, they are difficult to sell at the moment and so a wide variety from the rest of the world adds to the range. France includes a reasonable collection from Bordeaux, Burgundy and the Rhône with five vintages of Mas de Daumas Gassac adding interest. There are Martínez-Bujanda Riojas and Vega Sicilia from Spain, an exciting and good-value selection from Portugal and wines from Australia, Chile, Brazil and California. Training is a priority, so advice behind the counter should be reliable.

Best buys

Bairrada Montanha Garrafeira 1983, Portugal, £
Bodenheimer Heitersbrünnchen Scheurebe Kabinett 1990, Weingut Kuehling Gillot, Rheinhessen, £
Mas de Daumas Gassac 1988, Vin de Pays de l'Hérault, ££
Rüdesheimer Kirchenpfad Spätlese Trocken, Spätburgunder 1989, EB Erhardt, Rheingau, ££

The Wine Shop

7 Sinclair Street, Thurso, Caithness KW14 7AJ *Tel* (0847) 65657

Open Tue–Sat 10–1, 2.30–5.30 **Closed** Sun, Mon, Chr and New Year **Credit cards** Access, Visa; personal and business accounts **Discounts** Available on unmixed case **Delivery** Free within 10-mile radius of Thurso (min 6 bottles); otherwise £1.50 per case or part case within Caithness; quotes given for Sutherland **Glass hire** Free with order **Tastings and talks** Not available **Cellarage** Not available

We are delighted to welcome this new wine shop to the *Guide* – about as far north as you can go without getting on a boat. The proprietors are Jan and Martine Hughes; Jan has a full-time job as a chemist at the Dounreay Nuclear Establishment.

The range of wine is surprisingly wide and very well chosen with a keen eye on value. From France there is a reasonable collection of clarets, with Côtes de Bourg and Fronsac at the value end and Potensac and Pichon-Lalande for special occasions. Bouchard Père features among the burgundies and there are small but sound selections from the Rhône, Loire and Alsace. The German range goes straight for style with Bürklin-Wolf, Friedrich Wilhelm Gymnasium and Robert Weil. Italy includes the delightful Peppoli Chianti from Antinori and Tedeschi's sturdy Recioto della Valpolicella. There is a splendid Spanish selection with the well-known names of Torres, CVNE and Ochoa providing most of the flavours and two Priorato wines from Masia Barril adding interest. Australia and New Zealand are well represented by Brown Brothers and a few Penfolds wines, and there is a clutch of good wines from Chile. In a major town, this quality of this selection would be commendable, but in such a remote part of the country it indicates a singleminded determination to do things properly.

Best buys

Hill-Smith Chenin/Semillon Blanc 1989, Australia, £
René Barbier Reserva Tinto 1984, Penedès, Spain, £
Masia Barril 1987, Priorato, Spain, ££
Domaine de Couillaud 1990, Chardonnay, Vin de Pays du Jardin de la France, ££

Wines from Paris

The Vaults, 4 Giles Street, Leith, Edinburgh EH6 6DJ *Tel* 031-554 2652

Open Mon–Sat 10–7 **Closed** Sun, Christmas, New Year and Easter **Credit cards** Access, Visa; personal and business accounts **Discounts** 5% case discount for collections **Delivery** Free in Edinburgh (min 1 case) and free to mainland Scotland (min 2+ cases); mail order available **Glass hire** Free; breakages charged for **Tastings and talks** Various tastings organised during the year; to groups on request **Cellarage** Not available

For those who don't already know, the Paris in question is not the one with the Eiffel Tower. Judith Paris runs this business that operates out of historic vaults in Leith. Restoration has provided the perfect place to store wine, in a building with wine associations going right back to the twelfth century.

Despite the antiquity of the surroundings, the list takes a refreshing view of the world of wine: sensible, restrained buying with a keen eye on quality and value. The Loire looks good with a fair selection of reds as well as whites, and fans of Loire rosé are catered for, not with indifferent Anjou but with a single vineyard Sancerre. Chablis wines come from Jean Durup and there is a pleasant collection of domaine burgundies. Clarets head for second wines and the Côtes de Francs. The South and South-West provide great value with wines from Ch. la Jaubertie in Bergerac and Val Joanis from the Côtes du Lubéron. Spain and Italy have a select but focused range; Sardinia and Portugal round off Europe with Germany being strangely absent. Basic Australians come from reliable Tisdall and Hill-Smith but then the range heads straight up the quality scale with Tim Adams, Vasse Felix and Yarra Yering. With Ramos-Pinto ports, de Soto sherries and a selection of fine old malts, these vaults are still home to a serious wine business.

Best buys

Domaine des Pensées Sauvages 1989, Corbières, £
Tisdall Semillon/Riesling 1991, Victoria, Australia, £
MacRostie Chardonnay 1990, Carneros, California, ££
Ch. Laclaverie 1988, Côtes de Francs, ££

The Wine Society

BEST MAIL-ORDER MERCHANT AWARD

Registered office (mail order only)
Gunnels Wood Road, Stevenage,
Hertfordshire SG1 2BG

Tel (0438) 741177 (enquiries)
Tel (0438) 740222 (24-hour answering service)

Open Mon–Fri 9–5; Sat 9–1 (1 retail outlet in Stevenage); showroom open for collections **Closed** Sun, public holidays **Credit cards** Access, Visa; personal and business accounts **Discounts** £1.20 on 1 unmixed case; also £1 per case on 5–9 cases, £2 per case on 10 cases or more **Delivery** Free in UK (min 1 case or for orders of over £75); otherwise £3 **Glass hire** Free with 1-case order **Tastings and talks** Series of tastings for members (monthly in Stevenage and London); 30 tastings per year nationwide; also wine weekends in England and France **Cellarage** £3.96 per unmixed case per year

Formed in 1874, the International Exhibition Co-operative Wine Society Ltd, to give it its full name, exists as the oldest and largest 'wine club' in the world. A single £20 payment buys you membership for life and when you move on to that great vineyard in the sky, your grieving relatives can pick up the dividend which has accrued. In fact, you purchase a share in the business and from then on you can vote at meetings, elect the officials and even stand for the Committee of Management.

Membership also brings you three well-annotated lists per year and monthly newsletters focusing on different regions and wines. You can also attend one of the many tastings held at venues around the country.

The wines are well chosen, each one a good representative of its region. Claret has always been a sound area. Most of the wines on the main list are ready to drink, those for laying down are noted in a separate section at the back. The Rhône is a satisfying selection from Jaboulet, Guigal and Chave with a few extras such as the Domaine Font Michelle Châteauneuf-du-Pape. French country wines merit a large section, most wines are below the magic £5 mark and represent as good a selection as you are likely to find anywhere. Sherry has long been a strong point, and the Society's own-label wines are particularly impressive. The New World choice is wide and includes Yarra Yering from Victoria.

En primeur offers have been growing in recent years and now Rhônes, burgundies, Sauternes and clarets are offered in this way. The selection is wide, prices are reasonable and often there is the chance to buy six bottles instead of a whole case. Mixed cases are also available.

One criticism your co-editor has heard of the Wine Society is that it is expensive. Perhaps where good merchants are thick on the ground the competition may shave a little off prices, but try living ten miles or more from a supermarket or an interested wine merchant and the range and services offered by the Society become very attractive. Orders are taken very efficiently over the phone, information is readily available and prices include delivery. One of our readers summed it up so well: 'A society that is well worth belonging to.'

Best buys

Domaine du Belvezet, Côtes du Vivarais 1990, £
Willunga Hill Cabernet/Shiraz 1989, Australia, £
Stratford Chardonnay 1991, California, ££
Lar de Barros Tinto, Reserva 1986, Extremadura, Spain, ££

Wines of Interest

46 Burlington Road, Ipswich, Suffolk IP1 2HS *Tel* (0473) 215752
Hadleigh Wines, at above address

Open Mon–Fri 9–6; Sat 9–1 **Closed** Sun, public holidays **Credit cards** None accepted; personal and business accounts **Discounts** 5% on 1 unmixed case **Delivery** Free in City of London, Ipswich and central Norwich (min 1 case) and elsewhere (min 6 cases); otherwise at cost; mail order available **Glass hire** Free with suitable order **Tastings and talks** Regular series of tastings in London, Clacton and Norwich (approx £15 per person) **Cellarage** Not available

To persuade customers to try something different Wines of Interest has started a Sampling Club. Not the usual idea of a sip in the shop: here the customer joins the Club for a £10 annual subscription and can then buy a single bottle of one or two selected wines per month at half price.

Tim Voelkler, MD of Wines of Interest and its identical twin Hadleigh Wine Cellars, has assembled a good collection of wines and has tried to find a few from off the beaten track, such as a Côte Roannaise wine, made from Gamay, in the upper reaches of the Loire not too far from Beaujolais, and a Collioure from the South of France. Both are worth sampling. Generally, the range takes a fairly conventional tour around the vineyards adding one or two less usual wines here and there. So, in a range of only eight Italian wines, we find Aglianico del Vulture from the hot south and Antinori's Tuscan Tignanello. Spain includes Pata Negra, the big brother version of Señorio de los Llanos from Valdepeñas, and there is a single quinta Vinho Verde from Portugal. From Australia, a few unusual names are included such as Blewitts Springs, St Leonards and Wirra Wirra, as well as Peter Lehmann, Brown Brothers and Renmano.

Most of the main list concentrates on providing value and flavour at under £10 but there is a Fine Wine list to keep the interest going: classic clarets and burgundies, along with older vintages of estate German wines, and ports and madeiras rolling back through the years.

Best buys

La Gitana Manzanilla, Hidalga (half-bottle), £
Côtes Roannaise 1990, Serol, £
Pata Negra Gran Reserva 1978, Valdepeñas, ££
Chablis Première Côte de Lechet 1989, Domaine des Malandes, ££

Wines of Westhorpe

Field House Cottage, Birch Cross, Marchington, Staffordshire ST14 8NX — *Tel* (0283) 820285
Bond address for collections
Cargo Bonding Ltd, Derby Turn, Derby Road, Burton on Trent, Staffordshire DE14 2QD — *Tel* (0283) 64622

Case sales only **Open** Mon–Fri 9–6.30; also open at various times on Sat, Sun and some public holidays **Closed** Chr Day (and possibly between Chr and New Year) **Credit cards** Access, Visa **Discounts** Available **Delivery** National delivery, £3.60 for 1 case, free on 2+ cases, £2.40 discount on 5–10 cases, £3 discount on 11–15 cases, etc. **Glass hire** Not available
Tastings and talks Occasionally to groups on request **Cellarage** Not available

With its limited range and case-only sales, newcomers to Wines of Westhorpe might think it has very little to offer (mainly Bulgarian wine but with some from Hungary, Chile and Australia) but the main appeal is price.

The whole Bulgarian range is available, from the basic but good country wines right up to Special Reserves. On every wine the bottle price is less than at most High Street shops – by 25p or so at the bottom end but at the top end the difference can be as much as 80p a bottle. This is for exactly the same wines as those widely available.

The Chilean selection is from a little-known company Peteroa, but the wines are good and very reasonably priced. The Australian range is a new addition called Tatachilla Hill in South-East Australia. Mixed cases are available but these are pre-selected as 'tasting cases' and other combinations are just not available.

Best buys

Svischtov Cabernet Sauvignon Controliran 1986, Bulgaria, £
Peteroa Chardonnay 1991, Chile, £
Special Reserve Stambolovo Merlot 1987, Bulgaria, £

Wright Wine Company

The Old Smithy, Raikes Road, Skipton, North Yorkshire BD23 1NP
Tel (0756) 794175/700886

Open Mon–Sat and public holidays 9–6 **Closed** Sun **Credit cards** None accepted; personal and business accounts **Discounts** 5% on mixed/unmixed cases **Delivery** Free within 30-mile radius of Skipton; elsewhere at cost **Glass hire** Free **Tastings and talks** Not available **Cellarage** Available free for 1–2 years, after that negotiable

In 1992, Bob Wright decided to throw caution to the winds and print his list in letters big enough for people to read. It now uses four times as much paper but if that bothers you he is happy to supply you with just the pages you need. He has also acquired the property next door, which more than doubles the available space, and has provided an extra sales area and a tasting room. The name 'Wright Next Door' indicates a streak of humour here in Skipton.

If you are looking for claret this would be a good place to start. The range is particularly good among the 1985 vintage. Alsace seems to be a favoured region with a variety of producers but Domaine Schlumberger standing out among them. Burgundies are present in depth, with domaine wines sharing shelf space equally with *négociants'* wines. The Rhône seems less in favour but there are some good country wines to balance things out. Spain and Italy look good; there has been some work involved in getting off the beaten track although the 1952 Castillo Ygay Rioja may take a little time to sell at nearly £100 a bottle. Australia includes a round-up of some of the big names, Penfolds, Rosemount and Mitchelton.

Best buys

Jeunes Vignes, Mis en Bouteille à Ch. Cissac, £
Vin de pays des Collines Rhodaniennes, Les Sables 1989, Syrah, Vallouit, £
Santa Carolina, Cabernet Sauvignon, Los Toro Vineyard 1985, Maipo Valley, Chile, ££
Pouilly Fumé, Domaine des Berthiers 1991, Jean Claude Dagueneau, ££

Peter Wylie Fine Wines

Plymtree Manor, Plymtree, Cullompton, Devon EX15 2LE *Tel* (08847) 555

Open Mon–Fri 9–6; Sat (only by appointment) **Closed** Sun, public holidays **Credit cards** None accepted; personal and business accounts **Discounts** Available **Delivery** 1 case at £10, 2 cases at £6.50 per case, 3 cases at £5 per case **Glass hire** Not available **Tastings and talks** Tastings by invitation only **Cellarage** £5 per case per year

If we had to nominate a favourite cellar to get lost in, the one at Peter Wylie's home in delightful Devon would probably be it. With a choice of 15,000 classic wines from assorted vintages back to 1890 and beyond, there is a lifetime's tasting homework.

Peter Wylie specialises in fine and rare wines from Bordeaux, Burgundy and Champagne and in vintage port. The list concerns itself not just with the château name and vintage but with the liquid level of the wine – base of neck, upper shoulder and so on – and the condition of the label. For those of us who would drink the contents, the level in the bottle is important and gives an indication of the condition of the wine. The state of the label is more the concern of collectors, who would no more pull the cork than stick a Penny Black on an envelope. On any list of old wines it is the great names that dominate such as Yquem, Lafite and Latour and these antique gems don't come cheap, though there are some bottles at less than £100. Peter Wylie does not just deal in history, he has quite a collection of 1980 clarets, Sauternes and burgundies.

Best buys

Not really appropriate here, considering the individual nature of the stock.

Yapp Brothers

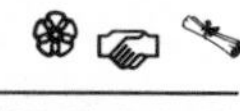

The Old Brewery, Mere, Wiltshire BA12 6DY *Tel* (0747) 860423

Case sales only **Open** Mon–Fri 9–5; Sat 9–1 **Closed** Sun, public holidays **Credit cards** Access, Diners Club, Visa; personal and business accounts **Discounts** Quantity and collection discounts available **Delivery** Free locally (Wiltshire, Dorset, Somerset); free on UK mainland (min 2 cases); otherwise 1 case £3; mail order available **Glass hire** Free **Tastings and talks** Occasional tastings, £5 per person (refundable on purchase) **Cellarage** £5 per case per year

Robin Yapp specialises in the wines of the Rhône and Loire, so when news of the disastrous Loire frosts in 1991 reached him he saw the distinct possibility of half his range disappearing. But Robin Yapp is loyal to his growers and they responded in like manner. To a man (or woman) the vignerons declared their intention to reserve enough stocks of the excellent 1990 vintage to supply Yapp. And so his most recent list barely registers that there was a frost.

It starts with some 1991 Domaine Muscadet that managed to escape the frost and gradually works up the river, calling in at vineyards where the people are friendly and wine quality is paramount. Coteaux du Layon from five different cuvées of the same property shows just how good this wine can get. Quarts de Chaume continues the tasting exercise and a 1947 Bonnezeaux demonstrates that these Loire whites can last for years. There are 10 wines from Savennières, a fine collection of Saumur Champigny and Vouvray in all its forms: sec, demi-sec, moelleux and sparkling.

The Rhône is explored with the same level of dedication. Condrieu and Ch. Grillet are listed in a choice of vintages, Gérard Chave provides his wonderful Hermitages, and there is his special Vin de Paille. Nine wines from Cornas, a hefty chunk from Châteauneuf-du-Pape and three wines from Brézème, a fairly rare and exciting discovery, add to the variety. One small criticism is that some wines in the list lose their growers' name, though these are often hidden in the text and where there is more than one supplier it can get confusing.

There are some good Côtes-du-Rhônes as well as domaine wines from Lirac, Côtes du Ventoux and Tricastin. Robin Yapp strays a little from his chosen path with a collection of Alsace wines from Schléret and the splendid Jacquesson champagnes.

Best buys

Saint Pourçain sur Sioule 1990, Union des Vignerons, £
Gamay de l'Ardèche 1991, Les Vignerons Ardéchois, £
Sancerre Les Perriers 1991, André Vatan, ££
Hermitage 1990, Chave, ££

Yorkshire Fine Wines

See Bibendum

WHO'S WHERE

This is a gazetteer of individual wine stockists listed in the *Guide*. See also the directory of chains and supermarkets that follows.

London

England

CHAINS AND SUPERMARKETS

Space does not permit us to list the addresses of all the branches of each chain, but details of the entry include the address and telephone number of the company's head office, from whom you will be able to find out your nearest branch.

Part IV

Find out more about wine

Find out more about wine

There is more activity than ever before for those who want to find out more about wine. You can join wine clubs and societies, you can go on wine courses, or you can travel to the vineyards in the company of like-minded wine lovers.

Some wine societies are independent organisations run by enthusiasts who arrange events throughout the year for their members. They will often sample wines from several merchants. Other clubs are run by wine merchants who also run tastings but they usually focus on their own ranges only.

This year we have decided to draw a distinction between these types of wine club. Both are valuable in the way they encourage wine drinkers to taste wines before they buy them.

There are also some 'wine clubs' which are really just mail-order merchants. These are to be found in the main WHERE TO BUY section of the *Guide* under their trading names.

INDEPENDENT WINE CLUBS

These are organised by wine enthusiasts and usually present a variety of tastings based around themes or presentations from different wine merchants throughout the year.

Bramhope Wine Appreciation Group
Kelvyn Chapman, 20 Ayresome Avenue, Leeds, W Yorks LS8 1BE
TEL (0532) 666322
Tutored tasting are held twice a month with the cost of wines shared (usually £3–£5 per session for six wines). Activities include visits from guest speakers, occasional visits to merchants, dinners and tours of wine-making regions abroad. Annual subscription £15. A smaller group also meets every Monday at the Garforth School Evening Centre during term-time.

Capital Wine Appreciation Group (CWAG)
R & A Sperry, 67 Wentloog Road, Rumney, Cardiff CF3 8HD
TEL (0222) 791088
Limited membership of up to 20 people. No membership fee but there is a supplement of £4 per meeting attended (held once a month) to cover the cost of the wines. Members are asked to make an annual contribution (£1) towards postal costs.

Cornwall Wine Tasting Group
Christopher James, 20 Lodge Drive, Truro, Cornwall TR1 1TX
TEL (0872) 71912
Although the group is affiliated to the Wine Society, membership is open. There is a one-off joining fee of £10 but a supplement is charged for each tasting attended. Meetings usually take place every six weeks.

The International Wine & Food Society
9 Fitzmaurice Place, Berkeley Square, London W1X 6JD
TEL 071-495 4191 FAX 071-495 4172
President: Michael Broadbent MW. Director: Hugo Dunn-Meynell. Membership terms on application; special rates for members under 25. The International Secretariat in London has a library, a club and hotel facilities. Nearly 200 regional branches organise dinners, tastings, lectures and visits. *The Annual*, regular newsletters and annual vintage guide to wine-buying are free to members.

The Lincoln Wine Society
8 Green Lane, North Hykeham, Lincoln, Lincolnshire LN6 8NL
TEL (0522) 680388
Chairman: Norman Tate. Meetings are held on the third Thursday of every month at St Mary's Guildhall, Lincoln. All aspects of wine appreciation are covered in a range of activities that include guest experts and wine merchants, fine wine and food evenings, trips to merchants and wine areas, and a grand annual dinner. Membership is £5 annually (£8 joint). (See also **The Lincoln Wine Course**.)

Martin Mistlin's Fine Wine Dining Club
41 Kingsend, Ruislip HA4 7DD TEL 081-427 9944 (day)
The Club specialises in wine and food events such as tastings, dinners and wine tours. The subscription in 1992 was £8 (£14 joint). (See also **Wine and Gastronomic Societies (WAGS)** and **Ordre Mondial des Gourmets Dégustateurs**.)

Nearly Private Wine Club
John Corliss, 309 Old Street, London EC1V 6LE TEL 071-613 0113
FAX 071-729 1390
Formerly just the Private Wine Club, this is a 'non-profit-making wine club consisting entirely of wine lovers'. Membership in 1992 was by a £10 donation to St Bart's Hospital children's wing. Members receive a quarterly newsletter, an invitation to the Great Beaujolais Breakfast and the Grand Annual Tasting in November.

Other events in 1992 included various Loire seminars, tastings of 1990 burgundies and wines from New Zealand, plus wine dinners.

North East Wine Tasting Society
Nigel Ellam (Secretary), 1 East View, High Heworth, Gateshead, Tyne & Wear NE10 9AR TEL 091-438 4107
Monthly meetings are held in Newcastle. Most members are 'enthusiastic amateurs' and the tastings are aimed at improving knowledge of wine-producing areas, grape varieties and the wines themselves. Annual membership £15 (£27 joint).

Northern Wine Appreciation Group
D M Hunter, 21 Dartmouth Avenue, Almondbury, Huddersfield, W Yorks HD5 8UR TEL (0484) 531228
Weekly meetings are held from September to June, 'to taste, assess and extend the members' experience of wine and food'. Graded tutored tastings and special events are held for new members. Activities include visits to merchants for tastings, and the planning of meals.

Ordre Mondial des Gourmets Dégustateurs
Martin Mistlin, 41 Kingsend, Ruislip, Middlesex HA4 7DD TEL 081-427 9944 (day)
This is a French wine guild with a British chapter (the headquarters are in Paris). Its aims are the promotion of the knowledge of fine wines and spirits. Varied, regular tastings and dinners are held with access to meetings abroad. Annual subscription is £65 for professionals, £45 for amateurs. (See also **Martin Mistlin's Fine Wine Dining Club** and **Wine and Gastronomic Societies (WAGS)**.)

The Petersham Wine Society
John Trigwell, Tanglewood House, Mayfield Avenue, New Haw, Addlestone, Surrey KT15 3AG TEL (0932) 348720 FAX (0932) 350861
This society was started in February 1991 and holds regular tastings in the cellars of the Petersham Hotel in Richmond (Surrey), followed by a small regional speciality dinner. Annual membership £7.50 (£12 joint at the same address). A charge is made for each tasting (about £20 per head).

Tanglewood Wine Society
Tanglewood House, Mayfield Avenue, New Haw, Addlestone, Surrey KT15 3AG TEL (0932) 348720 FAX (0932) 350861
This is a well-established wine club covering a large part of Surrey. The Society now has four branches (in Cobham, Ashtead,

Woking and East Grinstead) holding regular monthly tastings and social events. Annual membership costs £7.50 (£12 joint at the same address). A charge is made at each tasting, averaging £9 per head. The club attracts all levels of knowledge, from the beginner to the connoisseur. (See also **Tanglewood Wine Tours**.)

The Wine & Dine Society
96 Ramsden Road, London SW12 8QZ
TEL 081-673 4439
Weekly tastings of wines from all over the world, including fine and rare bottles. Guest speakers. Dinners in London follow an ethnic theme.

Wine and Gastronomic Societies (WAGS)
Martin Mistlin, 41 Kingsend, Ruislip, Middlesex HA4 7DD
TEL 081-427 9944 (day)
This society comprises the Alsace Club of Great Britain (President: Hugh Johnson), the Cofradia Riojana and the Gallo Nero Club of Great Britain (President: The Hon Rocco Forte). No annual subscription, but a joining fee of £10 allows members to attend tastings and dinners featuring wines from these regions, and occasional events based on other wine regions. A small supplement applies to certain events. Wine tours abroad and wine weekends in the UK feature in the clubs' activities. (See also **Martin Mistlin's Fine Wine Dining Club** and **Ordre Mondial des Gourmets Dégustateurs**.)

The Winetasters
P N Beardwood (Secretary), 44 Claremont Road, London W13 0DG
TEL 081-997 1252
Annual subscription £10 (£3 if you live more than 50 miles from London). This is a non-profit-making club which organises tastings, seminars, dinners and tours (the major tour for 1993 will be to German vineyards). Many of the members have academic connections.

Zinfandel Club
Spenser Hilliard (Hon. Secretary), 12A Russell Square Mansions, 122 Southampton Row, London WC1B 5AE TEL 071-797 7788 (work), 071-404 5690 (home)
Membership fee £5. Sporadic meetings to taste California wines, sometimes tutored. Occasional dinners with appropriate wines.

MERCHANTS' CLUBS

In assessing these clubs we were looking for a commitment from each merchant to organise proper tutored tastings on a regular basis, open to the general public. These tastings are usually priced to cover the cost of the wines tasted. Some merchants also run dinners, offer discounts and arrange trips to vineyards, and so on. See the WHERE TO BUY section for details.

Les Amis du Vin Wine Club
A & A Wines
The Bacchante Wine Club
Benedicts
B H Wines
Bibendum
Butlers Wine Cellar
Christchurch Fine Wine Co
Connolly's
County Wines of Hagley
Del Monico's
Direct Wine Shipments
Eldridge Pope
Farr Vintners
John Ford Wines
Garrards Wine Merchants
Gauntley's of Nottingham
Matthew Gloag & Son
Hampden Wine Company
Gerard Harris Fine Wines
John Harvey & Sons
House of Townend
S H Jones
King and Barnes
Mitchells Wine Merchant
Moreno Wines
Le Nez Rouge Wine Club
James Nicholson
Nickolls & Perks
The Nobody Inn
Portland Wine Co
Ravensbourne Wine Co
La Reserva
La Réserve
Robersons
The Sunday Times Wine Club
Helen Verdcourt Wines
La Vigneronne
The Vintner Wine Club
Wine Schoppen
Wine Society

WINE COURSES

Camberley Wine Courses
Lindum House, 27 Cambrian Close, Camberley, Surrey GU15 3LD TEL (0276) 23964
Introductory and fine wine courses are held generally in autumn and spring terms at Camberley Adult Education Centre. The Wine & Spirit Education Trust Higher Certificate course is also offered at Brooklands Technical College, Weybridge.

Christie's Wine Course
Caroline de Lane Lea (Secretary), 63 Old Brompton Road, London SW7 3JS TEL 071-581 3933
Principals: Michael Broadbent MW and Steven Spurrier. Christie's holds an Introduction to Wine Tasting course, concentrating on the principal wines of France. The course runs on five consecutive Tuesday evenings, lasting approximately two hours, six times a year, price £145. Christie's also offers Master Classes: specialist tastings of top-quality wines. There are places for 15-30 people, price £50-£60. Discussions and tastings are conducted by top wine experts.

Corney & Barrow's Wine Course
Judy Emerson, 12 Helmet Row, London EC1V 3QJ TEL 071-251 4051 FAX 071-608 1373
Aimed particularly at Corney & Barrow's younger customers and those within the hotel/restaurant trade, the four-session course – £25 per session or £75 for all four – covers the cost of the wines, tuition, information sheets, maps and glasses. Numbers are restricted to a maximum of 20. (See also the **Where to buy** section.)

Ecole du Vin, Château Loudenne, Bordeaux
Ecole du Vin, Château Loudenne, St-Yzans-de-Médoc, 33340 Lesparre, France TEL 010 33 56.09.05.03 FAX 010 33 56.09.02.87
Six-day courses (starting on Monday) are held for a dozen students five times a year at Gilbey's Château Loudenne, under the direction of Charles Eve MW. Accommodation in the Château. Aimed at the public and professionals, the lectures and tastings cover all aspects of viticulture and vinification, including other Bordeaux areas and châteaux. Price in 1992, which included all meals and drinks, was £1,295, plus travel to France. A short course is also available (£595 in 1992), as is a five-day Burgundy course.

Fulham Road Wine School
The Fulham Road Wine Centre, 899-901 Fulham Road, London SW6 5HU TEL 071-736 7009 FAX 071-736 6648
A selection of courses, from a straightforward introduction to identifying flavours and styles of wine, through to tastings covering grape types and classic wine regions in greater detail. Also how to match food and wine, and Saturday workshops from January to May: these consist of blind tastings under exam conditions, followed by a tutorial (people attending these sessions are studying for the Wine & Spirit Education Trust Diploma or Master of Wine exams). (See also the **Where to buy** section.)

German Wine Academy
German Wine Information Service, Chelsea Chambers, 262A Fulham Road, London SW10 9EL TEL 071-376 3329 FAX 071-351 7563
A twelfth-century German monastery is the setting for courses (delivered in English), which include lectures by wine experts, vineyard visits and tastings. The basic seven-day course is run throughout the year (£625) and is supplemented by more advanced courses and an extended, culturally oriented course conducted at a more relaxed pace.

Lay & Wheeler
6 Culver Street West, Colchester, Essex CO1 1JA TEL (0206) 764446 FAX (0206) 564488
Approximately 100 wine workshops are held throughout the year which aim to 'promote the enjoyment of wine through education'. They are presented by Lay & Wheeler's buying team and by their suppliers who travel from the New and Old World to host the tastings. Past speakers have included Baron Eric Rothschild from Château Lafite and Peter Sichel from Château Palmer. The tutored tastings are for a maximum of 50 people, and are followed by a two-course supper at Lay & Wheeler Wine Market in Colchester (cost about £25). Prices range from £18.50 for workshops aimed at the novice to £85 for the more prestigious tastings held at outside venues. Accommodation can be arranged. (See also the **Where to buy** section.)

Leith's School of Food and Wine
21 St Alban's Grove, London W8 5BP TEL 071-229 0177
Some of Leith's wine courses are for students of the School only, as part of their food and wine studies. However, at least two are available to outsiders: five two-hour evening sessions starting each January, leading to the award of Leith's Certificate (if you pass the exam); and ten two-hour evening sessions starting in

October, leading to Leith's Advanced Certificate of Wine, examined by Leith's Master of Wine, Richard Harvey. This is roughly analogous to the Wine and Spirit Education Trust's Higher Certificate, without the sessions on licensing and labelling laws, and with particular stress on tasting. Price £145 and £275 respectively. Other courses are also sometimes available.

The Lincoln Wine Course
Norman Tate, 8 Green Lane, North Hykeham, Lincoln, Lincolnshire LN6 8NL TEL (0522) 680388
A wine appreciation course is offered at North Hykeham Evening Institute (Tue p.m.) and at Yarborough Adult Education Centre, Lincoln (Wed p.m.), starting in September each year. This is a two-term course (20 weeks, two hours per week) with the emphasis on tasting as well as gaining a good general knowledge of wine. The price is divided between the course fee (£27) and a weekly supplement to cover the cost of the tastings. (See also **Lincoln Wine Society**.)

Sotheby's
Wine Department, No 5 Albion Wharf, Hester Road, London SW11 4AN TEL 071-924 3287 FAX 071-924 3110
Sotheby's Wine Seminars are held throughout the year at New Bond Street (London). These include tutored tastings with Serena Sutcliffe MW and top wine producers. Wine dinners are also held.

Tante Marie School of Cookery
Woodham House, Carlton Road, Woking, Surrey GU21 4HF
TEL (0483) 726957
Conal Gregory MW organises wine appreciation courses, generally during the autumn and winter, on three weekday evenings (lasting two hours), including extensive tutored tastings, aimed at those with modest knowledge.

The Wine School at Roberson
348 Kensington High Street, London W14 8NS TEL 071-371 2121
FAX 071-371 4010
The Wine School aims to 'banish all the mystique and snobbery that surrounds wine', and both introductory and more specialised courses are on offer, consisting of a short series of weekly evening or Saturday morning sessions, tasting around eight wines. Maximum of 16 people per course. Introductory session £18, others (three sessions) £55-£60. (See also the **Where to buy** section.)

The Wine Schoppen Wine Tasting Circle
Mrs Anne Coghlan (Managing Director), 1 Abbeydale Road South, Sheffield, S Yorkshire S7 2QL TEL (0742) 365684 FAX (0742) 352171
A wide range of tutored tastings is hosted by guest speakers. Also included in the programme are 'open days' (held on the first Saturday of each month, tasting one special or rare wine), cheese and wine tastings, and dinners. A wine tour abroad (to Portugal in 1992) and a wine weekend are organised annually. Annual fee £8.

Winewise
Michael Schuster, 107 Culford Road, London N1 4HL
TEL 071-254 9734
Promotes all aspects of tasting, understanding and appreciating wines and spirits. Regular tastings include two wine courses: a Beginners' Course (£90 for six evenings) and an Intermediate Course (£130 for six evenings). Each course is limited to 18 participants. Other tastings are held to examine the wines of individual properties and vintages, and to compare fine wines from around the world. There are blind tastings each spring, workshops on Saturday mornings, 'wine and food' events and fine wine tastings on late Sunday afternoons.

Wine World
Lilyane Weston, 'Owlet', Templepan Lane, Chandlers Cross, Rickmansworth, Hertfordshire WD3 4NH TEL/FAX (0923) 264718
Lilyane Weston runs a programme for 'those who wish to combine the theory and practice of learning about wines in a relaxed atmosphere'. Activities include fine wine tastings, workshops (on individual wines), and external tastings and lectures; 10-12 wines tasted on average, cost £15-£18 per session. Training also offered to restaurant staff to improve their wine knowledge. Tutorials given to candidates sitting for the Wine & Spirit Education Trust Diploma (£15 per session). Visits organised to UK and French vineyards.

WINE TOURS

Allez France
27 West Street, Storrington, West Sussex RH20 4DZ
TEL (0903) 745793/742345
The Allez France 'VINEscapes' individual wine holidays are for the independent-minded traveller to France, and are based on hotels chosen for their setting, cuisine, character and comfort in Alsace, Champagne, Burgundy, Rhône/Provence, Bordeaux and the Loire. These include a 'unique' selection of hotels with their

own vineyards. Travel arrangements are flexible but inclusive. Tailor-made wine tours for groups, clubs or associations can also be arranged.

Arblaster & Clarke Wine Tours
104 Church Road, Steep, Petersfield, Hampshire GU32 2DD
TEL (0730) 266883 FAX (0730) 268620
This small, family-run specialist tour operator offers four- and five-day tours to France, Spain, Portugal, Italy, California and, new for 1993, South Africa. Prices start from £399. There are also weekends in Champagne (tasting 25 different champagnes) and cookery weekends in Normandy, from £189. The tours are accompanied by a wine guide and tour manager, and visits are to the best cellars in the area. For those who prefer to go it alone, individual itineraries can also be organised.

Australia's Southern Tourism Promotion (Victoria & Tasmania)
Gemini House, 10-18 Putney Hill, London SW15 6AA
TEL 081-789 7088 FAX 081-780 1496
Australia's Southern Tourism Promotion produces a wine and food guide to Victoria with helpful notes on wineries and ideas for self-drive visits. It also has details of various rail and coach tours including brochures for Australian Wine Tours, Peter Heath's Unique Winery Tours, Winery Walkabout and Bogong Jack Cycling Winery Tours. It also assists in planning group tours around the state's 140 public wineries.

Australian Tourist Commission
Gemini House, 10-18 Putney Hill, London SW15 6AA
TEL 081-780 2227
The Tourist Commission can provide information on tours and holidays available through Australian travel firms (for a free Travellers Guide call 081-780 1424). For more specific information on wine tours, contact The Australian Wine Centre, South Australia House, 50 Strand, London WC2N 5LW (071-930 7471).

Blackheath Wine Trails
13 Blackheath Village, London SE3 9LA TEL 081-463 0012
FAX 081-463 0011
In 1992, wine tours were offered to Tuscany, Madeira, the Lisbon coast, Oporto, Madrid, Seville, Jerez, Rioja, Barcelona, Bordeaux, Burgundy, the Rhine and Mosel, northern Portugal, Israel and Australia. Prices start at £259 and tours vary from four to twenty days. For the independent traveller, fly-drive and self-catering options are also available.

Classic Wine Tours
Helen Gillespie-Peck, HGP Travel Services, 103 Queen Street, Newton Abbot, Devon TQ12 2BG TEL (0626) 65373 FAX (0626) 334749
Wine tours are offered to Bordeaux, Burgundy, Beaujolais, Champagne, Côtes-du-Rhône and Languedoc; 5 to 14 days, £245 to £580. Visits to other European wine regions in 1993 will be to Tuscany and northern Spain. Travel is by luxury coach and numbers are limited to a maximum of 32 per trip. Gastronomic weekends in Reims and Bordeaux are also offered.

DER Travel Service
18 Conduit Street, London W1R 9TD TEL 071-408 0111 FAX 071-629 7442
As well as Rhine cruises, DER arranges air and rail holidays in German and Austrian hotels, guesthouses or apartments, many of them in wine-growing areas, and with your own car you can tour the wine-growing areas of the Rhine and Mosel on the 'Wine Regions Tour'. An eight-night tour in 1992 costs from £230 (for five adults) to £276 (for two adults).

English Vineyards Association
38 West Park, London SE9 4RH TEL 081-857 0452
Many English vineyards are open to the public and offer guided tours, tastings and sales. A free pamphlet giving all these details is available from the address above (send an s.a.e.).

Eurocamp
Canute Court, Toft Road, Knutsford, Cheshire WA16 0NL TEL (0565) 650022 (Reservations only: 28 Princess Street, Knutsford, Cheshire WA16 6BG)
Eurocamp arranges self-drive camping and mobile home holidays at over 200 sites in Europe, many of which are 'almost among the grapes – and the more well-known grapes at that'. These include the Gironde, Saumur, Meursault, Bergerac, Cahors, Mosel, Bordeaux and Rhineland. 'Eurocamp Independent', tel (0565) 755399, offers a ferry/pitch reservations 'package' for campers and touring caravan-owners to over 250 sites in Europe.

Francophiles
Ron and Jenny Farmer, 66 Great Brockeridge, Westbury-on-Trym, Bristol BS9 3UA TEL (0272) 621975
The Farmers offer France 'lovingly packaged' on their personally escorted 'holidays of discovery in the regional heartlands'. Their clients are 'not usual coach holiday travellers but ones who

appreciate in-depth, unhurried visits and structured tastings'. Tours on offer include Alsace, Provence, Cévennes, Auvergne, Tarn, the Dordogne and the Jura.

Hide-a-Way Holidays in Burgundy
Maureen and Ken Deeming, Greenbank, Penrith Road, Keswick, Cumbria CA12 4LJ TEL (07687) 72522
One week 'Wine Appreciation Holidays' are offered in May, July and September to groups of six or more, based in a renovated 200-year-old cottage in southern Burgundy. On three of the days visitors are taken to vineyards of the Côte Chalonnaise, Côte de Nuits, Côte de Beaune and Beaujolais for tastings. The price is £225 per person and includes bed and continental breakfast and four evening meals.

KD German Rhine Line
G A Clubb Rhine Cruise Agency, 28 South Street, Epsom, Surrey KT18 7PF TEL (0372) 742033 FAX (0372) 724871
In 1992 a week-long 'Floating Wine Seminar' (cost from £635) visited six famous wine-growing areas from the Mosel, the Rhine, Alsace and Baden, which included lectures, tutored tastings and optional sightseeing tours.

Moswin Tours
Moswin House, 21 Church Street, Oadby, Leicestershire LE2 5DB TEL (0533) 719922/714982 FAX (0533) 716016
Fully inclusive tours of four to eleven days, by air or coach, to the Mosel and Rhine Valley, plus sightseeing tours, exclusive wine tastings and wine weekends, and autumn visits to vineyards, as well as wine festivals. Also available are tailor-made specialist wine tours (budget to luxury) – for individuals and groups – to other wine-growing regions in Germany, France and Italy.

Sonata Travel
227 Umberslade Road, Selly Oak, Birmingham, West Midlands B29 7SG TEL 021-472 8636
This specialist coach company offers group tours to French and German wine regions from four to seven days. Joining points are in the Midlands and London.

Tanglewood Wine Tours
Tanglewood House, Mayfield Avenue, New Haw, Addlestone, Surrey KT15 3AG TEL (0932) 348720 FAX (0932) 350861
This company specialises in coach tours to vineyards in France. In 1992 nine tours were offered to Burgundy and the Loire Valley,

which included a weekend in Chablis, a seven-day 'Summer Wine Spectacular' taking in the *marché médiéval* in Chinon, and a November trip to the wine auctions in Beaune. A tour of Alsace and Champagne is planned for 1993. (See also **Tanglewood Wine Society**.)

Wessex Continental Travel
PO Box 43, Plymouth, Devon PL1 1SY TEL (0752) 846880
FAX (0752) 845547
Described as 'holidays with wine', seven nine-day coach tours are offered around France – to the Midi, Alsace and Champagne, Beaujolais and the Northern Rhône, the Dordogne and St-Emilion, Bordeaux and Gascony, the Loire Valley, and Chablis and Burgundy. Prices are from £355 to £385, which includes continental breakfast and one main meal per day. Maximum of 36 people per tour. The pick-up point is in Portsmouth. For private/corporate groups, independent arrangements can be made to other wine regions of the world.

World Wine Tours
69-71 Banbury Road, Oxford, Oxfordshire OX2 6PE
TEL (0865) 310244 FAX (0865) 310299
World Wine Tours, now a subsidiary of Alternative Travel Group, offers a wide range of wine tours for the novice and connoisseur, each lasting from four to eight days. All tours are led by wine experts, most of whom are Masters of Wine. A maximum of 20 bookings are accepted on any one tour. Tours include visits to top wine estates and châteaux in France, Italy, Spain and Portugal. Courses are organised at Château Loudenne and the German Wine Academy (*q.v.*). There are also 'introduction to wine' and 'fine wine' weekends in the UK (prices from £350 to £1,350). Specially tailored tours can be arranged both for private groups of wine enthusiasts and as corporate incentives/hospitality. Visits to New Zealand and California are planned for 1993.

Wine glossary

abboccato (Italy) medium-dry
abocado (Spain) medium-dry
adega (Portugal) winery
almacenista (Spain) a small-scale sherry stockholder
amabile (Italy) medium or medium-sweet
amarone (Italy) dry passito (*q.v.*) wine from Valpolicella
amontillado (Spain) an aged fino (*q.v.*) sherry on which yeast flor (*q.v.*) has ceased to grow but which is matured further without flor to develop delicate nutty flavours; commercial 'medium amontillados' are not made in this way, but are blended, sweetened sherries
amoroso (Spain) medium-sweet style of sherry
Anbaugebiet (Germany) growing region
appassimento (Italy) drying of grapes to concentrate their sugars
appellation contrôlée (France) the best category of French wine, with regulations defining the precise vineyard area according to soil, grape varieties, yields, alcohol level, and maybe vineyard and cellar practices
Ausbruch (Austria) dessert wine, between Beerenauslese and Trockenbeerenauslese, from nobly rotten grapes
Auslese (Germany) wine from selected ripe grapes, possibly with noble rot (*see* botrytis)
barrique 225-litre barrel, usually of French oak, in which both red and white wines are matured and white wines sometimes fermented. Normally replaced every 2-3 years, as new barriques have more effect on taste
Beerenauslese (Germany) wine from specially selected ripe berries, probably with noble rot
Bereich (Germany) region, larger than Grosslage, smaller than Anbaugebiet (*q.v.*)
blanc de blancs white wine or champagne made from white grapes only
blanc de noirs white wine or champagne made from red grapes vinified without skin contact (the juice of most red grapes is colourless; all the colouring matter is found in the skins)
bodega (Spain) cellar, winery
botrytis a form of rot that shrivels grapes and concentrates their sugars ('noble rot')
botte/i (Italy) large oak or chestnut barrel/s
brut (Champagne) dry or dryish (up to 15g sugar/litre)
bual (Madeira) smokily sweet madeira
cantina sociale/cantine sociali (Italy) co-operative winery/ies
carbonic maceration fermentation of whole bunches of grapes in vat filled with carbon dioxide to give fruity wines with low tannin
cava (Spain) champagne-method sparkling wines; now a DO in its own right
chaptalisation the addition of sugar to the must to increase the final alcohol content of the wine
classico (Italy) heartland of a DOC zone, producing its best wines, e.g. Chianti Classico
clos (Burgundy) vineyard site that was walled in the past, and may still be walled
colheita (Portugal) vintage (table wine); single-vintage tawny(port)
cosecha (Spain) vintage
cream (Spain) sweet sherry
criadera (Spain) literally 'nursery'; signifies a stage in a sherry solera system (*q.v.*)

crianza, sin (Spain) without wood-ageing

crianza, vino de (Spain) basic wood-aged wine, with one year's oak-cask ageing and one year's bottle- or tank-ageing

cru (France) literally 'growth', meaning either a distinguished single property (as in Bordeaux) or a distinguished vineyard area (as in Beaujolais or Burgundy)

cru (Italy) wine from grapes of a single vineyard, usually of high quality. Term is in common use but not officially permitted

cru bourgeois (Bordeaux) 'bourgeois growth', indicating a wine from the bottom tier of the Médoc's secondary classification system

cru classé (Bordeaux) 'classified growth', indicating a wine from the Médoc's primary classification system, divided into five strata (premiers, deuxièmes, troisièmes, quatrièmes and cinquièmes crus classés); or from the classification systems of the Graves, Sauternes or St-Emilion

cru classé (Provence) estates bottling their own wines since 1953 (of little significance)

cru grand bourgeois (Bordeaux) 'a fine bourgeois growth', indicating a wine from the middle tier of the Médoc's secondary classification system

cru grand bourgeois exceptionnel (Bordeaux) 'exceptionally fine bourgeois growth', indicating a wine from the upper tier of the Médoc's secondary classification system

crusting/crusted (Portugal) a blend of port of different years for short-term cellaring; needs decanting

cuve close a method of making sparkling wines by carrying out the second fermentation inside a sealed tank rather than in bottle. Also known as the 'tank method' and 'Charmat method'

cuvée (France) vat or tank; sometimes means a 'selected' wine, but the term has no legal status on labels

demi-sec (Champagne, Loire) sweet (up to 50g sugar/litre)

Denominación de Origen (DO) (Spain) wines of controlled origin, grape varieties and style

Denominación de Origen Calificada (DOCa) (Spain) as DO, but entails stricter controls including bottling at source; so far, only Rioja has been given a DOCa status

Denominazione di Origine Controllata (DOC) (Italy) wine of controlled origin, grape varieties and style

Denominazione di Origine Controllata e Garantita (DOCG) (Italy) wine from area with stricter controls than DOC

domaine (Burgundy) estate, meaning the totality of vineyard holdings belonging to a grower or négociant

dosage (Champagne) the sugar added with wine to champagne after disgorgement, to determine the degree of sweetness of the final blend, from brut, through extra sec, sec, demi-sec to doux. Extra brut has no dosage

doux (Champagne, Loire) sweet to very sweet (over 50g sugar/litre)

Einzellage (Germany) single vineyard site

Eiswein (Germany) wine made from frozen grapes

English table wine (England & Wales) all English wines, including the very best, are, as yet, classed as 'table wine' by the EC. A pilot scheme for quality wine is being introduced for the 1992 vintage

erzeugerabfüllung (Germany) estate-bottled (co-

operative cellars may also use this term)
extra brut (Champagne) absolutely dry (no added sugar)
extra dry (Champagne) off-dry (12-20g sugar/litre)
fino (Spain) light, dry sherry matured under flor (*q.v.*)
flor (Spain) a layer of yeast growing on sherry in a part-empty butt; gives fino (*q.v.*) its character
frizzante (Italy) lightly sparkling
fusto/i (Italy) oak or chestnut barrel/s
garrafa (Portugal) bottle
garrafeira (Portugal) better-than-average table wine given longer-than- average ageing; a producer's selection of his best wine; a colheita port given bottle as well as cask age
generoso (Portugal, Spain) fortified wine
grand cru (Alsace) classified vineyard site
grand cru (Burgundy) finest category of named vineyard site
grand cru classé (Bordeaux) 'fine classed growth', indicating a wine from the second level of the St-Emilion classification system
grand vin (Bordeaux) 'fine wine': the top wine of a Bordeaux château, blended from selected cuvées only, as opposed to the 'second wine', which is blended from less successful cuvées and perhaps the wine of younger vines, and which is generally sold at a lower price; in other regions the term is used more loosely
gran reserva (Spain) red wine aged for a minimum of two years in oak casks and three in bottle; white (or rosé) wine aged for a minimum of six months in oak casks and three and a half years in tank or bottle
Grosslage (Germany) collective vineyard site
halbtrocken (Germany) semi-dry
Kabinett (Germany) first category of Prädikat wine (*q.v.*), light and delicate in style
kolektziono (Bulgaria) reserve
Landwein (Germany) country wine
Late-Bottled Vintage (LBV) (Portugal) a medium-quality red port of a single year
late harvest (Australia, New Zealand, North America) sweet wine made from grapes picked in an over-mature or maybe botrytised condition
lieu-dit (Burgundy) named, but unclassified, vineyard site
liquoroso (Italy) wines fortified with grape alcohol
maduro (Portugal) a term, meaning 'matured', used loosely of any non-verde (*q.v.*) white wine
malmsey (Madeira) the most sweet and raisiny of madeiras
malolactic fermentation a secondary, non-alcoholic 'fermentation' that converts malic acid into lactic acid and carbon dioxide. The process is accomplished by bacteria rather than yeast
manzanilla (Spain) salty fino from Sanlúcar de Barrameda
manzanilla pasada (Spain) aged manzanilla (*q.v.*)
méthode traditionnelle (France) replaces méthode champenoise in France to describe the champagne method
metodo classico (Italy) champagne-method sparkling wines
método tradicional (Spain) champagne-method sparkling wines
mis en bouteille par (France) bottled by
moelleux (France) medium-sweet to sweet
mousse (France) term used to describe the effervescence in sparkling wine

mousseux (France) sparkling
muffa nobile (Italy) noble rot
naturale (Italy) natural; describes non-sparkling or slightly sparkling Piemontese Moscato wines with lowish alcohol
négociant (France) wholesale merchant and wine trader
noble rot *see* botrytis
non-vintage (nv) a wine or champagne made from a blend of wines of different years
normale (Italy) non-riserva; most commonly mentioned for Chianti
nouveau (Beaujolais) new wine sold from the third Thursday in November after the harvest
novello (Italy) new wine, for drinking very young, on sale from October or November
Oechsle (Germany) measure of sugar in grape must; determines quality of wine in Germany and Austria; also used in New World
oloroso (Spain) sherry aged oxidatively rather than under flor (*q.v.*)
Palo Cortado (Spain) light and delicate style of oloroso (*q.v.*)
passerillage (France) the process of leaving grapes to dry and dehydrate on the vine with the eventual aim of producing a dessert wine from them
passito (Italy) dried or semi-dried grapes or wine made from them
perlant (France) with a slight prickle of gas, visible on the side of the glass
pipe (Portugal) a port cask containing between 534 litres (shipping pipe) and 630 litres (lodge pipe)
Port with an Indication of Age (Portugal) true tawny port, in four styles: 10 Years Old, 20 Years Old, 30 Years Old, over 40 Years Old
Prädikat (Germany) a category of German wine with a 'special attribute' based on natural sugar levels in must, such as Kabinett, Spätlese, Auslese, Beerenauslese, Trockenbeerenauslese or Eiswein
predicato (Italy) category of merit used for new-style Tuscan wines
premier cru (Burgundy) second highest category of named vineyard site. If no vineyard name is specified, wine made from a number of different premier cru sites
premier grand cru classé (Bordeaux) 'first fine classed growth', indicating a wine from the top level of the St-Emilion classification system
propriétaire (France) vineyard owner
puttonyos (Hungary) in practical terms, an indication of sweetness of Tokaj Aszú wines (*q.v.*). The more puttonyos specified (3-6), the sweeter will be the Tokaj
Qualitätswein (Germany) quality wine
Qualitätswein bestimmter Anbaugebiet (QbA) (Germany) quality wine from a specific region
Qualitätswein mit Prädikat (QmP) (Germany) quality wine with a 'special attribute' (*see* Prädikat)
quinta (Portugal) farm, estate. In the port context, any style may be branded with a quinta name, but 'Single Quinta' port generally refers to a single-farm port from a lesser year
rainwater (Madeira) a medium-dry madeira based on the Tinta Negra Mole variety
recioto (Italy) sweet passito (*q.v.*) wine from the Veneto
récolte (France) harvest
região demarcada (Portugal) demarcated (wine) region
reserva (Portugal) better-than-average wine; slightly higher (0.5%) in alcohol than legal minimum; at least one year old
reserva (Spain) red wine aged for a minimum of one year in oak

casks and two years in bottle; white (or rosé) wine aged for a minimum of six months in oak casks and one and a half years in tank or bottle

reserve (Bulgaria) wine which has spent two years (white) or three years (red) ageing in wood

reserve (Madeira) madeira with a minimum age of five years

réserve (France) 'reserve': this term has no legal status on labels

riserva (Italy) wines aged for longer than normal. If DOC wines are riserva, then a minimum (but variable) ageing period is laid down. Usually the best wines are held back for riserva

sec (Champagne, Loire) medium-dry (17g-35g of sugar per litre of wine); (other wines) dry

secco (Italy) dry

seco (Portugal, Spain) dry

second wine (Bordeaux) *see* grand vin

Sekt (Germany) sparkling wine

sélection de grains nobles (Alsace) wine made from botrytis-affected grapes (*see* botrytis)

semi-seco (Spain) medium dry

sercial (Madeira) the driest madeira, though cheap examples are rarely fully dry

solera (Spain) sherry ageing system which, by fractional blending, produces a consistent and uniform end product

sous-marque (France) a wine sold or labelled under a secondary, possibly fictional, name

Spätlese (Germany) wine from late-picked grapes, possibly with noble rot

special reserve (Madeira) madeira with a minimum age of ten years

spumante (Italy) sparkling

stravecchio (Italy) extra old

sulfites (US) sulphur dioxide, present in all wines (including organic wines), used as a preservative and disinfectant

supérieur (France) higher alcohol content than usual

'sur lie' (Loire) this should refer to a wine (generally Muscadet) bottled directly from its lees, without having been racked or filtered. The term has, though, been used in a lax fashion in recent years; grant it credence only in conjunction with an indication of domaine-bottling, such as 'mis en bouteille au domaine'

superiore (Italy) wine with higher alcohol, and sometimes more age

Super Tuscan (Italy) non-DOC wine of high quality from Tuscany

Süssreserve (Germany) unfermented grape juice which may be added to fully fermented wine to sweeten it; the process is known as 'back-blending'

Tafelwein (Germany) table wine

tank method *see* cuve close

tawny port (Portugal) basic light port. True wood-aged tawny ports are either marketed as colheitas (*q.v.*) or as Ports with an Indication of Age (*q.v.*)

transfer method a method of making sparkling wines in which the second fermentation takes place in bottle, but the sediment produced by this process is eliminated by decanting and filtering under pressure. The wine is then rebottled

trocken (Germany) dry

Trockenbeerenauslese (Germany) very sweet wine from raisined grapes affected by noble rot

varietal a wine based on a single grape variety

vecchio (Italy) old

velho (Portugal) old

vendange tardive (Alsace) 'late harvest', meaning wine made from especially ripe grapes

verde (Portugal) 'green', meaning young

verdelho (Madeira) medium-dry madeira
viejo (muy) (Spain) old (very)
vigna (Italy) vineyard or 'cru' (*q.v.*)
vigneto (Italy) vineyard or 'cru' (*q.v.*)
viña (Spain) vineyard
vin de pays (France) literally translates as country wine, and describes wine that is better than basic vin de table, with some regional characteristics. Usually vins de pays are determined by administrative geography, with more flexible regulations than for appellation contrôlée (*q.v.*)
vin de table (France) the most basic category of French wine, with no precise provenance other than country of origin given on the label
vin gris (France) pale rosé wine
vinifera (North America) a grape variety that is a member of the European *Vitis vinifera* family, as opposed to some of the other vine families (such as the native American *Vitis labrusca* family)
vinificato in bianco (Italy) juice from black grapes fermented without skin contact to make white wine
vino da tavola (VdT) (Italy) table wine: wine that is neither DOCG, DOC nor fortified nor sparkling nor low in alcohol. Quality may be basic or exceptionally fine
vino de la tierra (Spain) country wine
vino de mesa (Spain) table wine
Vino Kontrolirano (Bulgaria) Controliran wine, made from certain grape varieties in certain DGOs (*see below*)
Vino ot Deklariran Geografski (Bulgaria) Wine of Declared Geographic Origin (DGO)
vino santo (Italy) type of passito (*q.v.*) wine from Trentino, Tuscany and Umbria
vino tipico (Italy) new category for vino da tavola with some regional characteristics
vintage champagne champagne made from a blend of a single year, sold after at least three years' ageing
Vintage Character (Portugal) medium-quality red port. This style may cease to exist in the near future
vintage madeira (Madeira) the finest madeira; declared only after 20 years' maturation
vintage port (Portugal) very fine port, bottled young and requiring long cellaring (8 to 40 years); needs decanting
vitivinicoltura (Italy) the whole process of wine-making, from the vineyard through to the finished wine
VDQS (France) (Vin Délimité de Qualité Supérieure) covers the very much smaller category, below appellation contrôlée (*q.v.*), with very similar regulations
VQPRD (Italy) 'quality wine produced in a specified region'; EC term indicating appellation contrôlée, DOC, DOCG, DO, DOCa, RD and other similarly controlled quality categories
Weinbaudomäne (Germany) wine estate
Weingut (Germany) wine estate
Weinkellerei (Germany) wine cellar
Weissherbst (Germany) rosé
Winzergenossenschaft (Germany) growers' co-operative

INDEX

The index covers the **Taste of Wine** section only and includes principal areas, grapes and wine characteristics, as well as the names of wines themselves. See also the Glossary on page 487.

Report to the Editor *The Which? Wine Guide*

This report is

a new recommendation ☐

a comment on existing entry ☐

please tick as appropriate

name of establishment

address

tel no:

please continue overleaf

date of most recent visit

signed

I am not connected directly or indirectly with the management or proprietors

name *in block letters, please*

address

Send to: The Which? Wine Guide, Freepost, London NW1 4DF
(please note: no postage required within UK)

Report to the Editor *The Which? Wine Guide*

This report is

a new recommendation ☐

a comment on existing entry ☐

please tick as appropriate

name of establishment

address

tel no:

please continue overleaf

date of most recent visit

signed

I am not connected directly or indirectly with the management or proprietors

name *in block letters, please*

address

Send to: The Which? Wine Guide, Freepost, London NW1 4DF
(please note: no postage required within UK)